By Autho

THE

ARMY LIST

2001

Part I

LONDON: The Stationery Office

ISBN 0 11 772978 7

Printed in the United Kingdom by The Stationery Office
TJ005141   C35   08/01   19585   649272

iii

CONTENTS

iv

NOTES

General

The Army List is divided into three parts as follows:

a. *Part I*   Contains details of major appointments, headquarters and establishments and regimental and corps lists of officers of the British Active and Territorial Armies.

b. *Part II*   Contains an alphabetical list of non-effective officers in receipt of retired pay. The full list is published triennially, the intervening years being covered by a supplement.

c. *Part III* Contains the biographical list of serving active officers. (Restricted document).

Part I

Editing

Every effort has been made to make this edition as accurate as possible, and all information held on Officers' Record of Service (RoS) database as at 30 March 2001 has been included. It is therefore possible that some detail will be incorrect, as promotions, awards, etc promulgated prior to this date may not have been entered into the RoS. The Editor regrets this and any difficulties it may cause, and will endeavour to ensure that these changes appear in the next edition.

The Gradation List

This shows officers from Field Marshals down to and including major generals under their substantive ranks and in order of seniority. Brigadiers and Colonels are shown at the heads of their respective late regimental or corps lists. Lieutenant Colonels and below are shown under their parent regimental or corps lists.

Communications

Communications on all matters pertaining to officers' personal entries should be submitted in writing through commanding officers to: Officers' Record of Service, Kentigern House, Mail Point 430, 65 Brown Street, Glasgow G2 8EX. Any other queries should be addressed to Officers' Publications, MCM Occurrences, Mail Point 210 at the same address or telephone 0141 224 3089. Matters that cannot be resolved by the Editor will be referred to the Editorial Committee, chaired by SO1 DMS.

Amalgamated Regiments

Notes on amalgamated regiments are shown at the beginning of their respective entries. Disbanded regiments are included for 25 years.

Post Nominals

These are shown for all personnel, military or civilian. Honorary degrees are shown for general officers.

Editorial Staff

Editor	SO1 DMS Lt Col R J Knight *MBE* PWRR
Asst Editor	EO Mrs A M McIntyre
Sub Editor	AO Mr W McMillan

SYMBOLS AND ABBREVIATIONS
SYMBOLS - BRIEF CURRENT MEANING

Symbol	Short Title	Symbol	Short Title
adp	Advanced Automatic Data Processing Course	ph(cfs*)	Rotary Wing A1 Flying Instructor
ae	Long Aeronautical Engineering Course	pi	Long Petroleum Installation Course
aic	Long Armour/Infantry Course	pl	Fixed Wing Pilot
ais	Advanced Information Systems Course	pl(i)	Fixed Wing B1 Flying Instructor
asq	Aerosystems Course	pl(cfs)	Fixed Wing A2 Flying Instructor
ato	Ammunition Technical Officer's Course	pl(cfs*)	Fixed Wing A1 Flying Instructor
aws	Air Warfare Course	psc†	Army Staff Course (Division I or II at MCS followed by Staff College Camberley)
c	Long Civil Engineering Course		
cafs	Combat Arms Fighting Systems Course	psc()†	Army Staff Course (Division I or II at RMCS followed by Staff College in Australia, India or Pakistan)
cl	Post-Gradate Personnel Management Course		
df	Defence Fellow		
dis	Design of Information Systems Course	psc	Army Staff Course (Division III at RMCS followed by Staff College Camberley)
E	Long Electrical Engineering Course		
ee	Long Electronic Engineering Course	psc()	Army Staff Course (Division III at RMCS followed by Staff College in Australia, India or Pakistan. Alternatively Staff College in Canada or Germany without attending RMCS)
ENG	Long Engineering Course		
em	Long Electrical and Mechanical Course		
g†	Instructor-in-Gunnery (AA)		
g	Instructor-in-Gunnery (Field)		
g(a)	Instructor-in-Gunnery (Air Defence)	psc(n)†	Naval Staff Course (preceded by Division I or II at RMCS)
g(gw)	Instructor-in-Gunnery (Guided Weapons)		
g(s)	Instructor-in-Gunnery (Surface to Surface Guided Weapons)	psc(n)	Naval Staff Course (preceded by Division III at RMCS)
g(ss)	Instructor-in-Gunnery (Surface to Surface)	psc(a)†	Air Force Staff Course (preceded by Divisions I or II at RMCS)
g(y)	Instructor-in-Gunnery (Locating)		
gsd	Gun System Design Course	psc(a)	Air Force Staff Course (preceded by Division III at RMCS)
gw	Guided Weapons Course		
hcsc	Higher Command and Staff Course	psm	Advanced Certificate of Royal Military School of Music
hp	Half Pay		
I*	Interpreter First Class	ptsc	Technical Staff Course
I	Interpreter Second Class	qs	Staff Course RAF Staff College
idc	Imperial Defence College Course	rcds	Royal College of Defence Studies Course
ifp	International Fellows Programme	rly	Railway Course
im	Industrial Administration Course	s	Food Technology Course
jsc	Graduate of WRAC Staff College	sowc	Senior Officers' War Course
jsdc	Joint Services Defence College Course	sq	Staff qualified (other than at a Staff College)
jssc	Joint Services Staff College Course	sq(V)	Staff qualified (TA)
lc	Long Civil Catering Course	sq(W)	Staff qualified Weapons
lcc	LCL Command Certificate (Ocean Going)	svy	Army Survey Course
M	Long Mechanical Course	svy(cg)	Advanced Cartography Course
mda	Master of Defence Administration Course	svy(gy)	Advanced Geodesy Course
me	Long Mechanical Engineering Course	svy(pg)	Advanced Photogrammetry Course
mese	Military Electronic Systems Engineering Course	svy(pr)	Advanced Printing Course
		t	Advanced Transport Course
mvt	Military Vehicles Technology Course	t*	Advanced Transportation Course (US)
nadc	NATO Defence College Course	tacsc	TA Command and Staff Course
ndc	National Defence College Course	te	Telecommunicationns Engineering Course
ocws(US)	US Air War College	tem	Telecommunication Engineering Management Course
ocds()	Overseas College of Defence Studies		
odc()	Overseas Defence College Course	tn	Long Transportation Course
o	Ordnance Officers Course	tp	Empire Test Pilots' Course
osc()	Overseas Staff College	tt	Tank Technology Course
owc	LCL Watch-Keeping Certificate (Ocean Going)	y	Instructor in Counter-Bombardment
p	Officers Long Plant Course	(+)	Army Staff Course Div 1 or Div 2 RMCS
pc	Postal & Courier Officer	†	On probation
pfc	Long Finance and Accountancy Course	††	University Medical or Dental Cadets
ph	Rotary Wing Pilot	Ø	Denotes a female officer (not QARANC or WRAC)
ph(i)	Rotary Wing B1 Flying Instructor		
ph(cfs)	Rotary Wing A2 Flying Instructor	¶	Non-regular Permanent Staff (TA only)

ORDERS, DECORATIONS AND MEDALS IN COMMON USE

VC ......Victoria Cross

GC ......George Cross

KG ......Knight of the Order of the Garter

KT ......Knight of the Order of the Thistle

KP ......Knight of the Order of St Patrick

GCB .....Knight Grand Cross or Dame Grand Cross of the Order of the Bath

OM ......Member of the Order of Merit

KCB .....Knight Commander of the Order of the Bath

CB ......Companion of the Order of the Bath

GCMG ...Knight Grand Cross of the Order of St Michael and St George

KCMG ...Knight Commander of the Order of St Michael and St George

CMG ....Companion of the Order of St Michael and St George

GCVO ...Knight Grand Cross or Dame Grand Cross of the Royal Victorian Order

KCVO .Knight Commander of the Royal Victorian Order

DCVO ....Dame Commander of the Royal Victorian Order

CVO .....Commander of the Royal Victorian Order

GBE ....Knight Grand Cross or Dame Grand Cross of the Order of the British Empire

CH ....Member of the Order of the Companion of Honour

KBE .....Knight Commander of the Order of the British Empire

DBE ....Dame Commander of the Order of the British Empire

CBE .....Commander of the Order of the British Empire

DSO .....Companion of the Distinguished Service Order

LVO .....Lieutenant of the Royal Victorian Order

OBE .....Officer of the Order of the British Empire

ISO ......Companion of the Imperial Service Order

MVO .....Member of the Royal Victorian Order

MBE .....Member of the Order of the British Empire

CGC .....Conspicuous Gallantry Cross

RRC .....Member of the Royal Red Cross

DSC .....Distinguished Service Cross

MC ......Military Cross

DFC .....Distinguished Flying Cross

AFC .....Air Force Cross

ARRC ....Associate of the Royal Red Cross

DCM .....Distinguished Conduct Medal (Obsolete)

CGM .....Conspicuous Gallantry Medal (Obsolete)

GM ......George Medal

DSM .....Distinguished Service Medal (Obsolete)

MM ......Military Medal (Obsolete)

DFM .....Distinguished Flying Medal (Obsolete)

AFM .....Air Force Medal (Obsolete)

QGM ....The Queen's Gallantry Medal

BEM .....British Empire Medal (Obsolete)

RVM .....Royal Victoria Medal

TD ......Territorial Decoration or Efficiency Decoration

QVRM ...Queen's Volunteer Reserves Medal

• ......Denotes the award of a bar to a decoration or medal for valour. The award of additional bars is indicated by the addition of a further similar symbol for each award.

APPOINTMENTS TO THE QUEEN

ADC Gen .Aide de Camp General

ADC .....Aide de Camp

Eq ....Equerry

QHC .....Honorary Chaplain

QHDS ....Honorary Dental Surgeon

QHNS ....Honorary Nursing Sister

QHP .....Honorary Physician

QHS .....Honorary Surgeon

QHVS ....Honorary Veterinary Surgeon

REGIMENT AND CORPS ABBREVIATIONS

A and SH	The Argyll and Sutherland Highlanders (Princess Louise's) _ Scottish Division	IG	Irish Guards - Guards Division
AAC	Army Air Corps	KORBR	The King's Own Royal Border Regiment - King's Division
AGC	Adjutant General's Corps	KOSB	The King's Own Scottish Borderers - Scottish Division
AGC(SPS)	Adjutant General's Corps (Staff and Personnel Support Branch)	KINGS	The King's Regiment - King's Division
AGC(RMP)	Adjutant General's Corps (Royal Military Police)	KRH	The King's Royal Hussars - RAC
AGC(ETS)	Adjutant General's Corps (Educational and Training Services Branch)	LG	The Life Guards - Household Cavalry
		LD	The Light Dragoons - RAC
AGC(ALS)	Adjutant General's Corps (Army Legal Services Branch)	LI	The Light Infantry - Light Division
		OTC	Officers Training Corps
AGC(MPS)	Adjutant General's Corps (Military Provost Staff)	PARA	The Parachute Regiment
APTC	Army Physical Training Corps	PWO	The Prince of Wales's Own Regiment of Yorkshire - King's Division
AG CORPS	Adjutant General's Corps (Unclassified)		
Bda Regt	The Bermuda Regiment	PWRR	The Princess of Wales's Royal Regiment - Queen's Division
BW	The Black Watch (Royal Highland Regiment) - Scottish Division	QARANC	Queen Alexandra's Royal Army Nursing Corps
RHG/D	The Blues and Royals (Royal Horse Guards and 1st Dragoons) - Household Cavalry	QDG	1st The Queen's Dragoon Guards - RAC
		QGE	The Queen's Gurkha Engineers - Bde of Gurkhas
CA Mus	Corps of Army Music		
CHESHIRE	The Cheshire Regiment - Prince of Wales's Division	QOGLR	The Queen's Own Gurkha Logistic Regiment - Bde of Gurkhas
COLDM GDS	Coldstream Guards - Guards Division	QG SIGNALS	Queen's Gurkha Signals - Bde of Gurkhas
REME	Corps of Royal Electrical and Mechanical Engineers	QLR	The Queen's Lancashire Regiment - King's Division
RE	Corps of Royal Engineers	QRH	The Queen's Royal Hussars (The Queen's Own and Royal Irish) - RAC
D and D	The Devonshire and Dorset Regiment - Prince of Wales's Division		
		QRL	The Queen's Royal Lancers - RAC
DWR	The Duke of Wellington's Regiment (West Riding) - King's Division	R ANGLIAN	The Royal Anglian Regiment - Queen's Division
GSC	General Service Corps	RAC	Royal Armoured Corps
GH	The Green Howards (Alexandra Princess of Wales's Own Yorkshire Regiment) - King's Division	RAChD	Royal Army Chaplains' Department
		RADC	Royal Army Dental Corps
GREN GDS	Grenadier Guards - Guards Division	RAMC	Royal Army Medical Corps
HLDRS	The Highlanders (Seaforth, Gordons and Camerons) - Scottish Division	RAVC	Royal Army Veterinary Corps
		R SIGNALS	Royal Corps of Signals
INT CORPS	Intelligence Corps	RDG	The Royal Dragoon Guards - RAC

RG	The Royal Gibraltar Regiment
RGBW	The Royal Gloucestershire, Berkshire and Wiltshire Regiment - Prince of Wales's Division
RGJ	The Royal Green Jackets - Light Division
RGR	The Royal Gurkha Rifles - Bde of Gurkhas
RHF	The Royal Highland Fusiliers (Princess Margaret's Own Glasgow and Ayrshire Regiment) - Scottish Division
RHA	Royal Horse Artillery
R IRISH	The Royal Irish Regiment (27th (Inniskilling) 83rd and 87th and The Ulster Defence Regiment)
9/12th L	9th/12th Royal Lancers (Prince of Wales's) - RAC
RLC	The Royal Logistic Corps
RA	Royal Regiment of Artillery
RRF	The Royal Regiment of Fusiliers - Queen's Division
RRW	The Royal Regiment of Wales - Prince of Wales's Division
RS	The Royal Scots (The Royal Regiment) - Scottish Division
SCOTS DG	The Royal Scots Dragoon Guards (Carabiniers and Greys) - RAC
RTR	Royal Tank Regiment - RAC
RWF	The Royal Welch Fusiliers - Prince of Wales's Division
SG	Scots Guards - Guards Division
SASC	Small Arms School Corps
SAS	Special Air Service Regiment
STAFFORDS	The Staffordshire Regiment (The Prince of Wales's) - Prince of Wales's Division
WG	Welsh Guards - Guards Division
WFR	The Worcestershire and Sherwood Foresters Regiment - Prince of Wales's Division

TA
UNIT TITLES WHICH DIFFER FROM THOSE OF REGULAR UNITS

E and WRR	The East and West Riding Regiment
EER	The East of England Regiment
HAC	The Honourable Artillery Company
HIGHLAND	51st Highland Regiment
KCR	The Kings and Cheshire Regiment
LCV	The Lancastrian and Cumbrian Volunteers
LONDONS	The London Regiment
LOWLAND	52nd Lowland Regiment
QOY	The Queen's Own Yeomanry
RANGERS	The Royal Irish Rangers
R MON RE(M)	Royal Monmouthshire Royal Engineers (Militia)
R WX Y	The Royal Wessex Yeomanry
RMLY	The Royal Mercian and Lancastrian Yeomanry
RV	The Rifle Volunteers
RRV	The Royal Rifle Volunteers
RWR	The Royal Welsh Regiment
RY	The Royal Yeomanry
TYNE TEES	The Tyne Tees Regiment
WM REGT	The West Midlands Regiment

PRECEDENCE OF CORPS, ETC.

1) Life Guards and The Blues and Royals
2) Royal Horse Artillery (a)
3) Royal Armoured Corps
4) Royal Regiment of Artillery (Royal Horse Artillery excepted)
5) Corps of Royal Engineers
6) Royal Corps of Signals
7) Regiments of Foot Guards
8) Regiments of Infantry (b)
9) Special Air Service Regiment
10) Army Air Corps
11) Royal Army Chaplains Department
12) The Royal Logistic Corps
13) Royal Army Medical Corps
14) Corps of Royal Electrical and Mechanical Engineers
15) Adjutant General's Corps
16) Royal Army Veterinary Corps
17) Small Arms School Corps
18) Royal Army Dental Corps
19) Intelligence Corps
20) Army Physical Training Corps
21) General Service Corps
22) Queen Alexandra's Royal Army Nursing Corps
23) Corps of Army Music
24) The Royal Monmouthshire Royal Engineers (Militia) (Territorial Army)
25) The Honourable Artillery Company (Territorial Army)
26) Territorial Army (other than 24 and 25 above) (c)
27) The Royal Gibraltar Regiment
28) The Bermuda Regiment

(a) But on parade, with their guns, to take the right and march at the head of the Household Cavalry.

(b) Divisions of Infantry have precedence as shown in the Corps Warrant. The precedence of the individual infantry regiments remains as it was before the grouping of Infantry Regiments was introduced.

(c) In order of arms as for the Regular Army.

PRECEDENCE OF ROYAL ARMOURED CORPS REGIMENTS

1st The Queen's Dragoon Guards
The Royal Scots Dragoon Guards (Carabiniers and Greys)
The Royal Dragoon Guards
The Queen's Royal Hussars (The Queen's Own and Royal Irish)
9th/12th Royal Lancers (Prince of Wales's)
The King's Royal Hussars
The Light Dragoons
The Queen's Royal Lancers
Regiments of the Royal Tank Regiment

PRECEDENCE OF REGULAR INFANTRY REGIMENTS

The Royal Scots (The Royal Regiment)
The Princess of Wales's Royal Regiment (Queen's and Royal Hampshires)
The King's Own Royal Border Regiment
The Royal Regiment of Fusiliers
The King's Regiment
The Royal Anglian Regiment
The Devonshire and Dorset Regiment
The Light Infantry
The Prince of Wales's Own Regiment of Yorkshire
The Green Howards (Alexandra, Princess of Wales's Own Yorkshire Regiment)
The Royal Highland Fusiliers (Princess Margaret's Own Glasgow and Ayrshire Regiment)
The Cheshire Regiment
The Royal Welch Fusiliers
The Royal Regiment of Wales (24th/41st Foot)
The King's Own Scottish Borderers
The Royal Irish Regiment (27th (Inniskilling), 83rd, 87th and The Ulster Defence Regiment)
The Royal Gloucestershire, Berkshire and Wiltshire Regiment
The Worcestershire and Sherwood Foresters Regiment (29th/45th Foot)
The Queen's Lancashire Regiment
The Duke of Wellington's Regiment (West Riding)
The Staffordshire Regiment (The Prince of Wales's)
The Black Watch (Royal Highland Regiment)
The Highlanders (Seaforth, Gordons and Camerons)
The Argyll and Sutherland Highlanders (Princess Louise's)
The Parachute Regiment
The Royal Gurkha Rifles
The Royal Green Jackets

PRECEDENCE OF YEOMANRY REGIMENTS

The Royal Yeomanry
The Royal Wessex Yeomanry
The Royal Mercian and Lancastrian Yeomanry
The Queen's Own Yeomanry

PRECEDENCE OF TERRITORIAL ARMY INFANTRY REGIMENTS

52nd Lowland Regiment

3rd (Volunteer) Battalion The Princess of Wales's Royal Regiment (Queen's and Royal Hampshires)

The Royal Rifle Volunteers

The London Regiment

The Lancastrian and Cumbrian Volunteers

The Tyne-Tees Regiment

The West Midlands Regiment

The King's and Cheshire Regiment

The East of England Regiment

The Rifle Volunteers

The East and West Riding Regiment

The Royal Welsh Regiment

The Royal Irish Rangers

51st Highland Regiment

4th (Volunteer) Battalion The Parachute Regiment

SECTION I

THE QUEEN

COLONEL IN CHIEF: -LG (060252), RHG/D (010469), SCOTS DG (020771), QRL (060693), RTR (020653), RE (060252), GREN GDS (060252), COLDM GDS (060252), SG (060252), IG (060252), WG (060252), RWF (020653), QLR (250370), A and SH (220447), RGJ (010166), AGC (060492), RMLY (011192)

AFFILIATED COLONEL IN CHIEF: - QGE (070993)

CAPTAIN GENERAL:- RA (060252), HAC (060252), CCF (020653)

PATRON:- RAChD (060292)

Commonwealth Forces

COLONEL IN CHIEF:- The Governor General's Horse Guards (of Canada), Canadian Forces Military Engineers Branch, The King's Own Calgary Regiment, (RCAC), Royal 22e Regiment (of Canada), Governor General's Foot Guards (of Canada), The Canadian Grenadier Guards Le Regiment de la Chaudiere (of Canada)
The 2nd Bn Royal New Brunswick Regiment (North Shore)
The 48th Highlanders of Canada, The Argyll and Sutherland Highlanders of Canada (Princess Louise's), The Calgary Highlanders, Royal Australian Engineers, Royal Australian Infantry Corps, Royal Australian Army Ordnance Corps, Royal Australian Army Nursing Corps, The Corps of Royal New Zealand Engineers, Royal New Zealand Infantry Regiment, The Malawi Rifles, The Royal Malta Artillery

CAPTAIN GENERAL:- Royal Regiment of Canadian Artillery, Royal Regiment of Australian Artillery, Royal Regiment of New Zealand Artillery, Royal New Zealand Armoured Corps

MEMBERS OF THE ROYAL FAMILY

Her Majesty Queen Elizabeth The Queen Mother

COLONEL IN CHIEF:- QDG (010159), QRH (020993), 9/12 L (110960), KINGS (010958), R ANGLIAN (010964) LI (100768), BW (110537), RAMC (240242)

ROYAL HONORARY COLONEL:- The London Scottish (060535), RY (180767), Inns of Court and City Yeomanry (Squadron strength only, part of 71st (Yeomanry) Signal Regiment (Volunteers), Band part of The Royal Yeomanry

Commonwealth Forces

COLONEL IN CHIEF:- The Black Watch (Royal Highland Regiment) of Canada, The Toronto Scottish Regiment (Queen Elizabeth The Queen Mother's Own), Canadian Forces Medical Service, Royal Australian Army Medical Corps, Royal New Zealand Army Medical Corps

Field Marshal His Royal Highness The Prince PHILIP Duke of EDINBURGH
KG KT OM GBE AC QSO

Field Marshal (150153)

COLONEL IN CHIEF:- RGBW (270494), HLDRS (170994), REME (010769), INT CORPS (110677), ACF (150153)

DEPUTY COLONEL IN CHIEF:- QRH (020993)

COLONEL:- GREN GDS (010375)

ROYAL HONORARY COLONEL: City of Edinburgh Universities OTC (230394)

MEMBER: Honourable Artillery Company (1957)

Commonwealth Forces

FIELD MARSHAL:- Australian Military Forces (010454), New Zealand Army (110677)

COLONEL IN CHIEF:- The Royal Canadian Regiment (1953), The Royal Hamilton Light Infantry (Wentworth Regiment) of Canada (1978), The Cameron Highlanders of Ottowa (1967), The Queen's Own Cameron Highlanders of Canada (1967), The Seaforth Highlanders of Canada (1967),The Royal Canadian Army Cadets (1953), The Royal Australian Corps of Electrical and Mechanical Engineers (1959), The Australian Army Cadet Corps (1963)

ROYAL HONORARY COLONEL:- The Trinidad and Tobago Regiment (1964)

Major General His Royal Highness The Prince of Wales KG KT GCB AK QSO ADC

Major General:- (141198)
COLONEL IN CHIEF:- RDG (310792), CHESHIRE (110677), RRW (010769), PARA (110677), RGR (010794), AAC (060292)
DEPUTY COLONEL IN CHIEF:- HLDRS (170994)
COLONEL:- WG (010375)
ROYAL HONORARY COLONEL:- QOY (170600)
Commonwealth Forces
COLONEL IN CHIEF:- The Royal Canadian Dragoons, Lord Strathcona's Horse (Royal Canadians), Royal Regiment of Canada, Royal Winnipeg Rifles, Royal Australian Armoured Corps, 2nd Battalion The Royal Pacific Islands Regiment

His Royal Highness The Duke of York CVO ADC

COLONEL IN CHIEF:- R IRISH (010692), STAFFORDS (210489)
Commonwealth Forces
COLONEL IN CHIEF:- The Queen's York Rangers (1st AmericanRegiment), Royal New Zealand Army Logistic Regiment

Her Royal Highness The Princess Royal KG KT GCVO QSO

COLONEL IN CHIEF:- KRH (041292), RLC (050493), R SIGNALS (110677), RS (300683), WFR (280270)
AFFILIATED COLONEL IN CHIEF:- QGS (070993), QOGLR (050401)
COLONEL:- RHG/D (010998)
ROYAL HONORARY COLONEL:- University of London OTC (210489)
Commonwealth Forces
COLONEL IN CHIEF:- 8th Canadian Hussars (Princess Louise's), Canadian Forces Communications and Electronics Branch, The Grey and Simcoe Foresters, (RCAC), The Royal Regina Rifle Regiment, Royal Australian Corps of Signals, Royal New Zealand Corps of Signals, Royal New Zealand Nursing Corps, Royal Newfoundland Regiment

Her Royal Highness The Princess Margaret, Countess of Snowdon CI GCVO

COLONEL IN CHIEF:- RHF (200159), QARANC (280954), LD (250297)
DEPUTY COLONEL IN CHIEF:- R ANGLIAN (010964)
Commonwealth Forces
COLONEL IN CHIEF:- The Highland Fusiliers of Canada, The Princess Louise Fusiliers (of Canada), The Bermuda Regiment

Her Royal Highness Princess Alice, Duchess of Gloucester GCB CI GCVO GBE

COLONEL IN CHIEF:- KOSB (110537)
DEPUTY COLONEL IN CHIEF:- KRH (011292), R ANGLIAN (010964)
Commonwealth Forces
COLONEL IN CHIEF:- Royal Australian Corps of Transport

His Royal Highness The Duke of Gloucester KG GCVO

DEPUTY COLONEL IN C HIEF:- RGBW (270494), RLC (050493)
ROYAL HONORARY COLONEL:- R MON RE(M) (110677)

Her Royal Highness The Duchess of Gloucester GCVO

COLONEL IN CHIEF:- RADC (170600)
DEPUTY COLONEL IN CHIEF:- AGC (060492)
Commonwealth Forces
COLONEL IN CHIEF:- Royal Australian Army Educational Corps, Royal New Zealand Educational Corps

Field Marshal His Royal Highness The Duke of Kent KG GCMG GCVO ADC

FIELD MARSHAL: (110693)
COLONEL IN CHIEF: RRF (010769); D and D (110677)
DEPUTY COLONEL IN CHIEF: SCOTS DG (021293)
COLONEL: SG (090974)
Commonwealth Forces
COLONEL IN CHIEF: Lorne Scots (Peel, Dufferin and Hamilton Regiment)

Her Royal Highness The Duchess of Kent GCVO

Honorary Major General: (280267)
COLONEL IN CHIEF: PWO (070585)
DEPUTY COLONEL IN CHIEF: RDG (310792); AGC (060492); RLC (050493)

His Royal Highness Prince Michael of Kent KCVO

Major (retired): The Royal Hussars (Prince of Wales's Own)

Her Royal Highness Princess Alexandra, The Hon Lady Ogilvie GCVO

COLONEL IN CHIEF: KORBR (110677)
DEPUTY COLONEL IN CHIEF: QRL (250693); LI (100768)
DEPUTY ROYAL HONORARY COLONEL: RY (150475)
Commonwealth Forces
COLONEL IN CHIEF: The Queen's Own Rifles of Canada, The Canadian Scottish Regiment (Princess Mary's)

PERSONAL AIDES DE CAMP TO THE QUEEN

Maj Gen *HRH The Prince of* Wales *KG KT GCB AK QSO ADC*
Cdr *HRH The Duke of* York *CVO ADC*
Field Marshal *HRH The Duke of* Kent *KG GCMG GCVO ADC*
Capt M A P Phillips *CVO ADC* ret

AIDES DE CAMP GENERAL TO THE QUEEN

Gen *Sir* Rupert Smith *KCB DSO OBE QGM ADC Gen*
Gen *Sir* Michael Walker *GCB CMG CBE ADC Gen*
Gen *Sir* Sam Cowan *KCB CBE ADC Gen*

AIDES DE CAMP TO THE QUEEN

Brig J B A Bailey *MBE ADC*
Brig A E Whitley *CBE ADC*
Brig C J Burton *OBE ADC*
Brig A F Birtwistle *OBE ADC*
Brig *The Hon* S H R H Monro *CBE ADC*
Brig R J Croucher *ADC*
Brig C T Rogers *OBE ADC*
Brig T Dalby-Welsh *ADC*
Brig J R Thomson *TD ADC* TA
Brig W R Rollo *CBE ADC*
Brig R P D Folkes *OBE ADC*
Col K M Tutt *OBE ADC*
Col I G Henderson *OBE TD ADC* TA
Col A J Figg *OBE ADC*

4

EQUERRIES TO THE QUEEN

Crown Equerry

Lt Col S V Gilbart-Denham *CVO* ret pay

Equerry

Lt Col A C Richards *MVO* ret pay *(Deputy Master of the Household)*

Temporary Equerry

Capt J A E Rous COLDM GDS

Extra Equerries

Maj *Sir* Edward Ford *GCVO KCB ERD* ret pay
Lt Col *Sir* John Miller *GCVO DSO MC* ret pay
Lt Col *Sir* John Johnston *GCVO MC* ret pay
Lt Col *Sir* Blair Stewart-Wilson *KCVO* ret pay
Maj *Sir* Shane Blewitt *GCVO* ret pay
Lt Col G A A-R-West *CVO* ret pay
Lt Col *Sir* Malcolm Ross *KCVO OBE* ret pay
Maj Gen *Sir* Simon Cooper *GCVO* ret pay
Lt Col A C McC Mather *CVO OBE* ret pay
Lt Col *Sir* Guy Acland *Bt LVO* ret pay
Lt Col R G Cartwright ret pay
Maj Gen *The Lord* Michael Fitzalan Howard *GCVO CB CBE MC* ret pay

HONORARY CHAPLAINS TO THE QUEEN

The Ven J Blackburn *QHC* Chaplain-General
The Rev D E Wilkes *OBE QHC* Deputy Chaplain-General
The Rt Rev Mgr K Vasey *OBE VG QHC* Principal Roman Catholic Chaplain
The Rev P J Howson *QHC* Chaplain to the Forces 1st Class

HONORARY PHYSICIANS TO THE QUEEN

Brig D W Smith QHP
Brig G O Hopkins QHP
Maj Gen D S Jolliffe QHP
Brig J R Brown QHP
Brig A H McG Macmillan QHP
Col W J Freeman *TD* TA QHP
Brig I G Robertson *OBE TD* QHP

HONORARY SURGEONS TO THE QUEEN

Lt Gen R C Menzies *OBE* QHS
Brig I T Houghton QHS
Col P Roberts *MBE* QHS

HONORARY NURSING SISTERS TO THE QUEEN

Col B C McEvilly *ARRC* QHNS

HONORARY DENTAL SURGEONS TO THE QUEEN

Maj Gen J A Gamon QHDS
Brig S J Poole QHDS
Col M R Townsend QHDS

HONORARY VETERINARY SURGEON TO THE QUEEN

Brig A H Roache QHVS

HER MAJESTY'S BODY GUARD OF THE HON CORPS OF GENTLEMEN AT ARMS

(ESTABLISHED IN THE YEAR 1509)

Uniform - Scarlet   *Facings* - Blue Velvet

Agents - Lloyds Bank plc, Cox's & King's Branch

Captain
The Rt Hon Lord Carter 010597

Lieutenant
Col D V Fanshawe *OBE* ret pay *(late* GREN GDS) 021100

Standard Bearer
Maj *Sir* Timothy Gooch *Bt MBE* ret pay *(late* LG) 020600

Clerk of the Cheque and Adjutant
Maj J B B Cockcroft ret pay *(late* WG) 021100

Harbinger
Col J H Baker *MBE* ret pay *(late* IRISH GDS)..040900

Gentlemen-at-Arms
Col *Hon* R N Crossley *TD* ret pay *(late* 9 L) 260582
Col T J M Wilson ret pay *(late* RM)...090184
Lt Col *Hon* P H Lewis ret pay *(late* 9/12 L) 310388
Maj C J H Gurney ret pay *(late* RGJ)..101088
Lt Col J R Macfarlane ret pay *(late* COLDM GDS) 180290
Lt Col *Hon* G B Norrie ret pay *(late* RH) 310790
Col R J W ffrench Blake ret pay *(late* 13/18 H) 011090
Lt Col J H Fisher *OBE* ret pay *(late* RM)...051190
Maj P D Johnson ret pay *(late* SG) 231290
Lt Col R H Ker *MC* ret pay *(late* RGJ)..190692
Col *Sir* William Mahon *Bt* ret pay *(late* IG) 100493
Lt Col P G Chamberlin ret pay *(late* RGJ) 150693
Col *Sir* Brian Barttelot *Bt OBE* ret pay *(late* COLDM GDS) 110993
Maj R M O Webster ret pay *(late* RA) 031193
Col M J C Robertson *MC* ret pay *(late* RGJ) 140394
Maj J F Warren ret pay *(late* SG) 310196
Maj E M Crofton ret pay *(late* COLDM GDS)...050796
Col G R S Broke *LVO* ret pay *(late* RA)...220297
Maj J G Groves ret pay *(late* 17/21 L) 260397
Col *Sir* Charles Lowther *Bt* ret pay *(late* QRIH).....................................180597
Maj J F M Rodwell ret pay *(late* GREN GDS) 130498
Maj Gen J M F C Hall *CB OBE* ret pay *(late* RSDG) 080399
Col *The Rev* R H Whittington *MBE* ret pay *(late* RE)...............................240599
Maj O C Howard ret pay *(late* RH) 050600
Lt Col T C R B Purdon *OBE* ret pay *(late* WG) 040900
Maj *Hon* A F C Wigram *MVO* ret pay *(late* GREN GDS) 150900
Maj W G Peto ret pay *(late* 13/18 H) 021100

HM TOWER OF LONDON

Constable
Field Marshal *The Lor*d Inge *GCB DL* .... .030896
Constable Designate
Gen *Sir* Roger Wheeler *GCB CBE* (*late* R IRISH) .... .010801

Lieutenant
Lt Gen *Sir* Roderick Cordy-Simpson *KBE CB* (*late* LIGHT DRAGOONS) .... .010301

Resident Governor and Keeper of the Jewel House
Maj Gen G W Field *CB OBE* (*late* RE) .... .150894

Medical Officer
Dr J McGrath .... .181089

Chaplain
The Rev P R C Abram *MA (late* RA Ch D) .... .200896

Deputy Governor
Lt Col J R Dallow (*late* QLR) .... .011298

Operations and Security Manager
Lt Col R J D Reid *OBE* (*late* RE) .... .030700

THE QUEEN'S BODYGUARD OF THE YEOMAN OF THE GUARD

(INSTITUTED 1485)

Uniform - Scarlet   Facings - Blue Velvet

Agents - Lloyds Bank plc, Cox's & King's Branch

Captain
The Lord McIntosh of Haringey .... .020597

Lieutenant
Col G W Tufnell ret pay (*late* GREN GDS) .... .110993

Clerk of the Cheque and Adjutant
Col R S Longsdon ret pay (*late* 17/21 L) .... .110993

Ensign
Maj C R Marriott (*late* RB) .... .110993

Exons
Maj S C Enderby ret pay (*late* 9/12 L) .... .220187
Maj M T N H Wills (*late* COLDM GDS) .... .110993

WINDSOR CASTLE

Constable and Governor
   Air Chief Marshal *Sir* Richard Johns *GCB CBE LVO FRAES* 010500

MILITARY KNIGHTS OF WINDSOR

(INSTITUTED 1348)

Badges - (i) A Shield charged with Cross of St George
(ii) The Star of the Order of the Garter

Uniform - Scarlet   Facings - Blue

Governor
   Maj Gen *Sir* Michael Hobbs *KCVO CBE* ret pay (*late* Gren Gds)

Royal Foundation
   Hon Brig J F Lindner *OBE MC* ret pay (*late* RA)
   Maj W L Thompson *MVO MBE DCM* ret pay (*late* LG)
   Maj J C Cowley *OBE DCM* ret pay (*late* COLDM GDS)
   Maj G R Mitchell *MBE BEM* ret pay (*late* SG)
   Maj P H Bolton *MBE* ret pay *(late* R SIGNALS)
   Brig T W Hackworth *OBE* ret pay (*late* R SIGNALS)
   Maj R J Moore ret pay (*late* RCT)
   Lt Col R R Giles ret pay (*late* RHG/D)
   Maj R J de M Gainher ret pay (*late* QLR)
   Maj A H Clarkson ret pay (*late* RA)
   Col B E Colston ret pay (*late* RCT)
   Lt Col T B F Hiney *MC* ret pay (*late* RAChD)

THE QUEEN'S BODY GUARD FOR SCOTLAND
ROYAL COMPANY OF ARCHERS

ORGANISED IN THE YEAR 1676 (RECONSTITUTED 1703)

Uniform - Green   Facings - Black with Red Velvet

Captain-General and Gold Stick for Scotland

Maj *Sir* Hew Hamilton-Dalrymple *Bt KCVO* 310596
(*HM Lord-Lieutenant East Lothian*)

Captains

Silver Stick for Scotland
The *Duke of* Buccleuch and Queensberry *KT VRD* 210476
The *Rt Hon Earl of* Airlie *KT GCVO (HM Lord-Lieutenant Angus)* 230496
Capt *Sir* Iain Tennant *KT* 180497
The *Marquis of* Lothian *KCVO* 180497

Lieutenants

Commodore *Sir* John Clerk of Penicuik *Bt CBE VRD* 230496
The *Earl of* Elgin and Kincardine *KT CD JP* 230496
Col G R Simpson *DSO LVO TD* 180497
Maj *Sir* David Butter *KCVO MC* 180497

Ensigns

The *Earl of* Minto *OBE* 230496
Maj Gen *Sir* John Swinton *KCVO OBE* 230496
Gen *Sir* Michael Gow *GCB* 180497
Maj *The Hon Sir* Lachlan Maclean *Bt CVO* 140499

Brigadiers

The *Rt Hon Viscount* Younger of Leckie *KT KCVO TD* 240485
Capt G W Burnet *LVO (HM Lord-Lieutenant Midlothian)* 240485
The *Duke of* Montrose 300486
Lt Gen *Sir* Norman Arthur *KCB* 300488
The *Hon Sir* William Macpherson of Cluny *TD* 270489
The *Lord* Nickson *KBE* 260490
Maj *The Lord* Glenarthur 040593
The *Earl of* Dalkeith *KBE* 040593
Maj R Y Henderson *TD (HM Lord-Lieutenant Ayrshire & Arran)* 040596
Col H F O Bewsher *LVO OBE* 040596
The *Earl of* Dalhousie 180497
Brig C D M Ritchie *CBE* 180497
Brig *The Hon* S H R H Monro *CBE ADC* 140499

Adjutant

Brig *The Hon* S H R H Monro *CBE ADC* 120400

Secretary

Capt J D B Younger *(HM Lord-Lieutenant Tweeddale)* 200294

Surgeon

Maj W M Warrack 120400

Chaplain

The *Very Rev* William J Morris *KCVO DD* 200494
(Minister of Glasgow Cathedral)

FOREIGN SOVEREIGNS
AND
MEMBERS OF FOREIGN ROYAL FAMILIES

who are Colonels in Chief or hold Honorary Rank in the Army

His Majesty HARALD V KING OF NORWAY *GCVO*
    Colonel in Chief GH (060292)
    Honorary General (050794)

Her Majesty QUEEN MARGRETHE II OF DENMARK
    Colonel in Chief PWRR (250297)

His Majesty Sultan
HAJI HASSANAL BOLKIAH MU'IZZADDIN WADDAULAH SULTAN AND YANG DI-PERTUAN OF BRUNEI DARUSSALAM GCMG
    Honorary General (230284)

His Royal Highness Prince Mohamed Bolkiah of Brunei *CVO*
    Honorary Lieutenant IG (151171)

His Royal Highness THE GRAND DUKE OF LUXEMBOURG *KG*
    Honorary General (170395)

His Royal Highness Prince Henri of Luxembourg
    Honorary Major PARA (190789)

10

DISBANDED REGIMENTS

ROYAL MILITARY ACADEMY BAND CORPS
(Disbanded 1985)

The Royal Cypher within a circlet bearing the words ROYAL MILITARY ACADEMY
SANDHURST surmounted by a Crown Below the circlet a scroll bearing the words - SERVE TO LEAD

THE CAMERONIANS (SCOTTISH RIFLES)

THE YORK AND LANCASTER REGIMENT
(1. Both Regiment RHQs were finally disbanded 1987)

SECTION II

DEFENCE COUNCIL

The Right Honourable GEOFFREY HOON *MP*
    Secretary of State for Defence *(Chairman of the Defence Council)*

Mr ADAM INGRAM *MP*
    Minister of State for the Armed Forces

Lord BACH
    Minister of State for Defence Procurement

Dr LEWIS MOONIE *MP*
    Parliamentary Under-Secretary of State for Defence

Admiral Sir MICHAEL BOYCE *GCB OBE ADC*
    Chief of the Defence Staff

Mr KEVIN TEBBIT *CMG*
    Permanent Under-Secretary of State

Admiral Sir NIGEL ESSENHIGH *KCB ADC*
    Chief of the Naval Staff and First Sea Lord

General Sir MICHAEL WALKER *GCB CMG CBE ADC Gen*
    Chief of the General Staff

Air Chief Marshal Sir PETER SQUIRE *GCB DFC AFC ADC FRAeS*
    Chief of the Air Staff

Air Chief Marshal Sir ANTHONY BAGNALL *KCB OBE ADC FRAeS*
    Vice Chief of the Defence Staff

Sir ROBERT WALMSLEY *KCB FREng*
    Chief of Defence Procurement

Professor Sir KEITH O'NIONS *FRS*
    Chief Scientific Adviser

General Sir SAM COWAN *KCB CBE ADC Gen*
    Chief of Defence Logistics

Sir ROGER JACKLING *KCB CBE*
    Second Permanent Under Secretary of State

ARMY BOARD OF THE DEFENCE COUNCIL

The Right Honourable GEOFFREY HOON *MP*
    Secretary of State for Defence
    (Chairman of the Defence Council and Chairman of the Army Board of the Defence Council)

Mr ADAM INGRAM *MP*
    Minister of State for the Armed Forces

Lord BACH
    Minister of State for Defence Procurement

Dr LEWIS MOONIE *MP*
    Parliamentary Under-Secretary of State for Defence

—————————————————

General Sir MICHAEL WALKER *GCB CMG CBE ADC Gen*
    Chief of the General Staff

Sir ROGER JACKLING *KCB CBE*
    Second Permanent Under-Secretary of State *(Secretary of the Army Board)*

Lieutenant General Sir Timothy GRANVILLE-CHAPMAN *KCB CBE*
    Adjutant General

Major General D L JUDD
    Quartermaster General

Major General P GILCHRIST
    Master General of the Ordnance

General Sir MIKE JACKSON *KCB CBE DSO*
    Commander in Chief Land Command

Major General K O'DONOGHUE *CBE*
    Assistant Chief of the General Staff

EXECUTIVE COMMITTEE OF THE ARMY BOARD

Chairman . . . . Chief of the General Staff
Members . . . . The Second Permanent Under Secretary of State
                     The Adjutant General
                     The Quartermaster General
                     The Master General of the Ordnance
                     Commander-in-Chief Land Command
                     The Assistant Chief of the General Staff

15

MINISTRY OF DEFENCE

SECRETARY OF STATE FOR DEFENCE

SECRETARY OF STATE FOR DEFENCE . . . . . *The Right Honourable* GEOFFREY HOON *MP*
  Private Secretary . . . . .Mr Julian Miller
MINISTER OF STATE FOR THE ARMED FORCES
                            Mr ADAM INGRAM *MP*
MINISTER OF STATE FOR DEFENCE PROCUREMENT
                            Lord BACH
PARLIAMENTARY UNDER SECRETARY OF STATE
                            Dr LEWIS MOONIE *MP*
CHIEF OF THE DEFENCE STAFF . . . . .Admiral *Sir* MICHAEL BOYCE *GCB OBE ADC*
CHIEF OF THE NAVAL STAFF AND FIRST SEA LORD
                         Admiral *Sir* NIGEL ESSENHIGH *KCB ADC*
CHIEF OF THE GENERAL STAFF . . . . .General *Sir* MICHAEL WALKER *GCB CMG CBE ADC Gen*
CHIEF OF THE AIR STAFF . . . . .Air Chief Marshal *Sir* PETER SQUIRE
                          GCB DFC AFC ADC RAF
VICE CHIEF OF THE DEFENCE STAFF . . . . .Admiral *Sir* PETER ABBOTT *GBE KCB*
SECRETARY, CHIEFS OF STAFF COMMITTEE Group Captain M Swan *LLB*

PERMANENT UNDER SECRETARY OF STATE

PERMANENT UNDER SECRETARY OF STATE
                            KEVIN TEBBIT *CMG*
Second Permanent Under Secretary of State . . . .*Sir* Roger Jackling *KCB CBE*

CENTRAL STAFF
Defence Policy Staff

Policy Director . . . . .Richard Hatfield
Director General International Security Policy . . .Brian Hawtin
Director NATO . . . . .Air Commodore Lacey
Director for Central and Eastern Europe . . . . . .Malcolm Haworth
Director Europe . . . . .Ian Lee
Director of Proliferation and
  Arms Control Secretariat . . . . .Paul Schulte
Director of Chemical and
  Biological Warfare Policy . . . . .John Millen
Head Protocol . . . . .Colonel M A Corbet Burcher *OBE*
Assistant Chief of Defence Staff (Policy) . . . . . .Major General J G Reith *CB CBE*
Director of Policy Planning . . . . .Patrick Turner
Director of Nuclear Policy . . . . .Commodore T Hare
Director Force Development . . . . .Air Commodore McNicoll
Head of British Defence Staff (Washington) . . . .Air Vice Marshal J Thompson
Director General Joint Doctrine
  and Concepts Centre .Major General A A Milton *OBE*
Director General Corporate Communications . . .Mr John Pitt-Brooke
Director News . . . . .Martin Howard
Director Corporate Communications Services . . .Chris Williams
Director Corporate Communications (Navy) . . . .Commodore R Leaman
Director Corporate Communications (Army) . . . .Brigadier S J L Roberts *OBE*
Director Corporate Communications (RAF) . . . .Air Commodore D A Walker *OBE MVO BSc FRAeS MIPD* RAF

Deputy Chief of the Defence Staff (Personnel)

Deputy Chief of the Defence Staff (Personnel) . .Air Marshal *Sir* Malcolm Pledger *OBE AFC BSc FRAeS* RAF
Defence Services Secretary . . . . .Rear Admiral R B Lees
Director of Reserve Forces and Cadets . . . . . . .Brigadier R M Lang *TD* TA
Director of Military Outplacement Services . . . . .Brigadier D H Godsal *MBE BA(Hons)*
Director General Service Personnel Policy . . . . . .Mr B Miller
Director Service Personnel Policy,
  Pay and Allowances .Air Commodore D J Pocock *BA* RAF
Director Service Personnel Policy
  Service Conditions . . . . .Mr M Fuller
Director Service Personnel Policy
  Manning and Training . . . . .Commodore N C Preston-Jones
Director Service Personnel Policy
  Pensions and Welfare . . . . .Mr J Iremonger
Director Pay-As-You-Dine . . . . .Brigadier P J T Maggs *CBE*
Chief Executive Defence Housing Executive . . . .Mr J Wilson
Director of Service Liaison Defence
  Housing Executive . . . . .Brigadier C K Price
Chief Executive Armed Forces Personnel
  Administration Agency . . . . .Mr T S Lord
DCE AFPAA/Director Strategy . . . . .Commodore T A Spires
Director Operations . . . . .Air Commodore P R Thomas

Defence Commitments Staff

Deputy Chief of the Defence Staff (Commitments)
  Lieutenant General A D Pigott *CBE MA*
Assistant Chief of Defence Staff (Operations) . . .Air Vice Marshal G L Torpy *CBE DSO BSc(Eng)* RAF
Director Overseas Military Assistance . . . . .Air Commodore P D Luker *OBE AFC* RAF
Director of Operational Capability . . . . .Air Commodore P Walker *CBE MA* RAF
Director of Naval Operations . . . . .Commodore P L Wilcocks *DSC*
Director of Military Operations . . . . .Brigadier J N R Houghton *OBE*
Director of Air Operations . . . . .Air Commodore A P Waldron *CBE AFC* RAF
Director of Joint Warfare . . . . .Commodore A Nance *OBE*
Director General Operational Policy . . . . .Mr S Webb *CBE*

Defence Equipment Capability Staff

Deputy Chief of the Defence Staff
  (Equipment Capability) . . . . .Vice Admiral *Sir* Jeremy Blackham *KCB BA*
Capability Manager (Strategic Deployment) . . . .Rear Admiral R G J Ward *MA MSc FIEE*
Capability Manager (Manoeuvre) . . . . .Major General A C Figgures *CBE*
Capability Manager (Strike) . . . . .Air Vice Marshal S M Nicholl *CB CBE AFC BA* RAF
Capability Manager (Information Superiority) . . .Major General R H G Fulton
Director General (Equipment) . . . . .Mr M K J Witney
Director General (Research and Technology) . . . .Mr M Markin

Surgeon General's Department

Surgeon General . . . . .Lieutenant General R C Menzies
  OBE QHS MB ChB FrcPath DMJ(Path)
Chief of Staff . . . . .Rear Admiral C D Standford *MA FNI* RN

Defence Scientific Staff

Chief Scientific Adviser . . . . .Professor Sir Keith O'Nions *FRS*
Deputy Under Secretary (Science & Technology) Mr G Jordan
Assistant Chief Scientific Adviser (Nuclear) . . . .R W Roper
Director General (Scrutiny & Analysis) . . . . . . .Mr Tony Quigley
Director Science (Ballistic Missile Defence) . . . .Vacant
Director General (Research & Technology) . . . . .M Markin

17

ARMY DEPARTMENT

CHIEF OF THE GENERAL STAFF

CHIEF OF THE GENERAL STAFF . . . . .GEN *SIR* MICHAEL WALKER *GCB CMG CBE ADC Gen*
ASSISTANT CHIEF OF THE GENERAL STAFF .Maj Gen K O'Donoghue *CBE*

Director of Army Staff Duties . . . . .Brig B W Barry *OBE*
Director Royal Armoured Corps . . . . .Brig W R Rollo *CBE ADC*
Director Royal Artillery . . . . .Brig J B A Bailey *MBE ADC*
Engineer in Chief (Army) . . . . .Brig A E Whitley *CBE ADC*
Signal Officer in Chief (Army) . . . . .Brig C J Burton *OBE ADC*
Director of Infantry . . . . .Brig A D A Duncan *DSO OBE*
Director of Army Aviation . . . . .Brig R P D Folkes *OBE ADC*
Director Intelligence Corps .Brig C G Holtom
Director Royal Logistic Corps . . . . .Brig T Dalby-Welsh *ADC*
Director Electrical and Mechanical Engineers (Army) .Brig R J Croucher *ADC*
Director General Development & Doctrine . . . . .Maj Gen C L Elliott *CB MBE*
Director Land Warfare . . . . .Brig C S Grant *OBE*
Director Capability Integration (Army) . . . . .Brig C C Wilson
Director of Command and Control &
    Information Systems (Army) . . . . .Brig L M J Stone
Director Land Digitization . . . . .Brig G P Sheldon

PERSONNEL AND TRAINING COMMAND

HEADQUARTERS ADJUTANT GENERAL (PERSONNEL AND TRAINING COMMAND)

ADJUTANT GENERAL ....LT GEN *Sir* TIMOTHY GRANVILLE-CHAPMAN *KCB CBE* .190500

DEPUTY ADJUTANT GENERAL/DIRECTOR GENERAL
SERVICE CONDITIONS (ARMY) ....Maj Gen A P N Currie 010201
Chief of Staff ....Brig K H Cima 010201
Director Personal Services (Army) ....Brig N J Cottam *OBE* 081200
COMMAND SECRETARY ....Mrs E M McLoughlin *CBE*

DIRECTOR GENERAL
ARMY MEDICAL SERVICES ....Maj Gen D S Jolliffe *MB BS FRCP MRCS* 170200
Director of Army Dental Services ....Brig S J Poole *QHDS MSc MGDSRCSEng MGDSRCS(Edin)*
LDS 080101
Director of Army Nursing Services ....Col B C McEvily *ARRC QHNS* 010499
Director of Army Veterinary and
Remount Services ....Brig A H Roache *QHVS* 290997

CHAPLAIN-GENERAL ....The Ven J Blackburn *QHC* 120500
Deputy Chaplain-General ....The Rev D E Wilkes *OBE QHC* 050500
Principal Roman Catholic Chaplain ....The Rt Revd Mgr K Vasey *OBE VG QHC* 170597

CORPS OF ARMY MUSIC
Director Corps of Army Music ....Col R G Rowe *BA(Hons)* late R IRISH 100300

ARMY SPORT CONTROL BOARD
President ....
Chairman ....Maj Gen A P N Currie
Director ....Maj Gen S W ST J Lytle *CB* ret pay
Secretary ....Lt Col B Lillywhite ret pay

THE COLLEGE OF ARMS

Inspector of Regimental Colours ....P LI Gwynn-Jones *CVO* 021095

Deputy Inspector of Regimental Colours ......Maj D Rankin-Hunt *MVO MBE TD* 010595

DIRECTOR GENERAL ARMY TRAINING AND RECRUITING

Director General Army Training and Recruiting . .Maj Gen A M D Palmer *CBE* 220199

ARMS CENTRES

Armour Centre Bovington ....Col C J R Day....................................161296
RSA Larkhill ....Col P B Williams *OBE* 130498
RSME ....Brig D R Burns *OBE* 050198
RSS Blandford ....Col K J Hadfield 111298
ITC Catterick ....Col N C D Lithgow 120198
ITC Wales ....Col R F C Andrew *OBE* 240599
ITC Warminster ....Col D T I Glyn-Owen *OBE* 270996
SAAVN ....Col N D D Thursby 010496

ROYAL LOGISTIC CORPS TRAINING GROUP (RLCTG)

Comd RLCTG .... Brig T McG Brown OBE 180299
Comdt Sch of Log .... Col P D Verge 051098
Comdt AS of Cat .... Col D S Robertson 100498
CO AS of A .... Lt Col W G Withers RLC 111100

DEFENCE SCHOOL OF TRANSPORT (DST)

Comdt DST .... Col D J Kerr 280700

ROYAL ELECTRICAL AND MECHANICAL ENGINEERS TRAINING GROUP (REME Trg Gp)

Comd REME Trg Gp .... Brig S C Matthews late REME 100599
Comdt SEME .... Col R G Owen late REME 060599
Comdt SEAE .... Col G Hughes late REME 020899
Comdt SES(A) .... Col S A M Jarvis late REME 050600

ADJUTANT GENERAL'S CORPS TRAINING GROUP (AGC Trg GP)

Comd AGC Trg Gp .... Brig M St J Filler late AGC(ETS) 041099
Comdt DAC .... Col D A MacDonald late RAVC
CO ASTS .... Lt Col K G Lawson AGC(ETS)
CO DSL .... Cdr S E Airey RN
CO RMPTS .... Lt Col K T Bacon OBE AGC(RMP)
CO SET .... Lt Col J L Ransom MBE AGC(SPS)
CO SFM .... Lt Col J A Dathan AGC(SPCS)
OC ASE .... Maj C Douglas AGC(ETS)

HEADQUARTERS INITIAL TRAINING GROUP (HQ ITG)

Comd ITG .... Brig I D T McGill CBE ADC 150699
CO ATR Bassingbourn .... Lt Col I A J Condie R SIGNALS 010998
CO ATR Glencorse .... Lt Col R J Watson PWO 151298
CO ATR Lichfield .... Lt Col P R Farrar PARA 010499
CO ATR Pirbright .... Lt Col D D S A Vandeleur COLD GDS 260297
CO ATR Winchester .... Lt Col J A Athill RGJ 040497
CO Army Apprentice College .... Lt Col J W Mitchell RE 190698
CO Army Foundation College .... Lt Col I W Smith MBE PARA 010498

ROYAL MILITARY ACADEMY SANDHURST (RMAS)

Comdt RMAS .... Maj Gen P C C Trousdell CB 070101

PHYSICAL AND ADVENTUROUS TRAINING GROUP (PATG)

Comdt PATG .... Lt Col S J Hepton APTC 070898
CO ASPT .... Lt Col S J Hepton APTC 070898

INSPECTOR OF PHYSICAL & ADVENTUROUS TRAINING (ARMY) AND COMMANDANT ARMY PHYSICAL TRAINING CORPS

Trenchard Lines, Upavon, Pewsey, Wilts SN9 6BE (Tel: 01980-615152)

Inspector of Physical & Adventurous Training
(Army) and Commandant APTC . . . . .Brig J P Weller *MBE* 150997

Senior Master at Arms . . . . .Lt Col R A Steel APTC 040598

Inspector of Physical & Adventurous Training
(Army) and Assistant Commandant APTC . . . .Col R S Coward 210998

HEADQUARTERS RECRUITING GROUP (HQ RG)

Commander Recruiting . . . . .Brig A S Craig *OBE* 080897

ESTABLISHMENTS

ARMY SCHOOL OF TRAINING SUPPORT
Commanding Officer . . . . .Lt Col R K Morrison *MEd* AGC (ETS) 230996

ADJUTANT GENERAL'S CORPS

Director of Staff and Personnel Support (Army) . .Brig V Batchelor *OBE* 080600

Provost Marshal (Army) . . . . .Brig M Nugent 151099

Director of Educational and Training Services
(Army) . . . . .Brig P S Purves *CBE* 300699

Director of Army Legal Services . . . . .Maj Gen G Risius *CB* 010497

ARMY PERSONNEL CENTRE

MILITARY SECRETARY . . . . .Maj Gen A P Grant Peterkin *OBE* 011200

Chief of Staff . . . . .Col D J Clements *MBE* 080101

Deputy Military Secretary . . . . .Brig C M G Elcomb *OBE* 220199

Colonel Military Secretary (A) . . . . . .Col S F Sherry *OBE* 011299

Colonel Military Secretary (B) . . . . . . .Col M N Pountain 020401

No 1 Selection Board (Appointments and Promotion to Major General)

Chairman . . . . .The Chief of the General Staff (or, in his absence Commander-in-Chief Land
Command)

Members . . . . .The Commander-in-Chief Land Command
The Adjutant General
The Commander Ace Rapid Reaction Corps
Nominated Three Star Officer

Secretary . . . . .The Military Secretary

No 2 Selection Board (Appointments and Promotion to Brigadier and Colonel)

Chairman . . . . .Military Secretary

Members . . . . .Four Core Members:
The Chief of Staff, Headquarters Land Command
Director General Service Conditions (Army)
Director General Defence Logistics Support, Headquarters Defence Logistics
Organisation
Capability Manager (Manoeuvre)

An additional member drawn from the following:
The Chief of Staff PJHQ
The Commandant, Royal Military Academy Sandhurst
The Commandant, Royal Military College of Science
The General Officer Commanding 1st (United Kingdom) Armoured Division
The General Officer Commanding 2nd Division
The General Officer Commanding 3rd (United Kingdom) Division
The General Officer Commanding 4th Division
The General Officer Commanding 5th Division
The General Officer Commanding London District
The General Officer Commanding United Kingdom Support Command
(Germany)

Secretary . . . . .Deputy Military Secretary

The Board may co-opt additional members in the rank of Major General to assist
them in their duties

Composition of No 4 Selection Boards:

a   Boards will normally consist of a chairman and five members

b **Appointments Boards**

Chairman . . . .**DMS**

Membership: Five members
Weapons . . . .**DEC (IBE)**
                      As directed by CM(M)
AG . . . .**COS HQ AG**
                      ACOS Pol
DLO . . . .**D Tech**
                      D Sp Chain
LAND . . . .**ACOS Trg and Dev HQ LAND**
                      DIGTA

MOD CENTRE . . . .**DASD**

Regional Brigade Commanders (2, 15, 42, 43, 49, 51, 52, 143, 145 and 160 Brigades are held as Reserve Members)

c **Promotion Boards:**

Chairman: MS

Membership: Five members drawn from:
Arms Directors . . . .**DRAC**
                      DRA
                      EinC(A)
                      SOinC(A)
                      D Inf
                      DAAvn
                      DRLC
                      DEME(A)
                      Comd AGC Trg Gp
                      D INT CORPS
Ordinary Members . . . .**DCI (A)**
                      DPS(A)
                      DLW
                      DCIS(A)
                      Asst Comdt (Land) JSCSC
                      BGS HQ LAND
                      ACOS Pers HQ LAND
                      Dep Comdt RMCS
Regional Brigade Commanders . . .2, 15, 42, 43, 49, 51, 52, 143, 145 and 160 Brigades

d **Command Boards:**

Chairman . . . .**MS**

Membership: DMS and four core members:
Weapons . . . .**DEC (IBE)**
                      As directed by CM(M)
AG . . . .**COS HQ AG**
                      ACOS Pol
DLO . . . .**DTech**
                      D Sp Chain
LAND . . . .**DIGTA**
                      ACOS Trg and Dev HQ LAND

Other one star commanders may attend as board members if required and available. Special-to-Arm advice is provided by Arms Directors as required.

Secretariat: Col MS(B) acts as the Secretary for all Boards with SO1 MS4 acting as the Assistant Secretary.

No 5 Selection Board (Promotion to Major)

President . . . . .Deputy Military Secretary
Chairman . . . . .Colonel Military Secretary (B)
Members . . . . .Colonel Manning (Army)
                          Chief of Staff Royal Military Academy Sandhurst
                          Colonel nominated by Headquarters LAND
                          Colonel nominated by Headquarters Defence Logistics Organisation
Secretary SO1 MS5

The Army Staff Selection Board

President . . . . .Deputy Military Secretary
Chairman . . . . .Colonel Military Secretary (B)
Members . . . . .Division Director Joint Service Command Staff College
                          Military Director of Studies Royal Military College of Science
                          Director Exams and Courses (Army)
                          Deputy Chief of Staff/Chief of Staff Regional Division
Secretary SO1 MS5

MANNING AND CAREER MANAGEMENT

Director Manning and Career Management
Kentigern House, 65 Brown Street, Glasgow, G2 8EX (Tel: 0141-224 then Ext)
Room 4401   (Tel: 3040)
Deputy Military Secretary . . . . .Brig C M G Elcomb *OBE* 220199

Manning and Career Management Support Division
Room 4409   (Tel: 3053)
SO1 DMS .Lt Col R J Knight *MBE* PWRR 150500

Military Secretary (A)
Room 4010 (Tel: 3095)
Colonel MS(A) . . . . .Col S F Sherry *OBE* 011299

Military Secretary (B)
Room 4107   (Tel: 3110)
Colonel MS(B) . . . . .Col M N Pountain 020401

Royal Armoured Corps/Army Air Corps Manning and Career Management Division
Room 4107   (Tel: 3133)
Divisional Colonel . . . . .Col C H Vernon 210501

Royal Artillery Manning and Career Management Division
Room 5440   (Tel: 3169)
Divisional Colonel . . . . .Col C A Knightley 300501

Royal Engineers Manning and Career Management Division
Room 4402   (Tel: 3204)
Divisional Colonel . . . . .Lt Col G C Watts *MBE* 100401

Royal Signals/Intelligence Corps Manning and Career Management Division
Room 4322   (Tel: 3243)
Divisional Colonel . . . . .Col M J M Dyer *MBE* 201299

Infantry Manning and Career Management Division
Room 5323   (Tel: 3293)
Divisional Colonel . . . . .Col C G Le Brun 220500

Royal Logistic Corps Manning and Career Management Division
Room 4130   (Tel: 3376)
Divisional Colonel . . . . .Col I C Macfarlane 180900

Army Medical Services Manning and Careeer Management Division
Room 5168   (Tel: 3420)

Divisional Colonel . . . . .Col T S Pitcher 100300

Royal Electrical and Mechanical Engineers Manning and Careeer Management Division
Room 4220   (Tel: 3442)

Divisional Colonel . . . . .Col P T McCarthy 191197

Adjutant General's Corps Manning and Career Management Division
Room 4226   (Tel: 3463)

Divisional Colonel . . . . .Col W H Farrington 291199

Territorial Army and Reserves Manning and Career Management Division
GC5, Cadogan Street, Glasgow   (Tel: 8742)

Divisional Colonel . . . . .Col A P W Campbell 040400

PERSONNEL PAY AND PENSIONS ADMINISTRATION

Kentigern House, 65 Brown Street, Glasgow G2 8EX (Tel: 0141-224 then Ext)
Room 3407 (Tel: 3590)

Colonel Personnel Pay and Pensions
Administration ....Col C J Kitchener *OBE* 310500

ARMOUR CENTRE

Allenby Barracks, Wareham, Dorset BH20 6JA (Tel: Bindon Abbey (STD 01929) 403301)
Allied School - The Armoured School (Australia)

Headquarters

Commander . . . . .Col N Q W Beer 220101

AFV Driving and Maintenance School

Commanding Officer .Lt Col R J L Fellowes KRH 200600

AFV CIS School

Commanding Officer .Lt Col C P Donaghy R SIGNALS 011199

AFV Gunnery School

Commanding Officer .Lt Col N Grant-Thorold KRH 171298

Royal Armoured Corps Training Regiment

Commanding Officer .Lt Col A W Ledger QRH 170999

HEADQUARTERS DIRECTOR ROYAL ARTILLERY

Stirling Barracks, Larkhill, Salisbury, Wiltshire SP4 8QT

Director Royal Artillery . . . . .Brig J B A Bailey *MBE ADC* 020200
Chief of Staff . . . . .Col D G Lyon 101299
Col Force Dev . . . . .Col A D K Inkster 280200

REGIMENTAL HEADQUARTERS ROYAL ARTILLERY

Artillery House, Front Parade, RA Barracks, Woolwich, London SE18 4BH (Tel: 020-8781-3714)

Headquarters

Regimental Colonel . . . . .Col M B Cooper 221199

THE ROYAL SCHOOL OF ARTILLERY

Larkhill, Salisbury, Wilts SP4 8QT (Tel: 01980-675581)

Headquarters

Commandant . . . . .Col P B Williams *OBE* 200498

14 Regt RA

Commanding Officer .Lt Col M A L Milligan RA 100700

CENTRAL VOLUNTEER HEADQUARTERS ROYAL ARTILLERY

Royal Artillery Barracks, Woolwich, London SE18 4BB (Tel: 0208-781-3419)

Commanding Officer .Lt Col S N Upton RA 110900

REGIMENTAL HEADQUARTERS ROYAL ENGINEERS

Ravelin Building, Brompton Barracks, Chatham, Kent ME4 4UG (Tel: 01634-822227)

Regimental Colonel ....Col M H H Brooke *OBE* 040599

ROYAL SCHOOL OF MILITARY ENGINEERING

Brompton Barracks, Chatham, Kent ME4 4UG (Tel: 016340 822430)

Headquarters

Commandant ....Brig C M Sexton 011000

Construction Engineer School

Brompton Barracks, Chatham, Kent ME4 4UG (Tel: 01634-822381)

Colonel ....Col I M Tait 010599

1 RSME Regiment

Brompton Barracks, Chatham, Kent ME4 4UG (Tel: 01634-8223341)

Commanding Officer ....Lt Col D S Armitage *MBE* RE 190400

Combat Engineer School

Gibraltar Barracks, Blackwater, Camberley, Surrey GU17 9LP (Tel: 01252-863388)

Colonel ....Col M H G Croft 010799

3 RSME Regiment

Gibraltar Barracks, Blackwater, Camberley, Surrey GU17 9LP (Tel: 01252-863270)

Commanding Officer ....Lt Col P J Francis 010399

GEOGRAPHIC ENGINEER GROUP

Hermitage, Newbury, Berkshire RG16 9TP (Tel: 01635-204240)

Commander ....Col R N Rigby 120400

SIGNAL OFFICER IN CHIEF (ARMY)
Armstrong Building, Blandford Camp, Blandford Forum, Dorset DT11 8RH

Signal Officer in Chief (Army) . . . . .Brig C J Burton *OBE ADC* 020699
Chief of Staff . . . . .Col G J T Rafferty 201100
Colonel Command Support Development Centre .Col D M Mills 301198
Deputy Chief of Staff .Col G N Donaldson *OBE* 250900

REGIMENTAL HEADQUARTERS ROYAL SIGNALS
Blandford Camp, Blandfod Forum, Dorset DT11 8RH (Tel: 01258-482083)

Regimental Colonel . . . . .Col G N Donaldson *OBE* 021100

ROYAL SCHOOL OF SIGNALS
Blandford Camp, Blandford Forum, Dorset DT11 8RH (Tel: 01258-482212)

Headquarters

Commander . . . . .Col J K Ewbank 091000

11th Signal Regiment
(Tel: 01258-482553)

Commanding Officer .Lt Col R G Nicholson 270999

HEADQUARTERS INFANTRY

Imber Road, Warminster, Wilts BA12 0DJ   (Tel: 01985-222457 Fax: 01985-222374)

Chief of Staff ....Col M S Vine *OBE* 270600
Colonel Trg/Force Development ......Col A D Hutchison 041200
Deputy Chief of Staff G1 ....Col N J Mangnall *OBE* 131299

Divisional Offices

Foot Guards ....Lt Col J S Scott-Clarke GREN GDS 010799
Scottish ....Lt Col R M Riddell BW 110199
Queens ....Lt Col P D McLelland PWRR 010700
Kings ....Lt Col N J Rynn GH 280699
Prince of Wales's ....Lt Col P E W Smith WFR 060999
Light ....Lt Col P J Pentreath LI.............................130999
Parachute Regiment ....Lt Col S J Barry PARA 100100

Small Arms School Corps

Colonel Commandant ....Lt Gen C N G Delves *CBE DSO* 010401
Commandant ....Col M S Vine *OBE* 270600
Chief Instructor ....Lt Col G J Lacey *MBE* SASC 110199

Infantry Trials and Development Unit

Warminster, Wilts BA12 0DJ   (Tel: 01985-222000)
Commandant ....Lt Col A W Thornburn *MBE* D and D 260201

SCHOOL OF ARMY AVIATION

Headquarters

Commandant ....Col N J Caplin 130401

2 (Training) Regiment AAC

Commanding Officer ....Lt Col A R B Oatts AAC 140599

Flying Wing

Officer Commanding & Chief Flying Instructor
                     Lt Col H C Northam *MBE* AAC 251099

31

ESTABLISHMENTS

RMCS SHRIVENHAM
(Tel: Reception 01793 785408)

Commandant ....Maj Gen J C B Sutherell *CBE* 120399
Principal ....*Prof* P Hutchinson 010896
Director of Studies and
Deputy Commandant ....Brig W O Cook 191098

DEFENCE NUCLEAR BIOLOGICAL & CHEMICAL CENTRE
Winterbourne Gunner, Salisbury, Wilts SP4 0ES (Tel: 01722 436265)

Commandant ....Gp Capt I A McPhee RAF 150997

ARMY SCHOOL OF PHYSICAL TRAINING
Aldershot, Hants (Tel: 01252 24431)

Commandant ....Lt Col S J Hepton 070898

HEADQUARTERS JOINT SERVICE MOUNTAIN TRAINING CENTRE
Indefatigable, Plas Llanfair, LLANFAIR PG, Anglesey LL61 6NT

Officer Commanding ....Lt Col G S Nicholls D&D 260198

ARMY PROSECUTING AUTHORITY
RAF Uxbridge, Middlesex UP10 0RZ

Prosecuting Authority for the Army ....Maj Gen G Risius 010497
Brigadier Prosecutions ....Brig T Glynn 010497
Colonel Prosecutions (UK) ....Col D M Howell...010497
Colonel Prosecutions (Germany) .....Col A S Paphiti 200197

HEADQUARTERS ARMY MUSIC/ROYAL MILITARY SCHOOL OF MUSIC
Kneller Hall, Twickenham, Middx TW2 7DU
(Tel: Civ 020 8898 5533 Fax: 020 8898 7906)
(Tel: Mil Kneller Hall Ext 5533 Fax: Ext 8644)

Director Corps of Army Music and
Commandant Royal Military School of Music . .Col R G Rowe *BA(Hons)* late R IRISH 100300
Principal Director of Music (Army) . . . . Lt Col G A Kingston psm *C A Mus* 080500

HEADQUARTERS ARMY MUSIC
Chief of Staff . . . . Lt Col (Retd) R M McGhie *OBE* 151098
SO2 Manning and Recruiting . . . . Maj (Retd) C J Reeves 200798

ROYAL MILITARY SCHOOL OF MUSIC
Adjutant . . . . Maj R Archer RLC 050201
Chief Instructor . . . . Maj B D S Burton CA Mus. 131199

ARMY MEDAL OFFICE
Government Buildings, Droitwich Spa, Worcestershire WR9 8AU (Tel: 01905-772323 Ext: 8740)
Officer i/c . . . . Lt Col (retd) J P B Condon *MBE* 011193

HEADQUARTERS RECRUITING GROUP (CRG)

HQ RECRUITING GROUP (HQ RG)
Commander Recruiting Group (CRG)
Ministry of Defence, Building 38B, Trenchard Lines, Upavon, Wilts SN9 6BE
(Tel: 01980 61 8120 Mil (9) 4344 Ext 8120 PS Ext 8121)
(Fax: 01980 61 8166 Mil (9) 4344 Ext 8166)
Commander Recruiting Group (CRG) . . . . Brig S D Young *CBE* 151200
Colonel Army Recruiting (CAR)
Ministry of Defence, Building 38B, Trenchard Lines, Upavon, Wilts SN9 6BE
(Tel: 01908 61 8122 Mil (9) 4344 Ext 8122, PS Ext 8122)
(Fax: 01908 61 8166 Mil (9) 4344 8166)
Colonel Army Recruiting (CAR) . . . . Col W R Harber *OBE* 040599

HEADQUARTERS COMMANDER REGIONAL RECRUITING - LONDON
St Christopher House, Southwark Street, London SE1 0TD
(Tel: 020 7305 4415 Mil (9) 6305 Ext 4415)
(Fax: 020 7305 4314 Mil (9) 6305 4314)
Commander Regional Recruiting (London) . . . . . Lt Col T J D Holmes QDG 010400

HEADQUARTERS COMMANDER REGIONAL RECRUITING - NORTHERN IRELAND
Palace Barracks, BFPO 806
(Tel 02890 429 170 Mil Holywood Mil 43170)
(Fax: 02890 429 168 Mil Holywood Mil 43168)
Commander Regional Recruiting
(Northern Ireland) .Lt Col R F Rafferty R IRISH 101000

HEADQUARTERS COMMANDER REGIONAL RECRUITING - NORTH EAST
Segrave Road, Catterick Garrison, North Yorkshire DL9 3LB
(Tel: 01748 87 2268 Mil (9) 4731 Ext 2091)
(Fax: 01748 87 2268 Mil (9) 4731 Ext 2268)
Commander Regional Recruiting (North East) . . . Lt Col J M May *OBE* RLC 010400

HEADQUARTERS COMMANDER REGIONAL RECRUITING - NORTH WEST
Fulwood Barracks, Preston, Lancashire PR2 8AA
(Tel: 01772 260 556 Mil (9) 4554 Ext 2556)
(Fax: 01772 260 460 Mil (9) 4554 Ext 2460)

Commander Regional Recruiting (North West). . . Lt Col D M Braithwaite RLC 010400

HEADQUARTERS COMMANDER REGIONAL RECRUITING - WESSEX
D Block, Room 28, Dehli Barracks, Tidworth, Wilts SP9 7AB
(Tel: 01980 61 2271 Mil (9) 4342 Ext 2271)
(Fax: 01980 61 2260 Mil (9) 4342 Ext 2260)

Commander Regional Recruiting (Wessex). . . . . . Lt Col D E Roe KRH 010400

HEADQUARTERS COMMANDER REGIONAL RECRUTING - EAST
Building 289, Room 26, HQ Chilwell Station, Chetwynd Barracks, Beeston, Notts NG9 5HA
(Tel: 0115 957 2311 Mil (9) 4451 Ext 2311)
(Fax: 0115 957 2244 Mil (9) 4451 Ext 2244)

Commander Regional Recruiting (East). . . . . . . Lt Col R Evetts RLC 010400

HEADQUARTERS COMMANDER REGIONAL RECRUITING - LOWLAND
Hamilton Block, Craigiehall, South Queensferry, West Lothian EH30 9TN
(Tel: 0131 310 2182 Mil (9) 4740 Ext 2182)
(Fax: 0131 310 3626 Mil (9) 4740 Ext 3626/2312)

Commander Regional Recruiting (Lowland) . . . . Lt Col D K P Steele *MBE* A&SH 010400

HEADQUARTERS COMMANDER REGIONAL RECRUITING - WEST MIDLANDS
Copthorne Barracks, Shrewsbury, Shropshire SY3 8LZ
(Tel: 01743 26 2060 Mil (9) 4461 Ext 2060)
(Fax: 01743 26 2030 Mil (9) 4461 Ext 2030)

Commander Regional Recruiting
(West Midlands) . . . . .Lt Col L Anderson *MBE* LI 010400

HEADQUARTERS COMMANDER REGIONAL RECRUITING - HOME COUNTIES/SOUTH EAST
Block H, Clayton Barracks, Thornhill Road, Aldershot, Hants GU11 2BG
(Tel: 01252 348 541 Mil (9) 4222 Ext 3541)
(Fax: 01252 348 691 Mil (9) 4222 Ext 3691)

Commander Regional Recruiting
(Home Counties/South East) . . . . .Lt Col M E Bradley *OBE* GH 010400

HEADQUARTERS COMMANDER REGIONAL RECRUITING - WALES
The Barracks, Brecon, Powys LD3 7EA
(Tel: 01874 613 340 Mil (9) 4351 Ext 2340)
(Fax: 01874 613 467 Mil (9) 4351 Ext 2912)

Commander Regional Recruiting (Wales). . . . . . Lt Col E M Walters AGC(SPS). 010400

ARMY SCHOOL OF RECRUITING (ASR)
Stanley Barracks, Bovington Camp, Wareham, Dorset BH20 6JB
(Tel: 01929 40 3321 Mil (9) 4374 Ext 3321)
(Fax: 01929 40 3536 Mil (9) 4374 Ext 3536)

Commandant Army School of Recruiting . . . . Lt Col J M W Moody *OBE* R IRISH. 271000

ARMY CAREER ADVISERS (OFFICER) SCHOOL (ACA(O))

NORTH EAST . . . . .Col (Retd) J B Gunson. . . . . .Imphal Barracks, York
(Durham, East Riding of Yorkshire, Hartlepool, Kingston-upon-Hull,
Middlesborough, York, Northumberland, North Yorkshire, Redcar and
Cleveland, Stockton-On-Tees, Tyne and Wear, West Yorkshire, Darlington)

EAST MIDLANDS . . . . .Lt Col R J Christopherson. . . . . .HQ Chilwell Station
(South Yorkshire, South Humberside, South Derbyshire,
Nottinghamshire, Lincolnshire, Leicestershire and
Staffordshire)

EAST ANGLIA .... .Lt Col (Retd) G J Parker................................2 Glisson Road, Cambridge
(Bedfordshire, Norfolk, Cambridgeshire,
Suffolk, Essex and Hertfordshire (less Watford (WD) Postal Area))

LONDON .... .Col (Retd) K A Peacock *MBE*.........................Duke of York HQ, London
(Greater London (less the Boroughs of Bexley, Bromley, Croydon, Greenwich,
Lewisham and Southwark) plus the Watford (WD) Postal Area of Hertfordshire)

SOUTH (1) .... .Lt Col (Retd) I C Shuker...............................HQ R&LS South, Aldershot
(Buckinghamshire, Berkshire and Hampshire)

SOUTH (2) .... .Col (Retd) J N B Stuart
(Surrey, West Sussex and Isle of Wight)

SOUTH EAST .... .Lt Col (Retd) M C K Edwards.......................................ACIO Canterbury
(Kent, East Sussex and the London Boroughs of
Bexley, Bromley, Croydon, Greenwich
Lewisham and Southwark)

WESSEX .... .Lt Col (Retd) A J de Lukacs-Lessner....................Ward Barracks, Bulford
(Wiltshire, Dorset, South Gloucestershire, City and County of Bristol,
Bath and North East Somerset)

SOUTH WESTERN .... .Col (Retd) M A G Watts *MBE*.........................Wyvern Barracks, Exeter
(Somerset, Devon, Cornwall
and the Channel Islands)

SOUTH MIDLANDS .... .Lt Col (Retd) S F Thornton.......................St George's Barracks, Bicester
(Gloucestershire, Warwickshire
Oxfordshire and Northamptonshire)

WESTERN .... .Brig (Retd) A A Hedley *OBE*.......................................AFCO Shrewsbury
(Shropshire, West Midlands
Hereford, Worcester and Wales - Less those covered by ACA(O) NW)

NORTH WEST .... .Col (Retd) J C W Williams *MC*..ACIO Chester
(Cumbria, Lancashire, Merseyside, The Wirral,
Greater Manchester, Cheshire, Gwynedd, Isle of Anglesey, Isle of Man,
Flintshire, Denbighshire, Wrexham County and Conway County Borough)

NORTHERN IRELAND .... .Lt Col (Retd) P R West................................HQ R&LS Northern Ireland

SCOTLAND .... .Col (Retd) A P L Halford-Macleod...........................HQ R&LS Scotland

UNIVERSITY ARMY CAREERS ADVISERS (OFFICER) UNIVERSITY (ACA(O))

SCOTLAND AND NORTHUMBRIA .... .Lt Col (Retd) J A F Walpole.......................................HQ R&LS Scotland
(Scotland, Northumberland,
Tyne and Wear, Durham and Cleveland)

NORTH AND EAST MIDLANDS .... .Lt Col (Retd) J A Hodges...............Welby Lane Camp, Melton Mowbray
(North and West Yorkshire,
Humberside, Lincolnshire, Nottinghamshire,
Leicestershire and Rutland)

NORTH WEST .... .Brig (Retd) E C W Morrison *OBE*.......................................ACIO Chester
(Cumbria, Lancashire, Greater Manchester, Merseyside, Cheshire,
South Yorkshire, Derbyshire, Gwynedd, Isle of Anglesey, Flintshire,
Denbighshire, Wrexham County Borough and Conway County Borough)

LONDON AND EAST ANGLIA .... .Brig (Retd) H H Kerr *OBE*.............................Duke of York HQ, London
(Greater London, Essex, Hertfordshire,
Bedfordshire, Northamptonshire, Suffolk,
Cambridgeshire, Norfolk)

WESTERN .... .Brig (Retd) W H Backhouse...ACIO Worcester
(Wales - less those covered by ACA(O) NW,
Shropshire, Hereford, Staffordshire,
Warwickshire, West Midlands and Worcester)

SOUTH . . . . .Col (Retd) A G Platt. . . . . .HQ R&LS South, Aldershot
(Kent, Sussex, Surrey, Isle of Wight,
Hampshire, Berkshire, Oxfordshire,
Buckinghamshire, Dorset, Wiltshire,
Devon, Gloucestershire, Somerset,
Cornwall and Channel Islands)

NORTHERN IRELAND . . . . .Lt Col (Retd) P R West. . . . . .HQ R&LS, Northern Ireland

THE REGULAR COMMISSIONS BOARD
Leighton House, Westbury, Wiltshire BA13 3PS (Tel: 01373-828141)

President . . . . .Brig D A K Biggart *OBE* 060198
Vice Presidents . . . . .Col N H C Brown 080698
Col F R J MacLean 071298
Col S C Hearn *OBE* 140498

WELBECK COLLEGE
Worksop, Nottinghamshire S80 3LN (Tel: 01909 476326 Fax: 01909 530447)

Principal . . . . .Mr A Halliwell *BSc MA* 010199

DIRECTOR ARMED FORCES PERSONNEL ADMINISTRATION AGENCY (WORTHY DOWN SITE)
Bray House, Worthy Down, Winchester, Hants SO21 2RG (Tel: 01962-887642)

Headquarters
Director Armed Forces Personnel Administration
Agency (Worth Down Site) . . . . .Brig M L Ward 010497

Current Systems
Deputy Director (Current Systems) Armed Forces Personnel
Administration Agency (Worthy Down Site) . . . . .Col C T Oakley. 010498

ARMY MEDICAL SERVICES

Army Medical Directorate
former Army Staff College, London Road, Camberley GU15 4NP

Chief of Staff . . . . .Col A Hawley *OBE* L/RAMC 190299

RHQ RAMC
(Tel: 01276 63344)

Officer Recruiting . . . . .Col A P Willman ret pay 210194

RHQ QARANC
(Tel: 01276 63344)

Corps Recruiting & Liaison Officer . . . . .Maj T Collins QARANC 290101

RHQ RADC
(Tel: 01276 63344)

Recruiting . . . . .Capt J Sharp RADC 010700

Headquarters Army Medical Services Territorial Army
Imphal Barracks, Fulford Road, York YO10 4HD

Commander . . . . .Col M C Best L/RAMC 240397

Defence Animal Centre
Melton Mowbray, Leics LE13 0SL (Tel: 01664 63281)

Commandant . . . . .Col J A Kneale L/RAVC 011196

37

Consultants Emeritus to the Army

Rt Hon Lord Richardson *MVO (late Honorary Civilian Consultant Physician to the Army)*
Prof T C Gray *(late Honorary Civilian Consultant Anaesthetist to the Army)*
Mr T L T Lewis *CBE (late Honorary Civilian Consultant Obstetrician to the Army)*
Dr Walter Somerville *CBE (late Honorary Civilian Consultant Cardiologist to the Army)*
Mr R M Gibson *ERD TD (late Honorary Civilian Consultant Neuro-Surgeon to the Army)*
Prof J M Cameron *(late Honorary Civilian Consultant in Forensic Medicine to the Army)*
Prof R Williams *CBE (late Honorary Civilian Consultant in Medicine to the Army)*
Dr A Yates *(late Honorary Civilian Consultant in Rheumatology andRehabilitation to the Army)*
Dr P J Baskett *(late Honorary Civilian Consultant in Resuscitation to the Army)*

Honorary Consultants to the Army at Home

A&E Medicine . . . .*Mr* K Mackway-Jones
Alcohol and other Substance Abuse . . . .*Prof* C C H Cook
Anaesthetics . . . .*Prof* A P Adams
Aviation Medicine . . . .*Dr* K Edgington
Blood Transfusion . . . .*Dr* F E Boulton
Cardiology . . . .*Dr* D J Coltart
Cardiothoracic Surgery . . . .*Mr* G E Venn
Cardiothoracic Surgery . . . .*Mr* C P Young
Child & Adolescent Psychiatry . . . .*Prof* P Hill
Clinical Psychology . . . .*Prof* W Yule
Colon & Rectal Surgery . . . .*Mr* J Northover
Cytopathology . . . .*Dr* W Gray
Dental Education . . . .*Mr* D C Rule
Dermatology . . . .*Dr* M M Black
Diseases of the Chest . . . .*Dr* D M Geddes
Endocrinology . . . .*Prof* A M McGregor
Entomology . . . .*Prof* N R H Burgess
Forensic Medicine . . . .*Dr* P Vanezis
Forensic Psychiatry . . . .*Prof* J C Gunn *CBE*
Gastro-Enterology . . . .*Prof* M J G Farthing
General Practice . . . .*Dr* R G Hornung
Genito-Urinary Medicine . . . .*Dr* J S Bingham
Haemotology . . . .*Prof* A C Newland
Health Economics . . . .*Mr* J Hutton
Haematology Histopathology . . . .*Prof* I Lauder
Intensive Care Medicine . . . .*Prof* T W Evans
Malariology . . . .*Prof* D A Warrell
Medical Statistics . . . .*Dr* J Deeks
Medicine . . . .*Prof* L E Ramsay
Microbiology . . . .*Prof* R Wise
Neonatology . . . .*Dr* P Hamilton
Neurology . . . .*Dr* M Donaghy
Neurosurgery . . . .*Mr* G Neil-Dwyer
Nuclear Medicine . . . .*Prof* M N Maisey
Obst & Gynae . . . .*Mr* C D Sims
Occupational Medicine . . . .*Prof* J M Harrington *CBE*
Ophthalmology . . . .*Mr* P T Khaw
Oral Medicine . . . .*Prof* S J Challacombe
Oral Surgery . . . .*Dr* D W Patton *TD*
Orthodontics . . . .*Mr* N P Hunt
Orthopaedic Suregery . . . .*Mr* R H Vickers
Oto-Rhino-Laryngology . . . .*Mr* D Wright
Paediatrics . . . .*Dr* M J Dillon
Paed Ortho Surgery . . . .*Mr* G C Bennet
Paediatric Surgery . . . .*Prof* L Spitz
Pain Relief "Anaesthetist" . . . .*Dr* J R Wedley
Plastic Surgery . . . .*Mr* J D Watson
Psychiatry . . . .*Prof* J P Watson
Pub Health Medicine . . . .*Prof* J McEwen
Public and Media Relations . . . .*Mr* D Sharp
Radiothereapeutics . . . .*Dr* R H Phillips
Radiology . . . .*Prof* P Armstrong
Rehabilitation . . . .*Prof* D L McLellan
Restorative Dentistry . . . .*Prof* B G N Smith
Resuscitation . . . .*Mr* M F Ward
Rheumatology . . . .*Mr* B L Hazleman
Sports Medicine . . . .*Prof* W S Hills
Sports and Exercise Science . . . .*Prof* D A Jones

Surgery	.*Mr* B Jackson
Surgery	.*Prof* M H Irving
Surgery	.*Mr* W Owen
Travel Medicine	.*Dr* R H Behrens
Tropical Diseases	.*Dr* A D M Bryceson
Urology	.*Mr* H M Whitfield
Vacc & Immunisation	.*Prof* R E Spier
Vascular Surgery	.*Prof* K Burnand

To BFG Health Service

Paediatrics ....*Prof* K E Von Muhlendahl

To MDHU Northallerton

Oral Surgery ....*Mr* B S Avery

To Northern Ireland

Anaesthetics	.*Dr* H M L Johnston
Medicine	.*Prof* J R Hayes
Psychiatry	.*Lt Col* J N Scott *TD*
Surgery	.*Mr* A McMurray

To DCU MPH

Surgery ....*Prof* T G Parks

To DMS College Gosport

Wound Ballistics ....*Mr* L D Payne

To Scotland

Dermatology	.*Dr* R D Aldridge
ENT	.*Dr* B A B Dale
Medicine	.*Dr* E Housley
Ophthalmology	.*Dr* A D Adams
Orthopaedic Surgery	.*Lt Col* McDonald
Surgery	.*Dr* D A D Mcleod

ADJUTANT GENERAL'S CORPS CENTRE AND HEADQUARTERS WINCHESTER GARRISON

Worthy Down, Winchester, Hants SO21 2RG (Tel: 01962 887648 Mil Ext 2648)

Commander ....*Brig* D A Harrison *BA MSc(Econ) FIPD* 120197

ADJUTANT GENERAL'S CORPS TRAINING GROUP

Worthy Down, Winchester, Hants SO21 2RG (Tel: 01962 887686 Mil Ext: 2686)

Commandant ....*Col* M Nugent 101297

SCHOOL OF EMPLOYMENT TRAINING

Worthy Down, Winchester, Hants SO21 2RG (Tel: 01962 887238 Mil Ext: 2238)

Commanding Officer ....*Lt Col* J L Ransom *MBE sp pfc* AGC(SPS) 260599

SCHOOL OF FINANCE AND MANAGEMENT

Worthy Down, Winchester, Hants SO21 2RG (Tel: 01962 887651 Mil Ext: 2651)

Commanding Officer ....*Lt Col* P L d'A Willis AGC(SPS) 130798

ROYAL MILITARY POLICE TRAINING SCHOOL

Roussillion Barracks, Chicheste, West Sussex PO19 4BN (Tel: 01243 534204 Mil Ext: 4204)

Commanding Officer ....*Lt Col* K Bacon *OBE* AGC(RMP) 080598

MILITARY CORRECTIVE TRAINING CENTRE

Colchester (Tel: 01206 575121)

Commandant ....*Lt Col* S A Jasper RTR 051098

HEADQUARTERS BEACONSFIELD STATION AND DEFENCE SCHOOL OF LANGUAGES

Wilton Park, Beaconsfield (Tel: 014946 6121 Ext 3230)

Commander . . . . .Cmdr S E Airey *BA MA* RN 230399

RESETTLEMENT CENTRE CATTERICK

Hipswell Lodge, Catterick Garrison, North Yorkshire (Tel: Catterick Garrison 2898)

Commandant . . . . .Lt Col P R Thomas *MA* AGC(ETS) 121297

RESETTLEMENT CENTRE ALDERSHOT

Gallwey Road, Aldershot, Hants (Tel: 01252 24431)

Commandant . . . . .Lt Col P R Thomas *MA* AGC(ETS) 201296

HOME HEADQUARTERS AND MUSEUM ROYAL ARMY CHAPLAINS' DEPARTMENT

Armed Forces Chaplaincy Centre, Amport House, Amport, Andover, Hants SP11 8BG (Tel: 01264 773144)

Departmental Secretary . . . . .Maj (Retd) M Easey . . . .

ARMY SCHOOL OF EDUCATION

Worthy Down, Winchester, Hants SO21 2RG (Tel: 01962 887082 Mil Ext: 2082)

Officer Commanding . . . . .Maj C Douglas AGC(ETS) 140998

40

MISCELLANEOUS

THE NAVY ARMY AND AIR FORCE INSTITUTES
(A Company Limited by Guarantee)

Registered office: London Road, Amesbury, Wiltshire SP4 7EN
(Tel: 01980 627000)

PATRON . . . . .Her Majesty The Queen

Council

Service Members appointed by the Admiralty Board
Vice Admiral Peter Spencer *ADC*
Commodore Barry Bryant

Service Members appointed by the Army Board
Lt General *Sir* Timothy Granville-Chapman *KCB CBE*
Brigadier N J Cottam *OBE*

Service Members appointed by the Air Force Board
Air Marshal *Sir* John Day *KCB OBE DSc RAF*
Air Commodore M Good

Other Members appointed jointly by the Admiralty Board, Army Board and Air Force Board
Air Marshal *Sir* Malcolm Pledger *KCB OBE AFC BSc FRAeS RAF (President)*
D J M Roberts *MC (Chairman, Board of Management)*
G C Dart *CBE*
(Deputy Chairman, Board of Management)
Mr B Miller

Board of Management

Directors nominated by the Board of Management
N W McCausland *(Chief Executive)*
A H Vaughan *OBE BA FIMgt*
V Steel
A J Cole
T Morgan

THE SERVICES SOUND AND VISION CORPORATION
Chalfont Grove, Narcot Lane, Chalfont St Peter, Gerrards Cross, Bucks SL9 8TN
Tel: 01494 878 225 Fax: 01494 878 008
email: info@ssvc.com website: www.ssvc.com

PATRON . . . . .HRH The Princess Margaret

TRUSTEES AND MEMBERS OF THE SSVC BOARD OF MANAGEMENT

Chairman . . . . .David Hatch *CBE MA DipEd FRSA CIMgt JP*

Members . . . . .Brian Tesler *CBE MA*
Michael Andrae *Hon FCIM FMIS FRSA*
Howard Perlin *FCA*
Lt Gen *Sir* Roderick Cordy-Simpson *KBE CB*
Air Vice-Marshal Nigel Baldwin *CB CBE* RAF (Retd)
Captain Graham Robinson RN

Managing Director . . . . .Air Vice-Marshal D O Crwys-Williams
CB FIPD FIMgt RAF (Retd)

Vice Patrons .Vice Admiral P Spencer, ADC
(2 S/L and CinC Home Command)
Lt Gen *Sir* Timothy Granville-Chapman *KCB CBE*
(Adjutant General)
Air Marshal *Sir* John Day *KCB OBE*
(Air Member for Personnel)

Life Vice-Presidents . . . . .Group Captain *Sir* Gordon Pirie *CVO CBE DL* RAF (Retd)
General *Sir* Geoffrey Howlett *KBE MC*

41

THE ARMY BENEVOLENT FUND

41 Queen's Gate, South Kensington, London SW7 5HR
(Tel: 020-7591-2000 Fax: 020-7584-0889)
website: www.armybenevolentfund.com

PATRON	THE QUEEN
President	Field Marshal *The Lord* Inge *GCB DL*
Chairman Executive Committee	General *Sir* Jeremy Mackenzie *GCB OBE* ret pay
Controller	Maj Gen M D Regan *CB OBE* ret pay

THE NATIONAL ARMY MUSEUM

Royal Hospital Road, Chelsea, London SW3 4HT
(Tel: 020-7730-0717 Fax: 020-7823-6573)

PATRON	Field Marshal *HRH The Duke of* Kent *KG GCMB GCVO ADC*
Council	Parliamentary Under Secretary of State for Defence (Chairman)
	Adjutant General
	Command Secretary (Adjutant General)
	FM *Sir* John Chapple *GCB CBE DL*
	Mrs Sara Jones *CBE JP*
	The Right Revd Michael Mann *KCVO*
	Mr Richard Marriott *TD*
	The Hon David McAlpine
	Sir Nigel Mobbs *JP*
	Prof Hew Strachan *MA PhD FRHistS*
	Gen *Sir* John Waters *GCB CBE JP* (Deputy Chairman)
	One vacancy
Director	I G Robertson *MA FMA*

THE DUKE OF YORK'S ROYAL MILITARY SCHOOL

Dover, Kent CT15 5EQ (Tel: 01304-245029)
Journal: "The Yorkist"

President . . . . .Field Marshal *HRH The Duke of* Kent *KG GCMG GCVO ADC*

Commissioners

Ex Officio Members . . . . .The Chaplain General

In Attendance . . . . .Comd Sec (AG)
(Ex Officio) .DETS (A)

Special Commissioners . . . . .Maj Gen D A Grove *OBE* ret pay *Chairman*
Brig A Field *CB CBE* ret pay
Air Vice Marshal M R Jackson *CB* ret pay
Maj Gen A L Meier *CB OBE* ret pay
R Adm J A Trewby *CB* ret pay

Elected . . . . .Brig M A Atherton *CBE JP DL* ret pay
Sir John Carter
L C Stephenson Esq *CEng MRINA*
Mrs J B E Wells *MA JP*

Kent County Council . . . . .Vacant

Co-opted Member . . . . .D H Webb Esq *TD BSc Ceng FIMechE Fimgt*

Headmaster and Chief Executive . . . . .Mr J A Cummings *BA(Hons) MA* 010999

Bursar and Secretary to HM Commissioners
Lt Col R Say *FCMA ACIS Mimgt* ret pay 010798

QUEEN VICTORIA SCHOOL FOR THE CHILDREN OF SCOTTISH SAILORS, SOLDIERS AND AIRMEN

Dunblane, Perthshire FK15 0JY (Tel: 01786-822288)

Journal: "The Victorian"

Patron . . . . .Field Marshal *HRH The Prince* Philip *Duke of* Edinburgh
KG KT OM GBE AC QSO

President . . . . .The Secretary of State for Scotland

Commissioners . . . . .Lt Gen *Sir* John MacMillan *KCE CBE* ret pay *Chairman*
The Lord Justice Clerk *(ex officio)*
The GOC Scotland *(ex officio)*
Representative of the Scottish Office *(ex officio)*
Dr S E McClelland *CBE BSc PhD*
G F Belton Esq *OBE MA LLB FIMgt*
Mrs N H Howe
D MacLehose Esq
Maj Gen J D MacDonald *CB CBE DL* ret pay
Air Vice Marshal J Morris *CBE BSc* ret pay
Capt R A Smith RN ret pay
Sir Moray Stewart *KCB D.Litt*
W McD Moodie Esq *CBE QPM DL*
Mrs P McCabe
Rear Admiral N E Rankin *CB CBE*

Headmaster .B Raine Esq *BA(Hons) PGCE*

Bursar and Secretary to the Commissioners
Sqn Ldr I McGregor *MA Dip Mgmt*

ROYAL HOSPITAL CHELSEA

Commissioners

Ex officio . . . . .The Paymaster General
The Minister of State for the Armed Forces
The Parliamentary Under Secretary of State for Defence
The Governor of the Royal Hospital Chelsea
The Director General of Army Medical Services
Assistant Chief of the General Staff
The Command Secretary (Adjutant General)
The Lieutenant Governor of the Royal Hospital Chelsea

Specially appointed . . . . .Sir Idris Pearce CBE TD FRICS 101195
Gen Sir John Wilsey GCB CBE 010796
Field Marshal Lord Inge GCB 010398
Sir Michael Craig-Cooper CBE TD DL 151198
Sir Nigel Mobbs JP 010900
Mrs R Corben 010900
Mr I W Frazer Esq FCA 010900
M Gainsborough Esq 010301
Lord Glenarthur 010301

Governor . . . . .Gen Sir Jeremy Mackenzie GCB OBE 090899
Lieutenant Governor . . . . .Maj Gen J M F C Hall CB OBE ret pay 081297
Secretary . . . . .J M Legge CB CMG . . . .
Adjutant . . . . .Brig A G Ross OBE ret pay 010894
Physician and Surgeon . . . . .Lt Col W M Wallace ret pay 150598
Chaplain . . . . .Rev D Whittington MBE 290101
Assistant Physician . . . . .Col J S K Swanston ret pay 060999
Assistant Physician . . . . .Dr J P Jones 260600
Quartermaster . . . . .Lt Col N McCleery OBE ret pay 270300
Chief Clerk . . . . .I F Williamson Esq 010598
Chief Accountant . . . . .Maj P S D Sheehan ret pay 110396
Captains of Invalids . . . . .Col S R Daniell ret pay 211298
Maj H M Snow ret pay 210699
Maj J T Tatham ret pay 021192
Col N E Gilbert ret pay 170100
Lt Col A M Mackenzie MBE ret pay 020101

Consultants

Medicine . . . . .Col P Fabricus

Surgery . . . . .Col P Roberts MBE QHS

Honorary Consultants

Cardiology . . . . .Dr M M Webb-Peploe
Dermatology . . . . .Dr R C D Staughton
Psychogeriatrics . . . . .Dr R R Menon
Geriatric Medicine . . . . .Dr H Gillespie
Medicine . . . . .Dr R Zeegan OBE
Opthalmology . . . . .Dr D H Spalton
Radiotherapy and Medical Oncology . .Dr R H Phillips
Surgery . . . . .Prof T Allen-Mersh Honorary Physician
Thoracic Medicine . . . . .Dr J V Collins
Vascular Surgery . . . . .Prof R M Greenhalgh
Psychiatry . . . . .Dr O S Frank

DIRECTORATE GENERAL DEFENCE LOGISTIC SUPPORT
DLO Andover, Monxton Road, Andover, Hampshire SP11 8HT

DIRECTOR GENERAL DEFENCE LOGISTIC SUPPORT
Maj Gen T Cross *CBE* 010400
Director of Logistic Business Management
Mr S Wallace 010499
Director Defence Physical Supply Chain
Cdre N D Savage RN 151200
Chief Executive Defence Storage and Distribution Agency
Brig P D Foxton *CBE* 010499
Chief Executive Defence Transport and Movements Agency
Air Cdre P Whalley RAF 010400
Chief Executive British Forces Post Office
Brig B J Cash 080199
Director Defence Fuels Group
Air Cdre D P Hedges RAF 291199
Director Defence Catering Group
Air Cdre S Wood RAF 140200
Director Corporate Technical Services
Mr H W Perkins 231000
Director Pay As You Dine
Brig P J T Maggs *CBE* 250900
Director Defence Munitions
Mr A Blair 010401

DEFENCE STORAGE AND DISTRIBUTION AGENCY (DSDA)
DSDA, Ploughley Road, Lower Arncott, Bicester, Oxon OX25 2LD (Tel: 01869 256840)

Chief Executive ....Brig P D Foxton *CBE* 010499

Business Management Directorate
DSDA, Lower Arncott, Bicester, Oxon OX25 2LD

Director Business Management ......Mr P Clasper 010499

Plans Directorate
DSDA, Lower Arncott, Bicester, Oxon OX25 2LD

Director Plans ....Gp Capt D B Cannon RAF 010499

Operations Directorate
DSDA, Lower Arncott, Bicester, Oxon OX25 2LD

Director Operations ....Col J H O'Hare *OBE* 310301

Finance Directorate

Director Finance ....Mr J J Kelly 010499

Human Resources Directorate

Director Human Resources ....Mrs L A Gray 131100

Marketing Directorate
DSDA, Lower Arncott, Bicester, Oxon OX25 2LD

Director Marketing ....Mr M Waddleton 010900

DSDA (SC), Lower Arncott, Bicester, Oxon OX25 2LD

Director DSDA (SC) ....Wg Cdr S F Caunt RAF 310301

DSDA (G) Dulmen, BFPO 44

Director (DSDA(G) ....Lt Col M D Ingram *OBE* RLC 010499

DEFENCE STORAGE AND DISTRIBUTION CENTRES (Dsdcs)
DSDC Bicester, Oxon OX25 2LD (Tel: 01869 256849)

Director DSDC Bicester ....Col G A Hazlewood 010499

DSDC Donnington, Telford, Salop TF2 8JT (Tel: 01952 673000)
Director DSDC Donnington ....Col R W Bugler 240700

DSDC Ashchurch, Tewkesbury, Glos GL20 8LZ (Tel: 01869 258275)
Director DSDC Ashchurch ....Mr A Lavery 061299

DSDC Stafford, Beaconside, Staffs ST18 0AO
Director DSDC Stafford ....Gp Capt N W Cromarty RAF 030700

DSDC Llangennech, Llanelli, Dyfed SA14 8YP (Tel: 01554 822316)
Director DSDC Llangennech ....Mr G S Mabbett 010499

DSDC Aston Down, Stroud, Glas GL6 8HT (Tel 01285 760688)
Director DSDC Aston Down ....Mr J Roberts 010499

ARMY BASE REPAIR ORGANISATION
Monxton Road, Andover, Hants SP11 8HT (Tel: 01264 383118)

Chief Executive ....J R Drew *CBE* 060492

EQUIPMENT SUPPORT (LAND)

DIRECTOR GENERAL OF EQUIPMENT SUPPORT (LAND)
Maj Gen D L Judd 010400

Director Business Development	Brig S G Middleton	010400
Director Technical	Brig R I B Rickard	010400
Director Support Chain	Brig M J Wharmby	010400
Director Support Operations	Brig S J Tetlow *MBE*	111200
Director Munitions Corporate Business Unit	Brig C R Elderton *OBE*	010400
Director Resources	Mr K L Bellamy	010400
Director Commercial	Mr A Bevan	010400

REGIMENTAL HEADQUARTERS REME
Headquarters DEME(A), Box H075, Arborfield, Reading, Berks RG2 9NJ (Tel: 0118-976-0421)

Regimental Colonel . . . . .Col R B Peregrine 110800

HEADQUARTERS REME TERRITORIAL ARMY
Louisburg Barracks, Bordon, Hants GU35 0NE (Tel: 01403 3611)

Commander . . . . .Col J L Harvey *TD* 010799

DEFENCE PROCUREMENT AGENCY

MINISTRY OF DEFENCE

Defence Procurement Agency, Abbey Wood, Bristol BS34 8JH

Chief of Defence Procurement and Chief Executive
DPA CDP . . . .*Sir* Robert Walmsley *KCB*
Deputy Chief of Defence Procurement (Support) and Deputy
Chief Executive DCDP . . . . .John Howe
Executive Director XD1 . . . . .Ian Fauset
Executive Director 2 and Master General of the Ordnance
XD2/MGO . . . . .Maj Gen Peter Gilchrist
Executive Director 3 XD3 . . . . .Geoff Beaven
Executive Director 4 and Controller Navy
XD4/CofN . . . . .R Adm Nigel Guild
Executive Director 5 XD5 . . . . .Stan Porter
Executive Director 6 XD6 . . . . .Nick Evans
Engineering Advisor and President of the Ordnance Board
POB . . . . .Maj Gen Liam Curran

PEER GROUP A

Future Battlefield and Amphibious Support
Helicopter	IPT Chris Trout
Future Engineer Tank	IPTL Nigel Gilhead
MRAV	IPTL TBA
Tactical UAVs	IPTL Alan Baker
TRACER	IPTL Col Peter Flach

PEER GROUP B

Air Systems

PEER GROUP C

Air Systems
Battlefield Joint Trainers, Simulation and
Synthetic Environment   IPTL Neil McCabe

PEER GROUP D

Close Armour	IPTL Richard Brooks
Mobility	IPTL Roger Colebrook
Counter Mobility	IPTL Col Charles Hookey
EngineerVehicles and Plant	IPTL Phil Strudley
Battlefield Infrastructure	IPTL Les Lloyd

PEER GROUP E

Land Tactical Electronic Warfare
IPTL Col John Terrington
Command Support Info Systems
IPTL Peter Wakeling

PEER GROUP F

Sea Systems

PEER GROUP G

Sea Systems

PEER GROUP H

Infantry GW	IPTL Mike Hoskins
ASTOR	IPTL Gp Capt Stuart Black
Ground Based Air Defence	IPTL Dave Brewerton

PEER GROUP I

FAWS	IPTL Fred Edwards
Targetry	IPTL Col Andrew Johnstone
Combat Support Vehicles Heavy	
	IPTL Peter Jennings
Combat Support Vehicles Light	
	IPTL Col Jeff Little
Dismounted Close Combat	IPTL Col Robbie Scott-Bowden

PEER GROUP J

BOWMAN	IPTL Dr Iain Watson
Joint Battlefield Digitisation	IPTL Dr Iain Watson
Land C2IS	ITPL Dr Iain Watson
Datalinks Land/Air	IPTL Paul Blakiston
Long Range Terrestrial Radio	
	IPTL David King
Special Comms and Management	
Radio	IPTL Clive Tarver
Theatre and Formation Comms	
	IPTL John Turton
SATCOM	IPTL Keith Smith
Crypto	IPTL Dick Muggeridge
SANGCOM	IPTL Col Richard Holmes

49

LAND COMMAND

Erskine Barracks, Wilton, Salisbury SP2 0AG

COMMANDER IN CHIEF ....Gen *Sir* Mike Jackson *KCB CBE DSO* 010300

DEPUTY COMMANDER IN CHIEF ....Lt Gen C N G Delves *CBE DSO* 160301

STAFF

 Chief of Staff ....Maj Gen F R Viggers *MBE* 140200
 Deputy Chief of Staff ....Maj Gen P A Chambers *MBE* 141298
 Comds Sec ....Ms D J Seammen
 Brigadier General Staff ....Brig D R Bill 170100
 ACOS Ops ....Brig R M Brunt *CBE* 271100
 ACOS Trg & Dev ....Brig P T C Pearson *CBE* 080500
 ACOS G3 Res ....Brig A J M Durcan 270798
 ACOS Pers ....Brig J S Kerr *CBE* 131299
 Brigadier TA ....Brig J R Thomson *TD ADC* 010300

ARMS/SERVICE COMMANDERS

 Commander Arty ....Brig N B Philpott 150101
 Commander Engrs ....Brig M F N Mans 201299
 Commander Communications ....Brig J M Shaw *MBE* 120698
 Commander Med ....Brig A H M MacMillan *QHP* 240100
 Colonel Legal ....Col P D McEvoy *OBE* 120101
 ACOS Log ....Brig C M Steirn *CBE* 070301
 Commander ES ....Brig J C Campbell 111200

1ST (UNITED KINGDOM) ARMOURED DIVISION

British Forces Post Office 15

Headquarters

GOC ....Maj Gen R V Brims *CBE* 221100
COS ....Col J J Bucknall *MBE* 301198
Deputy Chief of Staff ....Col B W McCall 171100
Commander Artillery (Hereford Garrison) ......Brig C C Brown *CBE* 151199
Asst Comd ....Brig J E B Smedley 090697

HEADQUARTERS 4TH ARMOURED BRIGADE
British Forces Post Office 36
COMMANDER ....Brig N G Smith 051000

HEADQUARTERS 7TH ARMOURED BRIGADE
British Forces Post Office 30
COMMANDER ....Brig G J Binns *MBE MC* 111200

HEADQUARTERS 20TH ARMOURED BRIGADE
British Forces Post Office 16
COMMANDER ....Brig J R Cook *OBE MC* 051099

51

2ND DIVISION

Craigie Hall, South Queensferry, West Lothian EH30 9TN (Tel. 0131-310-ext)

Headquarters

GENERAL OFFICER COMMANDING . . . . . .Maj Gen R D S Gordon *CBE* 140599
(Governor Edinburgh Castle)
Chief of Staff . . . . .Col H C G Willing 290300
Deputy Chief of Staff .Col A K M Miller *OBE* 290300

HEADQUARTERS 15TH (NORTH EAST) BRIGADE

Imphal Barracks, Fulford Road, York YO1 4AU

COMMANDER . . . . .Brig A P Farquhar *MBE* 030600

HEADQUARTERS 42 (NORTH WEST) BRIGADE

Fulwood Barracks, Fulwood, Preston, Lancs (Tel: Preston 716543)

COMMANDER . . . . .Brig A F Birtwistle *OBE ADC* 010998

HEADQUARTERS 51 HIGHLAND BRIGADE

7 St Leonards Bank, Perth PH2 8EB (Tel: 01738-21281)

COMMANDER . . . . .Brig S R B Allen 131299

HEADQUARTERS 52 LOWLAND BRIGADE

The Castle, Edinburgh EH1 2YT (Tel: 0131-336-1761)

COMMANDER . . . . .Brig *The Hon* H B H E Monro *MBE* .161298

52

3RD (UNITED KINGDOM) DIVISION

Picton Barracks, Bulford Camp, Salisbury, Wilts SP4 9NY (Tel: Bulford Mil 2469)

Headquarters

GOC	Maj Gen J C McColl *CBE*	081100
Chief of Staff	Col D J Rutherford-Jones	171299
Deputy Chief of Staff	Col J G Askew *OBE*	221199
Comd Artillery	Brig C W Tadier *CBE*	060700
Asst Comd	Brig M N E Speller *MBE*	170100

HEADQUARTERS 1 MECHANIZED BRIGADE

Jellalabad Barracks, Tidworth, Hants SP9 7AB

COMMANDER . . . . Brig S V Mayall 260101

HEADQUARTERS 12 MECHANIZED BRIGADE

Arnham Barracks, Aldershot, Hants GU11 2AU

COMMANDER . . . . Brig J Cooper *DSO MBE* 151199

HEADQUARTERS 19 MECHANIZED BRIGADE

Smith-Dorrien House, Gaza Barracks, Catterick Garrison, N Yorks DL9 4AU

COMMANDER . . . . Brig N H Rollo 290400

HEADQUARTERS 43 (WESSEX) BRIGADE

Bldg 750, Picton Barracks, Bulford Camp, Salisbury, Wilts SP4 9NY

COMMANDER . . . . Brig A J Faith *OBE* 291098

4TH DIVISION

Steele's Road, Aldershot, Hants GU11 2DP (Tel: 01252-24431)

Headquarters

GENERAL OFFICER COMMANDING . . . . . . .Maj Gen J T Holmes *OBE MC*	.290101
COS . . . . .Col T J Checketts *OBE*	.210200
Deputy Chief of Staff . . . . .Col T P Grimshaw	.170500

HEADQUARTERS 2 (SOUTH EAST) BRIGADE

Shorncliffe, Folkestone, Kent CT20 3HJ

COMMANDER . . . . .Brig T J Minter *OBE* 101198

HEADQUARTERS 49 (EAST) BRIGADE

Chetwynd Barracks, Chilwell, Beeston, Notts NG9 2HA

COMMANDER . . . . .Brig D R Wilson 150500

HEADQUARTERS 145 (HOME COUNTIES) BRIGADE

Wavell House, Cavans Road, Aldershot, Hants GU11 2LQ

COMMANDER . . . . .Brig T D Gregg *CBE* 180398

5TH DIVISION

Copthorne Barracks, Copthorne Road, Shrewsbury SY3 8LZ
(Tel: Shrewsbury 236060)

Headquarters

GENERAL OFFICER COMMANDING . . . . . . .Maj Gen A G Denaro *CBE* 201200
Chief of Staff . . . . .Col D R L Bone 120500
Deputy Chief of Staff .Col D C Thorneycroft *OBE* 200398

HEADQUARTERS 143 (WEST MIDLANDS) BRIGADE

Copthorne Barracks, Copthorne Road, Shrewsbury
(Tel: Shrewsbury 236060)

COMMANDER . . . . .Brig A D Meek 030600

HEADQUARTERS 160 (WALES) BRIGADE

The Barracks, Brecon, Powys, Wales LD3 7EA
(Tel: Brecon 623111)

COMMANDER . . . . .Brig C T Rogers *OBE ADC* 230798

HEADQUARTERS 107 (ULSTER) BRIGADE

British Forces Post Office 808

COMMANDER . . . . .Brig D H Keenan *OBE* 020700

55

LONDON DISTRICT

Horse Guards, Whitehall, London SW1A 2AX (Tel: 020 7930 4466)

The City of London, the London Metropolitan Police Area,
and the Royal Borough of Windsor

Headquarters

GENERAL OFFICER COMMANDING LONDON DISTRICT AND MAJOR GENERAL COMMANDING THE
HOUSEHOLD DIVISION . . . . .Maj Gen C R Watt *CBE* 181200

Deputy Commander and
Commander London Area . . . . .Brig D R d'A Willis *CBE* 090499

Chief of Staff . . . . .Col J W M Ellery *CBE* 070200

Deputy Chief of Staff . . . . .Lt Col J J Purves *MBE* 280400

NORTHERN IRELAND
British Forces Post Office 825 (Tel: Lisburn 665111)

Headquarters

GENERAL OFFICER COMMANDING . . . . . .Lt Gen A S H Irwin *CBE* 061200
Chief of Staff. . . . . .Brig A D Leakey *CBE* 080201
Assistant Chief of Staff G1/G4 . . . . .Col R E Harrold *OBE* 150300
Assistant Chief of Staff G2/G3 . . . . .Col D St J Homer *MBE* 040900

HEADQUARTERS 3 INFANTRY BRIGADE
British Forces Post Office 809

COMMANDER . . . . .Brig A J N Graham *MBE* 061299
Deputy Commander . . . . .Col H M Purcell *OBE* 090499

HEADQUARTERS 8 INFANTRY BRIGADE
British Forces Post Office 807

COMMANDER . . . . .Brig P R Newton 121200
Deputy Commander . . . . .Col K G McCann *MBE* 010401

HEADQUARTERS 39 INFANTRY BRIGADE
British Forces Post Office 801

COMMANDER . . . . .Brig W E B Loudon *OBE* 061299
Deputy Commander . . . . .Col I R Liles *OBE* 130999

CORPS AND THEATRE TROOPS

HEADQUARTERS JOINT HELICOPTER COMMAND
Erskine Barracks, Wilton, Salisbury SP2 0AG

Commander . . . . .Air Vice Marshal D M Diven *CB CBE* 010598
Deputy Commander . . . . .Brig G R Coward *OBE* 100500

HEADQUARTERS TRAINING SUPPORT COMMAND (LAND)
WTC, Warminster, Wilts BA12 0DJ

Commander . . . . .Maj Gen B P Plummer 300899
Chief of Staff . . . . .Col D M Santa-Olalla *DSO MC* 161199

LAND WARFARE TRAINING CENTRE
WTC, Warminster, Wilts BA12 0DJ

Commander . . . . .Brig A A J R Cumming *CBE* 110498

LAND WARFARE SCHOOL
WTC, Warminster, Wilts BA12 0DJ

Commandant . . . . .Col W G Cubitt. 230401

LAND WARFARE COLLECTIVE TRAINING GROUP
WTC, Warminster, Wilts BA12 0DJ

Commandant . . . . .Col N R F Aylwin-Foster 241198

TRAINING SUPPORT COMMAND (GERMANY)
British Forces Post Office 16

Commander . . . . .Brig I A Johnstone *OBE* 140301

COMBAT MANOUEVRE SIMULATION CENTRE (GERMANY)
British Forces Post Office 16

Commandant . . . . .Col S P Hodder 010599

COMBINED ARMS FIELD TRAINING GROUP (GERMANY)
British Forces Post Office 16

Commandant . . . . .Col J K Tanner 171299

LAND WARFARE TRAINING CENTRE BATTLE GROUP
Commanding Officer IGH . . . . .Lt Col P T Roberts MBE 040199

WARMINSTER SUPPORT GROUP
Commanding Officer . . . . .Lt Col J K R Porter RRF 130300

HEADQUARTERS 16 AIR ASSAULT BRIGADE
Commander . . . . .Brig B W B White-Spunner 211200

HEADQUARTERS 2 (NC) SIGNAL BRIGADE
Commander . . . . .Brig N C Jackson *MBE* 080600

HEADQUARTERS 11 SIGNAL BRIGADE
Commander . . . . .Brig C L Le Gallais *CBE* 020101

HEADQUARTERS 101 LOGISTIC BRIGADE
Commander . . . . .Brig M D Wood *MBE* 171299

HEADQUARTERS 102 LOGISTIC BRIGADE
British Forces Post Office 47

Commander . . . . .Brig S P Cowlam *MBE* 151200

UNITED KINGDOM SUPPORT COMMAND (GERMANY)
British Forces Post Office 140 (Rheindahlen 2311)

Headquarters

GENERAL OFFICER COMMANDING . . . . . . .Maj Gen J D Moore-Bick *CBE* 240301
CHIEF OF STAFF . . . . .Col S J Marriner *MBE* 061100
DEPUTY CHIEF OF STAFF . . . . .Col R I Harrison *OBE* 080101

SERVICES
Assistant Chaplain General . . . . .Rev P J Cable 080199
Commander Medical . . . . .Col C G Batty *MBE* 230499
ALA NW Europe . . . . .Col A S Paphiti 201100

CIVIL SECRETARIAT
Civil Secretary . . . . .S W Beedle

DEPUTY JUDGE ADVOCATE GENERAL . . . .M A Hunter

BRITISH FORCES LIAISON ORGANISATION (GERMANY)
Commander . . . . .Brig R J Morris 111198

1ST SIGNAL BRIGADE AND RHINE GARRISON
Commander . . . . .Brig D McDowall *MBE* 100100

BRITISH FORCES GERMANY HEALTH SERVICE
Director . . . . .Mr D Roberts 040400
Director Primary and Community Care . . . . . . .Col J E Burgess 210998
Director Secondary Health Care . . . . .Brig C R Winfield *CBE* 010496
Director Primary Dental Services . . . . .Col C M James 161098

58

OVERSEAS COMMANDS

CYPRUS

HEADQUARTERS BRITISH FORCES

Administrator of the SBA and CBF Cyprus	Air Vice-Marshal T W Rimmer *OBE MA FRAeS* RAF	050900
Deputy Commander and Chief of Staff	Brig D E Radcliffe *OBE*	000000
Chief Officer SBA Administration	Mr D J Bonner	000000
Command Secretary	Mr A Kelly	261000
Commander Dhekelia Garrison	Col A M F Potter *OBE*	000000
Station Commander RAF Akrotiri	Gp Capt M W Halsall RAF	010201

BRITISH CONTINGENT-UNITED NATIONS FORCES IN CYPRUS

Commander	Col J C W Brooks	230899

GIBRALTAR

GOVERNOR AND COMMANDER IN CHIEF	Mr David R C Durie *CMG*	200300

BRITISH FORCES GIBRALTAR

Commander British Forces Gibraltar	Cdre A M Willmett *ADC* RN	160699
Chief of Staff	Col J D Sankey *OBE*	170197
Command Secretary	Col A L Moorby	120600
Station Command RAF Gibraltar	Wng Cdr D J T-Ryder	140800
Commanding Officer Gibraltar Regt	Lt Col F P Brancato ROYAL GIBRALTAR REGIMENT	011098

BRITISH FORCES FALKLAND ISLANDS

GOVERNOR	*His Excellency* D A Lamont	110599
COMMANDER BRITISH FORCES	Air Cdre J A Cliffe *OBE FRAeS* RAF	270101
CHIEF OF STAFF	Gp Capt P Hodgson RAF	100899
COMMAND SECRETARY	Mr D Halfpenny	100399
ACOS J2/J3, QHM	Cdr C J Martin RN	140300
ACOS J5/J7	Lt Col M P H Gouldstone *MBE* RGR	280201
ACOS J6	Wg Cdr Q Dixon RAF	181000
ACOS J1/J4	Lt Col M J Clews RLC	280201
CO FISU	Wg Cdr N G Branston RAF	060600
CO FIAW	Wg Cdr L Turner RAF	071100
CO JFLU	Wg Cdr A S Garner RAF	270600
ACOS J4 Estates	Lt Col N R Clark RE	271100
FIRST SECRETARY	Mr R T Jarvis	230297
COMMISSIONER TO SOUTH GEORGIA	*His Excellency* D A Lamont	110599

59

ALLIED COMMAND EUROPE

SHAPE BELGIUM

Deputy Supreme Allied Commander Europe
                                    Gen *Sir* Rupert Smith *KCB DSO* OBE QGM* 301198
Headquarters ACE Rapid Reaction Corps
Commander
ACE Rapid Reaction Corps (COMMARC) . . . . .Lt Gen *Sir* Christopher Drewry *KCB CBE* 310199
Chief of Staff
ACE Rapid Reaction Corps (COSARRC) . . . . . .Maj Gen A P Ridgway *CB CBE* 280498
Chief G6/Commander 1(UK) Signal Brigade . . . .Brig D McDowall *MBE* 240100
Deputy Chief of Staff for Support . . . . .Brig K Skempton *CBE* 160498
Chief Fire Coordination . . . . .Brig R M McQ Sykes 170100
Chief G3 Air . . . . .Brig M J Rutledge *OBE* 241199
Chief Engineer . . . . .Brig R A M S Melvin *OBE* 250800

60

JOINT SERVICE AND MISCELLANEOUS ESTABLISHMENTS

CENTRAL DEFENCE & JOINT SERVICE ESTABLISHMENTS

ROYAL COLLEGE OF DEFENCE STUDIES
Seaford House, 37 Belgrave Square, London SW1X 8NS (Tel: 020-7915-4800)

Commandant . . . . .Lt Gen (Retd) *Sir* Christopher Wallace *KBE*

Directing Staff

Senior Naval Member	Rear Admiral P A Dunt	301099
Senior Army Member	Maj Gen M A Charlton-Weedy *CBE*	040101
Senior Air Force Member	Air Vice-Marshal P W Roser *MBE* RAF	131299
Senior Civilian Member	Mr R J S Edis *CMG*	151297

PERMANENT JOINT HEADQUARTERS (UK)
Northwood, Middlesex HA6 3TJ (Tel: 01923 826161)

Chief of Joint Operations	V Adm *Sir* Ian Garnett *KCB*	100299
Chief of Staff	Maj Gen A R D Pringle *CB CBE*	031098
Civil Secretary	Miss J Binstead	130999
Assistant Chief of Staff J1/J4	Brig M Kerley *CBE QGM*	181200
Assistant Chief of Staff J2	Cdre D A Lewis	140499
Assistant Chief of Staff J3	Brig A R E de C Stewart *OBE*	081199
Assistant Chief of Staff J5	Cdre J R Fanshawe	180100
Assistant Chief of Staff J6	Air Cdre G Jones *MBE*	260499
Chief of Joint Force Operational Readiness and Training	AVM P V Harris *AFC*	060301
Director Joint Force Training and Standards	Brig A R Freer *OBE*	111200
Chief of Joint Force Operations	Brig P A Wall *OBE*	310301

JOINT SERVICES COMMAND AND STAFF COLLEGE
Shrivenham, Wilts SN6 8TS (Tel: 01793 788000)

Commandant	Air Vice-Marshal N K Burridge *CBE*	110100
Assistant Commandant (Land)	Brig N R Parker	251099

JOINT AIR RECONNAISSANCE INTELLIGENCE CENTRE
RAF Brampton, Huntingdon, Cambs PE28 4YG (Tel: 01480-52151)

Commanding Officer . . . . .Gp Capt M R Hallam 050199

JOINT AIR TRANSPORT EVALUATION UNIT
Brize Norton, Oxon OX18 3LX (Tel: 01993-896280 Fax: 01993 896281)

Commanding Officer . . . . .Lt Col T Mills *BSc(Eng) MSc CEng MRAeS* REME 230899

61

DEFENCE MEDICAL SERVICES

Defence Secondary Care Agency

St Christopher House, Southward Street, London SE1 0DT
(Military Network 96305-2083) (Fax: Military 96305-2111 Civil: 0207-305-2111)

Chief Executive	.Mr J F Tuckett	.190600
Director Personnel and Services	.Air Cdre W Pike RAF	.190499
Director Finance and Management Information	.Miss K Makin	.010199
Director of Corporate Development	.Mrs M Somekh	.010496

Defence Dental Agency

Lacon House, Theobalds Road, London WC1X 8RY

Chief Executive . . . . .AVM J S Mackay *QHDS* RAF

Medical Supplies Agency

DME Depot, Drummond Barracks, Ludgershall, Andover, Hants SP11 9RU

Chief Executive . . . . .Mr B Nimmick 010496

Headquarters Defence Medical Training Organisation

Brunel House, 42 The Hard, Portsmouth PO2 3DS
(Army Network Tel: 94295 5255 Civil Tel: 01705 82234/Ext 5255) (Fax: 01705 730579)

Director General . . . . .Maj Gen C G Callow *OBE* QHP L/RAMC 010496

Royal Defence Medical College

HMS Dolphin, Fort Blockhouse, Gosport, Hampshire PO12 2AB (Tel: 01705 765671)

Commandant . . . . .Surg Cdre I L Jenkins QHS 010496

Defence Medical Services Training Centre

Keogh Barracks, Ash Vale, Aldershot, Hants (Tel: 01252 340274)

Commander . . . . .Brig M J Ratcliffe L/RAMC 010496

62
DEFENCE EVALUATION AND RESEARCH AGENCY

ARMY ELEMENT SPONSORED BY AG

Farnborough, Hampshire (Tel: 01252 392000)

Incorporating
Defence Research Agency
Defence Test and Evaluation Organisation
Chemical and Biological Defence Establishment
Centre for Defence Analysis
Royal Aerospace Establishment
Royal Armament Research and Development Establishment
Royal Signals and Radar Establishment
Fighting Vehicles Research and Development Establishment
Military Engineering Experimental Establishment
Army Personnel Research Establishment
Defence Operational Analysis Centre
Directorate General of Test and Evaluation

Chief Executive (to be CE New Dera) . . . .*Sir* John Chisholm
Managing Director Security Div (to be CE/DSTL)
. . . . .Mr B C Clifford
Director Corporate Affairs . . . . .Mrs E Peace
Senior Military Officer . . . . .Cdre R C Pelly *MSc CEng* RN
Director Air Operations . . . . .Air Cdre N Wood *MRAeS* RAF
Military Resources Coordination Officer . . . . . . .Lt Col (retd) L S J T Gregory

Systems and Technology Sectors

Managing Director Solutions Division . . . . .Mr A C Sleigh
Senior RN Officer (Defence Solutions) . . . . .Capt S W Howick RN
Senior Army Officer (Defence Solutions) . . . . . . .Col J M Watson (*late* QRH)
Senior RAF Officer (Defence Solutions) . . . . .Gp Capt A Vincent RAF
Senior CIS Officer (Defence Solutions) . . . . .Gp Capt A Campbell RAF
Senior Military Officer CBD Sector . . . . .Capt I Jarvis RN
SO1(W) CES Sector . . . . .Lt Col S H P Sanderson *OBE*

Centre for Defence Analysis

Director CDA . . . . .Mr P Starkey
Senior Army Officer CDA . . . . .Col D W Lewthwaite (*late* RA)

NOTE: DERA due to be divided with effect 1 July 2001 into "New DERA plc" and "DSTL" (Defence Science & Technology Laboratory)

OFFICE OF THE JUDGE ADVOCATE GENERAL OF THE FORCES

(Lord Chancellor's Department)
(Joint Service for the Army and Royal Air Force)

22 Kingsway, London WC2B 6LE (Tel: 020-7218-8079)

JUDGE ADVOCATE GENERAL . . . .His Honour Judge J W Rant CB QC

Vice Judge Advocate General . . . . . .E G Moelwyn-Hughes
Judge Advocate M A Hunter (DJAG BRITISH FORCES IN GERMANY)
Judge Advocate J P Camp
Judge Advocate S E Woollam
Judge Advocate R C C Seymour
Judge Advocate I H Pearson
Judge Advocate R G Chapple
Judge Advocate J F T Bayliss

Legal Assistant . . . . .T S G Miller

Registrar . . . . .Miss J Norris

HEADQUARTERS DIRECTOR INTELLIGENCE CORPS AND DEFENCE INTELLIGENCE AND SECURITY CENTRE

Chicksands, Shefford, Beds SG17 5PR (Tel: 01462-752101)

Headquarters Director Intelligence Corps
Headquarters Defence Intelligence and Security Centre

Chief Executive/Commandant . . . . . . .Brig C G Holtom INT CORPS 171297
Chief of Staff . . . . .Gp Captain J Gimblett RAF 010200

Defence Intelligence and Security Centre Support Staff

Commanding Officer . . . . .Lt Col G Harwood *MBE* R SIGNALS 150201

Defence Intelligence and Security School

Chief Instructor . . . . .Lt Col C Tomlinson INT CORPS 010499

Joint Service Intelligence Organisation

Commanding Officer . . . . .Lt Col T M McMullen *MBE* INT CORPS 300699

Joint School Photographic Interpretation

Commanding Officer . . . . .Sqn Leader F Blake RN 011100

64

ORDER OF ST JOHN OF JERUSALEM & BRCS JOINT COMMITTEE SERVICE HOSPITALS WELFARE DEPARTMENT

5 Grosvenor Crescent, London SW1X 7EH (Tel: 020-7201-5132/6)

CHAIRMAN . . . .*Mrs* A K Stewart-Roberts *OBE JP LL*
Director . . . .*Mrs* S J Saunders *BA(Hons) MIWO*
Staff Officer . . . .*Mr* C M Gerry *FISM MIAP*
Training Officer . . . .*Miss* M Wilson
Secretary . . . .*Mrs* G Leoni

THE MOST VENERABLE ORDER OF THE HOSPITAL OF ST JOHN OF JERUSALEM

St John's Gate, Clerkenwell, London EC1M 4DA (Tel: 020-7253-6644)

Sovereign Head . . . . .HM THE QUEEN

Grand Prior . . . .*HRH THE DUKE OF* GLOUCESTER *KG GCVO*

Lord Prior . . . .*The Lord* Vestey *DL*
Chancellor . . . .*Professor* A R Mellows *TD*
Secretary General . . . .*Sir* Anthony Goodenough *KCMG*

The St John Ambulance

St John's Gate, 27 St John's Lane, Clerkenwell, London EC1M 4BU

Grand President . . . .*HRH THE PRINCESS* MARGARET *COUNTESS OF* SNOWDON

Commandant-in-Chief (Nursing) . . . . .HM QUEEN ELIZABETH THE QUEEN MOTHER

Commandant-in-Chief (Ambulance and Nursing Cadets)
                        HRH THE PRINCESS ROYAL *KG KT GCVO QSO*

Deputy Commandant-in-Chief (Nursing)
                        HRH PRINCESS ALICE, *DUCHESS OF* GLOUCESTER

Commander-in-Chief for Wales . . . . . .*HRH THE DUCHESS OF* GLOUCESTER *GCVO*

Chief Commander . . . .*The Baroness* Emerton *DBE DL*

The St John Eye Hospital

PO Box 1960, Jerusalem (Tel: 828325)

Hospitaller .Noel Rice Esq *MD FRCS FRCD*

THE ST ANDREW'S AMBULANCE ASSOCIATION

St Andrew's House, 48 Milton Street, Glasgow G4 0HR (Tel: 0141-332-4031)
(Fax: 0141 332 6582)

Patron . . . .*HM* QUEEN ELIZABETH THE QUEEN MOTHER

President . . . . .Capt *The Duke of* Buccleuch and Queensberry *KT VRD JP*
                        (HM Lord Lieutenant Selkirk) (Captain Queen's Body Guard for Scotland)
Chairman of Council . . . .*Dr* Ernest T Robinson *OBE TD KLJ MB ChB Dobst RCOG FRCGP*
Commandant-in-Chief . . . .*Mr* Rudy Crawford *BSc(Hons) MB ChB FRCS(Glas) FFAEM*
Chief Executive . . . .*Mr* Brendan J P Healy

THE BRITISH RED CROSS SOCIETY
9 Grosvenor Crescent, London SW1X 7EJ

Patron	HM THE QUEEN
President	*HM* QUEEN ELIZABETH THE QUEEN MOTHER
Deputy Presidents	*HRH Princess* Alexandra *The Hon Lady* Ogilvy *GCVO*
	The Countess Mountbatten of Burma *CBE CD JP DL*
Honorary Vice Presidents	*HRH Princess* Alice *Duchess of* Gloucester *GCB CI GCVO GBE*
	Lord Barnard *TD*
	The Rt Hon Baroness Chalker of Wallasey
	The Countess of Limerick *CBE*
Chairman of the Board of Trustees	*Mrs* E Thomas *CBE DL*

Vice Chairmen of the Board of Trustees

          Miss C Dixon-Carter *OBE*
          Sir Alan Munro *KCMG*
          Mr M Walsh

Director General . . . . *Mr* S Younger

WOMEN'S ORGANISATION
FIRST AID NURSING YEOMANRY (PRINCESS ROYAL'S VOLUNTEER CORPS)
Duke of York's Headquarters, Chelsea, London SW3 4RX
(Tel: Civ 020-7730-2058 Mil (9)4631 5400)

Commandant-in-Chief	*HRH* THE PRINCESS ROYAL *KG KT GCVO QSO*
Honorary Colonel	Maj Gen S R Carr-Smith
Chairman of the Advisory Council	Maj Gen P MacLellan *CB CVO MBE*
Corps Commander	*Mrs* L Rose
Deputy Corps Commander	*Miss* J M A Kauntze

COUNCIL OF VOLUNTARY WELFARE WORK
(For HM Forces)
Duke of York's Headquarters, Chelsea, London SW3 4RY
(Tel: 020-7730 3161 Fax: 020 7730 3161)

Chairman	*Sir* Kenneth MacDonald *KCB*
General Secretary	Brig W I C Dobbie
Representatives of	The Navy Department
	The Army Department
	The Air Force Department
	The Young Women's Christian Association
	The Salvation Army
	The Church Army
	The Methodist Church Forces' Committee
	The Church of England Soldiers' Sailors' and Airmens' Clubs
	Mission to Military Garrisons
	Royal Sailors' Rests
	Sandes Soldiers' and Airmens' Centres
	SASRA/Miss Daniell's Homes
	The Catholic Women's League
Associated	Women's Royal Voluntary Service

66

COMMONWEALTH WAR GRAVES COMMISSION

2 Marlow Road, Maidenhead, Berkshire SL6 7DX (Tel: 01628 634221)
Telex No 847526 COMGRA G   Fax No 01628 771208
E-mail: For general enquiries: general.enq@cwgc.org
For casualty and cemetery enquiries: casualty.enq@cwgc.org

President . . . . .FM *HRH The Duke of* Kent *KG GCMG GCVO ADC*

Members . . . . .The Secretary of State for Defence in the United Kingdom (Chairman)
General *Sir* John Wilsey *GCB CBE DL* (Vice Chairman)
High Commissioner for Australia
High Commissioner for Canada
High Commissioner for New Zealand
High Commissioner for the Republic of India
High Commissioner for the Republic of South Africa
Professor Robert J O'Neill *AO*
Mrs Llin Golding *MP*
John Wilkinson *MP*
Sir John Gray *KBE CMG*
Paul Orchard-Lisle *CBE TD DL*
Air Chief Marshal *Sir* Michael Stear *KCB CBE DL MA FRAeS*
Dame Susan Tinson *DBE*
Admiral *Sir* Peter Abbott *GBE KCB*

Director-General . . . . .R Kellaway (Secretary to the Commission)

Deputy Director-General . . . . .R J Dalley (Assistant Secretary to the Commission)

Legal Adviser and Solicitor . . . . .G C Reddie

*Director of Information
and Secretariat* . . . . .D R Parker

Director of Administration . . . . .R D Wilson *ACMA*

Director of Works . . . . .A Coombe

Director of Horticulture . . . . .D C Parker *Dip Hort (Kew) M.I.Hort.*

Director of Personnel . . . . .D G Stacey

*Personal Secretary to
Director-General* . . . . .Mrs H J Scott

Established under Royal Charter in 1917, whereby the Member Governments co-operate directly in the maintenance of war graves and memorials for those members of Commonwealth armed forces who died in the two World Wars.

ARMY COMMANDS OF COMMONWEALTH COUNTRIES
(The details in this list are based on information supplied by the Governments of the countries)

CANADA

GOVERNOR GENERAL AND COMMANDER IN CHIEF
Her Excellency The Right Hon Adrienne Clarkson
Secretary . . . .*Mme* Barbara Uteck

DEPARTMENT OF NATIONAL DEFENCE

MINISTER OF NATIONAL DEFENCE
The Honourable Arthur Eggleton *PC MP*

DEFENCE COUNCIL

CHAIRMAN
MINISTER OF NATIONAL DEFENCE . . . .*The Honourable* Arthur Eggleton *PC MP*

MEMBERS
Parliamentary Secretary to the Minister of National Defence
Mr John O'Reilly *MP*
Deputy Minister of National Defence . . . .*Mr* J A J Judd
Chief of the Defence Staff . . . . .General J M G Baril *CMM MSM CD*
Vice Chief of the Defence Staff . . . . .VAdm G L Garnett *CMM CD*

COMMAND AND STAFF APPOINTMENTS

Chief of the Defence Staff . . . . .General J M G Baril *CMM MSM CD*
Vice Chief of the Defence Staff . . . . .VAdm G L Garnett *CMM CD*
Deputy Chief of the Defence Staff . . . . .LGen R R Henault *OMM CD*
Assistant Deputy Minister
(Human Resources - Military) . . . . .RAdm G V Davidson *CD*
Surgeon General . . . . .Vacant
Director General Intelligence . . . . .BGen R G Meating *OMM CD*
Assistant Deputy Minister (Policy) . . . . .Dr K J Calder *PhD*
Assistant Deputy Minister (Materiel) . . . . . .*Mr* M S Williams
Chief of the Maritime Staff . . . . .VAdm G R Maddison *CMM MSC CD*
Chief of the Land Staff . . . . .LGen M K Jeffery *CMM CD*
Chief of the Air Staff . . . . .LGen L C Campbell *CMM CD*
Commander Maritime Forces Pacific . . . . . .RAdm R D Buck *OMM CD*
Commander Maritime Forces Atlantic . . . . .RAdm D E Miller *MSC CD*
Commander CanadianForces Recruiting
Education and Training Systems . . . . .MGen J R P Daigle *MSC CD*
Commander Headquarters Northern Region .Col K C McLeod
Commandant Canadian Forces College . . . .BGen J J R Gagnon *CD*
Commandant Canadian Forces Land
Command and Staff College . . . . .BGen J G M Lessard *CD*
Commandant Royal Military College . . . . . .RAdm D C Morse *OMM CMM CD*
Commandant Combat Training Centre
Gagetown . . . . .Col Isabelle
Commander Canadian Defence
Liaison Staff Washington . . . . .RAdm F W Gibson *OMM CD*
Commander Canadian Defence
Liaison Staff London . . . . .BGen W S Richard *CD*

68

AUSTRALIA

Governor General of the Commonwealth and
  Commander in Chief . . . . *His Excellency The Honourable Sir* William Deane *AC KBE*
Official Secretary to the Governor General . . .Mr R D Sturdey
House Manager . . . . .Mr G Mair
Minister for Defence . . . .*The Honourable* John Moore *MP*
Minister for Veterans Affairs - Minister Assisting
  the Minister for Defence . . . .*Senator The Honourable* Bruce Scott *MP*

AUSTRALIAN DEFENCE HEADQUARTERS

Chief of Army . . . . .Maj Gen P J Cosgrove *AC MC ndc(Ind) jssc psc(US)*
Deputy Chief of Army . . . . .Maj Gen P F Leahy *AM LCSC(j) acdss psc(US) psc BA(Mil) MMAS*

PRINCIPAL STAFF OFFICERS

DG Preparedness and Plans Army . . . . .Brig G Yacoub *CSC acdss jssc psc MMngt Econ Bbus Grad Dip Mngt
                                                              Studs*
DG Future Land Warfare & Concepts Pol . . . . .Brig M A Swan *acdss psc tem M Def Stud BSc(Mil)*
DG Reserves - Army . . . . .Brig N R Turner *RFD ADC BEng(Hons) MEng Sc*
DG Personnel - Army .Brig M Evans *DSC AM acdss psc Grad Dip Mngt Stud*
Judge Advocate General . . . . .Maj Gen K P Duggan *RFD*

LAND COMMAND
(Victoria Banks, Paddington, NSW)

Land Commander - Australia . . . . .Maj Gen P Abigail *AO acdss jssc psc BComm Grad Dip*

TRAINING COMMAND - ARMY
(Georges Heights, NSW)

Commander . . . . .Maj Gen F X Roberts *AM acdss psc G MSc BE(Civ)*

OFFICE OF THE MILITARY ATTACHE AND AUSTRALIAN STAFF (WASHINGTON)

Head of Australian Defence Staff . . . .
Australian Army Representative . . . . .Brig W J A Mellor *DSC AM jssc psc ph BA*

AUSTRALIAN DEFENCE STAFF - LONDON
Australia House, Strand, London WC2B 4LA (Tel: 0207-379-4334)

Head of Australian Defence Staff . . . . .Cdre G J Geraghty RAN
Army Adviser . . . . .Col D J Murray *CSC psc G MBA*

ARMY TRAINING CENTRES

ROYAL MILITARY COLLEGE
(Duntroon, ACT)

Commandant . . . . .Brig M R McNarn *AM acdss psc(SIN) MDef Stud MBA BA(Hons)
                                                              Grad Dip TSM Grad Dip Mngt Studs*

COMBINED ARMS TRAINING AND DEVELOPMENT CENTRE
(Puckapunyai, VIC)

Commandant . . . . .Col J P Cantwell *AM psc psc(j) MDef Stud Grad Dip Mngt Studs*

ARMY ALL CORPS PROMOTION TRAINING CENTRE
(Canungra, QLD)

Commandant . . . . .Col N S Bartels *psc ph jssc MSc BA(Hons) Grad Dip Strat Stud*

ARMY RECRUIT TRAINING CENTRE
(Wagga Wagga, NSW)

Commandant . . . . .Col M P Crane *jssc psc G BSc(Hons) MA(Strat Stud) Grad Dip Def Stud
                                                              Grad Dip Strat Stud*

ARMY COMBAT ARMS TRAINING CENTRE
(Puckapunyai, VIC)

Officer Commanding .Col P J Hutchinson *psc BE(Civ) M Bldg Sc Grad Dip Mngt Studs*

ARMY LOGISTIC TRAINING CENTRE
(Bonegilla, VIC)

Commandant . . . . .Col C J Anstey *CSC BA(Mil)(Hons) Grad Dip Def Stud Grad Dip Log
                                                              Mngt*

ARMY SPECIAL FORCES TRAINING CENTRE
(Singleton, NSW)
Commandant . . . . .Lt Col O P Richmond *psc qtc BA(Mil)*

PARACHUTE TRAINING SCHOOL
(Nowra, NSW)
Commanding Officer/Chief Instructor . . . . .Lt Col A A Nikolic *jssc psc lcsc(Phil) BA BSoc Sc MMng Stud(HRM) Grad Dip Mngt Studs Grad Dip Strat Stud*

ARMY COMMUNICATIONS TRAINING CENTRE
(Walsonia, VIC)
Commanding Officer/Chief Instructor . . . . .Lt Col J R Baker *psc BSoc Sc(HRD) Grad Dip TSM*

DEFENCE FORCE SCHOOL OF MUSIC
(Walsonia, VIC)
Commandant . . . . .Lt Col H Ward LTCL

ARMY MILITARY POLICE TRAINING CENTRE
(Ingleburn, NSW)
Commandant . . . . .Lt Col B J Cox *psc BA(Police Stud) M Def Stud*

ARMY AVIATION TRAINING CENTRE
(Oakey, QLD)
Commandant . . . . .Col T R Jones *CSC psc qtc ph(i) Grad Dip Mngt Stud*

DEFENCE INTELLIGENCE TRAINING CENTRE
(Canungra, QLD)
Commanding Officer/Chief Instructor . . . . .Lt Col S R Dowse *psc BA(Hons) Grad Dip Def Stud*

TRAINING TECHNOLOGY CENTRE
Commandant . . . . .Col W B Sercombe *AM CSC MEd MA BEd BApp Sc Grad Dip Furth Ed Grad Dip Lib Grad Dip Ed Admin Grad Dip Ed Stud(PD)*

JOINT SERVICE UNITS

HEADQUARTERS AUSTRALIAN THEATRE
(Potts Point, NSW)
Commander . . . . .AVM R B Treloar

DEPLOYABLE JOINT FORCE HEADQUARTERS
(Enoggera, QLD)
Commander . . . . .Maj Gen A J Molan *AO acdss jssc psc ph BA(Mil) BEc*

SUPPORT COMMAND - AUSTRALIA
(Victoria Barracks, VIC)
Commander Support - Australia . . . . .Maj Gen P F Haddad *AM jssc psc Im Bec MSc*
Support Commander - Army . . . . .Maj Gen M P J O'Brien *CSC acdss psc qtc BSc(Mil) MD*

DEFENCE INTELLIGENCE ORGANISATION
(Russell Offices, ACT)
Director . . . . .Mr F Lewincamp

70

NEW ZEALAND

GOVERNOR GENERAL AND COMMANDER IN CHIEF

His Excellency The Rt Hon Sir Michael Hardie Boys *GNZM GCMG*

DEFENCE STAFF

Chief of Defence Force ....Air Marshal C W Adamson *CNZM AFC* cndc psc
Deputy Chief of Defence Force ....R Adm R J Gillbanks *RNZN* psc
Asst Chief Personnel ....Air Cdre B R Ferguson *OBE AFC* rcds awc cfs
Asst Chief Development ....Brig I A J Marshall *MA Strat Stud Bsc(Mil)* jssc* psc(UK) G
Asst Chief Resources ....Cdre A J Peck *RNZN BA* rcds jssc* psc
Asst Chief Operations ....Brig C W Lilley hbs psc(AS)
Corporate Financial Officer ....*Mr* M Horner

THE ARMY GENERAL STAFF

Chief of General Staff ....Maj Gen M F Dodson *MC CBE BBS* hbs jssc psc(AS)
Acting Deputy Chief of General Staff
and ACGS (Ops) ....Col B L Fraher *BA(Mil)* jssc* psc(UK)
ACGS (Dev) ....Col R P Cassidy *ONZM MPhil MMS* psc(USMC)
ACGS (HR) ....Col P J Gibbons *ONZM* jssc* psc(Mal)

LOGISTIC EXECUTIVE

ACGS (Logistics) ....Col I J M Gordon *MA(Hons)* jssc* psc(AS) t(UK)

LAND COMMAND

Land Commander ....Brig J Mateparae *ONZM MA(Hons) AFNZIM* rcds jssc* psc(UK)
Chief of Staff ....Acting Col G K Milward *ONZM* psc(AS)
Acting Commander 2 Land Force Group ....Lt Col M Wheeler *RNZAC* psc(Mal)
Commander 3 Land Force Group ....Col M J A Dransfield *BA(Hons) DipMgmt GDipDef* jssc* psc(AS)
Commander Army Training Group ....Col T O'Reilly *BE AFNZIM* ptsc

New Zealand Defence Staff London

New Zealand House, London SW1Y 4TQ (Tel: 020-7930-8400)

Head ....Brig R R Ottaway *MBE* facdss jssc* psc(AS)

NEW ZEALAND ARMY INSTRUCTIONAL ESTABLISHMENTS

OFFICER CADET SCHOOL (WAIOURU)

Commandant ....Lt Col R J McElwain *RNZIR BSc* psc(US)

LAND OPERATIONS TRAINING CENTRE

Commandant ....Lt Col M J Baker *RNZA* psc(AS)

THE ARMY DEPOT

Commanding Officer ....Lt Col P F Cosgrove *RNZIR* psc

MILITARY STUDIES INSTITUTE

Director ....Lt Col C P Richardson *RNZ Sigs MA(Hons) ANZIM MDefStud* psc(AS)

71

SOUTH AFRICA

PRESIDENT AND COMMANDER IN CHIEF
Mr Thabo M Mbeki

Executive Deputy President . . . . Mr Jacob Zuma
Minister of Defence . . . . Mr Patrick Lekota
Deputy Minister of Defence . . . . Ms Nozizwe Mdadlala-Routledge
Secretary for Defence . . . . Mr J B Masilela
Chief of the National Defence Force . . . . General Siphwe Nyanda

Office of the South African High Commission in the United Kingdom

Trafalgar Square, London, WC2N 5DP   (Tel: 020 7451 7299)

THE REPUBLIC OF INDIA

PRESIDENT OF THE REPUBLIC OF INDIA . .Shri K R Narayanan
Military Secretary to President . . . . .Maj Gen Bhopinder Singh *AVSM*

ARMY HEADQUARTERS

CHIEF OF THE ARMY STAFF . . . . .Gen S Padmanabhan *PVSM AVSM VSM ADC*
Vice Chief of the Army Staff . . . . .Lt Gen Vijay Oberoi *PVSM AVSM VSM*
Deputy Chief of the Army Staff (T&C) . . . . . .Lt Gen R K Sawhney *PVSM AVSM*
Deputy Chief of the Army Staff (P&S) . . . . . .Lt Gen S S Mehta *PVSM AVSM** VSM*
Adjutant General . . . . .Lt Gen S S Grewal *PVSM AVSM SM VSM*
Director General (MP & PS) . . . . .Lt Gen H S Bagga *PVSM VSM*
Director General (DGDC&W) . . . . .Lt Gen C R S Kumar *PVSM AVSM VSM*
Quartermaster General . . . . .Lt Gen Krishan Pal *PVSM UYSM VSM***
Master General of Ordnance . . . . .Lt Gen J S Dhillon *PVSM YSM*
Military Secretary .Lt Gen D S Chauhan *UYSM AVSM VSM*
Engineer-in-Chief .Lt Gen Hari Uniyal

HEADQUARTERS EASTERN COMMAND
GENERAL OFFICER COMMANDING IN CHIEF
Lt Gen H R S Kalkat *PVSM AVSM*

HEADQUARTERS SOUTHERN COMMAND
GENERAL OFFICER COMMANDING IN CHIEF
Lt Gen N C Vij *PVSM UYSM AVSM*

HEADQUARTERS WESTERN COMMAND
GENERAL OFFICER COMMANDING IN CHIEF
Lt Gen Surjit Singh *PVSM VSM*

HEADQUARTERS CENTRAL COMMAND
GENERAL OFFICER COMMANDING IN CHIEF
Lt Gen P S Joshi *PVSM AVSM VSM*

HEADQUARTERS NORTHERN COMMAND
GENERAL OFFICER COMMANDING IN CHIEF
Lt Gen R K Nanavatty *PVSM UYSM AVSM*

HEADQUARTERS ARMY TRAINING COMMAND (ARTRAC)
GENERAL OFFICER COMMANDING IN CHIEF
Lt Gen H B Kala *PVSM AVSM SC*

DEFENCE SERVICES STAFF COLLEGE
(Wellington, Nilgiris, Tamil Nadu)
Commandant . . . . .Lt Gen S R R Aiyangar *PVSM AVSM VSM*

NATIONAL DEFENCE ACADEMY
(Pune)
Commandant . . . . .Lt Gen S B S Kochar *PVSM AVSM*

INDIAN MILITARY ACADEMY
(Dehradun)
Commandant . . . . .Lt Gen Y K Mehta *PVSM AVSM*

73

NATIONAL DEFENCE COLLEGE
(New Delhi)

Commandant . . . . .Air Mshl V G Kumar *PVSM AVSM VM*

COLLEGE OF COMBAT
(Mhow)

Commandant . . . . .Lt Gen V K Kapoor

INFANTRY SCHOOL
(Mhow)

Commandant . . . . .Lt Gen D B Shekalkar *AVSM VSM*

COLLEGE OF MATERIAL MANAGEMENT
(Jabalpur)

Commandant . . . . .Lt Gen T J S Gill

ARMY AVIATION TRAINING SCHOOL
(Agra)

Commandant . . . . .Vacant

ARMY SCHOOL OF PHYSICAL TRAINING
(Pune)

Commandant . . . . .Brig Bir Nath *SM*

CDR TPT MGT WG ASC CENTRE & COLLEGE
(Bangalore)

Commandant . . . . .Brig R K Gupta

ARMOURED CORPS CENTRE AND SCHOOL
(Ahmednagar)

Commandant . . . . .Lt Gen V K Sewal *PVSM*

SCHOOL OF ARTILLERY
(Deolali)

Commandant . . . . .Lt Gen Avtar Singh *PVSM*

COLLEGE OF MILITARY ENGINEERING
(Kirkee, Pune)

Commandant . . . . .Lt Gen R J Mordecai *PVSM AVSM*

MILITARY COLLEGE OF TELECOMMUNICATION ENGINEERING
(Mhow)

Commandant . . . . .Lt Gen Sudhir Kumar *PVSM*

ARMY SERVICE CORPS CENTRE & COLLEGE
(Bengalore)

Commandant . . . . .Lt Gen Jagdish Chander *AVSM VSM*

MILITARY COLLEGE OF ELECTRONICS & MECHANICAL ENGINEERING
(Secunderabad)

Commandant . . . . .Lt Gen Dharambir Singh *PVSM VSM*

ELECTRICAL & MECHANICAL ENGINEERING SCHOOL
(Vadodara)

Commandant . . . . .Maj Gen Vijay Krishna *AVSM*

MILITARY INTELLIGENCE TRAINING SCHOOL & DEPOT
(Pune)

Commandant . . . . .Maj Gen S T Manimala *VSM*

AEC TRAINING SCHOOL & CENTRE
(Pachmarhi)

Commandant . . . . .Brig R K Sehgal

CMP CENTRE AND SCHOOL
(Bangalore)

Commandant . . . . .Brig Atma Ram

COLLEGE OF DEFENCE MANAGEMENT
(Secunderabad)

Commandant . . . . .Maj Gen K C Padha *VSM*

Office of the Indian High Commission in London

India House, Aldwych, London, WC2B 4NA

Military Adviser . . . . .Brig Sudhir Sharma

SRI LANKA

COMMANDER OF THE ARMY	Lt Gen C S Weerasooriya *RWP RSP VSV USP ndc IG*
Chief of Staff	Maj Gen L P Balagalle *USP ndc IG*
Deputy Chief Staff	Maj Gen K J C Perera *RWP RSP USP rcds psc*
Military Secretary	Brig K J C Senaweera *RSP Ldmc*
Colonel MS	Col S A P P Samarasinghe *RSP psc*

DIRECTORS

Director, Operations	Brig N Wijesinghe *USP IG*
Director, Training	Brig S G Karunaratne *RWP RSP psc*
Director, Plans	Brig N Wijesinghe *USP IG*
Director Military Intelligence	Brig H K G Hendavitharane *USP*
Director, Psychological Operations	Brig M Wijeyewickrema *USP*
Director, Staff Duties	Brig E A D A S de Alwis *RSP USP*
Director, Budget and Financial Management	Brig A K Samarasekara *USP*
Director, Media	Brig W P P Fernando *USP psc*
Director, Personnel Administration	Brig G M Rockwood *RSP psc*
Director Army Medical Services	Col S D C de Silva *RWP RSP*
Director Dental Services	Brig S Jayaweera *USP*
Director, Legal Services	Col M A M Peiris
Director, Pay & Records	Col R K P Ranaweera *USP*
Director, Provost	Brig S I S Dassanayake *USP*
Director, Welfare	Brig W B Peiris *USP*
Director, Additional Welfare	Brig M R W de Zoysa *USP*
Director, Rehabilitation	Brig K D P Perera *USP*
Director, Humanitarian Laws	Brig L L A Fernando *USP*
Director, Recruiting	Brig W U B Edirisinghe
Director, Judge Advocate General	Brig H I G Wijeratne
Director, Army Quartering	Brig G W P Samaratunga *RSP USP ato*
Director, Supply & Transport	Brig H M N Krishnaratne *RSP*
Director, Movement	Brig G S M Ranatunga *USP*
Director, Engineer Services	Brig M D R Peiris *UPS*
Director, Ordnance Services	Brig D S G Kempitiya *USP ato*
Director, Electrical & Mechanical Engineers	Brig W P P Fernando *USP psc*

DIVISIONAL COMMANDERS

Commander, SF HQ (J)	Maj Gen A M C W B Seneviratne *USP psc*
Commander SF HQ (Wanni)	Maj Gen H N W Dias *RWP RSP VSV USP ndc IG*
GOC 11 Division	Maj Gen L C R Gunawardena *RSP USP ndc IG*
GOC 21 Division	Brig S D Tennakoon *RSP*
GOC 22 Division	Maj Gen D S K Wijesoorlya *RWP RSP USP psc*
GOC 23 Division	Maj Gen M D S Chandrapala *RSP USP psc*
GOC 51 Division	Brig G B W Jayasundara *RWP RSP*
GOC 52 Division	Brig P S B Kulatunga *RWP USP*
GOC 53 Division	Brig G Hettiarachchi *WWV RWP RSP USP*
Dy GOC 53 Division	Brig D Ratnasabapathy *USP*
GOC 54 Division	Brig K B Egodawele *RWP RSP USP*
Dy GOC 54 Division	Brig P P Fernando *RWP RSP psc*
GOC 55 Division	Brig S Wanigasekara *RWP RSP USP psc*
Dy GOC 55 Division	Brig D V S Y Kulatunga *RSP USP psc*
GOC 56 Division	Brig H B Thibbotumumuwe *USP IG*
Dy GOC 56 Division	Brig T T R de Silva *RWP RSP USP psc*
OCC	Maj Gen N R Marambe *RSP USP psc*
Dy OCC	Brig K J C Jayaratne *RSP*

SRI LANKA ARMY VOLUNTEER FORCE

Commandant	Maj Gen H N W Dias *RWP RSP VSV USP ndc IG*
Dy Commandant	Maj Gen S V Panabokke *KSV*

BRIGADE COMMANDERS
Commander 112 Brigade . . . . .Brig P Chandrawansa *RWP RSP USP psc*
Commander 211 Brigade . . . . .Brig T W Jayawardene *psc*
Commander 212 Brigade . . . . .Col D M D Alwis *USP*
Commander 213 Brigade . . . . .Col A M A Chandrasiri *RSP USP*
Commander 214 Brigade . . . . .Col H M H A Herath *psc*
Commander 215 Brigade . . . . .Lt Col S R Manawaduge *RSP psc IG SLA*
Commander 221 Brigade . . . . .Col E P de Z Abeysekara
Commander 223 Brigade . . . . .Col S M de A Rajapakse *RWP RSP*
Commander 224 Brigade . . . . .Lt Col K M Navaratne *USP SLSC*
Commander 231 Brigade . . . . .Col R M J A Ratnayake *RSP*
Commander 232 Brigade . . . . .Lt Col C Weeratunga *SLSC*
Commander 233 Brigade . . . . .Col A R Zacky *USP*
Commander 511 Brigade . . . . .Lt Col T F Meedin *RSP SLSC*
Commander 512 Brigade . . . . .Col D R A B Jayathilake
Commander 513 Brigade . . . . .Lt Col S A A L Perera *IG SLA*
Commander 515 Brigade . . . . .Lt Col H M R K Wanninayake *RSP GR*
Commander 521 Brigade . . . . .Lt Col V R L Anthonisz *RSP psc IG SLA*
Commander 522 Brigade . . . . .Col L W C B B Rajaguru *RWP RSP*
Commander 523 Brigade . . . . .Lt Col S A M T Seneviratne *RWP psc GW*
Commander 524 Brigade . . . . .Col J S Masakkara *RSP*
Commander CDO Brigade . . . . .Col K A N S Fernando *RSP USP*
Commander SF Brigade . . . . .Lt Col D R Wijesiri *RWP RSP SLAC*
Commander Air Mob Brigade . . . . .Col K S Fernando *RWP RSP*
Commander 533 Brigade . . . . .Lt Col A K S Perera *WWV RWP RSP GR*
Commander 534 Brigade . . . . .Col C R M Silva *WWV RWP RSP*
Commander 541 Brigade . . . . .Col W A A P B *Jayathilake RSP IG*
Commander 542 Brigade . . . . .Col L B R Mark *RSP*
Commander 543 Brigade . . . . .Col S Udumalagala *RSP*
Commander 544 Brigade . . . . .Col R N Ackmeemana *USP*
Commander 545 Brigade . . . . .Col L A D Amaratunga *RSP*
Commander 546 Brigade . . . . .Col S W L Daulagala *RSP*
Commander 551 Brigade . . . . .Lt Col N A J C Dias *RWP RSP GR*
Commander 552 Brigade . . . . .Lt Col U de Silva *RSP GW*
Commander 553 Brigade . . . . .Lt Col L K J C Perera *RSP SLSR*
Commander 561 Brigade . . . . .Col A Lankadeva *RSP USP*
Commander 562 Brigade . . . . .Col A W J C de Silva
Commander 563 Brigade . . . . .Lt Col K S Ratnayake *RWP RSP GR*
Commander 564 Brigade . . . . .Lt Col S P Chandrakumar *RSP SLE*
Commander Area HQ GLE . . . . .Brig M R U Bandaratilake *USP*
Commander Area HQ KDY . . . . .Brig P G Charles
Commander Area HQ DLA . . . . .Brig N A Ranasinghe *RSPUSP psc*
Commander Armr Brigade . . . . .Col R M Jayasinghe *USP psc*
Commander Arty Brigade . . . . .Brig V R Silva *RSP USP IG*
Commander Engr Brigade . . . .´. . .Brig V N Wijegunawardena *RSP USP*
Commander Sig Brigade . . . . .Brig Y S A de Silva *psc*
Commander MC Brigade . . . . .Brig S D Tennakoon *RSP*
Commander Log Comd . . . . .Maj Gen M G Muthalib *USP*
Dy Log Comd FMA(East) . . . . .Brig C S D Gunasinghe *USP*
Dy Log Comd FMA(North) . . . . .Brig L B Aluvihare *psc*
Dy Comd FMA(N/C) . . . . .Col D N Wijesuriya *USP*
Comd RP (TCO) . . . . .Lt Col P Udugampala *SLCMP*
Comd RP (VNA) . . . . .Lt Col H K N U Silva *SLAGSC*

TRAINING ESTABLISHMENTS
Commandant, Army Comd & Staff College . .Maj Gen G W W Perera *RWP RSP psc USAWC*
Commandant, Sri Lanka Military Academy . .Brig N A Ranasinghe *RSP USP psc*
Commandant, Army Training School . . . . . . .Lt Col W M S Gunaratne *psc SLSR*
Commandant, Infantry Training Centre . . . . .Col T B Morseth *RWP*
Commandant, Combat Training School . . . . .Lt Col V S P de Mel *CR*
Commandant, NCOs Training School . . . . . .Lt Col M S Illangamage *RSP VIR*

Office of the Sri Lanka High Commission in the United Kingdom
13, Hyde Park Gardens, London, W2 2LU (Tel: 020-7262-1841)

THE REPUBLIC OF GHANA

PRESIDENT AND COMMANDER IN CHIEF
His Excellency Mr John Agyekum Kufuor

CHIEF OF DEFENCE STAFF . . . . .Maj Gen S K Obeng
CHIEF OF STAFF (General Headquarters) . . . .Brig F K Mensah Yawson
Military Secretary . . . .
Director General (Joint Ops and Plans) . . . .
Director General (Logistics) . . . . .Cdre S V Adatsi
*Commandant Ghana Armed Force Command
and Staff College* . . . . .Maj Gen N C Coleman
*Commandant Military Academy and
Training Schools* . . . . .R/Adm J Y Adoko

COMMANDERS
Army . . . . .Brig C B Yaachie
Commander Northern Command . . . . .Brig G Aryiku
Commander Southern Command . . . . .Brig J B Danquah
Commander Support Services . . . . .Brig L E Attivor

Office of the Ghana High Commission in the United Kingdom
13 Belgrave Square, London SW1X 8PN (Tel: 020-7235 4142)

Defence Adviser . . . . .Cdre C B Puplampu

78

MALAYSIA

SUPREME COMMANDER . . . . .Seri Paduka Baginda Yang DiPertuan Agong

MEMBERS OF THE ARMED FORCES COUNCIL

MINISTER OF DEFENCE . . . . .YB Dato' Sri Mohd Najib bin Tun Hj Abdul Razak
DSAP SIMP SSAP PNBS DPMS

Chief of Defence Forces . . . . .Gen Tan Sri Dato' Seri Mohd Zahidi bin Hj Zainuddin
PGAT PSM SPTS SIMP SPKK DPTS PAT JSD PMP KAT AMN AMK
DPKT (Brunei) ndc jssc psc

Secretary General For Defence . . . . .Dato' Hashim bin Meon *DPMS KMN*

Chief of Army . . . . .Gen Dato' Seri Md Hashim bin Hussein
PGAT PSAT SPKK SPTS DPMJ DSAP PAT KMN BCK MA(King's College) mpat psc

Chief of Royal Malaysian Navy . . . . .Admiral Dato' Seri Abu Bakar bin Mohd Jamal
PGAT PSAT SPTS DPJM DIMP DPTS PAT JMN SMJ KMN PPA PPM rcds psc

Chief of Royal Malaysian Air Force . . . . .Gen Tan Sri Ahmad Saruji bin Che Rose
PGAT PSM PSAT SIMP SPTS DPTS PAT SDK KMN AMN BCK ABS ndc awc

Assistant Chief of Staff Personnel . . . . .Rear Admiral Dato' Engku Zainal Abidin bin Hj Engku Ngah
PSAT DPMT DIMP PAT KAT JMN KMN SMT PPA PPM acdss mpat nsc

Chief of Logistic, Army HQ . . . . .Maj Gen Dato' Abdul Wahid bin Haji Anwar
PSAT DPKK DPTS PAT PKK KMN AMN PPN UNOMIL MA(Lancs) psc

OTHER APPOINTMENTS

Deputy Chief of Army .Lt Gen Dato' Abdul Ghafir bin Abdul Hamid
DPMJ PAT KAT KMN AMN AMK MA(UKM) mpat psc

GOC Army Field Command . . . . .Lt Gen Dato' Seri Zaini bin Haji Said
PSAT SPMJ SPTS DPMJ DSAP DMSM PAT JSD DSM KMN BGP ndc mpat psc

GOC 1 DIV . . . . .Maj Gen Dato' Mohd Azumi bin Mohamad
DPTS KAT ACM AMP AMN jssc psc

GOC 2 DIV . . . . .Maj Gen Datuk Khairuddin bin Mat Yusof
PGDK KMN AMK PNBB psc MA(Lancs) Dip Int Rels(Lancs)

GOC 3 DIV . . . . .Maj Gen Datuk Abdullah bin Abdul Ghani
*PSAT DIMP DSDK PAT JSM KMN MSc(Leicester) ndu mpat Imt Dip Sis (PSK) Dip Mgm*t (MIM)

GOC 4 DIV . . . . .Maj Gen Dato' Sulaiman bin Yusof
DSPM PAT KMN BCK mpat psc

Office of the High Commissioner for Malaysia in the United Kingdom
45/46 Belgrave Square, London, SW1X 8QT (Tel: 0207-235 8033 Fax 0207-235-5161)

Defence Adviser . . . . .Col Kamaruddin Mattan
PAT KAT KMN AMN AMP mpat psc

Assistant Defence Adviser . . . . Maj M Zahari Jamaluddin *AMN psc RMAF*

79

THE FEDERAL REPUBLIC OF NIGERIA

PRESIDENT, COMMANDER-IN-CHIEF . . . . . .Chief Olusegun Obasanjo *GCFR*
Chief of Defence Staff .V/Adm I Ogohi *CFR*
Chief of Army Staff . . . . .Lt Gen S V L Malu *CFR*
Chief of Naval Staff . . . . .V/Adm V K Ombu *CFR*
Chief of Air Staff . . . . .AM I M Alfa *CFR*
Commandant National War College . . . . .R/Adm G A Shiyanbade
Commandant Nigerian Defence Academy . . . . .Maj Gen P G Sha *CFR*
Defence Adviser . . . . .Maj Gen A F K Akale

Office of the Nigerian High Commission in the United Kingdom

Nigeria House, 9 Northumberland Avenue, London WC2N 5BX (Tel: 020-7839-1244)

THE REPUBLIC OF CYPRUS

PRESIDENT . . . .*His Excellency* Mr Glafcos Clerides
Minister of Defence . . . . .Mr Socrates Hassikos

Office of the Cyprus High Commission in the United Kingdom

93 Park Street, London W1Y 4ET (Tel: 020-7499-8272)

THE REPUBLIC OF SIERRA LEONE

PRESIDENT OF THE REPUBLIC OF SIERRA LEONE
His Excellency *Dr* Alhaji Ahmad Tejan Kabbah

REPUBLIC OF SIERRA LEONE MILITARY FORCES

DEPUTY MINISTER OF DEFENCE . . . . .Capt (Rtd) Hinga Norman

Office of the Sierra Leone High Commission in the United Kingdom

245 Oxford Street, London W1R 1LF (Tel: 020-7287-9884 Fax: 020-7734-3822)

THE UNITED REPUBLIC OF TANZANIA

PRESIDENT OF THE UNITED REPUBLIC AND COMMANDER IN CHIEF OF THE ARMED FORCES
Mr Benjamin William Mkapa
MINISTER FOR DEFENCE . . . . .Prof Philemon Sarungi

Tanzania Peoples Defence Forces

CHIEF OF DEFENCE FORCES . . . . .Gen R P Mboma

Office of the Tanzanian High Commission in the United Kingdom

43 Hertford Street, London W1Y 8DB (Tel: 020-7499-8951)

Defence Adviser . . . . .Col G M S Komba

JAMAICA

GOVERNOR GENERAL . . . .*His Excellency The Most Hon Sir* Howard Felix
Hanlon Cooke *ON GCMG*

DEFENCE BOARD
PRIME MINISTER . . . .*The Rt Hon* Percival J Patterson *QC MP*
MINISTER OF DEFENCE . . . .*The Rt Hon* Percival J Patterson *QC MP*
MINISTER OF NATIONAL SECURITY . . . . . .*Hon* K D Knight *MP*
Permanent Secretary
Ministry of National Security . . . . .Ms Elaine Baker
Chief of Staff . . . . .Major General J I Simmonds ADC
Defence Adviser . . . . .Col L H Graham

Office of the Jamaican High Commission in the United Kingdom

1-2 Prince Consort Road, London SW7 2BZ (Tel: 020-7823-9911)

REPUBLIC OF TRINIDAD AND TOBAGO

PRESIDENT AND COMMANDER IN CHIEF OF THE ARMED FORCES
His Excellency Mr Arthur Napoleon Raymond Robinson

Minister of National Security . . . .*Honourable* Basdeo Panday, *Prime Minister* Trinidad and Tobago
Chief of Defence Staff . . . . .Brig Gen John C E Sandy *ED psc BSc*
Special Adviser National Security Council . . .Rear/Adm (Retd) Richard Kelshall *Ed psc HBM*
Vice Chief of Defence Staff . . . . .Col Ancil Antoine *ED psc MMAS BA*

Trinidad and Tobago Regiment
Commanding Officer . . . . .Col Peter Jospeh *Ed MBA*

Trinidad and Tobago Coast Guard
Commanding Officer . . . . .Capt Garnet Best *Ed psc MSc*

Office of the High Commission for Trinidad and Tobago in the United Kingdom

42 Belgrave Square, London SW1X 8NT (Tel: 020-7245-9531 Fax: 020-7823 1065)

REPUBLIC OF UGANDA

PRESIDENT AND COMMANDER IN CHIEF OF THE ARMED FORCES
His Excellency Lt Gen Yoweri Kaguta Museveni

Acting Minister of State for Defence . . . .*Hon* Kavuma Stephen

Uganda Peoples Defence Forces
Army Commander . . . . .Maj Gen Jeje Odongo
Army Chief of Staff . . . . .Brig James Kazini

Office of the Uganda High Commission in the United Kingdom

Uganda House, 58-59 Trafalgar Square, London WC2N 5DX (Tel: 020-7839-5783 Fax: 020-7839-8925)

KENYA

PRESIDENT AND COMMANDER IN CHIEF OF THE ARMED FORCES
His Excellency The Hon Daniel Toroitich arap Moi *CGH MP*

Office of the President (Department of Defence) Minister
Chief of the General Staff . . . . .Gen J R E Kibwana *MGH CBS* (Navy)

Kenya Army
Army Commander . . . . .Lt Gen L K Sumbeiywo

Office of the Kenya High Commission in the United Kingdom

45 Portland Place, London W1N 4AS (Tel: 020-7636-2371/5)

Kenya Defence Adviser . . . . .Col B Y Haj *AC psc(UK)*

MALAWI

PRESIDENT AND COMMANDER IN CHIEF AND MINISTER OF DEFENCE
His Excellency Dr Bakili Muluzi

Army Commander . . . . .Gen J G Chimbayo *OSC*
Deputy Army Commander . . . . .Lt Gen M D Chiziko *OSC*

Office of the Malawi High Commission in the United Kingdom

33 Grosvenor Street, London W1X 0DE (Tel: 020-7491-4172 Fax: 020-7491-9916)

Malawi Defence Adviser . . . . .Col H Odilo *OSC*

MALTA

PRESIDENT . . . .*His Excellency Professor* Guido de Marco
Prime Minister . . . .*The Hon Dr* Edward Fenech-Adami *KUOM BA LL.D MP*

The Armed Forces of Malta
Commander of the Armed Forces of Malta . . .Brig Rupert C Montanaro

Office of the Malta High Commission in the United Kingdom

Malta House, 36-38 Piccadilly, London W1J 0LE. (Tel: 020-7292-4800)

ZAMBIA

PRESIDENT AND COMMANDER IN CHIEF . .*President* F J T Chiluba

Zambia Defence Force
Minister of Defence . . . .*Hon* Chitalu M Sampa *MP*
Army Commander . . . . .Lt Gen G R Musengule
Air Force Commander . . . . .Lt Gen S Kayumba
Commandant Zambia National Service . . . . . . .Lt Gen W Funjika

Office of the Zambia High Commission in the United Kingdom

Zambia House, 2 Palace Gate, Kensington, London W8 5NG (Tel: 020-7589-6655)

THE GAMBIA

PRESIDENT . . . .*His Excellency* Col (Retd) Yahya A J J Jammeh
VICE PRESIDENT . . . . .Mrs Isatou Njie-Saidy

Office of the Gambia High Commission in the United Kingdom

57 Kensington Court, London W8 5DG (Tel: 020-7937-6316/7/8)

SINGAPORE

PRESIDENT . . . .*Mr* Sellapan Ramanathan
Minister for Defence . . . .*Dr* Tony Tan Kheng Yam

Office of the Singapore High Commission in the United Kingdom

9 Wilton Crescent, London SW1X 8SP (Tel: 020-7235-8315 Fax: 020-7245-6583)

GUYANA

PRESIDENT . . . .*His Excellency Mr* Bharrat Jagdeo
PRIME MINISTER . . . .*The Hon* Samuel A A Hinds *MP*

Office of the Guyana High Commission in the United Kingdom

3 Palace Court, Bayswater Road, London W2 4LP (Tel: 020-7229-7684 Fax: 020-7727-9809)

THE REPUBLIC OF BOTSWANA

PRESIDENT . . . .*H E Mr* Festus G Mogae
VICE PRESIDENT . . . .*Hon* Lt Gen S K I Khama *PH FOM DCO DSM*
Commander . . . . .Lt Gen L M Fisher *DCO GOM psc*
Chief of Staff and Deputy Commander . . . . .Maj Gen T H C Masire
Deputy Chief of Staff .Maj Gen B K Oitsile

Office of the Botswana High Commission in the United Kingdom

6 Stratford Place, London W1N 9AE (Tel: 020-7499-0031)

82

THE KINGDOM OF LESOTHO

HEAD OF STATE . . . .*His Majesty King* Letsie III
PRIME MINISTER . . . .*The Rt Hon* Mr Pakalitha Mosisili

COMMANDER . . . . .Maj Gen M Mosakeng
Office of the Lesotho High Commission in the United Kingdom
7 Chesham Place, Belgravia, London SW1 8HN (Tel: 020-7235-5686)

BARBADOS

GOVERNOR GENERAL . . . .*His Excellency Sir* Clifford Husbands *GCMG KA*
PRIME MINISTER . . . .*The Rt Hon* Owen Arthur *MSc MP*
Office of the Barbados High Commission in the United Kingdom
1 Great Russell Street, London WC1B 3ND (Tel: 020-7631-4975 Fax: 020-7323-6872)

REPUBLIC OF MAURITIUS

PRESIDENT . . . .*Mr* Cassam Uteem *GCSK*
PRIME MINISTER . . . .*Sir* Anerood Jugnauth *PC KCMG QC*
Office of the Mauritius High Commission in the United Kingdom
32/33 Elvaston Place, London SW7 5NW (Tel: 020-7581-0294/5 Fax: 020-7823-8437)

THE KINGDOM OF SWAZILAND

HEAD OF STATE . . . .*His Majesty King* Mswati III
PRIME MINISTER . . . .*The Rt Hon* Barnabas Sibusiso Diamini

COMMANDING OFFICER . . . . .Brig S Dlamini
Office of the Swaziland High Commission in the United Kingdom
20 Buckingham Gate, London SW1E 6LB (Tel: 020-7630-6611)

FIJI

PRESIDENT AND COMMANDER IN CHIEF . . *His Excellency The Rt Hon Ratu Josefa Uluivuda Iloilo*
PRIME MINISTER . . . .*The Rt Hon* Laisenia Qarase

Republic of Fiji Military Forces
COMMANDER . . . . .Cmde Ratu Voreque Bainimarama
Chief of Staff . . . . .Col Iowane Naivalurua
Office of the Fiji High Commission in the United Kingdom
34 Hyde Park Gate, London SW7 5DN (Tel: 020-7584-3661 Fax: 020-7584-2838)

THE PEOPLES REPUBLIC OF BANGLADESH

PRESIDENT AND SUPREME COMMANDER THE PEOPLES REPUBLIC OF BANGLADESH
His Excellency Shahabuddin Ahmed
Chief of Army Staff Bangladesh Army . . . . .Lt Gen Md Harun-Ar-Rashid *BP rcds psc*
High Commission for The Peoples Republic of Bangladesh
28 Queen's Gate, London SW7 5JA (Tel: 020-7584-0081)

83

THE BAHAMAS

A/GOVERNOR GENERAL ....*His Excellency Sir* Orville A Turnquest *GCMC QC*
PRIME MINSTER ....*The Rt Hon* Hubert A Ingraham *PC MP*
OFFICE OF THE DEPUTY PRIME MINISTER AND MINISTER OF NATIONAL SECURITY
Hon Frank Watson *MP Deputy Prime Minister*
Royal Bahamas Defence Force
COMMANDER ....Commodore D Rolle
Office of the High Commissioner for the Commonwealth of The Bahamas

Bahamas House, 10 Chesterfield Street, London W1J 5JL (Tel: 020-7408-4488 Fax: 020-7499-9937)

GRENADA

GOVERNOR GENERAL ....*His Excellency Sir* Daniel C Williams *GCMG QC*
PRIME MINISTER AND MINISTER OF NATIONAL SECURITY
Dr The Hon Keith C Mitchell
Office of the High Commissioner for Grenada in the United Kingdom

1 Collingham Gardens, Earls Court, London SW5 0HW (Tel: 020-7373-7809 Fax: 020-7370-7040)

ZIMBABWE

PRESIDENT AND COMMANDER IN CHIEF ..*His Excellency The Hon* Robert Gabriel Mugabe
MINISTER OF DEFENCE ....*The Honourable* M Mahachi
COMMANDER DEFENCE FORCES (CDF) ...Gen V M G Zvinavashe
ARMY COMMANDER ....Lt Gen C G Chiwenga
AIR FORCE COMMANDER ....Air Marshal P Shiri
Office of the Zimbabwe High Commission in the United Kingdom

Zimbabwe House, 429 Strand, London WC2R 0SA (Tel: 020-7836-7755 Fax: 020-7379-1167)

Defence Adviser ....Col J J Murozvi

ISLAMIC REPUBLIC OF PAKISTAN

PRESIDENT ....Muhammad Rafiq Tarar
Chief Executive, Chairman Joint Chiefs of Staff' Committee
and Chief of Army Staff ....General Pervez Musharraf *NI(M) T Bt*
Office of the Pakistan High Commission in the United Kingdom

35 Lowndes Square, London SW1X 9JN (Tel: 020-7664-9200)

Defence and Naval Adviser ....Vacant
Army and Air Adviser ....Colonel Zubair Mahmood Hayat

BELIZE

GOVERNOR GENERAL ....*Hon Sir* Colville M Young *GCMG MBE PhD*
PRIME MINISTER ....*Hon* Said Musa
BELIZE DEFENCE FORCE
COMMANDANT ....Brig Gen R S Garcia

HIS MAJESTY THE SULTAN 29TH SULTAN OF BRUNEI

SULTAN AND COMMANDER IN CHIEF ROYAL BRUNEI ARMED FORCES

Kebawah Duli Yang Maha Mulia Paduka Seri Baginda Sultan Haji Hassanal Bolkiah Mu'izzaddin Waddaulah Ibni Al-Marhum Sultan Haji Omar 'Ali Saifuddien Sa'adul Khairi Waddien *DKMB DK PSSUB DPKG DPKT PSPNB PSNB PSLJ SPMB PANB GCB GCMG DMN DK(kelantan), DK(Johor), DK(Negeri Sembilan), Collar of the Supreme Order of the Chrysanthemum, Grand Order of Mugunghwa, DK(Pahang), Bintang Republik Indonesia Adipurna, Collar of the Nile, The Order of Al-Hussein bin Ali, The Civil Order of Oman, DK(Selangor), DK(Perlis), DK(Perak), The Ancient Order of Sikatuna Rank of Rajah, Al Khalifia, Ouissam El Mohammdi Grand Collier, The Most Auspicious Order of the Rajamitrabhorn, DUBS(Sarawak), The Order of Temasek First Class, Nishan-E-Pakistan, DK(Terangganu), PGAT, Distinguished Service Order (Military) Sultan Dan Yang Di-Pertuan Negara Brunei Darussalam.*

85

DEFENCE AND MILITARY ADVISERS TO BRITISH HIGH COMMISSIONS WITHIN THE COMMONWEALTH

CANADA

OTTOWA

Defence and Military Adviser . . . . .Brig C J R Day 280301

AUSTRALIA

CANBERRA

Defence and Naval Adviser . . . . .Cdre A J Lyall *MBE* RN 130298
Military/Air Adviser .Gp Capt N C Rusling RAF 010699
(also Defence Adviser Papua New Guinea)

NEW ZEALAND

WELLINGTON

Defence Adviser and Head BDLS . . . . .Capt D A Wines RN 231098
(also Defence Attache Fiji and Tonga)

INDIA

NEW DELHI

Defence and Military Adviser . . . . .Brig S M A Lee *OBE* 251197
(also Defence Adviser Bangladesh)

SRI LANKA

COLOMBO

Defence Adviser . . . . .Lt Col M H Weldon 210401

GHANA

ACCRA

Defence Adviser . . . . .Lt Col S K E Clarke *OBE* 120101
(also Defence Attache Togo and Ivory Coast)

MALAYSIA

KUALA LUMPUR

Defence Adviser . . . . .Col R J Little 181099

KENYA

NAIROBI

Defence Adviser . . . . .Col T V Merritt *OBE* 050997
(also Defence Adviser Mauritius,Tanzania, Seychelles, and Defence Attache Eritrea and Ethiopia)

CYPRUS

NICOSIA

Defence Adviser . . . . .Col C S Wakelin *OBE* 070598

SINGAPORE

Defence Adviser . . . . .Gp Capt C B Le Bas RAF 010698

PAKISTAN

ISLAMABAD

Defence and Military Adviser . . . . .Brig E J Torrens-Spence 011200

NIGERIA

ABUJA

Defence Adviser . . . . .Col G G Davies 010599

UGANDA

KAMPALA

Defence Adviser . . . . .Lt Col C E Thom *OBE* R IRISH 041297
(also Defence Attache Burundi and Rwanda)

JAMAICA

KINGSTON

Defence Adviser . . . . .Col R A Hyde-Bales 140400
(also Defence Adviser Bahamas, Belize and DA British Dependent Territories Cayman Islands,Turks & Caicos)

ZIMBABWE

HARARE

Defence Adviser . . . . .Col J S Field *CBE* 010899
(also Botswana, Malawi and Mozambique)

BARBADOS

BRIDGETOWN

Defence Adviser . . . . .Capt P Jackson RN 140298
(also D Adv to States of Regional Security: Grenada, St Vincent, St Lucia, Dominica, Antigua & Barbuda, St Kitts)
D Adv to British Dependent Territories: British Virgin Islands, Anguilla, Montserrat also D Adv to Trinidad & Tobago,
Guyana, Surinam.
DVO to Guadaloupe, Martinique, Curacao, US Virgin Islands, Puerto Rico.

SIERRA LEONE

FREETOWN

Defence Adviser . . . . .Lt Col J J P Poraj-Wilczynski 270101
(also D Adv to Guinea)

SOUTH AFRICA

PRETORIA

Defence and Military Adviser . . . . .Brig M R Raworth 150399
(also Defence Adviser Lesotho and Swaziland)
Naval and Air Adviser . . . . .Wg Cdr T A Harper RAF 090201
(also Defence Adviser Namibia)

MILITARY ATTACHES TO EMBASSIES IN FOREIGN COUNTRIES

ABU DHABI (UAE)

Defence Attache . . . . .Col A V Malkin 051100

AMMAN

Defence, Naval and Military Attache . . . . . . .Col C R Romberg 070101

ANKARA

Defence and Military Attache . . . . .L/Brig K O Winfield 011199

ATHENS

Defence, Naval and Air Attache . . . . .Cdre J L Milnes RN 171298
Military Attache . . . . .Lt Col S W L Strickland OBE 031100

BAHRAIN

Defence Attache . . . . .Cdr M Dodds RN 030799

BANGKOK

Defence Attache . . . . .Col A R E Singer OBE 230899

BEIRUT

Defence Attache . . . . .Lt Col D J A Bergin OBE 250799

BELGRADE

Defence Attache . . . . .Col J H Crosland OBE MC 230899

BERLIN

Defence and Military Attache . . . . .Brig B R Isbell 150899

BERNE

Defence Attache . . . . .Lt Col E J Gould RTR 250198

BOGOTA

Defence Attache . . . . .Col R J Griffiths MBE 310599
(also DA Lima)

BRASILIA

Defence, Military and Air Attache . . . . .Col J M Bowles MBE 250199

BRATISLAVA

Defence Attache . . . . .Lt Col N S Southward OBE 130700

BRUNEI

Defence Attache . . . . .Capt P H Jones OBE RN 190799

BRUSSELS

Defence Attache . . . . .Col T E Hall CBE 300398
(also Defence Attache Luxembourg)

BUCHAREST

Defence Attache . . . . .A/Col A T Bruce MBE 131100
(also Defence Adviser Kishinev)

BUDAPEST

Defence Attache ....Col A T B Kimber 270498

BUENOS AIRES

Defence, Military and Naval Attache ......Col P A Reynolds RM 011200
Air Attache ....Gp Capt T P Brewer OBE RAF 171299
(also Defence Attache Paraguay and Uruguay)

CAIRO

Defence and Military Attache ....Col P E Dennison OBE 271199

CARACAS

Defence Attache ....Capt E F Searle RN 150800
(also Defence Attache Ecuador, Panama and Cuba)

COPENHAGEN

Defence Attache ....Cdr A C Gordon Lennox RN 130298

DAMASCUS

Defence Attache ....Col R C J Martin OBE 090201

DOHA

Defence Attache ....Wg Cdr P K Keating RAF 100199

DUBLIN

Defence Attache ....Col P B G Cummings 160301

GUATEMALA CITY

Defence Attache ....Col I C D Blair-Pilling OBE 020900
(also Defence Attache El Salvador, Honduras, Nicaragua and Mexico)

THE HAGUE

Defence and Naval Attache ....Capt N A M Butler RN 160301
Military and Air Attache ....Lt Col S J A Lloyd MBE RA 271198

HELSINKI

Defence Attache ....Lt Col G A B Grant RA 060498
(also Defence Attache Estonia)

JAKARTA

Defence Attache ....Col A J Roberts 111200

KATHMANDU

Defence Attache ....Col M Dowdle 031098

KIEV

Defence Attache ....Capt M N Littleboy RN 091098
Assistant Defence Attache ....Maj C A Bulleid PWRR 310898

KINSHASA

Defence Attache ....Lt Col C T B Brown 230201
(also Defence Attache Congo and Gabon)

KUWAIT

Defence Attache ....Col The Hon A J C Campbell 031298

LISBON

Defence Attache . . . . .Cdr A J Bull RN 281199

LJUBLJANA

Defence Attache . . . . .Lt Col A R Manton 050600

MADRID

Defence and Naval Attache . . . . .Capt A Croke RN 040900
Military and Air Attache . . . . .Col R J Lawson 120997

MANILA

Defence Attache . . . . .Capt C Peach RN 090998

MOSCOW

Defence and Air Attache . . . . .Air Cdre J C Jarron RAF 210899
Military Attache . . . . .Col C R Langton OBE 040398
Asst Military Attache . . . . .Maj P J F Daniell 100999
(MA is DA to Kazakhstan (Almaty), Kyrgyzstan (Bishkek), Tajikistan (Dushanbe), Turkmenistan (Ashkabad), and
Uzbekistan (Tashkent)
AMA is ADA to Turkmenistan (Ashkabad) and Uzbekistan (Tashkent)

MUSCAT

Defence and Military Attache . . . . .L/Brig M Smith CBE MC 260699

OSLO

Defence and Naval Attache . . . . .Cdr D L Stanesby RN 210499
Military Attache . . . . .Lt Col J A Poole-Warren RGJ 080898

PARIS

Defence and Air Attache . . . . .Air Cdre D N Adams RAF 010298
Military Attache . . . . .Brig R E Ratazzi CBE 011000

PEKING

Defence Military and Air Attache . . . . .Brig J G Kerr OBE QGM 150698
(also Defence Attache Mongolia)

PRAGUE

Defence Attache . . . . .Col D A Wynne-Davies 300301

RABAT

Defence Attache . . . . .Lt Col G D Duthoit R ANGLIAN .110600
(also Defence Attache Mauretania, Senegal)

RIGA

Defence Attache . . . . .Lt Col A S Tuggey RE 050999

RIYADH

Defence and Military Attache . . . . .Brig R I Talbot 230898
(also Defence and Military Attache Yemen)

ROME

Defence and Military Attache . . . . .L/Brig A L Mallinson 170700

SANTIAGO

Defence Attache ....Col R M J Rollo-Walker *OBE* 110800
(also Defence Attache Bolivia)

SEOUL

Defence and Military Attache ....Brig J G Baker *MBE* 121098

SKOPJE

Defence Attache ....L/Col M I V Dore RA 010599
(also Defence Attache Albania)

SOFIA

Defence Attache ....Col R Z A Claglinski 160201

STOCKHOLM

Defence Attache ....Wg Cdr J G Elliott *MBE* RAF 190998

TBILISI

Defence Attache ....Wg Cdr A W Kerr RAF 100699
(also Defence Attache Armenia and Azerbaijan)

TEL AVIV

Defence and Military Attache ....Col T M Fitzalan-Howard *OBE* 231000

TOKYO

Defence Attache ....Capt J A Boyd RN 121099

VIENNA

Defence Attache ....Lt Col J A Bourne AAC 030600

VILNIUS

Defence Attache ....Lt Col P R P Swanson *MBE* 260201

WARSAW

Defence and Air Attache ....Gp Capt M Mitchell RAF 160697
Naval and Military Attache ....Lt Col I F Watts INT CORPS 301000

WASHINGTON

Defence Attache and Head BDS ....A/VM J H Thompson *CB* RAF 250400
Military Attache and COMD BAS ....Brig A C Mantell *OBE* 040199
Assistant Military Attache ....Col T F L Weeks *OBE* 140700

ZAGREB

Defence Attache ....Lt Col S C H Cleveland *MBE* RRF 301197

SECTION III

SECTION III

GRADATION LIST

OFFICERS OF THE ARMY ON THE ACTIVE LIST

FIELD MARSHALS

His Royal Highness The Prince PHILIP Duke of EDINBURGH KG KT OM GBE AC QSO psc(n) 150153
CARVER The Lord GCB CBE DSO• MC idc jssc psc 180773
GIBBS Sir Roland GCB CBE DSO MC idc jssc psc 130779
BRAMALL The Lord KG GCB OBE MC idc psc 010882
STANIER Sir John GCB MBE DL idc jssc psc 100785
BAGNALL Sir Nigel GCB CVO MC• ADC idc jssc psc 090988
VINCENT The Lord GBE KCB DSO psc ptsc G(a) 020491
CHAPPLE Sir John GCB CBE MA df jssc psc 140292
His Royal Highness The Duke of KENT KG GCMG GCVO psc 110693
INGE The Lord Peter GCB DL jssc psc 150394
(Constable Tower of London)

FORMER CHIEFS OF STAFF

Guthrie General Sir Charles GCB LVO OBE (late WG) psc 130192
Wheeler General Sir Roger GCB CBE MA (late R IRISH) psc(AUS) 090795

GENERALS

Walker Sir Michael GCB CBE ADC Gen (late R ANGLIAN) psc† 020497

Cowan Sir Sam KCB CBE BA (late R SIGNALS) psc† 100998

Smith Sir Rupert KCB DSO OBE QGM (late PARA) psc hcsc 301198

Jackson Sir Mike KCB CBE BSocSc(Hons) (late PARA) ndc psc hcsc jsdc 010300

Deverell Sir John KCB OBE (late LI) psc(n) hcsc ..230301

LIEUTENANT GENERALS

Willcocks Sir Michael KCB BSc(Hons) (late RA) psc† hcsc 010399

Drewry Sir Christopher KCB CBE BA(Hons) (late WG) psc hcsc 260100

Menzies R C OBE QHS MB ChB FRC Path (late RAMC) 280200

Pigott A D CBE MA (late RE) rcds psc 090300

Granville-Chapman Sir Timothy KCB CBE MA(Hons) (late RA) rcds psc† hcsc 090500

Irwin A S H CBE MA (late BW) psc(PAK)+ psc hcsc 061200

Delves C N G CBE DSO (late D and D) psc hcsc ..120301

MAJOR GENERALS

Sulivan T J *CB CBE BSc(Hons) (late* RHG/D) psc(a) hcsc
. 210794
Elliott C L *CB MBE BSc(Eng) Hons MPhil (late* RE) df psc
hcsc 020395
Kiszely J P *MC (late* SG) psc hcsc 020395
O'Donoghue K *CBE BSc(Hons) (late* RE) nadc psc(CAN)
hcsc 020395
Denaro A G *CBE (late* QRIH) rcds psc† hcsc 220296
Trousdell P C C *CB (late* R IRISH) psc hcsc 220296
Chambers P A *MBE BA FIMGT FILOG (late* RAOC) rcds
psc hcsc 220296
Besgrove P V R *CBE BSc(Eng) Hons CEng MIEE (late*
REME) psc ee hcsc jsdc 240696
Searby R V *(late* 9/12 L) psc 160596
Risius G *CB (late* AGC(ALS)) 200297
Ramsay A I *CBE DSO (late* RHF) rcds ocds(US) psc jsdc
150597
Reith J G *CB CBE (late* PARA) psc hcsc 010797
Elliott C H *CBE (late* RRW) psc 120997
Pringle A R D *CB CBE BSc(Hons) (late* RGJ) rcds psc†
hcsc 141197
Raper A J *CBE MA (late* R SIGNALS) odc(AUST) psc†
hcsc 230298
Ridgway A P *CB CBE MPhil(Cantab) (late* RTR) psc ph
. 280498
Truluck A E G *CBE FIMGT (late* R SIGNALS) rcds psc†
hcsc 280498
Currie A P N *BA(Hons) (late* RA) psc† hcsc 020898
Watt C R *CBE MA (late* WG) psc PSC(J) hcsc . . .170898
HRH *The Prince of* Wales *KG KT GCB AK QSO ADC*
. 141198

Grant Peterkin A P *OBE BA (late* QOHLDRS) rcds
odc(Aust) psc(Ind) hcsc 040199
Dannatt F R *CBE MC BA(Hons) (late* GH) psc hcsc
. 150199
Palmer A M D *CBE (late* RGJ) rcds psc(PAK) hcsc
. 220199
Sutherell J C B *CBE BA(Hons) (late* R ANGLIAN) rcds psc
. 120399
Viggers F R *MBE* psc hcsc (late RA) 240399
Moore-Bick J D *CBE MA (late* RE) psc(GE) hcsc I*
. 190499
Gordon R D S *CBE MA* rcds psc† hcsc 140599
Plummer B P *BA(Hons) (late* RWF) jsdc hcsc(J) sq psc
rcds 310899
Judd D L *BSc(Eng) (Hons) CEng* rcds psc† hcsc . .101199
Brims R V *CBE* psc† hcsc 170100
Gilchrist P psc† aic hcsc 210100
Jolliffe D S *MB BS FRCP MRCS* 170200
Messervy-Whiting G G *MBE FIMGT MIL (late* INT
CORPS) jsdc psc(A) rcds 130300
Cross T *CBE MSc (late* RLC) rcds psc ato hcsc . . .170800
Figgures A C *CBE MA CEng FIMechE MIEE (late* REME)
rcds psc hcsc 260900
Laurie M I *CBE BSc(Hons) (late* INT CORPS) hcsc(J) psc
rcds 261000
McColl J C *CBE (late* R ANGLIAN) hcsc(J) psc .081100
Charlton-Weedy M A *CBE (late* RA) psc† rcds . . .040101
Gamon J A *QHDS MSc BDS (late* RADC) 080101
Holmes J T *OBE MC (late* SG) psc hcsc 290101

HOUSEHOLD CAVALRY

THE LIFE GUARDS

April 1922
The 1st Life Guards and
The 2nd Life Guards amalgamated to form:
The Life Guards (1st and 2nd)
June 1928
Redesignated The Life Guards

The Royal Arms

Dettingen, Peninsula, Waterloo, Tel-el-Kebir, Egypt 1882, Relief of Kimberley, Paardeberg, South Africa 1899-1900

*The Great War_* **Mons, Le Cateau,** Retreat from Mons, **Marne 1914, Aisne 1914, Messines 1914,** Armentieres 1914, **Ypres 1914, 15, 17,** Langemarck 1914, Gheluvelt, Nonne Bosschen, St Julien, Frezenberg, **Somme 1916, 18,** Albert 1916, **Arras 1917 18,** Scarpe 1917, 18, Broodseinde, Poelcappelle, Passchendaele, Bapaume 1918, **Hindenburg Line,** Epehy, St Quentin Canal, Beaurevoir, Cambrai 1918, Selle, **France and Flanders 1914-18**

*The Second World War_* Mont Pincon, **Souleuvre,** Noireau Crossing, Amiens 1944, **Brussels,** Neerpelt, Nederrijn, Nijmegen, Lingen, Bentheim, **North-West Europe 1944-45,** Baghdad 1941, **Iraq 1941, Palmyra, Syria 1941, El Alamein, North Africa 1942-43,** Arezzo, Advance to Florence, Gothic Line, **Italy 1944**

Gulf 1991, Wadi Al Batin

Regimental Marches

Quick Marches . . . .(i) Milanollo (ii) Men of Harlech

Slow Marches . . . .(i) The Life Guards Slow March (ii) Men of Harlech

Agents . . . . .Lloyds Bank plc Cox's & King's Branch

Headquarters Household Cavalry . . . .Horse Guards, Whitehall, London SW1A 2AX (Tel. 0207-414-2213)

Allied Regiment of the Pakistan Army

The President's Bodyguard

Colonel in Chief . . . . .THE QUEEN

Colonel . . . . .General *Sir* Charles Guthrie *GCB LVO OBE ADC Gen* 010199

Commander Household Cavalry . . . . . .Col H P D Massey RHG/D 181200

Colonels

Ellery J W M *CBE* psc jsdc 300693
Falkner P S W F *OBE* psc 300697

Lieutenant Colonels

De Ritter A P psc psc(a) 300688
Anderson C S K (SL) osc(P) I
300693
Doughty W S G psc (A/Col 280900)
300696
Scott H S J psc† jsdc 300696
Ridley N M A *MA* psc† 300697
Van Der Lande *M C MA(Cantab) MA*
psc† 300600

Majors

Hunter P R L psc(n)†. 300984
Stibbe G G E *BA(Hons) MA(Hons)* sq
270491
Griffin R R D MDA 300995

Smyth-Osbourne E A *MA* psc† psc	
	300995
Thorneycroft T E sq	300995
Wheeler J R psc(CAN)	300997
Fullerton H R D	300998
Gaselee J D A	300998
Briscoe H C B *BA(Hons)*	300900
Howson G W *BA(Hons)*	300900
Methven A B *BA(Hons)*	300900
Taylor R C *BA(Hons)*	300900

Captains

Allerton C E O *BSc(Hons)*	080396
Lawrence A *BA(Hons)*	120496
Fox-Pitt A J L	230697

Lieutenants

Kenyon W R G	090899

Regular Category Late Entry Officers

Majors

Mead A J	300996
Lodge J T	300900

Special Regular Officers Late Entry

Captains

Whatley M	140897
Holbrook J S (A/Maj 230600)	
	10498
Pickard D	10498

Intermediate Regular Officers

Captains

Barnard J R D	141296
Butah J B C	80897
Catsaras Z N *BA(Hons)*	100299
Peasgood R A H *BA(Hons)*	100299
Blount J H *BSc(Hons)*	060200
Trietline C J	140400
Rees-Davies J G *BSc(Hons)*	301100

Short Service Late Entry Officers

Captains

Lindsay W R	150698

Tierney J S — 150199
Waygood R G — 120400

Short Service Officers

Majors

Hammond J *MBChB* — 10898

Lieutenants

Bond E J *BA(Hons)* — 120897
Derry R S I *BA(Hons)* — 120897
Greany J R *BA(Hons)* — 130498
Berry M S P *BA* — 100898
Howell J E M *BSc(Hons)* — 121098
Brooks D S *BSc(Hons)* — 141298
Lipman D L *BSc(Hons)* — 141298

Instone S A *BA(Hons)* — 90899
Anderson J G K *BSc(Hons)* — 131299

2nd Lieutenants

Giffard T A — 100499
Wren C W — 120800

97
THE BLUES AND ROYALS
(ROYAL HORSE GUARDS AND 1st DRAGOONS)

On 29 March 1969
Royal Horse Guards (The Blues) and
The Royal Dragoons (1st Dragoons) amalgamated to form:
The Blues and Royals (Royal Horse Guards and 1st Dragoons)

The Royal Arms

Tangier 1662-80, Dettingen, Warburg, Beaumont, Willems, Fuentes D'onor, Peninsula, Waterloo, Balaklava, Sevastopol, Egypt, Tel-el-Kebir, Relief of Kimberley, Paardeberg, Relief of Ladysmith, South Africa 1899-1902

The Great War _ Mons, Le Cateau, Retreat from Mons, **Marne 1914**, Aisne 1914, **Messines 1914**, Armentieres 1914, **Ypres 1914, 15-17**, Langemarck 1914, **Gheluvelt**, Nonne Bosschen, St Julien, **Frezenberg, Loos, Arras 1917**, Scarpe 1917, **Somme 1918**, St Quentin, Avre, Broodseinde, Poelcappelle, Passchendaele, **Amiens, Hindenburg Line**, Beaurevoir, **Cambrai 1918**, Sambre, Pursuit to Mons, **France and Flanders 1914-18**

*The Second World War_* Mont Pincon, **Souleuvre**, Noireau Crossing, Amiens 1944, **Brussels**, Neerpelt, **Nederrijn**, Veghel, Nijmegen, **Rhine**, Lingen, Bentheim, **North-West Europe 1944-45**, Baghdad 1941, **Iraq 1941, Palmyra, Syria 1941**, Msus, Gazala, **Knightsbridge**, Defence of Alamein Line, **El Alamein**, El Agheila, **Advance on Tripoli, North Africa 1941-43, Sicily 1943**, Arezzo, Advance to Florence, Gothic Line, **Italy 1943-44**

Falkland Islands 1982

Regimental Marches

Quick Marches . . . . Regimental Quick March of The Blues and Royals
Grand March from Aida and The Royals

Slow Marches . . . . Slow March of The Blues and Royals

Agents . . . . Lloyds Bank plc Cox's & King's Branch

Headquarters Household Cavalry . . . . Horse Guards, Whitehall, London SW1A 2AX (Tel. 0207-414-2213)

Alliances

Canadian Armed Forces . . . . The Royal Canadian Dragoons
The Governor General's Horse Guards

Colonel in Chief . . . . THE QUEEN

Colonel . . . . *Her Royal Highness* The Princess Royal *KG KT GCVO QSO* 011098

Commander Household Cavalry . . . . . . Col H P D Massey RHG/D 181200
Reg

Brigadiers	Clee C B B *BSc(Hons) MSc* psc(a)† 300995	**Special Regular Officers Late Entry**
Rollo W R CBE MA psc hcsc(J)	Woyka G V DE LA F odc(AUST) 300995	*Captains*
300698	Lockhart C A 300998	Stretton P F *(A/Maj 300500)*
White-Spunner B W B *MA* psc 300600	Eyre J P 300999	231094
	Tomes S C *BA(Hons)* 300999	
	Hughes D E 300900	**Intermediate Regular Officers**
Colonels		*Majors*
Rogers P B *MPhil* psc jsdc 300693	*Captains*	Miller S ST M 300999
Massey H P D psc I 300698	Goodwin-Hudson M P *BA(Hons)* 110895	
Browne W T *LVO* sq jsdc 300600	Dick A D 151295	*Captains*
	Bartle-Jones W 90498	Philipson-Stow R R 290797
Lieutenant Colonels	Bedford P A *BEng(Hons)* 160698	Bedford O M *BSc(Hons)* 100299
Lukas F G S *MSc* psc† dis jsdc 300695	**Regular Category Late Entry**	Bellman J A S *BA(Hons)* 140699
Tabor P J *MVO BA(Hons)* psc aic 300696	**Officers**	**Short Service Late Entry Officers**
Stone C M *MBBS DRCOG* 140898	*Lieutenant Colonels*	*Captains*
Cowen S H *MA* psc† 300699	O'Halloran D A sq 10198	Manning R P 210998
		Haywood C T 101198
Majors	*Majors*	Burbidge A 80299
McCullough G M D osc(SP) ph 300994	Harding M A 300999	Maher V P 30400

Carpenter T M	140400	Birkbeck O B *BA(Hons)*	220201	Lewis R H A *(A/Capt 090600)*	
Boyd D R	170400	Harrison N P *BSc*	220201		120499
Fisher J C	260400			Scott D I *(L/Capt 010999)*	120499
Norris M J	180500			De St John-Pryce J E A *BSc(Hons)*	
Carney R J	261000				90899

Lieutenants

Short Service Officers

		Dollar M P F *BSc(Hons)*	120897	Lane-Fox E S *BA(Hons)*	90899
		Sturgis R T *BSc(Hons)*	120897	White J A M *BSc(Hons)*	90899
Majors		Heath M J *BA(Hons)*	131097	Williams P J *BA(Hons)*	90899
Haworth K J	10898	Hayward E P W *BA(Hons)*	140698		
		Snook W H A G *BSc(SocSciENCE)*			
Captains			141298	*Cornets*	
Townley P B A *BA*	41000	Gibbs R A *BSc(Hons)*	120499	Viney J R C P	150400

		Evetts R S *BA(Hons)*	100898

ROYAL ARMOURED CORPS

In front of two concentric circles broken and barbed at the top, a gauntlet, clenched, charged with a billet. Inscribed with the letters "RAC" the whole ensigned with The Crown

Alliances

Canadian Armed Forces . . . . .Armoured Branch
Australian Military Forces . . . . .The Royal Australian Armoured Corps

Colonel Commandant . . . . .Maj Gen P Gilchrist 070400

The origins of amalgamated Regiments now included in The Royal Armoured Corps are as follows:

1st THE QUEEN'S DRAGOON GUARDS

On 1 January 1959
1st King's Dragoon Guards and
The Queen's Bays (2nd Dragoon Guards) amalgamated to form:
1st The Queen's Dragoon Guards

THE ROYAL SCOTS DRAGOON GUARDS (CARABINIERS AND GREYS)

On 11 April 1922
3rd Dragoon Guards (Prince of Wales's) and
The Carabiniers (6th Dragoon Guards) amalgamated to form:
3rd/6th Dragoon Guards

On 31 December 1928 the Regiment was redesignated
3rd Carabiniers (Prince of Wales's Dragoon Guards)

On 2 July 1971
3rd Carabiniers (Prince of Wales's Dragoon Guards) and
The Royal Scots Greys (2nd Dragoons) amalgamated to form:
The Royal Scots Dragoon Guards (Carabiniers and Greys)

100

THE ROYAL DRAGOON GUARDS

On 11 April 1922
4th Royal Irish Dragoon Guards and
7th Dragoon Guards (Princess Royal's) amalgamated to form:
4th/7th Dragoon Guards

On 31 October 1936 the Regiment was redesignated
4th/7th Royal Dragoon Guards

On 11 April 1922
5th Dragoon Guards (Princess Charlotte of Wales's) and
The Inniskillings (6th Dragoons) amalgamated to form:
5th/6th Dragoons

On 31 May 1927 the Regiment was redesignated
5th Inniskilling Dragoon Guards

On 30 June 1935 the Regiment was redesignated
5th Royal Inniskilling Dragoon Guards

On 1 August 1992
4th/7th Royal Dragoon Guards and
5th Royal Inniskilliing Dragoon Guards amalgamated to form:
The Royal Dragoon Guards

THE QUEEN'S ROYAL HUSSARS
(THE QUEEN'S OWN AND ROYAL IRISH)

On 3 November 1958
3rd The King's Own Hussars and
7th Queen's Own Hussars amalgamated to form:
The Queen's Own Hussars

On 24 October 1958
4th Queen's Own Hussars and
8th King's Royal Irish Hussars amalgamated to form:
The Queen's Royal Irish Hussars

On 1 September 1993
The Queen's Own Hussars and
The Queen's Royal Irish Hussars amalgamated to form:
The Queen's Royal Hussars (The Queen's Own and Royal Irish)

9th/12th ROYAL LANCERS (PRINCE OF WALES'S)

On 11 September 1960
9th Queen's Royal Lancers and
12th Royal Lancers (Prince of Wales's) amalgamated to form:
9th/12th Royal Lancers (Prince of Wales's)

THE KING'S ROYAL HUSSARS

On 25 October 1969
  10th Royal Hussars (Prince of Wales's Own) and
  11th Hussars (Prince Albert's Own) amalgamated to form:
  The Royal Hussars (Prince of Wales's Own)

On 11 April 1922
  14th King's Hussars and
  20th Hussars amalgamated to form:
  14th/20th Hussars

On 31 December 1936 the Regiment was redesignated
  14th/20th King's Hussars

On 4 December 1992
  The Royal Hussars (Prince of Wales's Own) and
  14th/20th King's Hussars amalgamated to form:
  The King's Royal Hussars

THE LIGHT DRAGOONS

On 11 April 1922
  13th Hussars and
  18th Royal Hussars (Queen Mary's Own) amalgamated to form:
  13th/18th Hussars

On 31 December 1935 the Regiment was redesignated
  13th/18th Royal Hussars (Queen Mary's Own)

On 11 April 1922
  15th The King's Hussars and
  19th Royal Hussars (Queen Alexandra's Own) amalgamated to form:
  15th/19th Hussars

On 31 October 1932 the Regiment was redesignated
  15th The King's Royal Hussars

On 31 December 1933 the Regiment was redesignated
  15th/19th The King's Royal Hussars

On 1 December 1992
  13th/18th Royal Hussars (Queen Mary's Own) and
  15th/19th The King's Royal Hussars amalgamated to form:
  The Light Dragoons

THE QUEEN'S ROYAL LANCERS

On 11 April 1922
16th The Queen's Lancers and
5th Royal Irish Lancers amalgamated to form:
16th/5th Lancers

On 16 June 1954 the Regiment was redesignated
16th/5th The Queen's Royal Lancers

On 11 April 1922
17th (Duke of Cambridge's Own) Lancers and
21st (Empress of India's) Lancers amalgamated to form:
17th/21st Lancers

On 25 June 1993
16th/5th The Queen's Royal Lancers and
17th/21st Lancers amalgamated to form:
The Queen's Royal Lancers

ROYAL TANK REGIMENT

On 28 July 1917
The Tank Corps was formed from the Heavy Branch of the Machine Gun Corps

On 18 October 1923
The Corps was redesignated Royal Tank Corps

On 4 April 1939
The Corps was redesignated The Royal Tank Regiment

1st THE QUEEN'S DRAGOON GUARDS

The Imperial Eagle

'Pro Rege et Patria'

Blenheim, Ramillies, Oudenarde, Malplaquet, Dettingen, Warburg, Beaumont, Willems, Waterloo, Sevastopol, Lucknow, Taku Forts, Pekin 1860, South Africa 1879, South Africa 1901-02
*The Great War_* **Mons, Le Cateau,** Retreat from Mons, **Marne 1914,** Aisne 1914, **Messines 1914,** Armentieres 1914, **Ypres 1914, 15,** Frezenberg, Bellewaarde, **Somme 1916, 18,** Flers-Courcelette, **Morval,** Arras 1917, **Scarpe 1917, Cambrai 1917, 18,** St Quentin, Baupaume 1918, Rosieres, Amiens, Albert 1918, Hindenburg Line, St Quentin Canal, Beaurevoir, **Pursuit to Mons, France and Flanders 1914-18**
*The Second World War_* **Somme 1940,** Withdrawal to Seine, North-West Europe 1940, **Beda Fomm, Defence of Tobruk,** Tobruk, Relief of Tobruk, Msus, **Gazala,** Bir El Aslagh, Bir Hacheim, Cauldron, Knightsbridge, Via Balbia, Mersa Matruh, **Defence of Alamein Line,** Alam El Halfa, **El Alamein, El Aghella, Advance on Tripoli, Tebaga Gap,** Point 201 (Roman Wall), **El Hamma,** Akarit, El Kourzia, Djebel Kournine, **Tunis,** Creteville Pass, **North Africa 1941-43,** Capture of Naples, Scafati Bridge, **Monte Camino,** Garagliano Crossing, Capture of Perugia, Arezzo, **Gothic Line, Coriano,** Carpineta, **Lamone Crossing,** Defence of Lamone Bridgehead, **Rimini Line,** Ceriano Ridge, Cesena, **Argenta Gap, Italy 1943-45,** Athens, Greece 1944-45

Gulf 1991

Regimental Marches

Quick March	Regimental March of 1st The Queen's Dragoon Guards (Radetsky March and Rusty Buckles)
Slow Marches	(i) 1st Dragoon Guards Slow March (ii) 2nd Dragoon Guards Slow March
Agents	Lloyds Bank plc Cox's & King's Branch
Home Headquarters	Maindy Barracks, Whitchurch Rd, Cardiff, CF4 3YE (Tel. 02920 781213)

Alliances

Canadian Armed Forces	The Governor General's Horse Guards
Australian Military Forces	1st/15th Royal New South Wales Lancers
Pakistan Army	11th Cavalry (Frontier Force)
Sri Lanka Army	1st Reconnaissance Regiment
South African Defence Forces	1st Special Service Battalion

Colonel in Chief	*HM* QUEEN ELIZABETH THE QUEEN MOTHER
Colonel	Col J I Pocock MBE ret pay 010897

	Saker I R M *MSc* dis	300994	Robinson R G	100298
Colonels	Parry R J sq	300995	Hurley M W O	141298
	Pittman A J *MA* psc†	300995		
Macdonald H L A *OBE* psc 300698	Sugden H F A *BA(Hons)* PSC(J)		**Regular Category Late Entry**	
Hookey C A *BSc(Eng) MIMGT*		300996	**Officers**	
psc(AUS)† 300600	Fenton N J	300997		
Mayall S V *MA* psc 300600	Richmond A S *BA(Hons)* PSC(J)		*Majors*	
		300997		
———	Bouskell J H T	300998	Charleton W R	300996
	Grindle R G *BA*	300998	Brace W R BEM	300998
Lieutenant Colonels	Smart T A	300998	Burman S A	300900
Ward S A B sq aic 300696				
Andrews P J *OBE CGIA* psc†300697	*Captains*		**Special Regular Officers Late Entry**	
Baldwin J *MBE MBA* psc 300698				
Van Grutten M W sq 300600	Craven C F	151295	*Captains*	
Wilson T R *MA* psc 300600	McCulloch J W *BEng(Hons)*	100696		
	Meehan R D C *BA*	100696	Davies M D	250997
Majors	De Quincey-Adams J J	70896	Smith H C	10498
Russell D A *BA MSc* aic gw sq(w)	Seymour S C *BA(Hons)*	260398		
311278	Wickham P D W	111298	**Intermediate Regular Officers**	
Gates R A aic sq(w) 300679	Waggett C L *BSc(Hons)*	121298		
Deacon G H J *BA(Hons) MA FRGS*	Craven C E	90499	*Captains*	
FRAI psc† 300993	Roberts D P B	101299	Botsford M W L W	240397
Norris D W H *OBE LLB(Hons)*			Strachan R J *BA*	140699
(A/Lt Col 080101) 300993	*Lieutenants*		Cavill P C D	90200
Roxburgh A M *MA* psc† 300994	Bond P L C	120897	Duff D B *BA(Hons)*	90200

McDougall A J A *LLB*	130600	Gardner M D	180898	Fawcus S D *MEng(Hons)*	100298
				Perriss M D *MA(Hons)*	140698
2nd Lieutenants		**Short Service Officers**		Brown N G *BSc(Hons)*	100898
††Gates H J B	100900			Wood S D O *BCom(Hons)*	100898
		Captains		Boissard A M J	141298
Short Service Late Entry Officers		Thomas N *BSc(Hons)*	130600	Roberts L J	141298
		Coombes D C D *BA(Hons)*	080201	Walker H C *BSc(Hons)*	141298
Captains				Davidson J S *MEng(Hons)*	90299
		Lieutenants		Hulton A F *BA(Hons)*	90299
Grant G N	10496			Jones N M *MChem*	130699
Clegg I G T	290798	Stenhouse J G E *BSc(Hons)*	161297	Younger G J *BA(Hons)*	131299

THE ROYAL SCOTS DRAGOON GUARDS (CARABINIERS AND GREYS)

The Thistle within the circle and motto of the Order of the Thistle
In the first corner, White Horse of Hanover within a Scroll. In the second corner The plume of The Prince of Wales within a wreath of Roses, Thistles and Shamrocks upon a yellow ground. In the third corner, SCOTS DG in gold within a wreath of Roses, Thistles and Shamrocks upon a yellow ground. The Red Dragon of Wales within a Scroll.

Honorary distinction
A Napoleonic Eagle superimposed upon two carbines in Saltire upon a Plinth inscribed Waterloo

Blenheim, Ramillies, Oudenarde, Malplaquet, Dettingen, Warburg, Beaumont, Willems, Talavera, Albuhera, Vittoria, Peninsula, Waterloo, Balaklava, Sevastopol, Delhi 1857, Abyssinia, Afghanistan 1879-80, Relief of Kimberley, Paardeberg, South Africa 1899-1902

*The Great War_* Mons, Le Cateau, **Retreat from Mons, Marne 1914, Aisne 1914, Messines 1914,** Armentieres 1914, **Ypres 1914-15,** Nonne Bosschen, Gheluvelt, Neuve Chapelle, St Julien, Frezenberg, Bellewaarde, Loos, **Arras 1917,** Scarpe 1917, **Cambrai 1917-18,** Lys, Hazebrouck, **Somme 1918,** St Quentin, Avre, **Amiens,** Albert 1918, Bapaume 1918, **Hindenburg Line, Canal du Nord,** St Quentin Canal, Beaurevoir, Selle, Sambre, **Pursuit to Mons,** France and Flanders 1914-18

*The Second World War_* Caen, **Hill 112,** Falaise, Venlo Pocket, **Hochwald, Aller,** Bremen, North-West Europe 1944-45, **Merjayun,** Syria 1941, **Alam el Halfa, El Alamein,** El Agheila, **Nofilia,** Advance on Tripoli, North Africa 1942-43, **Salerno,** Battipaglia, Volturno Crossing, Italy 1943, **Imphal,** Tamu Road, **Numshigum, Bishenpur, Kanglatongbi, Kennedy Peak,** Shwebo, **Sagaing, Mandalay, Ava, Irrawaddy,** Yenangyaung 1945, Burma 1944-45.

Gulf 1991

Regimental Marches

Military Band

Quick March . . . ."3 DGs"
Slow March .The Garb of Old Gaul

Pipes and Drums

Quick March . . . . .Heilan' Laddie
Slow March .My Home

Agents . . . . .Holt's Branch, Royal Bank of Scotland plc, Lawrie House, Farnborough, Hants GU14 7NR

Home Headquarters . . . . .The Castle, Edinburgh, EH1 2YT (Tel: 0131 310 5100 Fax: 0131 310 5101)

Alliances

Canadian Armed Forces . . . . .The Windsor Regiment (RCAC)
Australian Military Forces . . . . .12th/16th Hunter River Lancers (RAAC)
New Zealand Army . . . . .The New Zealand Scottish (RNZAC)
South African Defence Force . . . . .The Natal Carbineers

Colonel in Chief . . . . .THE QUEEN

Deputy Colonel in Chief . . . . .FM HRH The Duke of Kent *KG GCMG GCVO ADC (P)* 031293

Colonel . . . . .Maj Gen J M F C Hall *CB OBE* 300698

		Majors		
			Alers-Hankey R R	300998
Brigadiers		Scrivener J R aic sq(w)	300980	Biggart J U	300998
Allen S R B rcds psc	300600	Dunkley N C W *MBE* sq I	300988	Cummins H *M A*	300998
		Ravnkilde K P M *MA(Hons)* sq(w) †			
Colonels			300990	*Captains*	
		Wheeler G F psc	300993		
Seymour N D A psc	300693	Blackman H H psc† psc (A/Lt Col		Bartholomew J G E *(A/Maj*	
Auchinleck M H psc(AUS) I		080101)	300994	*010201)*	110895
	311299	Cushnir J H M *BA(Hons)* sq(w) †		Williams K J *BEng(Hons)*	110895
			300994	Fair A G C *BSc(Hons)*	251095
———		Edwards B P *MA(Hons)* ocds(IND)		Allen D A J	141296
		psc(IND) *(A/Lt Col 170101)*		Mackinlay W G L	141296
Lieutenant Colonels			300994	Stephen A D G *(A/Maj 190301)*	
Vickers R P H *BA(Hons)* psc†		Brown T J S *MRAC* osc(FR)			80897
psc(J)	300696		300995	Clayton R L *BA*	80997
Allfrey H D *MBE FRGS MCGI*		Lambert C F *MA* psc(J)	300995	Bateman T J *MA*	191197
psc(J) sq(w) †	300697	Melville J L ph	300995	Spenlove-Brown T P	70898
Phillips A M psc	300697	Brannigan C T O *BA(Hons)* psc(J)		Davies W H L *MA(Hons)*	100299
Stagg C R M *OBE BA(Hons)*			300996	Boyle R M L	101299
odc(FR) sq	300698	Bulloch J D C psc(J)	300997	Matheson A I *BSc(Hons)*	80201
Bullen M P A *MBE* psc†	300600				

Lieutenants
Soulsby D B 90899
Walters S J *MEng* 90899

Regular Category Late Entry Officers

Majors
Crease A J *MBE BEM* 300990
Frew J 300999
Raitt W 300999
McGarrell C 300900

Special Regular Officers Late Entry

Captains
Robertson N H *BEM (A/Maj 130300)* 200497
Cameron A 10398

Intermediate Regular Officers

Captains
Macmillan R N *MA* 120496

Ridge B D A *MA* 120298
Cattermole B J *BA(Hons)* 140699
Blair A H 101299

Lieutenants
Turpin A C *(A/Capt 180300)* 100898

Short Service Late Entry Officers

Captains
Aitchison G 190497
Stewart A T 10199
Cochlan G 30300
Toward J R *MBE* 100300

Short Service Officers

Captains
Nicholls D M ph 111298
Renwick T E *MA(Hons)* 121099
Ambrose J S *BSc(Hons) MA* 130600
Macdermot-Roe C A *BA(Hons)* 130600

Lieutenants
Williams R T *BSc(Hons)* 160697
Hanlon J M *BA(Hons) (A/Capt 140101)* 161297
Lucas R S *BA(Hons)* 161297
Bishop J W H *BA* 100298
Ongaro R J *BA(Hons)* 100298
Ferndale M *LLB(Cantab)* 130498
Burnet N A *MA* 140698
Dobeson C G *BA(Hons)* 100898
Hayward M E *BA(Hons)* 100898
Kerrigan T E A *BSc(Hons)* 100898
Foulerton N G *BSc(Hons)* 141298
Trueman P W *BA* 141298
Gemmell A S *BSc(Hons)* 90299
McLeman J F S *MThEOL(Hons)* 90299
De Silva R J A *BSc(Hons)* 90899
Jameson M H S *BSc(Hons)* 90899
Le Sueur R F *BA(Hons)* 90899

2nd Lieutenants
Leek W R G 70899
Campbell-Davys I E 161200

107

THE ROYAL DRAGOON GUARDS

The Star of the Order of St Patrick

In the third corner The Harp and Crown. In the fourth corner The Coronet of Her late Majesty the Empress and Queen Frederick of Germany and Prussia as Princess Royal of Great Britain and Ireland **The Castle of Inniskilling with the St George's colours above the monogram "V.D.G"** the second corner "V. PCW. DG." on a blue ground, and in the third corner the Castle of Inniskilling also on a blue ground.

Boyne 1690, **Blenheim, Ramillies, Oudenarde, Malplaquet,** Elixem, **Dettingen,** Fontenoy, **Waterloo, Warburg, Beaumont, Willems, Salamanca, Vittorio, Toulouse, Peninsula,** Laffeldt, **Balaklava, Sevastopol, Tel-el-Kebir, Egypt 1882,** Elandslaagte, **Defence of Ladysmith, South Africa 1846-47, South Africa 1899-1902, South Africa 1900-1902**

*The Great War_* **Mons, Le Cateau,** Retreat from Mons, **Marne 1914, Aisne 1914, La Bassee 1914, Messines 1914,** Armentieres 1914, **Ypres 1914, 15,** Givenchy 1914, St Julien, Frezenberg, Bellewaarde, **Somme 1916, 18,** Bazentin, Flers-Courcelette, Morval, Arras 1917, Scarpe 1917, **Cambrai 1917, 18,** St Quentin, Rosieres, Avre, Lys, Hazebrouck, **Amiens,** Albert 1918, **Hindenburg Line,** St Quentin Canal, Beaurevoir, **Pursuit to Mons,** France and Flanders 1914-18

*The Second World War_* **Dyle, Withdrawal to Escaut, St Omer-La Bassee, Dunkirk 1940, Normandy Landing, Odon, Mont Pincon,** Seine 1944, **Nederrijn, Gellenkirchen,** St Pierre La Vielle, Lisieux, Risle Crossing, **Lower Maas, Roer, Rhineland, Cleve Rhine,** Bremen, Ibbenburen, North-West Europe 1940, North-West Europe 1944-45

The Hook 1952, Korea 1951-2

Regimental Marches

Quick March . . . . .Fare Thee Well Inniskilling
Slow March . . . . .4th Dragoon Guards Slow March and
7th Dragoon Guards Slow March combined

Agents . . . . .Holt's Branch, Royal Bank of Scotland plc, Lawrie House, Farnborough, Hants GU14 7NR

Home Headquarters . . . . .3 Tower Street, York, YO1 9SB (Tel: 01904 642036)

Alliances

Canadian Armed Forces . . . . .The Fort Garry Horse
The British Colombia Dragoons
Australian Military Forces . . . . .4th/9th Prince of Wales's Light Horse
3rd/9th South Australian Mounted Rifles
New Zealand Army . . . . .Queen Alexandra's Mounted Rifles
Pakistan Army . . . . .15th Lancers
Indian Army .The Deccan Horse

Colonel in Chief . . . . .HRH The Prince of Wales KG KT GCB AK QSO ADC

Deputy Colonel in Chief . . . . .Hon Maj Gen HRH The Duchess of Kent GCVO
who is known as the Colonel Duchess

Colonel . . . . .Maj Gen P A J Cordingley DSO 010100

	Carhart K R CD BA(Hons) psc 300697	Hyams T D MSc psc(J) 300996
Brigadiers		Young D N BSc(Hons) MDA psc(J) 300996
Torrens-Spence E J MSc hcsc(J) psc(Ind)† 300697	Clifford R C L OBE psc aic 300697	
	Freeman N C C BA psc† sq(w) 300698	Macfarlane P BA(Hons) 300998
Talbot R I psc hcsc(J) 300698	Millen N C T psc† 300698	Pendry S N BA(Hons) 300998
	Smailes M I T BSc(Hons) psc† 300699	Brooking J G 300999
Colonels		Carr-Smith J S A 300999
Day C J R MDA MSc psc 300694	Duckworth L sq 300600	Bailey C 300900
Anderson B R MVO sq 300697	Eaton R J C aic sq(w) † 300600	Campbell-Smith H 300900
Bone D R L psc I 300698		Craig Harvey T J 300900
Cardozo G C MBE psc I 300699	*Majors*	Dangerfield R C D 300900
Cary R A P psc† jsdc 300600	Sandbach C P L psc 300988	Rawlins D J BSc(Hons) 300900
Wathen J P G MBE psc jsdc 300600	Butler M T D sq 300991	Whitson R S M 300900
	Shelford M G M BSc(Hons) MA FRGS GCGI † 300993	*Captains*
Lieutenant Colonels	Baxter J W L MA psc(J) 300995	Langman B M W 70896
Gabbey H C G (SL) psc† 300690	Brown A N R MA psc(J) 300995	Piggott F A J CAFS 70896
Illingworth R H sq 300690	Cray J N A MSc 300995	Mallory H P 141296
Faulkner M W B psc 300693	Monier-Williams M J 300995	Etherington J S 121297
Roskelly C M D W psc (A/Col 011100) 300695	Russell T W LLB(Hons) psc(J) 300995	Ryan B D C BA(Hons) 120298
	Borneman C A MA psc(J) 300996	Clifton M J M BA(Hons) 100299
		Everard S R BA(Hons) 90200
		White J W B 90200

Addington-Smith J N *BA(Hons)*
    80201

**Regular Category Late Entry
Officers**

Majors

May P H K *MBE*   300900

Captains

Davis M W   *(A/Maj 210300)*
    10295
McKone M L   30696

Special Regular Officers Late Entry

Captains

Byres J S   40997
Port B J   10498

Intermediate Regular Officers

Captains

Rynehart M A *BA(Hons)*   10495

Mitchell M R C   140699
Lane J J S *BA(Hons)*   121099

Short Service Late Entry Officers

Captains

Barr W J *MBE (A/Maj 290101)*
    10498
McAllister R J   51199
Rowan J R   30400
Young V   180500
Best S F   220500
Carson P C   60700
Mouser P J   41200

Short Service Officers

Captains

Cuss C J *BA(Hons)*   140699
Proctor J A J *BSc(Hons)* ph   140699
Cake R P J *BSc(Hons)*   101000

Lieutenants

Ter Haar D S *BSc(Hons)*   120897

Potts J W *BSc(Hons)*   100898
Harvey A W *BA(Hons)*   141298
Smith R J A *BA(Hons)*   141298
Thacker P P *BA(Hons)*   141298
Howarth T H *MPH*   130699
Searle Y N   130699
Messum A C *BA(Hons)*   90899
Pearce Gould H *BSc*   90899
Hill S A *BSc(Hons)*   131299

2nd Lieutenants

Mack C D   111299
Ker M D   120800

Short Service Volunteer Officers

Lieutenants

Huddleston J C G   30400

THE QUEEN'S ROYAL HUSSARS
(THE QUEEN'S OWN AND ROYAL IRISH)

The White Horse of Hanover below the Angel Harp, both encircled by the garter of
The Order of the Garter, the whole surmounted by the Queen's Crown

'Mente et Manu'

Dettingen, Warburg, Beaumont, Willems, **Leswarree, Hindoostan,** Talavera, **Albuhera, Salamanca,** Vittoria, **Orthes, Toulouse, Peninsula, Waterloo,** Ghuznee 1839, **Afghanistan 1839,** Cabool 1842, **Moodkee, Ferozeshah,** Sobraon, **Chillianwallah,** Goojerat, Punjaub, Alma, **Balaklava,** Inkerman, **Sevastopol, Central India, Lucknow,** Afghanistan 1879-80, **South Africa 1900-02,** South Africa 1901-02, South Africa 1902

*The Great War_* **Mons,** Le Cateau, Retreat from Mons, **Marne 1914,** Aisne 1914, Messines 1914, Armentieres 1914, **Ypres 1914-15,** Langemark 1914, Gheluvelt, **Givenchy 1914,** St Julien, Bellewaarde, **Somme 1916, 18,** Bazentin, Flers-Courcelette, Arras 1917, Scarpe 1917, **Cambrai 1917,** Somme 1918, St Quentin, Bapaume 1918, Rosieres, Lys, Hazebrouck, **Amiens,** Albert 1918, Hindenburg Line, Canal du Nord, St Quentin Canal, Beaurevoir, Selle, Sambre, Pursuit to Mons, France and Flanders 1914-18, **Khan Baghdadi,** Sharqat, Mesopotamia 1917-18

*The Second World War_* **Villers Bocage,** Mont Pincon, Dives Crossing, Nederrijn, Best, Lower Maas, Roer, **Rhine,** North West Europe 1944-45, Egyptian Frontier 1940, Sidi Barrani, **Buq Buq, Beda Fomm,** Sidi Suleiman, **Sidi Rezegh 1941,** Relief of Tobruk, Gazala, Bir el Igela, Mersa Matruh, Defence of Alamein Line, Ruweisat, **Alam el Halfa, El Alamein,** North Africa 1940-41, North Africa 1940-42, North Africa 1942, **Citta della Pieve, Ancona,** Citta di Castello, **Coriano,** San Clemente, Rimini Line, Conventello-Comacchio, Senio Pocket, Senio, Santerno Crossing, Argenta Gap, Italy 1944, **Italy 1944-45,** Proasteion, Corinth Canal, **Greece 1941,** Crete, Pegu, Paungde, **Burma 1942**

Seoul, Hill 327, **Imjin,** Kowang-san, **Korea 1950-51,** Wadi al Batin, **Gulf 1991**

Honorary Distinction
Canadian Forces Unit Commendation

Regimental Marches

Quick March . . . . The Regimental Quick March of The Queen's Royal Hussars
Slow Marches . . . . (i) The 3rd Hussars Slow March
(ii) Litany of Loretto - Slow March of the 4th Hussars
(iii) The Garb of Old Gaul - Slow March of the 7th Hussars
(iv) March of the Scottish Archers - Slow March of the 8th Hussars

Agents . . . . Lloyds Bank plc Cox's & King's Branch

Home Headquarters . . . . Regents Park Barracks, Albany Street, London, NW1 4AL (Tel: 0207 414 8717)

Alliances

Canadian Armed Forces . . . . The Sherbrooke Hussars
The Royal Canadian Hussars (Montreal)
8th Canadian Hussars (Princess Louise's)
Australian Military Forces . . . . 3rd/9th South Australian Mounted Rifles
2nd/14th Light Horse (Queensland Mounted Infantry)
3rd Battalion The Royal Australian Regiment
Victorian Mounted Rifles Sqn, 4th/9th Prince of Wales's Light Horse
New Zealand Army . . . . Queen Alexandra's Mounted Rifles
South African Defence Force . . . . Natal Mounted Rifles
Umvoti Mounted Rifles
Light Horse Regiment

Colonel in Chief . . . . *HM* QUEEN ELIZABETH THE QUEEN MOTHER

Deputy Colonel in Chief . . . . Field Marshal *HRH The Prince* Philip *Duke of* Edinburgh *KG KT OM GBE AC QSO*

Colonel . . . . Maj Gen D J M Jenkins *CB CBE BA MPhil* 010999

Brigadiers	Bromley Gardner M R psc	300699	Currie R W psc aic	300697
Bellamy A N *BA(Hons)* rcds psc	Vernon C H psc†	300601	Swann D J L *MBE BA(Hons)* psc psc(J)	300697
311297	———		Metcalfe R J D *MSc* dis sq(w) †	
Smith N G psc† hcsc(J) 300600	*Lieutenant Colonels*			300698
	Varvill S P (SL) odc(US) psc 300689		Blackmore A C T psc	300699
Colonels	Thornely R M sq jsdc	300691	Comyn C L psc	300699
Beer N Q W *BA(Hons)* psc† 300696	Simson K B L sq	300693	Cuthbert A C *MA* psc†	300699
Crichton R F A *MA* sq aic sq(w)	Myatt T V psc(AUS)	300695	Forsyth J A L *BEd(Hons)* psc†	300699
300696	Jackson S *BSc(Hons)* psc(a)† aic jsdc	300696	Ledger A W sq	300699
Watson J M C *BSc(Eng)Hons* psc†			Bromley Gardner C A J *MBE*	
jsdc 300697	O'Reilly M S M sq	300696	*BSc(Hons)* psc†	300600

Majors

Watts T E A sq	300984
James R C D sq	300991
Noone R A psc	300991
Thomas N J	300993
Beckett T A *MA* psc†	300994
Easby T R	300994
Ormerod J C sq(w) †	300994
Troughton J B M ph sq(w)	300994
Labouchere D H *MBE MSc* psc(IND)	
	300995
Madden D A G *BSc(Hons)* sq(w)	
	300995
Coles C M B psc(J)	300997
Simson T M L *BA(Hons)*	300998
Coram-Wright E C *BA(Hons)*	
	300999
Redman S E J	300999
Scott J W E	300999
Bell R T G	300900
Mortimer I S *BEng(Hons)*	300900
Wilson A J I *BA(Hons)*	300900

Captains

Entwistle N (A/Maj 270899)	
	10495
Howard J R *BA(Hons)*	110895
Martin R C	110895
Cocup M R	151295
Greenwood R N H *BSc(Hons)*	
	110896
Vetch A H	141296
Roberts M J	111298
Briggs-Wilson P D F *BA(Hons)*	
	100299
De Morgan C G	90499
Hoult D M *BSc(Hons)*	140699
Miller J W C *BSc*	140699

Lieutenants

Oliver J N	130498
Penny R J	141298
Hatlem-Olsen S D *BA(Hons)*	90899

2nd Lieutenants

††Cowley N D G	220997

Regular Category Late Entry Officers

Lieutenant Colonels

Nunn P D *MBE*	10100

Majors

Dickenson P K	300995
Hodgson P E	300997
Hunt A S	300998
Deakin H K	300999

Special Regular Officers Late Entry

Captains

Walker J S	10498

Intermediate Regular Officers

Captains

Duff C E J *BA(Hons)*	110896
De Ferry-Foster R J *BEng(Hons)*	
	160698
Maggs S P *BA(Hons)*	100299
Gairdner E J *BA(Hons)*	130600

Lieutenants

Forsyth A V	131299

2nd Lieutenants

††Ford C D	100900

Short Service Late Entry Officers

Captains

Nicholl B E	120198
Hamilton T E C	10498
Vick A D	101198
Sparks D I	60899
Butler M E C	30100
Shearer M	30100
Austin J S	50100
Peters A	30400

Short Service Officers

Captains

Strickland W J *BA(Hons)*	101000

Lieutenants

McClellan M S *BSc(Hons)*	161297
Simpson R C *BA(Hons)*	161297
Vines R E *BSc(Hons)*	100898
Cox P M *BSc(Hons)*	141298
Jefford T E *BA(Hons)*	141298
Steel S A *BSc(Hons)*	141298
Henwood C J T *BSc(Hons)*	220299
Weaver L C	100400
Porter A J H	220900

2nd Lieutenants

Wildman C P J	100499

111

9th/12th ROYAL LANCERS (PRINCE OF WALES'S)

The Plume of the Prince of Wales upon two lances crossed in saltire, within the Garter
The Cypher of Queen Elizabeth the Queen Mother, The Cypher of Queen Adelaide reversed and interlaced.
Sphinx superscribed "Egypt"

Salamanca, Peninsula, Waterloo, Punniar, Sobraon, Chillianwallah, Goojerat, Punjaub, South Africa 1851-53, Sevastopol, Delhi 1857, Central India, Lucknow, Charasiah, Kabul 1879, Kandahar 1880, Afghanistan 1878-80, Modder River, Relief of Kimberley, Paardeberg, South Africa 1899-1902.

*The Great War_* **Mons**, Le Cateau, **Retreat from Mons, Marne 1914, Aisne 1914**, La Bassee 1914, **Messines 1914,** Armentieres 1914, **Ypres 1914, 15,** Neuve Chapelle, Gravenstafel, St Julien, Frezenberg, Bellewaarde, **Somme 1916, 18,** Pozieres, Flers-Courcelette, **Arras 1917,** Scarpe 1917, **Cambrai 1917, 18,** St Quentin, **Rosieres,** Avre, Lys, Hazebrouck, Amiens, Albert 1918, Hindenburg Line, St Quentin Canal, Beaurevoir, **Sambre, Pursuit to Mons,** France and Flanders 1914-18

*The Second World War_* **Dyle,** Defence of Arras, Arras Counter Attack, **Dunkirk 1940, Somme 1940,** Withdrawal to Seine, **North -West Europe 1940, Chor es Sufan,** Saunnu, **Gazala,** Bir el Aslagh, Sidi Rezegh 1942, Defence of Alamein Line, **Ruweisat,** Ruweisat Ridge, Alam el Halfa, **El Alamein,** Advance on Tripoli, Tebega Gap, **El Hammas,** Akarit, El Kourzia, Djebel Kournine, **Tunis,** Creteville Pass, **North Africa 1941-43,** Citerna, Gothic Line, Coriano, Capture of Forli, Lamone Crossing, Pideura, **Defence of Lamone Bridgehead,** Conventello-Comacchio, **Argenta Gap, Bologna,** Sillaro Crossing, Idice Bridgehead, **Italy 1944-45**

Regimental Marches

Quick March . . . . .God Bless The Prince of Wales

Slow March . . . .(i) Men of Harlech - Slow March of 9th Lancers
(ii) Coburg - Slow March of 12th Lancers

Agents . . . . .Lloyds Bank plc Cox's & King's Branch

Home Headquarters . . . . .TA Centre, Saffron Road, Wigston, Leicester LE18 4UX (Tel: 0116 278425)

Alliances

Canadian Armed Forces . . . . .The Prince Edward Island Regiment

Pakistan Army . . . . .12th Cavalry

Colonel in Chief . . . .*HM* QUEEN ELIZABETH THE QUEEN MOTHER

Colonel . . . . .Brig H W K Pye 010195

Woolley M R	300999	**Regular Category Late Entry Officers**
Brodey A C *BA(Hons)*	300900	
Fooks W J O *BD*	300900	

Brigadiers

Majors

Short J H T *OBE ADC BSc(Hons)*
psc† hcsc(J)   300695
Rutledge M J *OBE MA* psc†
hcsc(J)   300699

Kirkbride S J   300994
Sewell J R *BEM*   300997

Captains

Special Regular Officers Late Entry

Lieutenant Colonels

Crofton *The Lord* aic sq(w) 300693
Mackaness J R S D *MBE* rcds psc
                            300696
Abraham A M *MBE BA(Hons) MBA*
psc   300698
Martin J M *BSc(Hons)* psc 300699

Captains

Fuller J E J	141296
Farrer J A	141097
Goggs D M *BEng(Hons)*	120298
Simpson A E B *BA(Hons)*	20498
Jones T R	90498
Gasson-Hargreaves J R	111298
Croft N S *BA(Hons)*	100299
Craggs H D B	90200

Hartwell R A   10496
Pearce J   10498

Intermediate Regular Officers

Captains

Majors

Woodbridge I R psc   300991
Bailey N J W psc   300994
Bennett D M *BA(Hons)* psc†
                       300994
Charrington R A *MA MSc* psc†
                       300994
Stafford N M T *FRGS* psc† 300994
Crewdson C W N *MBE* psc 300995
Robinson T P *LLB(Hons)* psc(J)
                       300997

Lieutenants

Lort-Phillips H P F *BSc* 120897
Hood G J F *(A/Capt 110799)*
                       130498
Searby H L *BA(Hons)* 90899

2nd Lieutenants

††Doherty D J   220997
††Doherty O B   50999
Simpson H G   111299

Bannister K L CAFS *(A/Maj
280799)*   180396
Lyle T S D *BArch(Hons)* 120496
Russell K M   121297
Clifford G D H *BA(Hons)* 140699

Short Service Late Entry Officers

Captains

Reid G S   10498
Watson P A   71298
Duff J A P   40199
Harrison M A   10499

| Crofts S M *MBE* | 110699 |
| Bilyard F H | 160600 |

Short Service Officers

Captains

Durie R J A *BA(Hons)*	121099
Campbell-Barnard J R *BSc(Hons)*	
	90200
Croft C	90200

Tubbs A C *BSc*	230700
Preston C B R *MA(Hons)*	101000
Inglefield E H S *MA*	11200

Lieutenants

Carpenter A M	140497
Wilby N E G *BA(Hons)*	120897
Cathey J D *BA(Hons)*	161297
Corcoran P *MA(Hons)*	130498

Campbell-Collins G I	141298
Preston B H R	141298
Wall M G *BA*	141298
Vale P	50199
Willis T D *BSocSc(Hons)*	130699
Evans R M *BA(Hons)*	90899
Eyre-Brook M G *BSc(Hons)*	131299
Jacobs J E *BA(Hons)*	131299
Doherty S P	100400
Hubbard T A P	80800

113

THE KING'S ROYAL HUSSARS

A Prussian Eagle Sable royally crowned Or grasping in the dexter claw a Sceptre and in the sinister an Orb both Gold on the Eagle's breast the Cipher "FR" also Gold, The Sphinx superscribed Egypt

Warburg, Beaumont, Willems, Vimiera, Douro, Talavera, Fuentes D'Onor, Salamanca, Vittoria, Pyranees, Orthes, Peninsula, **Waterloo, Bhurtpore, Chillianwallah, Goojerat,** Punjaub, **Alma, Balaklava, Inkerman, Sevastopol, Persia, Central India, Ali Masjid,** Afghanistan 1878-79, **Egypt, Egypt 1884, Suakin 1885, Relief of Kimberley, Relief of Ladysmith, Paardeberg,** South Africa 1899-1902, South Africa 1900-1902, South Africa 1901-1902

*The Great War_* **Mons,** Le Cateau, Retreat from Mons, **Marne 1914, Aisne 1914, Messines 1914,** Armentieres 1914, **Ypres 1914, 15,** Langemarck 1914, Cheluvelt, Nonne Bosschen, France and Flanders 1914-18, Neuve Chapelle, Ypres 1915, St Julien, Frezenberg, Bellewaarde, Loos, **Somme 1916, 18,** Flers-Courcelette, **Arras 1918,** Scarpe 1917, **Cambrai 1917, 18,** St Quentin, Avre, **Amiens,** Albert 1918, Bapaume 1918, **Arras 1918,** Drocourt-Queant, Hindenburg Line, St Quentin Canal, Beaurevoir, Selle, **Sambre,** Pursuit to Mons, **Tigris 1916, Kut al Amara 1917, Baghdad,** Mesopotamia 1915-18, **Persia 1918**

*The Second World War_* Somme 1940, **Villers Bocage,** Bourguebus Ridge, Mont Pincon, Jurques, Dives Crossing, La Vie Crossing, Lisieux, La Toques Crossing, Risle Crossing, Roer, **Rhine,** Ibbenburen, Aller, NorthWest Europe 1940, North West Europe 1944-45, **Egyptian Frontier 1940,** Withdrawal to Matruh, Bir Enba, Sidi Barrani, Buq Buq, Bardia 1941, Capture of Tobruk, **Beda Fomm,** Halfaya 1941, Sidi Suleiman, Tobruk 1941, Gubi I II, Gabr Saleh, **Sidi Rezegh 1941,** Taieb el Essem, Relief of Tobruk, **Saunnu,** Msus, **Gazala,** Bir el Aslagh, Defence of Alamein Line, Alam el Halfa, **El Alamein,** Advance on Tripoli, El Hamma, Enfidaville, El Kourzia, Djebel Kournine, **Tunis,** North Africa 1940-43, North Africa 1942-43, Capture of Naples, Volturno Crossing, Coriano, Santarcangelo, Cosina Canal Crossing, Senio Pocket, Cesena, Valli di Commacchio, **Bologna, Medicina, Argenta Gap,** Italy 1943, Italy 1944-45, Italy 1945

Gulf 1991, Wadi al Batin

Regimental Marches

Quick March .The King's Royal Hussars
Slow March .Coburg

Agents . . . . .Lloyds Bank plc, Cox's & King's Branch

Home Headquarters . . . . .North - Fulwood Barracks, Preston, Lancs PR2 8AA
(Tel: Preston Military ext 2310)
South - Peninsula Barracks, Winchester, Hants, SO23 8TS
(Tel: Winchester Military ext 5140)

Affiliated Regiment

The Royal Gurkha Rifles

Alliances

Canadian Armed Forces . . . . .1st Hussars
Australian Military Forces . . . . .10th Light Horse
2nd/14th Light Horse (Queensland Mounted Infantry)
New Zealand Army . . . . .Queen Alexandra's Mounted Rifles
Pakistan Army . . . . .The Guides Cavalry (Frontier Regiment)
Zambia Army . . . . .Zambia Armoured Car Regiment

Colonel in Chief . . . .*HRH* THE PRINCESS ROYAL *KG KT GCVO QSO*

Deputy Colonel in Chief . . . .*HRH Princess* Alice *Duchess of* Gloucester *GCB CI GCVO GBE*

Colonel . . . . .Brig E C W Morrison *OBE* 011297

	Lieutenant Colonels		Howard J A F *BA(Hons)* psc(AUS)
	Fellowes R J L psc aic	300691	300696
	East R H (SL) sq	300692	Wade M W E *MBE BA(Hons)* psc†
Brigadiers	Suchanek S W G *BSc(Hons)* psc†		300696
Price C K *CBE* psc 300695	*(A/Col 050201)*	300692	Polley N G T *BA(Hons) MDA* psc†
Morris R J *BA(Hons)* rcds odc(US)	Tennent C M I psc jsdc	300693	MDA 300697
psc hcsc(J) 300698	Darell C H D *BA(Hons)* aic psc(Ind)†		Powe J J *OBE* psc† psc *(A/Col*
Shirreff A R D *CBE BA(Hons) MA*		300694	*290101)* 300697
psc† hcsc(J) 300698	Rogers J J *OBE BA(Hons)* psc *(L/Col*		Palmer J R M psc(GE) psc(J)
	010700)	300694	300698
Colonels	Ashbrooke A F B *BA(Hons)*		Allen T C psc 300699
Flach P R C *MBE* psc† aic 300699	*MA(Hons) MPhil* psc	300695	Grant Thorold N psc jsdc 300699
Singer A R E *OBE* psc jsdc ph	Garbutt P D W *CGIA* aic sq(w) †		
300600		300695	*Majors*
Tilney G H R *MBE* psc jsdc 300600	Bradshaw A J *OBE BSc(Hons) MA*		Scott T P *MIMGT* psc ph 120979
———	psc psc(J) ph *(A/Col 210800)*		Eliott-Lockhart P N *AIMGT* psc
		300696	sq(w) 300981

Lang S E L *MIMGT* sq	300985
Tayler T C *BA CGIA* psc†	300987
Wicks H A O sq	300989
Danvers C H D sq	300992
Moir J D S *MBE BA(Hons) MA* psc†	300993
Bridge S T W *BA(Hons) MA* psc(J)	300995
Hannay R J cafs psc(J)	300995
Orr J N N psc(J)	300995
Ross A C G I	300995
Gedney F G *BSc(Hons) MSc* psc(J)	300996
Joynson H R D J	300996
Ross E T *MSc* dis	300996
Todd R A U *BA MA* psc(J)	300997
Arrowsmith S T	300998
Denning J C V	300998
Hunter N W *BSc(Hons)*	300998
Berchem N P F *BSc(Hons)*	300999
Harman A C	300999
Potts A T L *BA(Hons)*	300999
Rayner M S	300999

Captains

Williams C J M *BA(Hons)*	110895
Mallinson T G	110497
Preston G R O *(A/Maj 181200)*	110497
Willis H J *BA(Hons)*	211097
Holloway T M *BA(Soc)Hons*	120298
Slack R O *MA(Hons)*	120298
Carey-Hughes J E M *BSc(Hons)*	131098
Macgregor C S *BSc(Hons) (A/Maj 280900)*	100299
Perry N C L *BA(Hons)*	100299
Kingsford J N J *BA(Hons)*	140699
Valdes-Scott C A J ph	60899
Biddulph A G	90200
Stephenson J A	90200
Jackson R M	140400

Lieutenants

††Tilney A M A	220997

Regular Category Late Entry Officers

Lieutenant Colonels

Draper B J M *MBE*	140798

Majors

Davies K sq(w)	300996

Captains

Halffman E M *(A/Maj 200300)*	270995
Kalewski R E	250796

Special Regular Officers Late Entry

Captains

Ashton D *MBE*	10298
Penkethman S	10498
Wild S *BEM*	10498

Interemediate Regular Officers

Captains

Senior J M *BA(Hons)*	170699
Buczacki J N E *BA(Hons)*	130600

Lieutenants

Hope-Hawkins R M *(A/Capt 090600)*	141298

Short Service Late Entry Officers

Majors

Tyson R F *FMS*	300998

Captains

Lister G S	261098
Oliver D M	10199
Hardbattle I J	10600
Smith A E	140700
Lewis L E	71200
Simpson I	141200

Short Service Officers

Captains

Stanley-Smith C M D *BA(Hons)*	170699
Mainwaring H A K *MA(Hons)*	130600
Ulster A P G *BA(Hons)*	101000
Cullinan R J *BSc(Hons)*	80201
Dean E R E *BSc(Hons)*	80201
Smith C D W *BSc(Hons)*	80201

Lieutenants

Michael A H L *BSc*	161297
Banks T C *BA(Hons)*	100898
Hackney A R *BA(Hons)*	100898
Smith J R L *BA(Hons)*	100898
Hay J C	90899
Hayman-Joyce A R *BA(Hons)*	90899
Sharman A E *BA(Hons)*	90899
Smith P D E *BSc(Hons)*	90899
Sutcliffe S P	131299
Grey B N A	121200

2nd Lieutenants

Ashby C W R	70899

115

THE LIGHT DRAGOONS

The monogram LD encircled by a wreath of Laurel and surmounted by the Crest of England,
all upon a Maltese Cross. The Elephant superscribed Assaye
"Viret in Aeternum" "Merebimur"

Emsdorf, Mysore, Assaye, Villers-en-Cauchies, Willems, Seringpatam, Egmont-op-Zee, Sahagun, Albuhera, Vittoria, Orthes, Toulouse, Niagara, Peninsula, Waterloo, Alma, Balaklava, Inkerman, Sevastopol, Afghanistan 1870-80, Tel-el Kebir, Egypt 1882-85, Nile 1884-85, Abu Klea, Defence of Ladysmith, Relief of Ladysmith, South Africa 1899-1902

*The Great War_* Mons, Le Cateau, Retreat from Mons, Marne 1914, Aisne 1914, Messines 1914, Armentieres 1914, La Bassee 1914, 15, **Ypres 1914-15**, Gravenstafel, St Julien, Frezenberg, **Bellewaarde**, Langemark 1914, Gheluvelt, Nonne, Bosschen, **Somme 1916, 18**, Flers-Courcelette, Arras 1917, **Cambrai 1917, 18**, St Quentin, Rosieres, Amiens, Albert, Bapaume 1918, **Hindenburg Line**, St Quentin Canal, Beaurevoir, **Pursuit to Mons, France and Flanders 1914-18, Kut al Amara 1917**, Baghdad, Sharqat, Mesopotamia 1916-18

*The Second World War_* Dyle, **Withdrawal to Escaut, Ypres-Comines Canal, Normandy Landing, Seine 1944**, Bretteville, Hechtel, **Caen**, Bourguebus Ridge, Nederrijn, Venraji, **Mont Pincon**, St Pierre la Vielle, **Gellenkirchen, Roer, Rhineland**, Waal Flats, **Hochwald, Goch, Rhine, Ibbenburen, Aller**, Bremen, **North-West Europe 1940, 44-45**

Regimental Marches

Quick March . . . . .Balaklava
Slow March . . . . .Denmark - 19th Hussars Slow March

Agents . . . . .Lloyds Bank plc Cox's & King's Branch

Home Headquarters . . . . .Fenham Barracks, Newcastle-upon-Tyne NE2 4NP (Tel: 0191 239 3138/3140/3141)

Alliances

Canadian Armed Forces . . . . .The Royal Canadian Hussars (Montreal)
The South Alberta Light Horse
Australian Military Forces . . . . .1st/15th Royal New South Wales Lancers
Indian Army .Skinner's Horse (1st Duke of York's Own Cavalry)
Pakistan Army . . . . .6th Lancers
19th Lancers
Malaysian Armed Forces . . . . .2nd Royal Armoured Regiment

Colonel in Chief . . . . .HRH The Princess Margaret *Countess of* Snowdon *CI GCVO*
Colonel . . . . .Lt Gen *Sir* Roderick Cordy-Simpson *KBE CB* 220500

	Nutting R C B psc† aic	300692	Matthews R C psc† †	300995
Brigadiers	Quicke R N B sq jsdc	300694	Whitaker C J S psc	300995
Gregg T D *CBE* psc 300696	Tabor A J *BA(Hons)* psc	300696	Frost E J S	300996
Stewart A R E DE C *OBE* rcds psc	Cusack D J *MBE MDA* aic MDA		Mayo C E A	300996
hcsc(J) 300696	sq(w) psc†	300699	Watson H A *BA(Hons)* psc(J)	
	Ledger S W sq	300699		300997
Colonels	Levey S R odc(AUST) psc aic		Coughlan S J P P *BA(Hons)*	300998
Mallinson A L *BA* psc *(L/Brig*		300699	Hamilton A J E *BSc(Hons)*	300998
010899) 300693	Ogden J W *BA(Hons)* psc†	300699	Deakin G A *NDA*	300999
Selfe J A M A *BA(Hons) FIMGT*	Polley R D S *MA* psc(n) osc(FR) I		Pery The Hon cafs	300999
psc(n)† jsdc 300694		300699		
Gillman J C W *OBE BSc(Eng)Hons*	Amos D R psc	300600	*Captains*	
psc† 300695	Ellwood O C B psc	120201	Moon T E G	130496
Webb-Bowen R I psc(a)† ph			Plant S J *BA(Hons)*	100696
300698	*Majors*		Nurton O J F	110896
Checketts T J *OBE* psc† psc(J)	Prestwich C T S *MBE* sq	300983	Van De Pol J R *BEng(Hons)*	110896
300600	Mackie A R *MBE* sq	300984	Warrack B J *BA(Hons) (A/Maj*	
Rutherford-Jones D J psc hcsc(J)	Brook M B sq(w) *(A/Lt Col 011100)*		*070101)*	131296
300600		300985	Pearce A C B *BA(Hons)*	131098
——	Browell M H aic sq(w) †	300991	Courage M A *BSc(Hons)*	100299
	Good M R psc† psc (A/Lt Col		Sapwell J R	60899
Lieutenant Colonels	010201) 300992			
Southward N S *OBE* psc(PAK) jsdc	Scott-Masson P A B G sq	300992	*Lieutenants*	
300689	Good C P ODC(EG) sq	300993	Hawkins G W P	90299
Le Hardy C A (SL) odc(BE) sq jsdc	Chitty R O M *BScEng(Civil)* sq(w)			
300690		300994	*2nd Lieutenants*	
Portman M B (SL) sq 300690	Judd G A psc† *(A/Lt Col 040101)*		†Scrope R W M	100995
Brook-Fox V J (SL) odc(BE) sq		300994	†Smith A J	50999
300691	Edwards M S *BSc(Hons)* psc(J)	300995		

Regular Category Late Entry Officers

Majors

Davies S P *MBE*	300993
O'Neill H S *MBE*	300993
Milnes P	300997
Taylor S D *BEM*	300997
Hawley S *BEM*	300999
Tazey M *MBE*	300900

Intermediate Regular Officers

Captains

Kennedy E J R *GCGI*	110497
Palmer C *BA(Hons)*	100299
Godfrey J *BEng(Hons)*	140699
Smith A J *BSc*	130600

Short Service Late Entry Officers

Majors

Rouse B R *MBE*	300998

Captains

Black G	70498
Lee A	250199
Summerscales S W	310799
Wiles S P	100300
Wiles R E	250400

Short Service Officers

Captains

Chandler J E *BSc(Hons)*	101099
Coke N C S *BEng(Hons)*	90200
Robson A L *BA(Hons)*	90200
Norton H P D S	161200

Hayman-Joyce R L *BA(Hons)*	80201
McAdam W K *BA(Hons)*	80201
Robb T R *BA(Hons)*	80201
Ward S J A *BA(Hons)*	80201

Lieutenants

Colbeck C T *BSc(Hons)*	161297
Whittall P J K *MEng(Hons)*	140698
Amos H A P *BSc(Econ)Hons*	100898
Dalby-Welsh T J *BA(Hons)*	141298
King O G H *BSc(Hons)*	141298
Smail T C A *BSc(Hons)*	90299
Brooks T O *BA(Hons)*	90899
Lawrence E J P *BA(Hons)*	131299
James W D M	80800

2nd Lieutenants

Barber D M G	100499
Jelf C E	111299

THE QUEEN'S ROYAL LANCERS

Death's Head *'Or Glory'* with crossed lances behind

Blenheim, Ramillies, Oudenarde, Malplaquet, Beaumont, Willems, Talavera, Fuentes D'Onor, Salamanca, Vittoria, Nive, Peninsula, Waterloo, Bhurtpore, Ghuznee 1839, Afghanistan 1839, Maharajpore, Aliwal, Sobraon, Alma, Balaklava, Inkerman, Sevastopol, Central India, South Africa 1879, Suakin 1885, Khartoum, Defence of Ladysmith, Relief of Kimberley, Paardeberg, South Africa 1899-1902

*The Great War_* **Mons, Le Cateau, Retreat from Mons, Marne 1914, Aisne 1914, Messines 1914,** Armentieres 1914, **Festubert 1914, Ypres 1914, 15, Somme 1916, 18,** Gheluvelt, St Julien, **Morval, Bellewaarde, Arras 1917,** Scarpe 1917, **Cambrai 1917, 18, St Quentin, Avre, Lys, Hazebrouck, Amiens,** Hindenburg Line, St Quentin Canal, Beaurevoir, **Canal du Nord, Pursuit to Mons, France and Flanders 1914-18, NW Frontier India 1915, 16**

*The Second World War_* **Tebourba Gap, Bou Arada, Kasserine, Thaia, Fondouk, El Kourzia,** Kairouan, **Bordj, Djebel Kournine, Tunis,** Hammam Lif, Gromballa, Bou Ficha, **North Africa 1942-43, Cassino II, Liri Valley,** Monte Piccolo, **Capture of Perugia,** Arezzo, **Advance to Florence, Argenta Gap,** Fossa Cambalina, Traghetto, **Italy 1944-45.**

Gulf 1991, Wadi Al Batin

Regimental Marches

Quick March . . . . .Stable Jacket
Slow March .Omdurman

Agents . . . . .Lloyds Bank plc, Cox's & King's Branch

Home Headquarters . . . . .Prince William of Gloucester Barracks, Grantham, Lincs NG31 7TJ
(Tel: 0115 9573195)

Alliances

Canadian Armed Forces . . . . .Lord Strathcoma's Horse (Royal Canadians)
Australian Military Forces . . . . .12th/16th Hunter River Lancers

Colonel in Chief . . . . .THE QUEEN

Deputy Colonel in Chief . . . .*HRH Princess* Alexandra *The Hon Lady* Ogilvy *GCVO ADC*

Colonel . . . . .Lt Gen *Sir* Richard Swinburn *KCB* 011195

Colonel Designate . . . . .Brig W J Hurrell *CBE* 140501

	Bate N *BSc(Hons)* psc† †	300995	**Regular Category Late Entry**
Brigadiers	Cockram D D L *BA(Hons)* psc†		**Officers**
Cumming A A J R *CBE* psc hcsc(J)		300995	
	300691	Hankinson P D P *MBE* psc†	300995	*Majors*
	Hughes A G *MBE BSc(Hons)* psc†		Willmore A L P	300996
Colonels		300995	Adkins J G	300998
	Wills N H C psc†	300995	
Finlayson A I *OBE* psc jsdc	300699	Gibb I J psc(J)	300996	*Captains*
Wertheim R N *MA* psc†	300699	Nixon-Eckersall R B cafs psc(J)		Needle A W *(A/Maj 140100)*
		300996		220296
	Dart J F *BSc(Hons)*	300997	
Lieutenant Colonels	Watson R G J	300998	
	Harrison G R M cafs	300999	**Special Regular Officers Late Entry**
Templer J M (SL) *MBE* odc(US) psc†	Kettler J J R *BSc(Hons)*	300999	
	300686	Trant R B cafs	300999	*Captains*
Campbell P MACL aic jsdc sq(w)	Ball C B C *BA(Hons)*	300900	Major W L	250796
	300690	Coward R J	300900	Oneill M J	10498
Marriott P C *OBE* psc(CAN)†	Todd M *MBE BA(Hons)*	300900	Oswin N *MIMGT*	10498
	300697			
Eadie D J psc†	300698	*Captains*	
Everard J R *OBE MA GCGI* psc†			
	300699	Clark J E *BA(Hons)* *(A/Maj 080101)*		**Intermediate Regular Officers**
Newitt C N psc†	300600		110895	
Fattorini C S *MA* psc†	300601	Thompson I M	130496	*Majors*
		Woolgar N R E	70896	Kierstead S M *BA(Hons)*	10185
		Mack E R J *BSc(Hons)*	110896	
Majors	Sharifi K D *BA(Hons)*	170797	*Captains*
Wieloch W R *BA BA(Hons)* psc† psc	Best N J	121297	
(A/Lt Col 220101)	300991	Portess J J R *BA(Hons)*	120298	Blakey C J	141296
Harding-Rolls M A C sq	300992	Lodge D P *BA(Hons)*	131098	Cushing G S *BA(Hons)*	141097
Pinney G R *BSc(Hons)* psc†	300993	Walker J A K *BA(Hons)*	231198	Cripps J E O *BEng(Hons)*	90200
English W P O *MSc* psc(IND)		Barrington-Barnes D T cafs	90499	
	300994	Burbridge C W	90200	

118

Short Service Late Entry Officers

Captains

Snelling P J	10498
Dzierozynski R T	60498
Brown G W	160899
Davies M A	61299
Smith D J	30400
Griffin K A	140400

Short Service Officers

Captains

Dowson C P *BSc(Hons)*	130600

Bowyer A M *BA(Hons)*	80201
Bramall S G *BSc(Hons)*	80201
Hodson J D F *BA*	90201

Lieutenants

Martin A T *MA(Hons)*	160697
Melson N J M *BSc(Hons)*	161297
Badcock C	140698
Woolley B A V *BA(Hons)*	100898
Cossens B M J *BA(Hons)*	121098
Faraday G M *BSc(Hons)*	141298

Graves R A *BA(Hons)*	130699
Bigg J B T *BA(Hons)*	90899
Foden A N B *BA(Hons)*	90899
Horne B S	121199
Scott J P R	131299
Burton H T	80800
Mudd M J	121200

2nd Lieutenants

Lukey J R	100499

ROYAL TANK REGIMENT
A tank encircled by a wreath of laurel and surmounted by The Crown
"Fear naught"

*The Great War_* Somme 1916, 18, Arras 1917, 18, Messines 1917, Ypres 1917, Cambrai 1917, St Quentin 1918, **Villers Bretonneux, Amiens, Bapaume 1918, Hindenburg Line,** Epehy, Selle, **France and Flanders 1916-18,** Gaza
*The Second World War_* Arras counter attack, Calais 1940, St Omer-La Bassee, Somme 1940, Odon, Caen, Bourguebus Ridge, Mont Pincon, Falaise, Nederrijn, Scheldt, Venlo Pocket, Rhineland, **Rhine,** Bremen, **North-West Europe 1940, 44-45, Abyssinia 1940,** Sidi Barrani, Beda Fomm, Sidi Suleiman, **Tobruk 1941,** Sidi Rezegh 1941, Belhamed, Gazala, Cauldron, Knightsbridge, Defence of Alamein Line, Alam el Halfa, **El Alamein,** Mareth, Akarit, Fondouk, El Kourzia, Medjez Plain, Tunis, **North Africa 1940-43,** Primosole Bridge, Gerbini, Adrano, **Sicily 1943,** Sangro, Salerno, Volturno Crossing, Garigliano Crossing, Anzio, Advance to Florence, Gothic Line, Coriano, Lamone Crossing, Rimini Line, Argenta Gap, **Italy 1943-45, Greece 1941, Burma 1942**

Korea 1951-53

Regimental Marches

Quick March	Regimental March of the Royal Tank Regiment - My Boy Willie
Slow March	Royal Tank Regiment Slow March
Agents	Holt's Branch, Royal Bank of Scotland plc, Lawrie House, Farnborough, Hants GU14 7NR
Regimental Headquarters	Stanley Barracks, Bovington, Wareham, Dorset BH20 6JB (Tel: 01929 40 3348/3448/3360)

Alliances

Canadian Armed Forces	12e Régiment Blindé du Canada RCAC
Australian Military Forces	1st Armoured Regiment RAAC
New Zealand Army	Royal New Zealand Armoured Corps
Indian Army	2nd Lancers (Gardner's Horse) Indian Armoured Corps
Pakistan Army	13 Lancers, Pakistan Armoured Corps

Colonel in Chief	THE QUEEN	
Colonel Commandant	Maj Gen A P Ridgway *CB CBE*	160799
Deputy Colonels Commandant	Maj Gen P Gilchrist	020400
Deputy Colonels Commandant	Brig A D Leakey *CBE*	160799

	Kendell R N *MBE* sq 300694
	Caraffi S *MBE BA(Hons)* psc *(A/Col 151100)* 300695
Brigadiers	Harrison S J D *MBE BA(Hons)* psc I* sq(w) 300696
Leakey A D *CBE MA* rcds psc hcsc(J) 300695	Bangham P H odc(FR) sq 300697
Brummitt R W *MBE* psc 300698	Chapman A D H psc 300697
Smedley J E B *BA(Hons)* sq jsdc 300698	Coombe T B J *BSc(Hons)* sq(w) † 300697
Speller M N E *CBE BSc(Hons)* psc(n)† 300698	Dixon R G *LLB(Hons)* psc(n)† 300697
	Garnett J W *MBE BSc(Eng)* psc† 300697
Colonels	Millington R D F *MBE CGIA* psc† aic 300697
Hall T E *CBE* psc jsdc 300695	Tustin S R psc(IND) 300697
Rodley I J *MBE BSc* df psc† *(A/Brig 180900)* 300698	Allison P J psc psc(J) 300698
Stevens I P G psc aic 300698	Chesterfield R T psc† aic 300698
Aylwin-Foster N R F *BA(Hons)* psc† 300699	Deverell C M *MBE BA(Hons) M A (Oxon) MCGI* psc† 300698
Lemon J R psc psc(PAK) 300699	Jasper S A *BA(Hons)* psc† jsdc 300698
Eccles D C *OBE BA(Hons)* psc† 300600	Shapland M P *MBE* psc† osc(KU) 300698
———	Ellis A M psc(n)† 300699
	Green B J W psc 300600
Lieutenant Colonels	Jammes R F *BA BA(Hons)* psc 300600
Patey C G (SL) *OBE* psc 300688	Wallis J A *BA(Hons)* psc† 300600
Carroll A G R psc 300689	Wilson S B *BA MSc* psc(IND) † 300600
Gould E J psc I 300690	
Hine R N *OBE* sq jsdc 300690	

Majors

Owen J M psc 240582
Masters M D psc 300984
Trape J A R *LLB(Hons)* sq 300984
Lewis N A E sq aic 300986
Mason N B psc† aic 300987
May S J sq(w) † 300988
Vesey Holt G M *MBE BA(Hons)* osc(FR) I sq(w) † 300988
Fyfe A W sq 300989
Gent S M psc *(A/Lt Col 260201)* 300990
Thornton J P *BA(Hons)* psc† *(A/Lt Col 100101)* 300990
Butterworth P J *BA(Hons)* sq(w) 300992
Charlesworth J R sq 300993
Macleod A *BA(Hons) MA* psc† † 300993
Mason K J S J *MSc* sq(w) † 300993
Ness T J sq aic 300993
Spicer P G 300993
Brown G F *BEng(Hons) MSc* psc(J) gw 300995
Couzens D M A *MSc* psc† 300995
De Bretton Gordon H S *BSc(Hons)* 300995
Gash A S *MA* psc(J) 300995
Hall S J osc(MAL) 300995
Hendry A P *BA(Hons)* psc† † 300995

Kidd P J *BA(Hons) MA(Hons)* psc† † 300995
Laver I C *BA(Hons)* † 300995
Patterson J R *MA MBA* psc(J) 300995
Williams M H psc(J) 300995
Hoskins D E W B *BA(Hons) MA* psc(J) 300996
Hunt J C A *BA(Hons)* cafs 300996
Catmur D A *BEng(Hons) MSc* psc(J) 300997
Davies G H cafs 300997
Hall C J *BA(Econ)Hons* 300997
Macro P J W 300997
Pollington S T *BA(Hons)* 300997
Clooney I G *BSc(Hons)* 300999
Large A D T cafs 300999
Leslie A J 300999
Thompson G J *BA(Hons)* 300999
Woodward R J R cafs 300999
Billings J D *BSc(Hons)* 300900
Briggs T A 300900
Cookson B G A 300900
How T D 300900

Captains

Gould R A *(A/Maj 011100)* 130495
Ozanne A M ph 110895
McAfee A J M 151295
Britton A M *BCom(Hons)* 140396
Williams J M cafs 70896
Bisset C A *BA(Hons)* ph 110896
Heywood A C R *MA* 131296
Craddock C J cafs 110497
Metcalfe A D *BA(Hons)* 141097
Willis M J *BA(Hons)* 120298
Evans M H *BA(Hons)* 160698
Goodwin J V *BA(Hons)* 160698
Grimshaw J A *BA(Hons)* 160698
Longman M J L *BSc(Hons)* 160698
Fox M J *BA(Hons)* 131098
Medhurst-Cocksworth C R *BA(Hons)* 100299
Maynard A M 140400
Michelin A C ph pl 140400
Phipps A S 140400

Lieutenants

Mackay G J *BA(Hons)* 120897
Miller T J 121200

Regular Category Late Entry Officers

Lieutenant Colonels

Lyman J *MBE* sq 241299

Majors

Hepburn C E 300993
Allum C D 300996
Wilding G K 300996
Orcheston-Findlay G G sq(w) 300997
Scully P R 300997
McGinn A J E sq 300998
Gamble R L 300998
McIntyre P A 300999
Cray M P A 300900

Captains

King S A S 30895

Special Regular Officers Late Entry

Majors

Greaves S G *BSc* sq 300998

Intermediate Regular Officers

Captains

Wesson R P *BSc(Hons)* 110895
Phillips M C E *BA(Hons)* 140699
Taylor M J H *BA* 121099
Cowey N J *BA(Hons)* 90200
Mayne B E O *BA(Hons)* 130600
Waugh W J L *BSc(Hons)* 130600
Porter J D H *BA* 180700
Thompson I M 141100

Lieutenants

Miles J P *(A/Capt 151200)* 130498

Short Service Late Entry Officers

Majors

Richart P V *QGM BEM* 300994

Captains

Fisher A D 10498
Larcombe D J 10498
Kellett N H 240498
Horton H B 10199
Clarke A G 200199

Buckley P J 10299
Connor B T 10499
Metcalf S J 140699
Russell S I 220699
Taylor R J 160300
Ashbridge L P *MBE* 180400
Bird G E 31100
Hynds B 301100

Short Service Officers

Captains

Lyon R R *BSc(Hons)* ph 60894
Cameron A J *BSc* 100299
Dening-Smitherman R P *BSc(Hons)* 100299
Hazan J A *BCom(Hons)* 90200
Smith M J T *BA(Hons)* 90200
Evans C D P *BSc(Hons)* 130600
Fake I C *BSc(Hons)* 231100

Lieutenants

Fisher J R C *MA(Hons)* 160697
Beaves P R *BA(Hons)* 161297
Gilhespy J M *BSc(Hons)* 161297
Fisher C J *BA(Hons)* 130498
Kaufman S M *BSc* 130498
Back J D *BA(Hons)* 100898
Ridgway S A *BA(Hons)* 100898
Davies J R *BSc(Hons)* 141298
Fowler J E *BSc(Hons)* 141298
Jones C H 290399
Bagshaw C E I *BSc(Hons)* 90899
Collins J J *B Sc (Hons)* 90899
Howard J R *BA(Hons)* 90899
Ridgway N P *BA(Hons)* 90899
Fielder M T *BA(Hons)* 131299
Purnell J M 171100

2nd Lieutenants

Hodgkiss B A F 100499
Gadsby Vicomte De St Quentin W J A 111299
Morris G A 161200

Short Service Volunteer Officers

Lieutenants

Halford-Macleod J P A *(A/Capt 261299)* 21095

ROYAL REGIMENT OF ARTILLERY

A Gun between two scrolls, that above inscribed UBIQUE, that beneath inscribed QUO FAS ET GLORIA DUCUNT;
the whole ensigned with The Crown all Gold

Regimental Marches

Quick March .... .The RA Quick March
Slow March .... .Royal Artillery Slow March

Agents .... .Lloyds Bank plc Cox's & King's Branch

Regimental Headquarters .... .Artillery House, Front Parade, RA Barracks, Woolwich, London SE18 4BH
(Tel: 020-8781-3714)

Alliances

Canadian Armed Forces .... .The Royal Regiment of Canadian Artillery
Australian Military Forces .... .The Royal Regiment of Australian Artillery
New Zealand Army .... .The Royal Regiment of New Zealand Artillery
Fiji .... .The Fiji Artillery
Indian Army .... .Regiment of Artillery
Pakistan Army .... .Artillery of Pakistan
Sri Lanka Army .... .The Sri Lanka Artillery
Malaysian Armed Forces .... .Malaysian Artillery
Singapore Armed Forces .... .The Singapore Volunteer Artillery
Malta .... .Armed Forces Of Malta
Colonial Forces .... .The Royal Gibraltar Regiment
South African Defence Force .... .South African Artillery Corps

Captain-General .... .THE QUEEN

Master Gunner, St James's Park ..... .Gen *Sir* Alex Harley *KBE CB* ret pay .... .010101

Colonels Commandant .... .Maj Gen M F L Shellard *CBE* ret pay .... .010493
Maj Gen A C P Stone *CB* ret pay .... .010493
Maj Gen M T Tennant *CB* ret pay .... .011094
Maj Gen I G C Durie *CBE* ret pay .... .010996
Lt Gen *Sir* Edmund Burton *KBE* ret pay .... .010198
Lt Gen *Sir* Michael Willcocks *KCB* .... .310300
Brig M G Douglas-Withers *CBE* ret pay .... .010900
Brig M S Rutter-Jerome ret pay .... .011000
Maj Gen N W F Richards *CB CBE* ret pay .... .010101

Hon Colonels Commandant .... .Brig P D Orchard-Lisle *CBE TD DL* .... .010186
Col M J E Taylor *CBE TD DL* .... .010394
Col A C Roberts *MBE TD JP DL* .... .010496

Brigadiers

Raworth M R rcds psc hcsc(J)
300692
Kerr G L *OBE* rcds psc hcsc(J)
300693
Radcliffe D E *OBE* psc hcsc(J)
300693
Cook W O psc† hcsc(J)
300695
Keeling J J psc(n)† 300695
Richards D J *CBE BA(Hons)* psc
hcsc(J) 300695
Ritchie A S *CBE BA(Hons)* psc
hcsc(J) 300696
Campbell I D S rcds psc 300697
Lambe B C *CBE* rcds psc hcsc(J)
300697
Wheelwright B D *BA(Hons) FIMGT*
psc† jsdc
Bailey J B A *MBE ADC BA(Hons)*
psc hcsc(J) 311297
Smith R J S *OBE QGM* psc† 311297
Applegate R A D *OBE BA(Hons)*
CGIA psc† hcsc(J) 300698

Wilson C C *CGIA* rcds psc† 300698
Brown C C *CBE LLB(Hons) CGIA*
psc† hcsc(J) I 300699
Faith A J *OBE* rcds psc odc(AUS)
300699
Lunn C D rcds psc 300699
Sykes R M M psc 311299
Philpott N B *BSc(Hons)* psc† jsdc
300600
Prentice K H N *OBE BSc(Hons)*
CGIA psc† 300600
Tadier C W *CBE* psc(AUS) hcsc(J)
300600

Colonels

Kelly R V *BSc(Eng)Hons* psc†
300691
Moorby A L psc 300691
King-Harman A W psc† 300692
Rice A J ocds(US) sq jsdc 300693
Williams R K *FIMGT* psc† sq G jsdc
300693
Corbet Burcher M A *OBE BA(Hons)*
rcds psc psc(a) 300694
Fairman B J *OBE* odc(US) sq
300694

Price K A *MCGI CGIA* psc†
300694
Williams P B *OBE* ocds(US) psc†
300694
Coats C M B *CGIA* psc† 300695
Molyneaux P C C psc(a)† 300695
Barry P G *CGIA* psc† 300696
Deuchar A D psc† 300696
Dutton J R W psc† jsdc 300696
Gledhill S M *BA(Hons)* psc 300696
Marwood P H *BSc(Hons)* psc†
300696
Wilton T J *MBE BSc* sq jsdc sq(w)
300696
Cooper M B sq 300697
Kazocins J *OBE BA(Hons)* psc
(A/Brig 150201) 300697
Smith P H J *BA(Hons)* psc(a)†
300697
Villalard P C psc jsdc 300697
Arnold K D psc 300698
Blease D H A *MSc MSc MInstD*
MCGI psc(AUS)† 300698
Nicholls C J *BSc(Hons)* psc† 300698
Wilson J D *BA MPhil* psc jsdc
300698

Young G A *MA* psc jsdc 300698
Clissitt N A psc osc(KU) 300699
Hutchinson S C J *BSc* psc† 300699
Kingdon W J F *MA MA* psc† 300699
Lewthwaite D W *BSc(Eng)* psc† 300699
Lyon D G psc† 300699
Manson M P *MA* psc† 300699
Moore W H *BA(Hons) FIMGT MCGI* psc† hcsc(J) 300699
Prior W G *CGIA* psc† jsdc 300699
Romberg C R *BA(Hons)* psc I* 300699
Thomas S O psc† 300699
Baxter J R J *OBE BA(Hons)* psc 300600
Berragan G W psc 300600
Bounsall R H *BSc(Eng)Hons* psc† 300600
Foster A J *MBE BSc(Hons)* psc† 300600
Gregory A R *MA* psc† 300600
Inkster A D K *BA(Hons)* psc† 300600
Potts D R *MBE BA(Hons) CGIA* psc† 300600
Pountain M N *BA(Hons)* psc(GE) I 300600
Purdy R W H *OBE MA* psc(a)† 300600
Reed S C *BA(Hons)* psc 300600
Sinclair I R *BA* psc 300600

_____

Lieutenant Colonels

Harris S P (SL) psc 300686
Shaw-Brown R D (SL) *BA(Hons)* psc 300687
Lang N G W *BA PGCE* sq 300688
Morgan M J (SL) sq 300688
Harrington J E (SL) *CGIA* psc† 300689
Manton A R *MBA* sq jsdc 300689
Stevenson K A P (SL) psc† 300689
Bazzard J A C odc(US) sq 300690
Clarke T P *MDA* psc† MDA 300690
Dore M I V *BSc* sq 300690
Goodfellow M R (SL) sq jsdc 300690
Happe E G psc† ato 300690
Howard-Vyse J C (SL) psc(n) 300690
Kirke C M ST G *MA CGIA* df psc† 300690
White R J (SL) *MSc* gw sq(w) 300690
Anderson M H (SL) sq sq(w) 300691
Burdick M W sq G(a) 300691
Carter M N (SL) *MBE* sq 300691
Fielding R E (SL) *MSc* sq (L/Col 051297) 300691
Gillett G M V *BSc(Eng)Hons MDA* psc† 300691
Hodkinson G A (SL) sq G sq(w) 300691
Rooke J L K (SL) sq 300691
Vere Nicoll I A *MBE* sq jsdc 300691
Arthur D R (SL) *MBE* sq 300692
Bonney C P (SL) sq 300692
Healey M R *BA MIMGT* G sq(w) 300692

Hobden D J (SL) sq ph sq(w) 300692
Hurst P J H (SL) G sq(w) 300692
Raley I D *BA(Hons)* sq jsdc 300692
Williams P R psc(IT) 300692
Ewence M W (SL) G sq(w) 300693
Gibbon J H psc† 300693
Gillespie A E *MSc* psc 300693
Sinclair T J B *BA(Hons)* psc† 300693
Cooke N D psc 300694
Eggar R N M *BA(Hons) MA* psc† G 300694
Grant G A B *MBISC* sq jsdc 300694
McKitrick R A S S (SL) sq G(y) sq(w) adp 300694
Nelson C J W *BSc(Hons)* psc† G(gw) 300694
Pedder A V *BSc(Hons) MBA CGIA* psc† 300694
Pope M D M psc† (A/Col 010201) 300694
Reynolds P W *MSc* sq I MDA 300694
Townend W A H *BA(Hons)* psc 300694
Watson J N E *BA(Hons)* psc(n)† jsdc 300694
Forster M J D *BA(Hons)* psc ais 300695
Hamilton R A *CGIA* psc(IND)† 300695
Jammes R R psc 300695
Johnson M sq 300695
Young S A J psc 300695
Adams D C B *BSc(Hons)* sq 300696
Bone G D F *BSc(Eng)Hons* psc† 300696
Brealey B psc† (A/Col 050201) 300696
Bruce A T *MBE* sq (A/Col 131100) 300696
Budd A D H psc† 300696
Challes D N *CGIA* psc† 300696
Duncan P A *MBE BA(Hons)* psc 300696
Harvey K M *BA(Hons)* psc† 300696
Knightley C A psc(a) G (A/Col 300501) 300696
Lane P R L *BSc(Hons)* psc† (A/Col 020101) 300696
Lyne-Pirkis C J A *BA(Hons)* sq 300696
Relph M D *MBE* psc jsdc (A/Col 250800) 300696
Shaw D A H psc† (A/Col 021000) 300696
Sweet T J psc 300696
Vacher M J *OBE* psc† (A/Col 150900) 300696
Atwell P V *BSc(Eng)Hons MSc PhD CEng MIEE MBCS* dis sq(w) 300697
Banham M P *MBE* psc† jsdc 300697
Barnard A P *BA(Hons)* psc† 300697
Barrons R L *OBE BA(Hons) MDA(Cantab&Oxon)001 MDA* psc MDA 300697
Brundle C J psc psc(J) 300697
Foster N J sq 300697
Fox P A *BA(Hons)* psc† G 300697

Lipscombe N J *MSc* psc(IND) 300697
Mears A J psc jsdc 300697
Pritchard D J psc 300697
Robinson W K M *MA* psc† 300697
Sims J C psc† psc 300697
Tomlinson P H *MA* psc† 300697
Waring M E psc 300697
Bayless I J psc 311297
Bleasdale J D sq G sq(w) 311297
Gower J R M sq 311297
Weldon M H DE W psc† 311297
Abraham K D *MA* psc† psc(J) 300698
Bate S C *BA BA(Hons)* psc 300698
Cowgill D B *MSc* dis sq(w) 300698
Dowdeswell I M *MSc* dis sq G sq(w) 300698
Dutton R K G sq sq(w) 300698
Eeles N H *BSc(Hons)* psc† 300698
Fleetwood T M A psc 300698
Hile N F W *BSc(Hons)* psc† 300698
Lawford H R *BA(Hons)* psc† 300698
Lloyd S J A *MBE* sq 300698
Milligan M A L *BA(Hons)* psc† 300698
Morris A D *LLB(Hons)* psc† 300698
Robson R W psc† G 300698
Tinsley I *BA(Econ)Hons* psc† 300698
Weighill R P M psc† 300698
Wilson L R *MBE* osc(FR) ph 300698
Ashmore N D *BA(Hons)* psc 300699
Best N C *BSc(Hons)* psc† 300699
Cook S K G sq(w) adp 300699
Dickey R C psc 300699
Dixon M S *BSc(Hons) MSc* psc† dis 300699
Donaldson S G sowc sq 300699
Francis D R K *BA(Hons)* psc† 300699
Greenwood D J sq jsdc 300699
Jackson R S *MBE* psc 300699
Jones R L *MA(Hons)* psc† 300699
Marjot T *BSc(Hons)* psc jsdc 300699
Morris T H psc 300699
Redmond M G psc G 300699
Sharp J psc(GE) G(gw) 300699
Slinger N J B *BA(Hons)* sq 300699
Stock C B W *MSc* sq(w) † 300699
Vincent M A F *MBE MSc* psc† dis 300699
Vye M A sq 300699
Caldwell R B psc† 300600
Cullen D M *MBE* psc 300600
Evans D R *BSc(Hons)* sq(w) † 300600
Grew A L *BA(Hons)* psc† G(a) 300600
Holdom G J L *MBE BSc(Hons)* sq(w) † 300600
James S G *BSc(Eng)Hons MSc* psc† G 300600
Jefferson N T *BSc(Hons) MSc* psc† 300600
Kidwell T G psc† 300600
Lacey M G *MA* psc† 300600
Neate M C psc 300600
Park R J J *BA(Hons)* sq 300600
Price T J E psc† G 300600
Pugh G M *BA(Hons) CGIA* psc† 300600

Smart M J *MBE BA(Hons) MDA* psc
300600
Upton S N *BSc(Hons)* sowc sq G
300600
Waddell G W C *BA(Hons)* psc
300600
Winchester R A psc† G 300600
Wolsey S P *BA(Hons)* psc† 300600
Butt G L *MBE* sq 300900

Majors

Tulloch J S M *MIMGT MIPD* sq
300679
Afford N A *MBE* sq 311279
Akhurst G R *MBE* sq G 300980
Gibbins J B G(a) gw sq(w) 300980
Hopkin S P M sq G(gw) 300980
McLaren D E G sq 300980
Morris M D A *MBE* sq ph 300981
Powrie I G C psc 300981
Hunter J A G *MBA* psc(CAN)
300982
Lang J D sq 300982
Ashton T C psc 300983
Fowler C P W sq G 300983
Graham D *BSc(Eng)Hons MSc* mvt
sq(w) 300983
Radice R J *MBE* sq 300983
Ellis Jones E O sq G(gw) 300984
Ratcliffe N G D sq 300984
Reglar M P J sq G 71184
Johnson C D sq 190985
Badham-Thornhill M L *MIMGT*
MIPD G sq(w) *(L/Lt Col 240898)*
300985
Clark R C D *MBE MDA MIPD* sq G
MDA 300985
Russell G W G sq(w) 300985
Sparkes S *BA* sq 300985
Turner T D R *BSc* G(a) sq(w)
300985
Begbie R M G sq(w) 300986
Cooke D J A sq G(a) 300986
Haynes R J H psc(a) 300986
Mehers S I *BA* osc(MAL) sq sq(w)
300986
Sanderson S C psc 300986
Taylor T H P *MBE BA(Hons) MDA*
psc sq *(A/Lt Col 311000)* 300986
Wadsworth G R sq 300986
Cameron A G H sq *(A/Lt Col*
090301) 300987
Leeming C F G(a) sq(w) 300987
Nicol W D sq 300987
Nicol J *BSc* G sq(w) 300987
Ramsay P G G sq(w) 300987
Swinton K sq G 300987
Angus P J *MBE BSc(Eng) MSc*
MCGI mvt sq(w) 300988
Austin C G *MSc* psc† dis *(A/Lt Col*
020101) 300988
Boyes R M L psc 300988
Collett J A *MBE BSc* sq(w) 300988
Drage B K sq 300988
Geary P J *BA(Hons)* G sq(w)
300988
Holland C G G sq(w) 300988
Robinson C N sq 300988
Ross C A M G sq(w) 300988
Stadward J N J *MSc MCGI* psc gw
sq(w) 300988
Stanley P K sq 300988

Tate J R sq G(a) 300988
White A J *BSc(Eng)* sq(w) † 300988
Worsley P S P sq 300988
Archer B B *MBE* sq 300989
Cogan P J cafs sq 300989
Forsyth W D S G sq(w) 300989
Glover P A *BA(Hons)* sq(w) 300989
Houghton M A sq 300989
Liddicoat M R H sq sq(w) 300989
Templeton G K sowc sq G(a)
300989
Van Poeteren J S M G G sq(w)
300989
Wheeler-Mallows K J *(L/Lt Col*
040900) 300989
Astbury A psc 300990
Bower J D *MBE* sq 300990
Caiger J G sq G 300990
Clark C R sowc sq G 300990
Cox S J *MCGI* psc† 300990
Dyer T J *MBE BSc(Hons)* psc†
300990
Hacon A N *BA(Hons) MBA* psc†
300990
Heath P B sq G(a) 300990
Potter J A H sq sq(w) † 300990
Taylor D C G sq(w) 300990
Abbott J C G(a) sq(w) 300991
Bates P N *MA* sq(w) † 300991
Carter M G J psc(n) *(A/Lt Col*
041200) 300991
Davies S H L sq 300991
Ellen T A sq G 300991
Lukes A W sq(w) 300991
Quaile M H K sq(w) † 300991
Stone R Q J psc 300991
Stroud-Turp J R *BA(Hons)* sq G
300991
Valenzia M D sq G 300991
Waddell A O M sq 300991
Wentworth M D *MA MSc* gw sq(w)
300991
Cameron A H M sq 300992
Haly R S O *BA(Hons)* psc† 300992
Hibbert N S G sq(w) 300992
Hinton G P P G *BSc(Hons)* sq
300992
Howard M R J *BA(Hons) M A*
(Oxon) psc† 300992
Iffland D M psc 300992
Jacobs C M *BA(Hons)* osc(FR) sq
300992
Jones D B *BScTech(Hons)* G 300992
Purdy A J *BSc(Eng)Hons MAPM*
psc † *(A/Lt Col 050301)* 300992
Robinson P D sq 300992
Ross M C *BA(Hons)* psc† 300992
Walsh C N P *BSc(Hons)* sq 300992
Walton M R *MC* sq 300992
Willcock C P *BA(Hons) PGCE* G
300992
Calderwood C G(a) 300993
Coups J M 300993
Drage J W *BSc(Hons)* psc† G
300993
Duhig K A 300993
Eve R R T G 300993
Ingle J F G(a) 300993
Lowles D J sq 300993
Mileham P C E *BA(Hons)* sq(w) †
300993

Muntz S G A G 300993
Napier G R *BA(Hons)* psc† 300993
O'Gorman S J *BA(Hons)* 300993
Rafferty A C *BSc(Hons)* sq G sq(w)
300993
Servaes M J P *BA(Hons)* sq 300993
Shepherd A J *BA(Hons) MA* psc†
300993
Sibbald J *MSc FInstD* dis G sq(w)
300993
Tyson E J *BA* 300993
Wakefield R J *MSc* psc† dis G(a)
300993
Bradley C D G 300994
Field A J *BSc(Hons) MSc* G(y) sq(w)
300994
Grace E C psc† psc 300994
Gray S J G 300994
Gunning C P *BA(Hons)* 300994
Hamer-Philip A J *BA(Hons)* psc†
300994
Herbert J J *BA(Hons) MA* psc† *(A/Lt*
Col 190201) 300994
Hercus D J *BA(Hons) PGDA*
psc(GE) 300994
Keleghan P S *MDA MSc* sq(w) ais
300994
Lee A P G sq(w) 300994
Luck D W *MA* psc† 300994
Mason S E G 300994
Peek N M 300994
Shapland G D 300994
Smith A M G 300994
Thorne P *MSc* psc† *(A/Lt Col*
161000) 300994
Vosper-Brown G psc 300994
Waller A J *BA(Hons)* psc(J) sq G
300994
Warren R P G 300994
Williams N K 300994
Wood T M *BA(Hons)* 300994
Wright P H D *BA(Hons) MPhil* sq G
300994
Ambrose G A *BA(Hons) MA GCGI*
G(ss) sq(w) 300995
Badman S J G *BSc(Hons)* G 300995
Baker R *BA(Hons)* 300995
Baker P H S *BA(Hons) MA* psc(J)
300995
Barker C H *BSc MDA* MDA 300995
Bell I R psc(J) 300995
Bolton R B 300995
Butt S R *BSc* 300995
Calder-Smith J D psc(CAN) 300995
Campbell J C *BSc(Hons) MA* psc(J)
300995
Canning S J *BA(Hons)* G 300995
Carwardine A V *MSc* psc(J) 300995
Edwards T C G(a) 300995
Fitzgerald N O psc psc(J) 300995
Fox D P *BA(Hons)* sq(w) 300995
Free J R *BEd(Hons)* psc† † 300995
Gamble M J psc(J) 300995
Haines S R G(a) 300995
Haldenby R *BA(Hons) MA* psc(J) sq
300995
Hall S R *MSc* psc(J) 300995
Hammond D psc(IT) sq(w) 300995
Harrington D R 300995
Harrison I G *MBE* psc 300995
Hewitt R W *MBE BA(Hons) MDA*
psc 300995

Hickie P L   sq(w) ais   300995
Hudson D J *MBE* psc   300995
Hutchinson A S L   300995
Ingham C R   300995
Ingram P H   300995
Jenkins B W psc   300995
Keeling P *MISM MIAM* G   300995
Long S R *BSc(Hons)*   300995
Makin N S *BSc(Hons)* sq(w)   300995
Marshall N *MA* psc(J)   300995
Mears C J *BSc(Hons) MDA* sq   300995
Metcalfe R S G   300995
Miller T L sq   300995
Neale A D G   300995
Nugee R E *MBE BA(Hons) GCGI*
  psc† *(A/Lt Col 040101)*   300995
Scouller D J *BSc(Hons) MA* psc(J)   300995
Swinhoe-Standen R A P *BSc MA*
  psc† psc   300995
Thompson P R C *BA(Hons) MA*   300995
Ware R E *BSc(Hons)*   300995
Welsh A C   300995
West S R *BSc(Hons)* psc†   300995
Wood C M cafs   300995
Butcher C S ph   300996
Cole G *BSc(Hons) MSc* psc(J)   300996
Connell W J G   300996
Gammon M C B *BSc(Hons)* psc(J)   300996
Greenwood N R *BEd(Hons)* sq   300996
Harden T P odc(AUST) G(a)   300996
Humphrey S L *MSc* psc(J)   300996
Kelly M J *BA(Hons)*   300996
Kingdom J M *BSc(Hons) MSc* psc(J)   300996
Lee R M *BA(Hons) MA* psc(J)   300996
McRobb N P *BA*   300996
McRory P G   300996
Murphy T P G(a) sq(w)   300996
Norton M A psc(J)   300996
Osmond G I P *BA(Hons)* G   300996
Reynolds A M H R *BA* psc(J)   300996
Shepherd R C G *MA(Hons)* G   300996
Skeates S R *BA(Hons) MSc* psc(J)
  MDA   300996
Storey D N   300996
Tilley P H   300996
Waymouth M R *BA(Hons)* cafs
  psc(J)   300996
Welch E J *BSc(Hons)* psc(J)   300996
Whelan D V   300996
Wiles J P H G sq(w)   300996
Wilson N A psc(J)   300996
Wordsworth T N J G   300996
Atkinson S *BA(Hons)*   300997
Barber J G M   300997
Bramble W J F *MSc* psc(J)   300997
Brown M E   300997
Clunie D M C *BSc(Hons) MSc CEng*
  MIEE gw sq(w)   300997
Collins S M C G(a)   300997
Cotterill J W S *BA(Hons)* G(a)   300997

Couzens R C *MA* psc(J) G(a)   300997
Dunk S P *BSc(Hons)* G   300997
Ford L K *BSc(Hons)*   300997
Greaves N *BSc(Hons) MA MSc*
  psc(J) dis   300997
Heath R D *BEng(Hons) MSc MSc*
  sq(w)   300997
Heath S G *BA(Hons)* G   300997
Jackson N R A   300997
Kernohan D A *BEng(Hons) MDA* G
  MDA   300997
Musgrave J B *BA(Hons)* psc(J) G   300997
Papenfus J R   300997
Pizii R L *BSc(Hons)* psc(J)   300997
Roper C B *BA(Hons)* MDA   300997
Shepheard-Walwyn P G   300997
Speirs I K G   300997
Thornhill M J psc(J)   300997
Torrents A C J *BA* osc(SP)   300997
Warner C R psc(J)   300997
Adams O J   300998
Armitage P A   300998
Belcourt P L *BSc(Hons)* G(a)   300998
Burn F W G *BA(Hons)* G   300998
Carter E H J *BA(Hons)*   300998
Carter R J *BA(Hons)*   300998
Colyer S P D *BA(Hons)*   300998
Cornock J E J   300998
Everett J M *BA(Hons)*   300998
Harrison P   300998
Learmont J J   300998
Lefever A J H   300998
Lewis A M   300998
Mackay D J   300998
Morgan H C *BA(Hons)*   300998
Pond N S *BA(Hons)*   300998
Reavill A ST J   300998
Ridgway T R D   300998
Robinson S J sq   300998
Ross M L *BA(Hons)*   300998
Southby A M *RVM*   300998
Stremes J T *BA(Hons)*   300998
Tombleson P *BA(Hons)*   300998
Whatmough G J *BA(Hons)* G   300998
Wilman N A *BA(Hons)*   300998
Bennett J M J *BA(Hons)*   300999
Bennett B W   300999
Brockman E G S   300999
Brown A J   300999
Collinge J R   300999
Comber I M   300999
Crisp M J   300999
Day C G *LLB(Hons)*   300999
Freeborn A M   300999
Grimwood R J G   300999
Haws D J cafs G   300999
Hodgson J F   300999
Huthwaite C S   300999
Maxwell D C G(a)   300999
Mooney P N G   300999
Phillips J I R *BA(Hons)*   300999
Radwell K D G(a)   300999
Rosier S D *BA(Hons)*   300999
Smith R M *BA(Hons)*   300999
Squier C J M *BSc(Hons)*   300999
Wilkinson G P *BSc(Hons)*   300999
Wilkinson H J P *BA(Hons)*   300999
Willsher B D cafs   300999

Allott M J *BSc(Hons)*   300900
Bates P R *BEng(Hons)*   300900
Bengtsson E J *BSc(Econ)Hons*   300900
Bergqvist P *MBE*   300900
Bowman K P   300900
Fraser S D   300900
Ganner R B *BSc(Hons)* G(a)   300900
Holden J *BSc(Hons)*   300900
Hudson S J *BA(Hons)*   300900
Jones D A E   300900
Kettler C C R   300900
Law T F *MA(Hons)*   300900
Legh-Smith M R   300900
Lord A D P G ph   300900
Macdonald N A G   300900
Maclean A G   300900
Murphy J D *BA(Hons) Dis*   300900
Palmer C *BSc(Hons)*   300900
Parrott J D *BSc(Hons)*   300900
Phillips A B *BA(Hons)*   300900
Pritchett J C R G im   300900
Smith M J   300900
Spence N A *BA(Hons)*   300900
Taylor T D K G(a)   300900
White M P   300900
Williams R B *BSc(Hons)*   300900
Williams S C   300900
Woods P D   300900

Captains

Craig A K G *(A/Maj 190201)*   101294
Brumwell A A *BSc(Hons)*   10495
Dawes A P L *BSc(Hons)*   10495
Heath A L *BSc(Hons)*   10495
Whiting F W G *BSc(Hons)*   10495
Dawes E J M *BEng(Hons)*   310795
Perry R L   40895
Clarke D S *BA(Hons)*   110895
Hendrickse R W *BSc(Hons)*   110895
Hodkinson A F *BA(HonsCantab)*
  (A/Maj 260300)   110895
Oates A G *BA(Hons)*   110895
Renyard N Z C *BA(Hons)*   110895
Vigne J E H *BSc(Hons)*   110895
Gorton C M *BSc(Hons)*   31095
Simpson C L *BSc(Hons)*   141295
Champken S D   151295
Culver S C D   151295
Hill J D *BSc(Hons)*   151295
Perry E T   110396
McCauley S P *BSc(Hons)*   120496
Christopher R J *BSc(Hons)*   130496
Day M J   130496
Dixon M J D   130496
Grant S G   130496
Hayhurst R M *(A/Maj 261000)*   130496
Richards J A D ph   130496
Mackenzie-Crooks M R *BSc(Hons)*   300796
Manley C R   70896
Roberts W P C J *BSc(Hons)*   70896
Alsworth R J *BA(Hons)*   110896
Clements R M *BSc(Hons)*   110896
Jordan R J P *LLB(Hons)*   110896
Relph D C J *BSc(Hons)* *(A/Maj
  190201)*   110896
Sawyer N T *BEng(Hons)*   110896
Taylor A J *BA(Hons)*   110896
Curtis P N   281196

125

Sanderson J S *BA(Hons)*	291196
Searle J M D *BEng(Hons)*	131296
Skinner C J *BA(Hons)*	131296
Jones P	141296
Mead J R *BSc (L/Maj 200101)*	141296
Swannell M J	141296
Andrew N P	110497
Perkins M L *BSc(Hons)*	110497
Sherrard D W *LLB(Hons)*	220797
Harding J A H *BSc(Hons)*	80897
Masters D R *BEng*	80897
Newsham A J K	80897
Whittle M H G	80897
Wood G M	80897
Brunswick J I *BSc(Hons)*	141097
Gee N M *BSc*	141097
Thomson A R *BA(Hons)*	141097
Venn N S C *BSc(Hons)* ph	141097
Wallwork R D *BEng(Hons)*	141097
Hollinrake R F	151197
Armstrong N R *BEng(Hons)*	121297
Farr C M P	121297
Mason T N	121297
Mawdsley J C W	121297
Ross W J	121297
Thomas S P	121297
Ø.Burley E L *BA(Hons)*	120298
Daly T P *MEng(Hons)*	120298
Elviss M R *BSc(Hons)*	120298
Murphy M J P *BSc(Hons)*	120298
Parrott J M *BSc(Hons)*	120298
Bridges D P *LLB(Hons)*	90498
Datson F N K *MBE*	90498
Graham D M	90498
Lucas C I	90498
Brown A R *BA(Hons)*	160698
Cook J P *BA(Hons)*	160698
Oxley P J *BSc(Hons)*	160698
Taylor G *BA(Hons)*	160698
Lynskey M J *BA(Hons)*	100998
Ø.Baker A *BSc(Hons)*	131098
Cassidy J J *BSc(Hons)*	131098
Killick M P D *BA(Hons)*	131098
Oldroyd J E K *BSc(Econ)Hons*	131098
Burton T L	111298
Francis D K *BSc(Hons)*	111298
James C P *BSc(Hons)*	100299
Sargent M J *MA(Hons)*	100299
Harris K R	90499
Kemp T	90499
Reader S W L *BSc(Hons)*	140699
Lamb S C	60899
Priddis M K	131299
Cresswell J P *BA(Hons)*	90200
Hepburn N *BEng(Hons)*	90200
Jones I L M *MA(Hons)*	90200
McCleery J W *BA(Hons)*	90200
Morris B E M *BA(Hons)*	90200
Relph J E *BSc(Hons)*	90200
Robinson F A *BEng(Hons)*	90200
Young M E J *BA(Hons)*	90200
Briant M I	120800
Estick S J *BSc(Hons)*	181100
Mabbott M J	161200
Swannell A D	161200
Dupuy P M *BSc(Hons)*	80201

Hewitt C A *BSc(Hons)*	80201
Wilson A N *BA(Hons)*	80201

Lieutenants

Wood M W *MEng(Hons)*	140698
Derbyshire C	100898
Forster R A *BA(Hons)*	100898
Young A P	100898
Alston R N *BA(Hons)*	90899
Ø.Stevens B L *(L/Capt 021200)*	131299
Gent C	121200

2nd Lieutenants

†Crawford R H	220997
Griffith D J A	100499
††Budd N J M	50999
Ø.Hart S J	50999
††Toms C D	50999

Regular Category Late Entry Officers

Lieutenant Colonels

Falzon J F *BEM* sq	30797
Winch B	60898
Bowater I G sq	10199
Smith L *MBE*	50199
Carter P sq	80200
Absolon S J DE M *MBE BEM* sq	140401

Majors

McPherson I	300988
Grant D R	300989
Witham M A	300989
Ravenhill G W	300991
Taylor R J	300992
Churchley C J	20793
Cook P J *MBE*	300993
Westwell F	300993
Moore B W	300994
Whiteway R J *MBE*	300994
Francis J	300995
Tate I E	300995
Wilson L C	300995
Brawn C W	300996
Everitt P J *MBE*	300996
Ferguson J H R *MBE*	300996
Parker A J	300996
Reeve R H J	300996
Roberts R M	300996
Beswick T R *MBE*	300997
Bond H	300997
Cutter G	300997
Lord K R	300997
Mott A N	300997
Parker R J *G(a)*	300997
Ransom J D	300997
Wallis S *MBE*	300997
Wright I C	300997
Allan D L *MBE*	300998
Bartholomew D	300998
Gledhill P	300998
Lewis G *QGM*	300998
McPherson R A GT	300998
Palmer C C D	300998
Parvez A	300998
Bacon C	300999
Dawson J F	300999
Gillett W J	300999

Haynes D L *MBE* GT	300999
Horner R H *MBE* sq	300999
Lambert-Gorwyn M	300999
Robson C A *MBE* GT	300999
Bond R J	300900
Hamzat R A GT	300900
Ives A H	300900
Manning H E *BA BSc(Hons)* GT(A)	300900
Porter G C	300900

Captains

Bonner W I GT	240296
Hayes G D	160596
Valentine J H GT(Y)	11196
Porter G W *MBE* GT(Y)	130397
McCormack L GT	91097

Technical Instructors in Gunnery

Comben M GT sq(w) *Lt Col 010999*	40382
Macallister N J *BSc* GT(Y) sq(w) *Maj 150292*	10484
Price G C *MBE* GT sq(w) *Maj 300989*	10484
Skerry G M GT sq *Lt Col 310197*	10486
Jones G *MBE* GT(Y) *Maj 300992*	10489
Hill R J T *MBE* GT *Maj 300994*	10191
Wilson D P GT sq(w) *Maj 300994*	10191
Linge N D *MBE* GT *Maj 300996*	10194
Lane K F *MBE* GT sq *Maj 300995*	10195
Warne C J GT *Maj 300900*	10195
Saward K L GT *Maj 300900*	10196
Krstic S A *MBE* GT *Capt 240295*	10197

Technical Instructors in Gunnery (AD)

Denton R GT(A) *Maj 290794*	10487
Conn N A C GT(A) sq *Lt Col 061200*	10191
Macaulay I R GT(A) *Maj 300998*	10196
Paylor J A GT(A) *Maj 300900*	10196

Special Regular Officers Late Entry

Majors

Cromwell B GT(A)	300900

Captains

Blake K S GT(A)	30495
Place L *MBE*	30795
Brook A H GT	220196
Goldsworthy A P GT	80496
Cattermole A J GT	260796
Groom I A	290796
Holland R GT(Y)	211196
McMurdo R J GT	100497
Lee R	30797
Haensel D G GT	40897
Fox M GT	110897

Roberts I P GT 110398
Glennon V M GT 220398
Welbourne C GT 250398
Ashford N GT 10498
Betty S A GT 10498
Boyle D S 10498
Durrant A GT 10498
Gaze N GT 10498
Greene P W GT 10498
Grendall E J 10498
Kalies N P GT 10498
Kirkpatrick T W 10498
Lindsay G M GT 10498
Lynch D J 10498
McCall D 10498
McLeavy J A 10498
Mills R J GT(A) 10498
Morson S W GT 10498
Mullin I M GT 10498
Ransom D L 10498
Sherrell P D 10498
Steadman C J GT 10498
Stuart P E GT 10498
Sweeney J P 10498
Trench J S 10498
Wright S M GT 10498
Young K GT 10498
Atkins C S 10998

Intermediate Regular Officers

Majors

Boxell P J BA PGCE 300994
ØAtkinson C R 300996
Casey S P 300998
Taylor A J BA(Hons) MSc dis 300998
Armstrong M cafs G 300999
Wilks M C BEd(Hons) G 300999
Gilmour A R BA(Hons) 300900

Captains

Sandells A J G 70893
Tivey M E BSc(Hons) G(a) 10495
ØWatson-Mack E L BSc(Hons) 10495
Wood A R BA(Hons) 10495
Jelley H W BA(Hons) 70995
Brimacombe R E P 50296
Brown S W BSc(Hons) 110896
Smith M A BA(Hons) 291196
Dickie G M A BA(Hons) 131296
Holah R E BA(Hons) 131296
Pearson M J 141296
Carter G R 110497
Gillen J N 110497
Marchant-Wincott A C 110497
Parkinson C E A 110497
Welstead J G 110497
Spaul A D 10697
Alderson C 290797
ØBrook C BSc(Hons) 141097
Giemza-Pipe J C BA(Hons) 141097
Roughton N H BA(Hons) 141097
Lovick C 201197
Doherty J W 121297
Ingham S A M 121297
Macintosh A K 171297
Recchia C J 221297
Bate A G E BSc(Hons) 120298
Brining S N G BSc(Hons) 120298

Crookbain S BA(Hons) 120298
Ventham T J BA(Hons) 120298
Botterill E B J BSc(Hons) 90498
Day C B 90498
Bolam W BA(Hons) 160698
Docherty J A BEng 160698
Harrison D E BEng(Hons) 160698
Horne A D E BA(Hons) 160698
Philpott A H BA(Hons) 160698
Rimmer M J G LLB(Hons) 160698
ØWalker C L BSc(Hons) 160698
Snodgrass P A BA(Hons) 60898
Dimmock A 70898
Howell B L 240998
Evans R D BA(Hons) 131098
Loose D A BSc(Hons) 131098
Mathieson G A BSc(Hons) 131098
Pitt A R BSc 131098
Welfare A P BA(Hons) 131098
ØWorsley N J BA(Hons) 131098
Parks A F W 111298
Bianconi G BA 100299
Brett M W BSc(Hons) 100299
ØForbes R H BSc(Hons) ph 100299
Miles S N BSc(Hons) 100299
Moore M J BSC(LANMAN)Hons 100299
ØParkes Z E C BA(Hons) 100299
Sharpe J E G BA(Hons) 100299
Snape-Johnson R J BSc(Hons) 100299
Wilson J BA(Hons) 100299
Foy R D BA(Hons) 260399
Constable N J BSc(Hons) 140699
Mayes J R P BSc(Hons) 140699
Nicolson G J BSc 140699
Pullan M BA(Hons) 140699
Rhys-Evans G L BA(Hons) 140699
Riley R H G BA(Hons) 140699
Salisbury T S BSc 140699
Tillotson C BA(Hons) 140699
ØWalker V L LLB(Hons) 140699
Turnbull C L 60899
Forshaw M P BSc(Hons) 121099
Haigh A W BSc(Hons) 121099
Longfield R N BSc(Hons) 121099
Potter S H BA(Hons) 121099
Sempala-Ntege N M BA(Hons) 121099
ØThomson R B BSc(Hons) 121099
Sharples A J 101299
ØBurt L S BSc(Hons) 90200
Clarke A J BSc(Hons) 90200
Lynch W R BSc 90200
Rees J J BSc(Hons) 90200
Rumbold S A MA(Hons) 90200
Sargent N P BSc(Hons) 90200
ØShepherd S J BSc(Hons) 90200
White D R BSc(Hons) 90200
Talbot-King P F 140400
Anderson C P M BA(Hons) 130600
Meldrum T S BA(Hons) 130600
Parker N J BA(Hons) 130600
Robinson G J MA(Hons) 130600
Shanklyn E M BEng(Hons) 130600
Wheale J P BSc(Econ)Hons 130600
Martin J W BSc(Hons) 90200
Miller G T 110800
Marshall S J 120800

Birch M J BSc(Hons) 101000
Edwards M K G BA(Hons) 101000
Hurndall J M L BA(Hons) MA 101000
ØWaddie A I BSc(Hons) 101000
Ward D N BSc(Hons) 101000

Lieutenants

Conlan M S (A/Capt 051098) 161297
Fisher S J 161297
Hinds S S (A/Capt 140200) 130498
Jennings D J (A/Capt 100100) 130498
Davis A K (A/Capt 150500) 100898
Webber N C (A/Capt 061100) 100898
Gracey A J 301098
Knowles M A 120499
McCaffrey P S (A/Capt 210900) 120499
Armstrong M A W BEng(Hons) 90899
Coton C L BEng(Hons) 90899
Nuttall D J BEng(Hons) 90899

2nd Lieutenants

Vincent J H BEng 90899
Layden A J 131299
Murray L K 131299
McDonald H B W 100400
Morton N I 100400
Sheldon K A 100400
Briffa D M 100900
Vincent T G 100499
Brooks N C 111299
Piercy R S 111299
††Powell S 100900
ØColley B L 161200

Short Service Late Entry Officers

Majors

Byford S P MBE 300998
Quartermaine P A D 300998
Bolderson M T GT 300900

Captains

Halpin D M GT 290495
Tippett J E GT 280396
Wilmot S D 10997
Chadwick G 10498
Dawson M 10498
Melville J 10498
Schofield P A 10498
Stubbins M L 10498
Underhill C E GT 10498
Pinkney J MBE GT 140998
Young J GT 210998
Haddock J W S 211098
Flear C A 150399
McCarthy M P GT 270399
Huish B G 10499
Ransom B D MBE 60499
Chadwick C 120499
Dryburgh F C GT 120499
Tobin M 120499
Sherburn A GT 130699
Markham G 140699
Lane B C GT 20899

Name	No.
Keizer P	10999
Glen A GT	11099
Corr I	41099
Clifford C F	240100
Le Feuvre J E *MBE* GT	240100
Hazell T	10300
Hatton L M	170400
Marsh R S	170400
Law D J GT	240400
Mann F D *BEM*	240400
Maple G P GT	240400
Morgan S R GT	240400
Bayliss M GT	20500
Greenhow F W	100500
Hood J A M	50600
Harfoot S M GT	100600
Hardicre S J	30700
Gaughan C A	100700
Roworth S A	170700
Parks P T GT	280700
Gamble-Thompson J M	40900
Morris W A GT	40900
Scoins K A	40900
Purvis C A	110900
Marshall A GT(A)	250900
Hall G T	21000
Gee M	41000
Ingleton G	81100

Short Service Officers

Captains

Name	No.
Bryant R A J *BA(Hons)*	141295
Cohu J J C *BA(Soc)Hons* ph	141295
Hopkinson J P *BA(Hons)* ph	141295
Powell D W *BSc* ph	301196
Morelli C J W ph	131296
Stewart A G *BSc(Hons)*	131296
Bradley G I *BA(Hons)* (L/Maj 190201)	141097
Cane O W S ph	160698
McGilton G D *BSc(Hons)* ph	160698
Millard-Smith R P ph	70898
Chapman P I *BSc(Hons)*	131098
Lott D J *BA(Hons)*	131098
Wood A B *BA(Hons)*	131098
Sweet M L	111298
Simon M P	110199
Taylor A R *BA(Hons)*	100299
Tapp P D *BA(Hons)*	260399
Cheesman J A *BSc(Hons)*	270399
Drew-Bredin H A *BSc*	140699
Riley A J *BA(Hons)*	140699
Tampin D *BSc*	140699
Raw P D *BA(Hons)*	90999
Batson R J *BSc(Hons)*	121099
Roberts J P *BA(Hons)*	121099
Holden D J *BSc(Hons)*	161099
ØMason C D *BA(Hons)*	161099
Granville W R	101299
Fox K M *BSc*	90200
Hawkins S M J *BSc*	90200
Ingham B M D *BA(Hons)*	90200
Luker T E *MA(Hons)*	90200
Magro A J *BSc(Hons)*	90200
Mardlin J E *BA(Hons)*	90200
ØRecchia F *BA(Hons)*	90200
Taffs J *BSc(Hons)*	90200
Withington C M *BEng(Hons)*	90200
Barber G R *BA(Hons)*	130600
Foster C F *BSc(Hons)*	130600
Wright R A *MA(Hons)*	130600
Dornan M A A *BA(Hons)*	90700
Morgan C G *BSc(Hons)*	200700
Bryant M H ph	120800
Blackburn D O *BEng(Hons)*	101000
Boag J J *BSc(Hons)*	101000
Cross N *BSc(Hons)*	101000
Davies T M D *BSc(Hons)*	101000
Jarman N J *BSc(Hons)*	101000
Karalus J S *BSc(Hons)*	101000
Nicolle G R L *BA(Hons)*	101000
ØNorman J K *BA(Hons)*	101000
Simons A C I *BSc(Hons)*	101000
Whitbread P A *BA(Hons)*	101000
Bridges J S	240101
Bower H S J *MA(Hons)*	80201
ØBurrows F J *BSc(Hons)*	80201
Haslam M J	80201
Pizii E V J *BA*	80201
ØHarrop J *BA(Hons)*	80201
Jenner G E J *BSc(Hons)*	80201
ØMackenzie L E *BA(Hons)*	80201
Mansbridge S J *BSc(Hons)*	80201
Moore R J *MA(Hons)*	80201
Smith D K *BSc(Hons)*	80201
ØSwindell N J *BA(Hons)*	80201
Watson S M *BSc(Hons)*	80201
Hansford D R *BSc(Hons)*	220201
Hurst J B H *BA(Hons)*	220201

Lieutenants

Name	No.
ØAlexander R A *BA(Hons)*	120297
Geoghegan A D *BSc(Hons)*	120297
Buckley D M *MA(Hons)*	160697
Macneil I H *BA(Hons)*	160697
Palmer J G K *BA(Hons)*	160697
ØYoulten A C *BA(Hons)*	160697
ØDe Renzy Channer R V *BA(Hons)*	120897
Rafferty K P *BSc(Hons)*	120897
Trevor-Barnston E C H *BA(Hons)*	120897
Boothroyd P R J *BA(Hons)*	131097
Edwards P G *(A/Capt 120700)*	141197
Kemp E M C *(A/Capt 080101)*	291197
Batchelor P R A	161297
Beaumont P *BA(Hons)*	161297
ØBolton L M *BA*	161297
Catto W J *BSc(Econ)Hons*	161297
Diamond J F F *BEng(Hons)*	161297
Hodge M J G *BA(Hons)*	161297
Howell A J *BA(Hons)*	161297
Malec G H *BSc(Hons)*	161297
Penney M R R *BSc*	161297
ØPryce S E J *BA(Hons)*	161297
Richardson B L *BSc(Hons)*	161297
Stewart C J M ph	161297
Webb M C M *BSc(Hons)*	161297
Armstrong R M *BA(Hons)*	100298
Cameron A C *BSc(Hons)*	100298
Craven J F *BA(Hons)*	100298
Salter B R *BA(Hons)*	100298
Wade R A *BSc(Hons)*	100298
Jones D M	90498
Power J L	90498
Foss-Smith T P *BSc(Hons)*	130498
ØFox A M *BSc(Hons) PGCE*	130498
ØJohnson F K *BSc(Hons)*	130498
ØKeats E J *BSc(Hons)*	130498
Orvis R J *BSc(Hons)*	130498
Pattison A J C *BSc(Hons)*	130498
ØTyson A C *BA(Hons)*	130498
Um M *BA(Hons)*	130498
Walker D I B *BA(Hons)*	130498
Morrison A W	270498
Hamilton A M *BSc(Hons)*	140698
Bedford G H C *DipLA BA(Hons)*	100898
Burlingham A C R *BSc(Econ)Hons MA*	100898
Cartwright S J E *BSc(Hons)*	100898
Edward M G *BA(Hons)*	100898
Garton J P	100898
Good C D *BA(Hons)*	100898
ØGorman J L *BSc(Hons)*	100898
ØLoveridge K J *BSc(Hons)*	100898
Nelson E M *BSc(Hons)*	100898
Sempala-Ntege B S *BA(Hons)*	100898
ØYoung C R *BSc(Hons)*	100898
Jagger W H G *BSc*	121098
ØUrry P L	131198
Strong W J T *BSocSc*	21298
Harrop I J *BScEng(Civil)*	141298
Hart R P *BA(Hons)*	141298
Holland T C *BSc(Hons)*	141298
Johnson A R *BEng(Hons)*	141298
Oldfield R T *BA(Hons)*	141298
Stones J J *BSc(Hons)*	141298
Cooper P J	20299
Byron S G *BA(Hons)*	90299
Curtis A P *BA(Hons)*	90299
Forrest R J *LLB(Hons)*	90299
Sparks A E T	140299
Evans J W *BSc(Hons)*	220299
Hockaday D N	220299
Graham R	230299
Atherton C E *BA(Hons)*	120499
Brotherton A C *BSc(Hons)*	120499
Dawson B G *BEng(Hons)*	120499
Elliott M D *BA(Hons)*	120499
Entwisle M I J *BSc(Hons)*	120499
Hakes C J *BSc(Hons)*	120499
Sheffield A J *BSc(Hons)*	120499
Thompson A S *LLB(Hons)*	120499
Franks K A *BSc(Hons)*	130699
Perris E J *BA(Hons)*	130699
ØRobb V M	130699
Stickley M A *BEng(Hons)*	130699
Cornes E N	80799
Clarke T N *BSc(Hons)*	90899
Baker J A *BA(Hons)*	131299
Donohoe G R *BA(Hons)*	131299
Haines R E *BSc(Hons)*	131299
Haswell M D *BA*	131299
Janes C M *(A/Capt 260201)*	131299
ØMontgomery G C M *BSc(Hons)*	131299
Neylan A J	131299
Phillips K J *BSc(Hons)*	131299
Reade T *BSc(Hons)*	131299
Rigby M J *BSc(Hons)*	131299
Southall J E *BSc(Econ)Hons*	131299
Wiseman A	310300
Lunn C J	100400
Taylor C P	100400
Hedges G A	80800

Field J	150900	Davidson D R	120800	**Rec Res (RARO)**	
Rowe C C	121000	Ferguson D W	120800		
ØCrawford M L	111100	Kennedy C C	120800		
Nicholson S J	11200	Lightfoot T G	120800	*Majors*	
Crookes B D F	121200	Sharp M J	120800		
Newby Grant A W	121200	Deninson J *BSc(Econ)Hons*	161200		
				Smith K M psc	291090
2nd Lieutenants				Dobbs M J *TD*	120297
Osman T R	100499				
Sutherland R D	100499	**Short Service Volunteer Officers**			
ØSmith A Z	70899				
Hallatt B P	111299	*Lieutenants*		*Captains*	
Leeming M J	111299	Ricketts P R	50298		
ØKealy A A	160300	Taylor R I	10600	Pirie M W	200900

CORPS OF ROYAL ENGINEERS

The Royal Arms and Supporters - *"Ubique"* and *"Quo Fas et Gloria decunt"*

Regimental March

Quick March .... Wings
The British Grenadiers
Agents .... Lloyds Bank plc Cox's & King's Branch
Corps Headquarters .... Brompton Barracks, Chatham, Kent ME4 4UG (Tel: Medway 01634-822298)

Alliances

Canadian Armed Forces .... Military Engineering Branch
Australian Military Forces .... The Corps of Royal Australian Engineers
New Zealand Army .... The Corps of Royal New Zealand Engineers
Indian Army .... Indian Engineers
Pakistan Army .... Pakistan Engineers
Sri Lanka Army .... The Sri Lanka Engineers
Malaysian Armed Forces .... Malaysian Engineer Corps
Zambian Army .... Zambia Corps of Engineers
South African Defence Force .... South African Engineer Corps
Gibraltar .... The Royal Gibraltar Regiment

Affiliated Regiment

The Queen's Gurkha Engineers

Colonel in Chief .... THE QUEEN
Chief Royal Engineer .... Lt Gen *Sir* Scott Grant *KCB* ret pay 100599
Colonels Commandant .... Maj Gen R A Oliver *CB* ret pay 100599
Lt Gen A D Pigott *CBE* 141097
Maj Gen C L Elliott *CB MBE* 051100
Maj Gen M P B G Wilson ret pay 020797
Maj Gen K J Drewienkiewicz *CMG CB* ret pay 311297
Maj Gen J A J P Barr *CB CBE* ret pay 050493
Maj Gen R Wood ret pay 010993
Maj Gen D A Grove *OBE* ret pay 010295
Maj Gen G W Field *CB OBE* ret pay 250396
Maj Gen P J Sheppard *CB CBE* ret pay 010496
Maj Gen P J Russell-Jones *OBE* 070100

Brigadiers

Hutchinson A R E *BSc(Eng)* psc† jsdc   300692
McGill I D T *CBE BSc(Eng)Hons CEng FICE FIMGT MIPD* psc c hcsc(J)   300693
Isbell B R *BSc(Eng) MSc* psc psc(IND) hcsc(J) nadc   300694
Wildman P R *OBE BSc(Eng)Hons* psc SVY   300694
Craig A S *OBE BSc(Eng)Hons* psc hcsc(J)   300695
Pridham R *OBE BSc CEng FICE* rcds psc†   300695
Whitley A E *CBE ADC* psc   300696
Wilson A A *OBE BSc(Eng)Hons MIHT* psc(n)†   300696
Cima K H *BA(Oxon) M A (Oxon) MBA CEng MIMechE* rcds psc(a)†   300697
Bill D R *BSc(Eng)Hons* psc hcsc(J)   311297
Baker J G *MBE BSc(Eng)Hons* psc†   300698

Burns D R *OBE BSc(Eng)* psc† hcsc(J)   300698
Hoskinson J P *OBE BSc(Eng)Hons* rcds psc†   300698
Innes D R FF *BSc(Eng)Hons* rcds psc   300698
Wall P A *OBE MA* psc† hcsc(J)   300698
Foulkes T H E *BSc(Eng) MBA CEng FICE FIMechE* rcds psc†   300699
Mans M F N *FIMGT FCIPD* rcds psc hcsc(J)   300699
Mantell A C *OBE MA* psc(n)† hcsc(J)   300699
Rollo N H *BScEng(Civil)* psc† hcsc(J)   300699
Hughes M A C *OBE BSc(Eng)Hons* psc†   300600
Melvin R A M S *OBE MA* psc(GE) hcsc(J) I*   300600
Walker A P *OBE BSc(Eng)Hons FRGS FRICS FIMGT* psc† SVY   300600

Colonels

Ludlam T J *OBE BSc(Eng) MCIT MILT* sq jsdc   300691

Anderson J D C *BSc(Eng)Hons* psc(n)†   300692
Foster M W *BSc(Hons) FICE* sq C   300692
Brooke M H H *OBE FIMGT* jssc sq   300693
Farmer A C *BSc(Hons)* psc† jsdc   300693
Field J S *CBE MBA* psc osc(ZIM) jsdc   300693
Haskell C W *BSc(Hons)* psc† aic   300693
Hyde-Bales R A   psc   300695
McAslan A R R *BSc(Eng)Hons* psc†   300695
Sandy R J *BSc(Eng) MIMGT* sq   300695
Durance J R *BSc(Hons)* rcds psc   300696
Griffiths R J *MBE* psc jsdc   300696
Reynolds M D *BSc(Eng) (EURING) CEng FICE FIPlantE* sq c 300696
Sexton C M *MA* ocds(IND) psc (A/Brig 231000)   300696
Sheridan P A J *BSc(Eng)Hons MBA FIMGT* psc†   300696
Watt R *BSc(Hons) CEng FIMechE MIMGT FIEE* EM sq(w)   300696

Whittington I F G *BSc(Eng) MSc*
ARICS MIMGT MIOP SVY(pg)
sq(w)   300696
Carruth A P *BTech(Hons) CEng*
MIMechE psc EM   300697
Kershaw G C *BSc(Eng)Hons*
DipEngMAN CEng MICE c sq(w)
    300697
Lilleyman P *MBE BSc(Eng)Hons*
psc† aic   300697
Little R J *BSc(Eng)Hons* sq   300697
Bailey W A *MBE BSc(Eng)* psc
sq(w)   300698
Dawson G W *BSc(Eng)Hons* psc†
    300698
Dorman C G *BSc(Eng)Hons MSc*
FRGS ARICS sq SVY   300698
Peebles A A *BSc(Eng)* sq jsdc 300698
Sherry S F *OBE* psc(CAN)   300698
Tait I M *BSc(Eng)Hons CEng MICE*
sq c jsdc   300698
Wilson A R M *BSc(Hons) (EURING)*
CEng MICE c sq(w)   300698
Caws I M *OBE BSc(Eng)Hons CEng*
MICE psc c   300699
Duffus J B *MSc* psc† dis SVY
    300699
Grossmith G B *MBE BSc(Eng)Hons*
psc   300699
Harking A D *OBE BSc(Eng)* psc†
    300699
Heron J M *MBE BSc(Eng)Hons*
MIMGT psc†   300699
Hodder S P *BSc(Hons) AMICE* psc c
    300699
Macklin A D *MA* psc(a)† jsdc
    300699
Thorn J W R *BSc(Eng)Hons* psc†
    300699
Wootton J D *MBE BA(Hons)* psc†
    300699
Brown A *BSc* psc jsdc   300600
Croft M H G *BSc(Hons)* sq   300600
Dodds G C W *OBE BSc(Eng)Hons*
psc†   300600
Grimshaw T P psc†   300600
Marsh P C *BSc(Eng)Hons CEng*
MICE c sq(w)   300600
Nield G A *OBE BSc(Hons)* psc†
    300600
Rigby R N *BSc(Hons) ARICS* psc
SVY   300600
Stevens D C *OBE MSc* psc† gw
    300600
Taylor G *OBE MA CEng MICE* psc
c   300600

Lieutenant Colonels

Bray P M (SL) *BSc* c sq(w)   300686
Campbell M S *BSc(Hons)*
DipEngMAN (EURING) CEng
MAPM MICE MIMGT c sq(w)
    300687
Johnson I H (SL) *BSc(Hons) MICE*
MINSTAMDip c sq(w)   300687
Warren M W M (SL) *MA* psc 300687
Mackenzie A M (SL) *MBE* sq
    300688
Dudin R A (SL) *MBE BSc(Eng) CEng*
MICE psc† c   300689

Lester R M S (SL) *BSc(Eng)Hons*
MSc dis sq(w)   300689
Rayner J M *BSc(Eng) CEng*
MIMechE MInstPet FEANI EM
    300689
Tuggey A S *BSc(Eng)* osc(MAL) sq
    300689
Clarke S K E *OBE* sq   300690
Crosskey R M *BSc(Eng) MICE* sq c
    300690
Edwards I D (SL) *BSc(Hons) MICE* c
sq(w)   300690
Hart R C *OBE* psc   300690
Ross I A M *MAppSci* sq(w) SVY
SVY(cg)   300690
Stafford-Tolley R E (SL) *MCIOB* sq
    300690
Cooper M D (SL) *MBE*
BSc(Eng)Hons CEng MIMechE
FIPlantE EM sq(w)   300691
Court S C *BSc(Hons) MSc(DIS)* dis
sq(w)   300691
Farley S L *BSc(Eng)* sq SVY
    300691
Pickles C S *BSc(Eng) CEng FEANI*
MICE c sq(w)   300691
Holman C N psc   300692
McCabe M C *BSc(Eng)Hons* psc†
    300692
Attwater D H E *MA* psc† SVY
    300693
Beazley M G *MBE* psc   300693
Braithwaite R I *BSc(Hons)* psc†
    300693
Clarke P W psc(GE) I   300693
Fairclough N M *OBE BA(Hons)*
CGIA psc† (A/Col 070201) 300693
Forrestal N R *MIMGT* sq   300693
Hayward-Broomfield P W (SL) sq
    300693
Anderson S M *BSc(Hons)* psc SVY
    300694
Bend R M *BEng CEng MIMechE*
EM I sq(w)   300694
Bouwens C P *MDA* sq   300694
Crompton J F *MBE BSc(Eng)* psc
    300694
Cross A P *BSc(Eng)Hons MSc* sq
SVY(pg) SVY   300694
Lodge P *BSc(Eng)Hons MSc*
psc(IND)   300694
Murphy S P *BSc(Eng)Hons CEng*
MICE c sq(w)   300694
Wheeley J F *MBE* psc   300694
Williams R H (SL) *OBE*
BSc(Eng)Hons (EURING) CEng
MICE c   300694
Davies P M *MBE BSc(Hons)* psc
    300695
Dickinson R L F *BSc(Eng)Hons*
MDA sq MDA   300695
Edwards N J *MA* psc   300695
Lane G S *MA MBA* psc†   300695
Larkin N H *BSc(Hons)* psc   300695
McNamara G M sq   300695
Sage J W *BSc(Hons)* psc†   300695
Sykes S W *BArch(Hons) BSc(Hons)*
sq(w) SVY   300695
Watts G C *MBE* sq jsdc   300695
Armstrong P M *BSc(Eng)Hons*
MICE c sq(w)   300696

Bayliss A H *MA CEng MICE* sq c
    300696
Blad T J *MA* psc†   300696
Burnside A P *BSc CEng MICE* sq c
    300696
Fitzgerald J F H *MSc ACGI* dis sq(w)
SVY   300696
Mullin J G *MBE MA* psc† (A/Col
050301)   300696
Naile S L *BSc(Eng)Hons* sq jsdc
    300696
Nicklin R M P *MAppSci MASI*
ARICS sq(w) SVY   300696
O'Sullivan J P J *MBE* psc   300696
Olley J B *BSc(Hons) MSc FRGS*
ARICS MIL psc SVY(gy) SVY
    300696
Poole P A H *BSc(Hons) MDA* psc†
    300696
Pope A C *MBE BSc(Eng)Hons MSc*
psc† (A/Col 100301)   300696
Prain J F *MA MSc FRGS FRICS*
MIMGT MRIN sq SVY(gy) SVY
    300696
Stewart R J N psc   300696
Strong J A R *MA CEng MCIBSE* EM
sq(w)   300696
Boag C J psc(J)   300697
Bowen D C *MBE* sq   300697
Carter M P *BSc(Hons)* psc jsdc
(A/Col 100700)   300697
Gibbs G K psc   300697
Gibson R D *MBE BSc* psc†   300697
Gunns J M *MBE BSc(Hons)* psc
    300697
Hall R G R *QGM* psc(CAN)   300697
Heminsley W J *OBE BSc(Eng)* nadc
sq   300697
Holland N M *BSc(Hons) FRGS*
psc(a)†   300697
Jenkinson R J *BSc(Hons)* c sq(w)
    300697
Killick R W *OBE BSc(Eng)Hons*
MDA MIMGT psc† MDA   300697
Le Grys B J *MBE BA(Hons)* psc(J)
j sdc   300697
Mills A M *BSc* psc†   300697
Naylor P M *OBE MILOG* jsdc sq(w)
    300697
Ogden I A *BSc(Eng)Hons CEng*
MICE c sq(w)   300697
Taylor D W *BSc(Eng)Hons MSc*
(EURING) CEng MICE MIMGT c
sq(w)   300697
Underwood I D *TD BSc CEng*
MIMINE EM   300697
Wright I D *BEd* psc   300697
Andrews M B *BSc(Econ)* sq
    300698
Cobbold R N *BSc(Eng)Hons CEng*
MICE c sq(w)   300698
Fenn N H W sq jsdc   300698
Francis P J *BSc(Hons)* psc†300698
Freeland S C *MBE MIMGT CGIA*
psc†   300698
Gilson M W *BSc(Eng)Hons MSc* sq
SVY(pg) SVY   300698
James I S *MBE BSc(Hons) MSc* psc†
    300698
McIlroy J D *BSc (EURING) MICE* c
sq(w)   300698

Mitchell J W BSc(Eng)Hons psc
SVY   300698
Montagu N E MA(Hons) CEng
MIMechE EM sq(w)   300698
Nell P G R sq(w) ais   300698
Rose C J BSc(Hons) psc†   300698
Shanahan J W MBE MBA psc
                                       300698
Sheppard A C MBE psc   300698
Sloane C R J OBE BSc(Hons)
psc(AUS)   300698
Thomas A D L BSc(Hons) psc†
                                       300698
Wakefield T J BSc sq   300698
Wallace-Tarry P A MBE sq   300698
Wilson A D sq   300698
Wright I R A BEng(Hons) CEng psc
EM   300698
Armitage D S MBE MSc psc†
                                       300699
Blanks I J MBE BSc(Eng)Hons psc†
                                       300699
Burley S A MBE psc psc(J)
                                       300699
Cockerill C M BSc(Hons) AMICE c
sq(w)   300699
Davis R R MBE MSc psc†   300699
Duggleby T R BSc(Hons) CEng
MICE c   300699
Hignett J J MDA sq   300699
Lemay J J J BEng MSc psc†   300699
Montgomery K H BSc(Hons) MBA
MIMGT psc†   300699
Morris W M G MBE BSc(Eng)Hons
(EURING) CEng MICE
DipEURHum c sq(w)   300699
Pope C M BSc(Eng)Hons MSc psc†
                                       300699
Ruddy J M BA(Hons) GCGI psc†
                                       300699
Shuler RR MSc sq   300699
Swanson R C MBE BSc(Eng)Hons
sq(w)   300699
White J R MBE BSc(Eng)Hons psc†
                                       300699
Wilks C L MBE MA CEng MIEE
MIE(AUST) psc EM sq(w) †
                                       300699
Whitchurch M W MBE sq   311299
Allen M K MIMGT sq   300600
Bowden J A MA psc   300600
Brand T S psc   300600
Brand G K BA(Hons) psc   300600
Burrows M R R H BSc(Hons) MA
psc(n) SVY   300600
Chapman L W MSc sq   300600
Clark N R BSc(Hons) CEng c
                                       300600
Cripwell R J BEng(Hons) MSc psc†
                                       300600
Edington A J S BSc psc   300600
Hainge C M BSc(Eng)Hons psc†
                                       300600
Hitchcock I G psc   300600
Jones G B O R BSc(Hons) CEng
MICE c sq(w)   300600
Lewis J D BSc(Hons) psc   300600
Miller A M O sq   300600
Pelton J F MBE BSc(Eng)Hons MA
(EURING) CEng MICE ACGI psc c
                                       300600
Putter E K MSc sq SVY   300600

Ruxton S J BSc CEng MICE sq c
                                       300600
Welch J A H MBE BA(Hons) psc
                                       300600
Wilmshurst-Smith G E BSc(Hons)
CEng MIMechE   300600
Baxter G H L MA MSc CEng
MIMechE psc†   300900
Tonkins R M BSc sq   311200
Fuller P J BSc(Hons) MA psc†
                                       130201

Majors

Thackwell W T R BSc(Eng)Hons
CEng MICE sq c   300980
Lewin R A BSc(Eng) ARICS MIMGT
MIOP MIMATM SVY(pr) SVY
                                       300981
Mackenzie J F BSc(Eng)Hons MSc
CEng MIE(AUST) c   300981
Mosedale M J Q BTech CEng MICE
sq c   300981
Flower L T MBE aic sq(w)   300982
Smale J F sq   300983
Boydell A P sq P AIS   300984
Bratt A D BA(Hons) sq   300984
Jones A J sq   300984
Kay A BSc(Hons) CEng MIMechE
EM   300984
Beaumont J D BEng(Hons)
BA(Hons) psc   300985
Keeley A BSc(Hons) PGCE sq CG
SVY SVY(cg)   300985
Luscombe P D BSc (EURING) CEng
MIMINE ELECIE sq EM 300986
McConaghy A J W sq   300986
Vernon M R sq   300986
Woollven R C J BSc(Eng)Hons psc†
                                       300986
Painter N J BEng(Hons) CEng
psc c   300987
Bailey C W BScEng(Civil) MSc dis
sq(w)   300988
Chambers P B BSc(Eng) CEng MICE
c sq(w)   300988
Cobley I S P sq(w) (A/Lt Col
020101)   300988
Crook P E sq (A/Lt Col 011000)
                                       300988
Davies S J MDA sq   300988
Dennis A P sq   300988
Perkins S P BSc CEng c sq(w)
                                       300988
Sheldon R P BSc(Eng) MSc CEng
MICE c sq(w)   300988
Chick J A sq   300989
Dunford M A BSc(Hons) CEng
MIMechE dis sq(w)   300989
Souter A M BSc(Hons) sq   300989
Wood J F sq   300989
Young M W BA(Hons) MSc sq   300989
Castle J W MBE MSc sq   300990
Fennell J H C BSc(Eng)Hons
MInstCES sq(w) SVY   300990
Hannington A J psc(a)   300990
Mozley R J D BSc sq   300990
Riches P J BSc(Eng)Hons CEng c
sq(w)   300990
Tenison S G BSc(Hons)Hons MSc
psc†   300990

Whiting W D BSc(Eng)Hons CEng
MICE c sq(w)   300990
Williams R J BSc(Eng)Hons psc† aic
                                       300990
Block S J BSc(Hons) CEng
MIMechE EM   300991
Cox M J BSc(Hons) c   300991
Ince C D S MBE BSc(Hons) sq(w)
                                       300991
Inglis N MBE BSc(Hons) c   300991
Law M C sq   300991
Nichols R M BA(Hons) sq   300991
Sonnex P S sq   300991
Thomas M F MA psc   300991
Ainslie R L BSc(Hons) psc   300992
Beaumont C M BSc(Hons) sq(w)
                                       300992
Caulfield D A psc   300992
Coutts G M L MSc psc†   300992
Fenn M A BSc(Eng)Hons MSc sq(w)
                                       300992
Greaves J J sq aws   300992
Honey A P BEng(Hons) MSc G(ss)
sq(w) SVY   300992
Marsh R J MSc psc(a)†   300992
Othen A BSc(Hons) MSc SVY sq(w)
                                       300992
Passmore J E MBE psc(CAN)
                                       300992
Richardson M G H BSc(Eng)Hons c
pc   300992
Smith N C R G BSc(Eng)Hons MICE
c   300992
Sole S J BSc psc(PAK)   300992
Stevenson M   300992
Cannons S R BSc(Hons) (EURING)
CEng MICE c   300993
Cooke S BSc MA   300993
Derben S J BSc MA psc†   300993
Gidney M A J sq   300993
Gimson S G S BSc(Eng)Hons MSc
psc†   300993
Gooding A C P BSc(Hons) CEng
MIMechE EM (A/Lt Col 230101)
                                       300993
Kedar J D BSc(Eng)Hons psc SVY
(A/Lt Col 050301)   300993
Levett-Scrivener M J BSc   300993
Piper R A BSc(Hons) MA psc†
                                       300993
Redwood I D   300993
Simonds J D BSc(Hons) CEng MICE
c   300993
Skeat C N R BSc(Eng)Hons MSc
psc†   300993
Stanton I P ais   300993
Stratford-Wright K P BSc(Hons) sq
                                       300993
Taylor A P psc†   300993
Tetley C M H BSc(Hons) MSc psc†
                                       300993
Thomas I M BSc(Eng)Hons MSc
psc†   300993
Vaughan T D MBE MA psc†   300993
Walne J N BSc(Hons) psc   300993
Wastie L F BSc(Hons)   300993
Wilman C J BSc(Eng)Hons MSc psc†
                                       300993
Abbott R J BSc(Hons) c   300994
Baveystock N G psc   300994

Bigger D L D psc† 300994
Cliffe A M *MBA MSc* psc† 300994
Cottee T R sq 300994
Daubney M E *MBE* 300994
Fawcett S A M *MIPlantE* P 300994
Green F J *BSc* c 300994
Hudson D C *MBE* 300994
Jones D M *BSc(Hons)* psc 300994
Marot G L psc† psc(J) 300994
Morris D *BSc(Hons) (EURING)*
MIMechE MCIOB MIMGT MCI
WEM EM 300994
Myers D S 300994
Page N A psc† 300994
Parker H J P sq(w) 300994
Parker A G *BSc* P 300994
Phillips R E *BSc(Hons)* sq
300994
Potts J N *BSc(Hons) MSc* psc†
300994
Stevens A T *BSc(Hons) ALCM CEng*
MIEE EM 300994
Strawbridge D L *MBE BEng(Hons)*
MSc psc† 300994
Thurlow R D *BSc(Hons)* sq sq(w)
SVY 300994
Treanor T L V *MA* psc 300994
Troulan A G L P sq 300994
Wakeman A J *MBE BSc MICE* c
300994
Wright S A *MSc* psc† 300994
Bellingall A D *MBE MSc* psc† dis
300995
Bowyer D G *MA* psc(a)† 300995
Boyd S P W *BSc(Hons) CEng*
MAPM EM 300995
Buckingham G E L *BA BAI MSc*
300995
Buckley D *BSc(Hons) CEng MIEE*
EM 300995
Burnet R J D J *BA(Hons)* sq(w)
300995
Burnett M *BSc(Hons)* c 300995
Cavanagh N J *BA(Hons) MA* psc(J) †
300995
Dainty A W 300995
Dash R G SVY sq 300995
Dickinson A S psc(CAN)† 300995
Elliott N K *BEng(Hons)* psc(J)
300995
Erskine J H *BSc(Hons)* psc†
300995
Finch M J *BSc(Hons) MIPlantE*
psc(J) P 300995
Gladen A P *BSc(Hons)* sq 300995
Grealy V M *BSc(Hons)* SVY
300995
Harris S P F *BA(Hons) PGCE*
300995
Howard J A *BSc(Hons) CEng MICE*
ACGI psc c 300995
Hutchison I *BSc(Eng)Hons MSc*
psc(J) 300995
Ingram C W *BEng(Hons) MIMechE*
MIMGT 300995
Jackson M C F *BEng MDA MIMGT*
psc 300995
Kemp J A *BSc(Hons)* SVY
300995
Killip J Q *BSc(Hons) MA*
300995
Knox T H *MSc* psc† 300995

Kuhle C G *BSc(Hons)* psc(J)
300995
Lane J F *BSc(Hons) MSc* 300995
Lowth R G *BA(HonsCantab) MA*
GCGI psc† *(A/Lt Col 271100)*
300995
Moore A M 300995
Morgan S D cafs 300995
Noble F R *MSc* psc† psc(J) dis
G(gw) 300995
Phillips A W *BA(Hons)* 300995
Prichard J L *BEng* c 300995
Quinn L T *MBE BEng(Hons) MSc*
CEng MICE c 300995
Richardson N J *BSc* psc(J) im
300995
Rider R J *BA(HonsCantab)* psc(GE)
300995
Roberts J A *BEng(Hons) MSc* psc†
300995
Ropel M A *BSc BEng(Hons)* EM
300995
Sealy-Thompson N J 300995
Semple R J *BSc MDA* psc 300995
Swan R I A *BSc(Eng)Hons MSc*
CEng MICE MIMGT FCIArb c
300995
Tickell C L *MBE* psc† 300995
Tomlinson R K *MBE BSc(Hons) MSc*
300995
Tresidder M O 300995
Tuson L S *BEng MA AIMGT* psc(J) †
300995
Urch T R *MBE BEng(Hons) MA*
CEng MICE MIMGT c psc psc(J)
300995
Ward H M *BEng(Hons) MSc*
300995
Williams A D H *BEng(Hons) MA*
psc† 300995
Williams L H *BSc* psc(J) 300995
Wilman J G *BEng(Hons) MA MSc*
psc psc(J) 300995
Winkworth S A *MA* psc† 300995
Ashcroft P S *BSc(Hons) MA*
300996
Barr A J P *BSocSc MA* psc(J) *(A/Lt*
Col 221100) 300996
Brambell D J *BSc(Hons)* c 300996
Brent R P *BEng(Hons)* psc(J)
300996
Cowan S C sq SVY 300996
Danby R L psc(J) 300996
Elliott T J *BSc(Hons)* 300996
Garwood D J *BSc(Hons) MSc* psc(J)
dis 300996
Gibson D C R *BSc(Hons) MDA*
psc(J) 300996
Godsall-Stanton P J M P 300996
Griffin M J *BSc* 300996
Hilton A C *BEng(Hons)* psc(J)
300996
Jackson A G *BEng(Hons)* 300996
Jones I B L *BEng(Hons)* psc(J)
300996
Lang W R S *BEng(Hons) CEng* c
EM 300996
Langford P J 300996
Lewis R G psc(J) 300996
Newsome J M *BSc(Hons)* c 300996
Pardy D C 300996
Peet R J *MSc* psc(J) dis 300996

Smith J P *BSc(Hons)* SVY adp
300996
Stanley P M 300996
Steed J D *AIIRSM* 300996
Sullivan M A P 300996
Thackway C S E *BSc(Hons) MDS*
psc 300996
Wildish T C L *BEng(Hons)* psc(J)
300996
Williams R E *BSc(Eng)Hons* EM
300996
Acornley J D *MA* psc(J)
300997
Bird J E H SVY 300997
Brammer J S *BEng(Hons)* SVY
300997
Brookes A D *BEng(Hons) MSc*
MRIN MInstCES SVY 300997
Buttery P A *BSc(Hons)* psc(J)
300997
Casey D D *BEng(Hons) MSc*
300997
Chapman T 300997
Finch G J *BA(Hons)* psc(J) 300997
Fox A S K 300997
Francis I D *BA(Hons)* E 300997
Fryer P D SVY 300997
Glasgow A C *BEng(Hons) MSc*
CEng MICE c 300997
Hargreaves D S P 300997
Jackson A J *BMet* 300997
Johnson-Ferguson M E *BA(Hons)*
MA c 300997
McKeown D *MBE BSc* psc(J)
300997
Moreton D A 300997
Morris A M 300997
Pullman R W *MSc ARICS* 300997
Scott T M *BSc(Eng) MSc* psc(J) dis
300997
Sherwood P E *BSc(Hons) MSc*
psc(J) 300997
Sutherland N *BSc(Hons)* 300997
Taylor J E S *ARICS* SVY 300997
Thornley M T *MA* 300997
Tilley M N *BSc(Hons)* EM 300997
Underwood T J *BEng* EM 300997
Webster T P G 300997
Wilson D *BTech(Hons)* 300997
Balgarnie A D 300998
Beaumont R G *MEng* 300998
Benfield C C *BEng(Hons)* 300998
Bilous A 300998
Blackstock R I *BEng(Hons)* c
300998
Browse S J *BA* c 300998
Campbell A G *BSc(Eng) CEng*
MCIBSE EM 300998
Carson N S 300998
Crawford J *BSc(Hons) MIMechE* EM
300998
Crook A W *BSc(Hons) MSc* SVY
300998
Daniell P J F *BA(Hons)* 300998
Fuller P T *MSc* SVY 300998
Fuller M R 300998
Hemmings B R E *BSc(Hons)*
300998
Higgens S G cafs 300998
Hourahane R S *BEng(Hons)* 300998
Livesey G M *BSc(Hons) MSc* SVY
300998

Marks N D *BSc(Hons) MSc* SVY 300998
McDougall I A *MSc* SVY 300998
Noble A J *BSc(Hons)* 300998
Page A G *BEd(Hons)* 300998
Prowse G J *MSc* EM 300998
Robertson S W *BSc(Hons)* 300998
Stanton L J *BEng(Hons) MBA* 300998
Stewart I K *BSc(Hons)* 300998
Strain S M *BSc(Hons) CEng MIMechE MIMGT* EM 300998
Turner M A *BEng(Hons)* 300998
Wardlaw R *BEng(Hons)* 300998
Weeden J C *BEng(Hons)* 300998
Wilby A R *BEng(Hons)* 300998
Wood T J *BSc(Hons)* 300998
Barry P N 300999
Bazeley M T G *BSc(Hons)* 300999
Brown P L O 300999
Currie K D 300999
Davies B E *BEng(Hons) MSc* SVY 300999
Dickinson M D *BEng(Hons)* 300999
Greene R S F *MBE* 300999
Hay A H *BSc(Hons) (EURING) CEng MICE* c 300999
Honnor A M F *BEng(Hons) CEng MICE* 300999
Howard A G *BSc(Hons)* 300999
Hulme S J 300999
Lawrence S A *BSc(Hons)* 300999
Lockhart J K *BSc(Hons) MIMechE* EM 300999
Maclachlan A J A 300999
Mainwaring W H K *BSc(Hons)* 300999
Neely J S *BEng(Hons)* SVY 300999
Orr R J *BEng(Hons) MSc* EOE 300999
Quare M 300999
Ricketts H T S 300999
Sladden C P *BSc(Hons) MSc* SVY 300999
Southall D W *BSc(Hons) MInstAM MISM* 300999
Sparks R J 300999
Stephens R A C *BSc(Eng)Hons* c 300999
Szabo A N *BEng(Hons) CEng MIMechE* EM 300999
Tait A *BEng(Hons)* 300999
Terry J S 300999
Turner J J *BSc(Hons)* 300999
Voase A D *BA(Hons)* 300999
White J V *BEng(Hons)* c 300999
Young N A *BEng(Hons)* 300999
Young R P *BEng(Hons)* EM 300999
Adamson I H *BEng(Hons) MSc* 300900
Bell S L *BSc(Eng)Hons* 300900
Boyle A D *BEng(Hons)* c 300900
Cribb N J 300900
Earnshaw J J *BEng(Hons)* ato 300900
Fountaine P V *MIMechIE* 300900
Garner D C 300900
Hislop A R *BEng* 300900
Hughes B J *BA(Hons)* 300900
Hunter C W *BEng(Hons) CEng MICE* c 300900

Morton R S *BSc(Hons)* 300900
Myres C C L *BEng(Hons)* 300900
Noble P R *BSc(Hons) MSc* 300900
O'Neill V K *BEng(Hons)* 300900
ØOrrell-Jones V F H *BEng(Hons)* 300900
Owens J P C *BScEng(Civil) MSc FRGS* 300900
Rhodes J C 300900
Stromberg A *BEng(Hons) MSc* SVY 300900
Sturgeon M J M *BSc(Hons)* 300900
Tate J *BEng(Hons) MSc* SVY 300900
Tingey L *BEng(Hons)* 300900
Veitch A B *BEng(Hons)* 300900
Walton-Knight R J *BSc(Hons)* 300900
Walton-Knight M P *BEng(Hons) (EURING) CEng MICE MCIWEM* c 300900
Wellard B P *BA(Hons)* 300900
Yearsley J H *BEng(Hons)* 300900

Captains

Rowlands D L *MSc* SVY 40494
Craddock L P *BEng(Hons)* c 60894
Ross Russell D *MEng* 60894
Thomson R C *LLB* 60894
McPhee M N J *BEng(Hons)* 101294
Millard J R *MSc* SVY (A/Maj 031200) 101294
Cockwell D R *MA BA(Hons)* 10495
Copsey K M 10495
Devey A R *BSc* (A/Maj 021198) 10495
Humphries R D *BEng(Hons)* 10495
Jarvis T J *LLB* ph 10495
Oldridge J A *BEng(Hons)* 10495
Schofield M D W 10495
Thomas S J *BEng(Hons)* 10495
Tomlinson C R *BEng(Hons)* 10495
Walters D A *BSc(Hons)* 10495
Williams R B *BEng(Hons)* 10495
Youngman P B 120495
Wood S D *BA(Hons)* 60695
Baker G V *BEng(Hons)* 110895
Dilworth R J *BEng(Hons)* 110895
Nicholson P B 110895
Thompson G W *BEng(Hons)* 110895
Fernandes J E R *BA* 30995
Massetti S M *BSc(Hons)* 81095
Evans J R *BSc(Hons)* 111095
Clee A C *BSc(Hons)* 131095
ØRoberts V J *BSc(Hons) MSc* SVY 181095
Brown R C *BSc(Hons)* 91195
Doherty A J 141195
Crick P E *BEng(Hons)* 181195
Fawcus R C D *BSc(Hons)* 181195
Story C R M *BEng(Hons)* (A/Maj 030101) 181195
Martin L J 191195
Stockley S P *BSc(Hons)* 151295
Edrich N *BEng* 130496
Ross F J 130496
Smith B *BEng* 130496
Lord D S *BSc(Hons)* 140796
Hanna A J 270796
Crow R A 70896
Davison P J 70896

Hones J A *BA(Hons)* 130896
ØJackson K *BA(HonsCantab)* 130896
ØLove D *BSc(Eng) MSc* 130896
Merer E R *BEng(Hons)* 130896
Parkinson R I B *BSc(Hons)* 140896
Douglas R A *BSc ARICS* 160896
Roose J J *BA(Hons)* 281196
White S W *BA(Hons)* 121296
Friend A R *BEng(Hons)* 141296
Frost K D *BEng(Hons)* 141296
George S B *BSc(Hons)* 141296
Hatcher G P *BEng(Hons)* 141296
Voase T S *BA(Hons)* 151296
Browning S C *MEng* 191296
Pullen D J *BSc(Hons)* 191296
Robinson E G *BSc* 191296
Teeton A J *BEng(Hons)* 191296
Kerr J R *BEng(Hons)* (A/Maj 041200) 211296
Matten S D *BA(Hons)* 281296
Bennett N A J *BSc(Hons)* (A/Maj 120201) 110497
Johnston B J R *BEng(Hons)* 110497
Sudding C J *BEng(Hons)* 110497
Whitticase S M *BEng(Hons)* 110497
Hammond K E *BEng(Hons)* 80897
Threapleton C M *BEng(Hons)* 80897
Fletcher N *BEng(Hons)* (A/Maj 121200) 91097
Burridge R D *BEng(Hons) AMIEE ACGI* 101097
Pickup M B *BEng(Hons) MSc* 141097
Cartmill P B *BEng(Hons)* 151097
ØMoss E H *BEng(Hons)* 151097
Blunt R M 121297
Ellisdon C L *BEng* 121297
Campbell-Colquhoun B H G *BEng(Hons)* 120298
Fox J S *BEng(Hons)* 120298
Hewett M A *BEng(Hons)* 120298
Houlston P E *BSc(Hons)* 120298
Mason A J *BEng(Hons)* 120298
Morris C E G *BEng(Hons)* ph 120298
ØPage A J *MEng(Hons)* 120298
Quaite P T *BEng(Hons)* 120298
Milner S A *BEng(Hons)* 190298
Springett B *BEng(Hons)* 190298
Sturrock A J W *BA MEng* 270298
Macgill A S 90398
Budinger A K *BEng(Hons)* ph 160698
Hindmarsh N J *BEng* 70898
Smallwood W N *BEng(Hons)* 70898
Taylor M J *BEng(Hons)* 70898
Walker R G *BA(Hons)* 131098
ØSeymour E J *BEng(Hons)* 100299
Leonard C R 90499
Forster M P *BSc* 140699
Lambert M G *BEng(Hons)* 140699
Williams A D *BEng(Hons)* 140699
Everett M D 60899
Smith M R 60899
ØBennett N M *BEng(Hons)* 121099
Fortey C *BEng(Hons)* 121099
Hannay S R R 121099
Witcombe N D *BSc(Hons)* 121099
Brogan C S *BSc(Hons)* 101299
Carpenter S A G 101299

Blunden G P J *BSc(Hons)* 90200
Croall D M 90200
Kerr J *BA(Hons)* 90200
Lacken J F *BL* 90200
ØNgwenya L F *BA MA* 90200
Woods D L *BA(Hons)* 90200
McCallion S E J 120400
Macdonald S A 140400
Wilkinson M R *MEng* 130600
Williams R *BEng(Hons)* 130600
Jarvis A R G *BSc(Hons)* 200700
ØDzisiewska I K *BEng(Hons)* 101000
Hawkins R B *BSocSc(Hons)* 101000
Llewelyn J A 161200
Cox T M *BEng(Hons)* 80201
Fossey J E *BSc* 80201

Lieutenants

Hoban D M *MEng (A/Capt 021000)* 120297
Scott J H *BEng(Hons)* 120897
Coen D J *BEng(Hons)* 131097
Lederer P *BEng(Hons)* 131097
ØPlummer J C *MEng(Hons)* 131097
Chapman S M *BEng(Hons)* 161297
Jones S I *BEng(Hons)* 161297
Sheppard B D E *BEng(Hons) (A/Capt 010400)* 161297
Steel T G 161297
Whishaw E A H 161297
Ainsworth A C J *BSc(Hons)* 100298
†Clark J L 100298
Kelly M B *BSocSc(Hons)* 130498
ØScotter F J *BSc(Hons)* 130498
Ash S P 140698
Ainley J *BEng(Hons)* 100898
McKenzie L R 100898
Ward K C *BEng(Hons)* 100898
Hughes S D *BEng(Hons)* 141298
Short M T J *(L/Capt 270300)* 141298
Thompson J I 141298
Warhurst C I *(A/Capt 160899)* 141298
Day B J W 90299
ØWollaston M F *BEng(Hons)* 90299
Ackerman C N 120499
Doyle S P M 120499
Ghinn M *BSc(Hons)* 90899
Legge T C 90899
Sanders P J 131299
Jones D E 80800
Millbank R G 121200

2nd Lieutenants

†Jenkins L D *BA(Hons)* 120992
††Duffus E J 110994
†Dent C J 80996
†McCarthy M D 80996
†Waight D C 80996
†Cohen L Q B 220997
†Gwyther R J 220997
†Johnson S G 220997
††Lakin N P H 220997
††Smallman M W E 220997
†Allen G W 60998
†Cheales A J 60998
†Coulthard J S 60998
†Gout R J 60998
†Harwood D J 60998

††Manchester N D 60998
††McKenzie R S 60998
††Nash J N 60998
ØBeszant R E 50999
††Buckley J M 50999
††Crossley J B A 50999
ØGraham-Brown C S 50999
††Williams T R W 50999

Regular Category Late Entry Officers

Lieutenant Colonels

Jordan N A sq(w) 10198
Townsley J M H *DMS MIMGT MCIM* 80498
Tarr K B 20598
Talbot L A 220798
Clayton P S 10299
Hamilton D N *MBE* 50599
Ness S J 70899
Wood M A *BEM MILT MInstAM MISM MILOG* 11199
Mitchell H J 120200
Heal R E 70300
Ellis P G B *QGM•* 10400
Palmer A R *IEng AMICE* sq 010400
Walker C K *MBE* 10400
Stables E C 120800
Rush W M *MBE* 280800
Neary D P 260900
Barker J *IEng AMICE* 170101

Majors

Burman F E 50392
Compton F S 300992
Hughes J V M 300992
Mollison R J 300992
Rainey R K 180293
Peters R A 220993
Cawson R W 300993
Corbet A L 300993
Derrick P I C 300993
Donohoe J K 300993
Lowe E A *BEM* 300993
Williams D H 300993
Nicholson B 070394
Andrews T R 300994
Boldock W *MIIRSM* 300994
Brown T C B 300994
Chatten R E 300994
Harrington D C 300994
Doig M J 300995
Ferguson W H M *DipHE* sq(w) 300995
Jones M R *MBE* 300995
Merrett G W 300995
Mullins R S *MISM AMILOG* 300995
Palmer R A 300995
Andrews B G 300996
Bassett M R *BEM* 300996
Clayton C G sq 300996
Falinski J H 300996
Gill P *MBE* 300996
Mummery N J 300996
Nicholls P J 300996
Pendlebury P A 300996
Ransom M 300996
Selmes D A *MBE BSc MCIOB* 300996

Thomas L R sq 300996
Thurgate I A 300996
Wilkinson D N 300996
Dawes S P *AMICE* 300997
Heseltine J 300997
Lisle R 300997
Maye P *MSc* adp 300997
Orchard R M *FIMechIE* 300997
Sauberlich P W G 300997
Simonini S P *BEM* 300997
Smith A B 300997
Strettle G J D *BEM* 300997
Thomis G S 300997
Atkinson I *MISM LCGI* 300998
Burke J *DipTPM MICE FInstCES* c 300998
Coles D J 300998
Dent D *AMICE MCIOB NEBOSH* 300998
Drake K I 300998
Gallagher T 300998
Hair F J *BEM* 300998
Hemingway M P 300998
Matthews R J 300998
Tomiczek E H *BEM* 300998
Daire A L 300999
Davey P D 300999
Ferguson G *MBE BEM* 300999
Kerr J S 300999
McEleny E *BEM* 300999
Nelson L J *MISM* 300999
Quinn D *BEM* 300999
Renwick T P 300999
Soper W J 300999
Williams N T *MBE* 300999
Wilson R M *MBE BEM•* 300999
Wright D G 300999
Adlington J N *MBE* 300900
Bagley N S *MIIRSM DipRSM* 300900
Collins N J 300900
Gosling C M P *MBE* 300900
Handscomb M S 300900
Hogan P J 300900
McEldon P 300900
Perkins A B 300900
Shay W J 300900
Shields P *QGM* 300900
Sinclair I *MBE* 300900
Swales F R 300900
Vowles P P *BEM* 300900

Captains

McCormick I G 170991
Thompson A *(A/Maj 260201)* 30894
Philips S *(A/Maj 041200)* 161194
Inglis J A *(A/Maj 120301)* 160495
Berrill M D *(A/Maj 030400)* 280695
Alexandre M J 30995
Hewson A *MBE IEng AMICE MISM AIIRSM (A/Maj 010400)* 30995
Atkinson D 130296
Sweeney C G 130296
Skelton K A 80496
Middlehurst P *MBE BEM* 110496
Walsh A J 80596
Hollman F J *IEng MIMechIE* 220796
Cunningham C A *BEM* 120896
McClellan P A 30297

Thompson J A 20597
Trussler P J 20597
Diggins D A (A/Maj 010400) 90597
Stevenson A V (A/Maj 200300) 90597
Roberts M W BEM•. 120697
McConnachie R J 190697
Hunter G W 201197

Special Regular Officers Late Entry

Majors

Harrison P G 300900
Jones G B 300900

Captains

Angus K D 80594
Barrett R M 80594
Clemens P 80594
Hayter R J AMILOG DipRSM (A/Maj 280998) 50295
Pulsford J F 221195
Brady T J 50196
Dunning J A 130296
Brown P L 100396
Burrow K W 270496
Matthews D R 240696
Webster W S J 60796
Prentice C 280796
Freeman W H MBE 190896
Sherrington B J 10996
Bridewell S C 51096
Watts D M 51096
Wood G A 301096
Sherlock T 81196
Pemberton S M 301196
Ruffle D B 90597
Connell J S (A/Maj 190201) 290597
Roe A B 260697
Topping R W 270697
Reilly W 10997
Gadd S N 310398
Gill M J 310398
Aspray M 10498
Bramhald H 10498
Brown R 10498
Burke N J BEM 10498
Cliffe L A IEng MIEIE 10498
Coe P D 10498
Dargavel J 10498
England M R BEM 10498
George I L 10498
Goucher A T 10498
Green P T 10498
Hammond V K 10498
Henderson T F 10498
Herrington M S 10498
Heyes P A MBE MIMGT 10498
Huish M 10498
Jones A B BEM 10498
Ladds P 10498
Liley G N MISM 10498
Melnyk L D 10498
Murray A W 10498
Peploe D 10498
Phillips S L BSc 10498
Pincombe I J 10498
Provan M 10498
Reed P M 10498

Reed A P 10498
Reynolds J R 10498
Roberts A P 10498
Roberts H R 10498
Rock S G 10498
Waters M 10498
Westwood P R IEng MIEIE 10498
Wheeler W G 10498
Worthington R J 10498
Ball K BSc 70498
Hoyle N 80498
Black D A 110598
Jackson P 210798
Hannah E K 240898
Borthwick K 040998
Eley P C 121098
Hill M J 301198
Mortlock C J 301198

Intermediate Regular Officers

Majors

Beck S J 300995
Howard A J 300999
Nichols I E S 300999
Norris A D 300999
Taylor J J BEng(Hons) CEng MIMechE EM 300999
Whitlock S J 300999
Johnson K BSc 300900

Captains

Manners W J (A/Maj 010198)
Sinclair D G BSc(Hons) (A/Maj 200300) 191294
Scott G P 130495
Holman J D 251295
Edmunds-Mcclune T D 10296
Lappin R G 310396
Davies S W P 90496
ØGauci P E BA(Hons) MA(Hons) MSc 130896
Masson C P BA(Hons) 130896
Macdonald-Willia E N BSc(Hons) 141296
Brain P C E BEng(Hons) 191296
Allewell C J BSc(Hons) 211296
Marshall C J BEng(Hons) 211296
Thomson R BSc(Hons) 211296
Aberdeen J J BEng(Hons) 271296
White S P 110497
Arnison C N BA 91097
Salway D M BSc(Hons) 131097
Gladwin R J BSc(Hons) 141097
Moxham A W BSc(Hons) 141097
McCarthy H BSc 301097
Barter D J BSc(Hons) 120298
Hemming D A BEng(Hons) 120298
Hemns S M BEng(Hons) 120298
Lewis M D BEng(Hons) 120298
Orr P A B BSc(Hons) 120298
Quinn D E BA(Hons) 120298
Shearman K R BA(Hons) 120298
Whishaw B W D BEng(Hons) 120298
McCallum G A R BSc(Hons) (A/Maj 060200) 20498
Bremner A J BEng 160698
Cunniff S E LLB(Hons) 160698

McKechnie A R I BA(Hons) MSc 160698
ØBell L N BSc(Hons) SVY 131098
Church I J BA(Hons) 131098
Mifsud N D BEng(Hons) 131098
Charles M A BEng(Hons) 100299
Ridge J H 100299
Robinson S BSc(Hons) 100299
Wallace P J 100299
Knights A P BEng(Hons) 260399
Acton M J BSc(Hons) 140699
Brown G D BEng(Hons) 140699
Foley A J 140699
ØHanlin C L BSc(Hons) MSc 140699
Hewson R J BEng(Hons) 140699
McMonagle L M BEng(Hons) 140699
Page R M BEng(Hons) 140699
Simonian S 140699
Brown S C 60899
White J P 270999
Watson M R 261199
Byron H J 40200
Jourdan D F BSc(Hons) 90200
Marsden T G J BA(Hons) 90200
Pratt J E H BSc(Hons) 90200
Scobie R A BAcc 90200
Walden S J BEng(Hons) 90200
ØWhiteman H D BA(Hons) 90200
Stuthridge S R 120400
Rowell P J 30500
Atkinson R J BEng(Hons) 130600
Baldwin G M 130600
Brown R M BSc(Hons) 130600
Clugston D W A 130600
Reid A M BA 130600
Robinson W H BEng(Hons) 130600
Green R J 270700
Booker M E 11000
Michael C L 31000
Archer M J BA(Hons) 101000
Brown I C BEng(Hons) 101000
Macdonald R J BEng(Hons) 101000
Rees T J BSc(Hons) 101000

Lieutenants

Douglas A S BEng(Hons) (L/Capt 290500) 120897
Boyes O J 131097
Richards M (A/Capt 220399) 141197
ØConcannon T J BEng(Hons) 161297
Ellison D B E (A/Capt 300498) 161297
Marsden G J (A/Capt 080399) 161297
Webster J D BEng(Hons) (A/Capt 040101) 161297
Budden M (A/Capt 210699) 230398
Holt C (A/Capt 170699) 130498
Bickers D J BEng(Hons) 100898
Gossage J P R BEng(Hons) 100898
Corbett C R BEng(Hons) 141298
Hay L A W (A/Capt 040101) 120499
Arnold G J BEng(Hons) 90899
Bradley P A BEng(Hons) 90899
Carter N P BEng(Hons) 90899
ØJoannou E BEng(Hons) 90899

Salberg T J *BEng(Hons)*	90899	
Smith R C *BEng(Hons)*	90899	
Smith J B *BEng(Hons)*	90899	
Walker G J *BEng(Hons)*	90899	
Carvel S J	131299	
Neville S M	131299	
Martindale T G	150300	
Lawes R A	121200	

2nd Lieutenants

Robinson A J	111299
ØWarren K	111299
McKay G A	120800
ØBlott C S	100900
††Hoey R A	100900
ØJoyce C F A	100900
ØOneill C N	100900
††Pask A R	100900
††Pope J L	100900
ØRickman G C	100900
††Clarke R A	110900

Short Service Late Entry Officers

Majors

Rutherford L M	300996

Captains

Teeling C G	270595
Steel R J	120995
McIlveen P A *IEng FIIE(MECH)*	60696
Caskie I R	10498
Gordon S M	10498
Hesketh P G	10498
Wilkin R M	10498
Taylor P D	70498
Starbuck J A	200498
Bell G W	270598
Hicketts J L	270798
Croll D	10998
Rushton D J	91198
Fowke M C	60199
Robertson L J H	20399
Richardson P A	160499
Foran J A *MM*	260499
Moore P E	260499
Artis C S	50599
Mellor A D	60599
Smalley T J	100599
Wallace M J	100599
Foster R B	210599
McCann E L	20699
Reddick A H	170699
Robinson K	260799
Dickerson P L	20899
Costen M D	40899
Calvert G J	60899
Frost R B	160999
Ironton B E	81199
Mortimore M A	240100
Philpots D G	240100
Coles M G *BEM*	140200
Matheson K J	140200
Lakey G	280200
Lowerson K	280200
Solomon N K	270300
McGinnis D A	310300
Lee T R	10400
Wharton J	100400

Easingwood A M	20500
Barrett C P	220500
Quince M G *IEng MIIEE ACIBSE*	50600
Scrivens I H	50600
Tustin A M *MBE*	120600
Bevan N P	160600
O'Connell T D	190600
Andrews G G	260600
Beddoe K	260600
Davidson P A *BSc*	30700
Garrett R J	30700
Pearce A M	100700
Rowlands P	100700
Allen D A	170700
Cork A J *BEM*	40800
Richardson M E	250900
Dalton B G	91000
Thomas M R	231000
Grantham K J *MBE QGM•*	131100
Hone S	131100
Poole T P	201100
Williams M A	201100
Dexter A	41200
Jenkins M G	41200
Mackinnon J *MBE*	41200
Baxter M A	151200
Larsen A A	151200
Leigh P J	220101

Short Service Officers

Captains

Hill R J A *BSc(Hons)*	91097
Hewins D J *BSc(Hons)*	160698
Barker R J P *BEng(Hons)*	131098
Ferguson D J	130499
Talbot D P *BEng(Hons)*	310599
Macmillan H J B *BSc(Eng)Hons* *SVY*	30699
Allin S D *BEng(Hons)*	140699
Coventry A D *LLB(Hons)*	150899
Taylor M *BA(Hons)*	290999
Bond G S *BSc(Hons)*	90200
Cox L B *BA(Hons)*	90200
Greaves A J *BSc(Hons)*	90200
Gregg C J *MA*	90200
Hardwick B C *BSc(Hons)*	90200
Janaway A S *BA(Hons)*	90200
Moore I *BEng(Hons)*	90200
Scoble M C *BEng(Hons)*	90200
Seabrook D Y *BSc(Hons)*	90200
Swain A W *BL*	90200
Bennett K *DipTPM*	130600
Bradley S N *BSc*	130600
Lumley S R *BEng(Hons)*	130600
O'Brien V P *BA(Hons)*	130600
Profit R W *BSc(Hons)*	130600
Walker D G *BEng(Hons)*	130600
Workman M H W *BSc(Hons) PhD*	130600
Battey C W	120800
Bolton S G W *BEng(Hons)*	101000
Evans G *BSc*	101000
Gifford B R J *BSc*	101000
Hawkins J W *BSocSc(Hons)*	101000
Holl J D *BA(Hons)*	101000
ØLloyd R M	101000
Millar E N S *MA(Hons)*	101000
ØNissen J R *BEng(Hons)*	101000
Richards G P *BA(Hons) MA*	101000
Grove P L *BSc(Hons)*	181100

Adams C B *BEng(Hons)*	80201
Davies M *BSc(Hons)*	80201
ØDenham M J *BSc(Hons)*	80201
Eade A J *BA(Hons)*	80201
Hayhurst R A *BEng(Hons)*	80201

Lieutenants

Torbet A T *BSc(Hons)*	10996
Garrow A A *DTFLA*	160697
Hunter D K *BEng(Hons)*	160697
Kerr G J *BEng(Hons)*	160697
ØParker E A *BSc(Hons)*	160697
Selley K A	160697
Wasilewski C T J *BA(Hons)*	160697
West J R *BSc(Hons)*	160697
Williams A M *BEng(Hons)*	160697
Back S C *BEng(Hons)*	120897
Commander M J L *BEng(Hons)*	120897
Helme P M *BEng(Hons)*	120897
Bracey J C *BSc(Hons)*	61097
Elsegood C J *BEng(Hons)*	161297
Luddington C *BEng(Hons)*	161297
Smith M J E *BSc(Hons)*	161297
ØBenn A E C *MA(Hons)*	100298
Eyre C A *BSc(Hons)*	100298
Eytle M G *MEng(Hons)*	100298
Greyling G A *BScEng(MECH)*	100298
ØLoyd T J *BA(Hons)*	100298
ØMacPhee K R *BA(Hons)*	100298
Ness P A *BEng(Hons)*	100298
O'Neill S S M *BEng(Hons)*	100298
Cradden D C *BSc(Hons)*	130498
Davies J C *BSc(Hons)*	130498
Day A S *BSc(Hons)*	130498
Jarvill C M *BEng(Hons)*	130498
Jenkins I G *BEng(Hons)*	130498
ØLincoln R V *BSc(Hons)*	130498
Longfellow J D *BA(Hons)*	130498
Phillips S P J *BSc(Hons)*	130498
Small E P	130498
Mayes S O L	140698
Pietrzak H A *MEng(Hons)*	140698
Boxall G J *BSc(Hons)*	100898
Boyce T D *BSc(Hons)*	100898
Coats C D *BSc(Hons)*	100898
ØFoad C B B *BA(Hons)*	100898
Harvey R *BEng*	100898
Humphreys D J *BEng(Hons)*	100898
McComb S J G *BSc(Hons)*	100898
Roberts A *BSc(Hons)*	100898
Scott P D G *BA(Hons)*	100898
ØUnsworth K B *BSc(Hons)*	100898
Hill A J *BA*	110898
ØBenefield L L *BEd(Hons)*	121098
McGhee S M *BSc(Hons)*	121098
White A D H *BSc(Hons)*	121098
James E R *BA(Hons)*	161198
Brown A D *BSc(Hons)*	141298
Green A S *BEng(Hons)*	141298
ØGross C L	141298
ØGuest C I N *BSc(Hons)*	141298
King P G *BSc(Hons)*	141298
Rowson A C J *BA(Hons)*	141298
ØBeattie L J *B Sc (Hons)*	90299
Carter R D *BEng(Hons)*	90299
Edwards B *BEng(Hons)*	90299
Farrell T S *BEng(Hons)*	90299
Robinson S D *MEng*	90299
Smith N *BA(Hons)*	90299
ØSteele F C M *MA BA(Hons)*	90299

Anson S J *BA*	120499	Lloyd G P *BEng(Hons)*	90899	Millar S D *(A/Capt 290900)*	
Baker M A S *BA(Hons)*	120499	Moore N A F *BEng(Hons)*	90899		100300
Beaumont P *BEng(Hons)*	120499	Parkinson D J *BSc(Hons)*	90899	Allardice D N	40700
Copland E P *BEng(Hons)*	120499	Reeve A J R *BEng(Hons)*	90899	Baxter J E	150900
Coughlan J J *BSc(Hons)*	120499	Robinson E J	90899	Canham M J	121200
Hammett P M *BSc(Hons)*	120499	ØTerrot S A *BEng(Hons)*	90899		
Lusi P J *BSc*	120499	Barnard C J	260999		
Young P A *BTech*	120499	Hayward J D	71099	*2nd Lieutenants*	
Bailey D W *MEng(Hons)*	130699			ØPotts L M	91098
ØCooper A M *BSc(Hons)*	130699	Donohoe T A *(A/Capt 010800)*		Lawes A C	150399
Francis N A *MEng(Hons)*	130699		101299	Stroud-Caules T D	100499
ØHain V M *BEng*	130699	Ankers C R *BSc(Hons)*	131299	Hart A S	280899
McConnell J J *BSc(Hons)*	130699	Buckett J A *BSc(Hons)*	131299	Normile M J	161199
ØRowbotham V S *MA(Hons)*		ØElliott L J *BSc(Hons)*	131299	Astbury D J *BEng(Hons)*	150400
	130699	Howard N R J *BEng(Hons)*	131299	Rider T C R	150400
Stuart J D *BSc(Hons)*	130699	Mayers M G *BEng(Hons)*	131299	Milner J M	120800
ØGissing J *BEng(Hons)*	90899	ØPlimmer C L K *BA(Hons)*	131299	Evett J P	161200
Gooch A A *BEng(Hons)*	90899	Teeton M W *BEng(Hons)*	131299		

ROYAL CORPS OF SIGNALS

The figure of Mercury holding a Caduceus in the left hand the right hand aloft poised with the left foot on a globe all silver, above the globe a Scroll inscribed *'Certa Cito'* and below on each side six laurel leaves all gold, the whole ensigned with The Crown in gold

Regimental Marches

Quick March . . . . .The Royal Signals March - Begone Dull Care
Slow March . . . . .HRH The Princess Royal

Agents . . . . .Lloyds Bank plc Cox's & King's Branch

Regimental Headquarters . . . . .Blandford Camp, Blandford Forum, Dorset DT11 8RH
(Tel: Blandford Military 2083)

Alliances

Canadian Forces . . . . .The Communications and Electronics Branch Canadian Forces
Australian Military Forces . . . . .The Royal Australian Corps of Signals
New Zealand Army . . . . .Royal New Zealand Corps of Signals
Indian Army . . . . .Corps of Signals
Pakistan Army . . . . .Signal Corps
Sri Lanka Army . . . . .The Signal Corps
Malaysian Armed Forces . . . . .Malaysian Signal Corps
Zambia Army . . . . .Zambia Corps of Signals

Affiliated Regiment
Queen's Gurkha Signals

Colonel in Chief . . . .*HRH* THE PRINCESS ROYAL *KG KT GCVO QSO*

Royal Signals Corps Committee

Master of Signals	.Maj Gen I O J Sprackling *OBE*	.300697
Representative Colonel Commandant . .	.Brig A P Verey *QVRM TD*	.010598
Chairman Royal Signals Association . .	.Maj Gen A H Boyle *CB*	.161195
Chairman Royal Signals Institution . . .	.Maj Gen W J P Robins *CB OBE*	.191196
Chairman Finance Committee	.Maj Gen J D Stokoe *CB CBE*	.010698
Colonel Commandant	.Maj Gen S R Carr-Smith	.010796
Colonel Commandant	.Brig N F Wood	.021098
Signal Officer in Chief (Army)	.Brig C J Burton *OBE ADC*	.020699
ACOS G6 CIS HQ LAND	.Brig J M Shaw *MBE*	.300695
Secretary	.Col A F Carter *MBE*	.011196

		Kimber A T B sq	300694	Neale P B *MA MSc* psc† dis	300699
Brigadiers		Merrick A W *MBE* psc I	300694	Oldfield P J psc	300699
		Blake J psc†	300695	Rouse P A R sq jsdc	300699
Lee S M A *OBE* psc†	300692	Evans R J *OBE BSc(Econ)Hons*		Thomas J E *MBE MSc CEng FIEE*	
Shaw J M *MBE* psc hcsc(J)	300695	*MInstD FIMGT MCGI* psc†	300695	jsdc MDA sq(w) TEM *(A/Brig*	
Burton C J *OBE ADC* psc†	300697	Innocent P T *FIMGT CGIA MCGI*		*020101)*	300699
Hughes S G *CBE BSc(Eng) CEng*		psc†	300695	Dyer M J M psc	300600
MIEE FIMGT psc†	300697	Dent M J *CBE FIMGT* sq	300696	James G A *BSc* psc†	300600
Baxter R *CBE* psc† hcsc(J)	300698	Hadfield K J psc	300696	Moseley P J *OBE MA* psc†	300600
Cook J R B *FIMGT FCIPD* psc†		Richardson T E M psc†	300696	Parfitt P *BSc(Hons)* sq sq(w) TEM	
jsdc	300698	Shipley G M S ocds(US) psc†			300600
Lynam D A *MBE BSc(Eng)Hons*			300696	Rowlinson D E *BSc(Eng)Hons* psc†	
psc†	300698	Stretch M K sq	300696		300600
Ham H H *CBE BSc* psc†	300699	Wilkinson M C *MA CEng MIEE* psc		Russ A W *BSc(Hons)* psc†	300600
McDowall D *MBE* psc(a)†	300699	sq(w) TEM	300696	Steele D M *MBE BSc(Hons) CEng*	
Grey A J *BSc(Eng)Hons CEng MIEE*		Kidner S J *BSc(Hons)* psc	300698	*MIEE MIMGT* psc†	300600
psc†	300600	Pratley P A *MBE BSc(Eng)Hons*		Terrington J A *CGIA* psc†	300600
Jackson N C *MBE* psc	300600	*AMIEE* psc† hcsc(J)	300698		
Le Gallais C L *CBE BSc(Eng)* rcds		Crombie R M psc psc(J)	300699		
jsdc sq(w)	300600	Ewbank J K sq jsdc	300699	*Lieutenant Colonels*	
		Inshaw T G *BSc(Eng)Hons* psc†			
Colonels			300699	Hughes D P (SL) *OBE BSc(Eng)*	
		Johnstone A H *BA(Hons)* psc†		*CEng MIEE* sq sq(w) CISEM	
Holmes R J *MBE* psc†	300693		300699		300686
Paul S S *BSc(Eng)* nadc psc†	300693	Mills D M *MSc* psc	300699	Wallace A M *BSc(Eng)Hons*	
Donaldson G N *OBE* sq jsdc	300694			psc(CAN) jsdc sq(w)	300686

Conlon C P sq 300688
Spencer C I *BSc(Eng)Hons CEng*
FIEE sq(w) TEM 300688
Thwaites R C A (SL) *BSc(Eng)Hons*
(EURING) CEng FIEE sq(w)
300688
West R J R *MCGI* psc† 300689
Reid M S psc† 300690
Rutherford R F (SL) sq 300690
Symonds R D sq 300690
Brewin W E sq ph 300691
Goodman G H (SL) sq I* I sq(w)
300691
Richards P sq 300691
Strong I M G *MBE* sq 300691
Fish T G B (SL) sq 300692
Hoole R T *MIMGT CGIA* psc†
300692
Hryhoruk P J sq 300692
Scott-Morton B J psc† 300692
Amberton J R S (SL) sq 300693
Crowley W P *BSc(Eng)Hons CEng*
MIEE psc† 300693
Ellis R J J *BSc(Hons) CEng MIEE*
MBCS sq(w) TEM *(A/Col 220101)*
300693
Hancock H A R psc† 300693
Hewitt R S *BA(Hons)* sq 300693
Hewitt B *BSc MIMGT AMIPD* psc†
300693
Holmes R R *BSc(Eng)Hons MSc*
psc† dis 300693
Palmer D F *BSc(Eng)* sq(w) TEM
300693
ØRelph L A *FIMGT* psc *(A/Col
120201)* 300693
Batho R W sq jsdc 300694
Donaghy C P sq 300694
Griffiths I W *BSc(Eng)Hons MSc*
CEng MIEE dis sq(w) 300694
Hutt A J sq 300694
Thurston R M *BSc(Eng) MBA* sq(w)
† 300694
Binham R F *MBE BSc(Eng)Hons*
CEng MIEE sq sq(w) TEM
300695
Fletcher J L *MA* sq 300695
Hargreaves D A *MA* psc† 300695
Noble I A (SL) sq 300695
Canham T W psc† 300696
Cary G J *OBE BSc(Eng) CEng MIEE*
psc† TEM *(A/Col 090101)* 300696
Evans R O N *BSc(Eng)Hons* psc†
300696
Hudson J P *BSocSc(Hons)* psc
300696
Little M A *BSc MBA* jsdc sq(w) TEM
300696
Mackenzie I W *BSc(Eng)Hons MDA*
jsdc sq(w) *(A/Col 061200)* 300696
Rimell T P psc† 300696
Roberts A P R *MBE* jsdc sq(w) †
300696
Steed R J *MBE* sq jsdc 300696
Whittaker C J *BSc(Eng)Hons MSc*
psc† dis 300696
Barton-Ancliffe B J *BA* sq(w) TE
TEM 300697
Bryning T J P *BSc(Eng) CEng MIEE*
sq(w) TEM 300697
Couch N D psc† *(A/Col 021000)*
300697

Eaton P H *BA(Hons) MA* psc†
300697
Flint E M *MA MSc* psc† *(A/Col
010800)* 300697
Lithgow M *MBE BSc(Eng)* psc(n)†
300697
Llewellyn M P *FRGS GCGI* psc†
300697
Manders T R *BSc(Hons)* sq(w) TEM
ais 300697
McKee J K *MBE BSc(Hons) MBA*
MSc dis sq(w) 300697
Meyer D P psc† 300697
Parsons K K W sq(w) ais 300697
Proctor D G sq 300697
Rafferty G J T *BSc(Eng)Hons* psc†
(A/Col 201100) 300697
Wakerley C *MBE* sq jsdc ph 300697
Walker P G psc 300697
Whitby D J *BSc(Eng)Hons MSc* psc†
MESE *(A/Col 120101)* 300697
Cameron-Mowat I *MA(Hons)* psc I
300698
Colborn H N S psc† 300698
Condie I A J *BSc(Hons)* psc† 300698
Coupar M A sq 300698
Dryburgh J sq 300698
Grogan P J psc 300698
Harrison N P *MBE BA MIMGT* sq(w)
TEM 300698
Jones D A H odc(AUST) psc†
300698
Morphet A N *MIL* psc(GE) I*
300698
Rough M A *BSc(Eng)Hons CEng*
MIEE psc† 300698
Thomas R G sq 300698
Turner C H *BA(Hons) MDA* sq
300698
Watts T J P *BSc(Hons) MSc CEng*
MIEE psc dis 300698
Westerman I D *MSc* psc† 300698
Clapp R N *MBA MSc(Eng) CEng*
MIEE psc† MESE 300699
Clark J W sq 300699
Davies P J *MA* psc† 300699
Davis R B *BSc(Eng)Hons AKC CEng*
MIEE sq(w) TEM 300699
Gillespie P *MA* psc† 300699
Harwell A A S *MA* psc 300699
Keegan C B *BSc(Hons) MSc* dis
sq(w) 300699
Kendall A E *BSc(Hons)* psc† 300699
Pope N A W *MA MA* psc† 300699
Richards C C *BSc(Hons) MSc* psc†
300699
Richardson J E *MBE* psc 300699
Sharman S R *MBE BA DipLA* sq
sq(w) 300699
Smith G *BA* sq(w) † 300699
Strawbridge R F *MBE BSc(Eng)Hons*
sq(w) † 300699
Sullivan D A sq(w) † 300699
Towers P R *MA(Cantab) MSc* psc†
dis 300699
Trimble A K sq sq(w) 300699
Turpin S J *MSc* MESE sq(w)
300699
Wilson J P *BSc(Eng)Hons MSc* psc†
psc dis 300699
Bristow A P psc† 300600
Complin M R sq sq(w) 300600

Croft S *BSc(Hons) MSc* sq 300600
Davis E A *BSc(Hons) LLB(Hons)*
odc(AUST) psc(PAK) 300600
Ewell A A sq sq(w) ais 300600
Macrostie S K *MBE MA GCGI*
psc(n) † 300600
Mather R G *BSc* psc† 300600
McComb A W T *BSc(Hons) MSc*
psc† 300600
Metcalfe N P *MBE QGM MA* psc†
300600
Richardson S J *BSc(Eng) MSc* psc†
300600
Sharp R A *MBE BSc* sq(w) † 300600
Smith G M *BSc(Hons)* psc† 300600
Sparshatt R G C *MSc* psc† dis
300600
Thackray C J *BEng(Hons) MSc* psc†
300600
Wallis S P *MBE* sq sq(w) 300600
Johns S C sq 300900

Majors

Danby K G *MA* odc(IT) sq I*
300679
Sanders R J sq 300980
Wallis M S *BSc(Eng)Hons* sq(w)
TEM 300980
Bowles P J sq 300981
Emslie M J M sq 300982
Helm A *BA* sq 300982
Grey P J *MA CEng MIEE* sq(w)
TEM 300983
Gorford P K *BA MDA DipLP* sq
MDA 300984
Johnston M N *BSc* sq(w) 300984
Ross H A sq 300984
Brannigan R V J sq 300985
Robertshaw P sq 300985
Brown I R C sq 300986
Harris J A *MInstD* 300986
Smith S J sq(w) TEM 300986
Williamson R J sq sq(w) 300986
Bardell H J *FRGS* sq 300987
Bowering A J sq 300987
Andrews S I *BSc(Eng)Hons MDA*
sq(w) TEM 300988
Goodfellow K W *BSc(Eng) CEng*
MIEE sq(w) TEM 300988
Riley F T J A sq 300988
Wilson K G *BSc(Eng)* sq(w) TEM
300988
Butler M *BSc(Eng)Hons MSc* dis
sq(w) TEM 300989
Edwards M W *MDA MAPM MIMGT*
sq 300989
Gale J M sq 300989
Hunt S P *BSc(Hons)* sq(w) 300989
Lawrence C R sq(w) TEM 300989
Plumb L J *BSc(Hons) MAPM* sq(w)
TEM 300989
Pritchard K sq(w) 300989
Tuson A J *BSc(Hons) MSc* dis sq(w)
TEM 300989
Bateson N J *BSc(Hons)* sowc sq
300990
Green S C *BSc(Hons) IEng AMIEE*
MIIEE sq(w) TEM 300990
Larkam D W sq(w) 300990
Osment P A *BA(Hons)* psc† 300990
Pearce A L sq(w) TEM 300990

Rock A J sq   300990
Seraph I W R sq   300990
Thatcher V J *BSc(Hons) MDA* sq(w)
                                300990
Avison B P *BSc(Eng)* TEM *(A/Lt Col 020301)*   300991
Heritage E *BA MBA PGCE GCGI* psc† psc   300991
Keen N *BA* psc   300991
Leigh S A *BSc* sq(w) TEM *(A/Lt Col 050799)*   300991
Leyland G R sq(w) TEM   300991
Mason G R *BSc(Hons)* sq(w) TEM
                                300991
May S J psc   300991
McNeill G J sq(w) TEM   300991
Nicholson R G *(A/Lt Col 111099)*
                                300991
Brand A G *BSc(Eng)Hons MSc CEng MIEE* dis sq(w) *(A/Lt Col 030400)*
                                300992
Bucklow I K *BSc(Eng)Hons MSc MSc MIEE MIMGT* dis sq(w)
                                300992
Gill N W *MSc MIMGT* psc(a)† †
                                300992
Macaulay D G *BSc(Hons)* sq(w)
                                300992
Miller C W S sq   300992
Purser S J sq(w) AIS   300992
Rowley J *BSc(Eng)Hons* sq(w) TEM
                                300992
Thornber K P sq(w) TEM   300992
Wood A J *BScTech MSc* dis sq(w)
                                300992

Body J E *BSc(Eng)* odc(AUST)
                                300993
Bradshaw I J *BSc* sq(w)   300993
Hodges S D psc *(A/Lt Col 220101)*
                                300993
Hudson A P *MBE* sq(w) *(A/Lt Col 280400)*   300993
Owen C R *BSc(Eng)Hons MSc* psc† dis   300993
Pender-Johns T W *BSc(Hons) MSc MESE*   300993
Renfrey S R sq(w) TEM   300993
Rodgers A H *BA(Hons) MDA PGCE* sq G(ss)   300993
Shaw M G sq(w)   300993
Stephenson P *BA(Hons)* sq sq(w)
                                300993
Stuart J S *BSc(Hons)* sq(w) TEM
                                300993
Turner J sq(w)   300993
Whimpenny D I sq(w)   300993
Borrill N J *BSc(Hons) MSc* psc†
                                300994
Bunce J R C *MSc* psc†   300994
Campbell-Black A H *BEng(Hons)* psc(GE)   300994
Dakin J W *MSc* dis   300994
Eaton M A *BSc(Eng)Hons MSc* dis sq(w)   300994
Giles R P *BA(Hons) MSc* dis sq(w)
                                300994
Glibbery P W *BSc(Hons) MSc* psc† *(A/Lt Col 111200)*   300994
Griffiths M *MSc* psc†   300994
Halstead D G *BEng(Hons) MSc* psc†
                                300994

Hearn G *BSc(Hons) BA(Hons) MIMGT DMS* sq   300994
Lapslie R W *MBE BSc(Eng)Hons MSc MESE* sq(w)   300994
Raleigh D S *BSc* sq(w)   300994
Turnbull S J psc   300994
Whitehead K *BEng(Hons) MSc* psc† dis *(A/Lt Col 041200)*   300994
Adams M W G *BSc(Hons) MSc*
                                300995
Adsett W E H *BSc MA* sq(w)
                                300995
Appleton R S psc†   300995
Baines M *BSc(Hons) AMIEE* psc†
                                300995
Billingham M G   300995
Blackwell A R *BSc(Hons) MA* psc(J)
                                300995
Burgin A D *BSc* sq(w)   300995
Charnock J S *MA* psc(J) †   300995
Complin G J psc(CAN)   300995
Cooper J W   300995
Davis M *BEng(Hons) MSc MESE* sq(w)   300995
Fensom M J psc(J)   300995
Grant G R *LLB(Hons) MDA* sq
                                300995
Gregory S *BA MDA MA* psc(J)
                                300995
Griffiths N J sq(w) TE   300995
Hooper I *BSc(Hons)* psc† † *(A/Lt Col 161000)*   300995
Hudson D B *BA(Hons) MSc CDipAF* psc†   300995
Hutchinson S G *MBE*   300995
Kelly P M *CD BA MDA*   300995
Lawrence I G *BSc(Hons) MSc* dis G(ss) sq(w)   300995
McIntosh C J *BSc(Hons) MSc* dis sq(w)   300995
Meinertzhagen R D *BSc(Hons) MSc* sq(w)   300995
Metcalfe A *MSc* psc(J) dis   300995
Norton G R *BSc* psc(J)   300995
Peel P D *BEng(Hons) MSc FIQS* psc(J) dis sq(w)   300995
Quinlan R J *BSc(Hons) MSc* dis sq(w)   300995
Roberts M C *BEng(Hons) MSc* psc(J)
                                300995
Robson D G psc(J)   300995
Somerville D W *BSc(Hons)* sq(w)
                                300995
Standen I G *BA(Hons) MSc* psc†
                                300995
Vickery S J *BEng(Hons)* psc(J)
                                300995
Vingoe I P F *BSc(Hons) MA* psc†
                                300995
Warne D B *BEng(Hons) MSc* psc(J) † adp   300995
Watt P J *MA*   300995
Wilson R P *MSc* psc†   300995
Workman S R *BEng(Hons) MDA* sq(w)   300995
Adams J S *BA(Hons) MA MSc* psc(J)
                                300996
Botterill A J *BSc(Hons) MSc* psc(J) dis   300996
Burke M C *BA(CombHons)* osc(FR)
                                300996

Compston J A *MBE BSc(Hons) MSc* dis sq   300996
Cooper T C *BEng(Hons) MSc* dis sq(w)   300996
Craft D A   300996
Duncan A J   300996
Favager I G *BEng(Hons)*   300996
Forrest J D *BSc(Hons) MSc* dis sq(w)
                                300996
Freeman R J *BEng(Hons) BEng(Hons) MSc* dis sq(w)   300996
Hanson M G *BSc(Hons)*   300996
Healey R J psc(J)   300996
Hill A G *BEng(Hons) MSc* psc(J)
                                300996
Hodges J M *BEng(Hons) MSc AMIEE* psc psc(J) MESE sq(w)   300996
Jenkins H A *BA(Hons) M A (Oxon) MSc* psc(J)   300996
Kinnaird D J *BSc(Hons) MSc* psc(J) dis   300996
McConnell S J   300996
Paterson C S K *BEng(Hons) MSc* psc(J)   300996
Ross A G *BEng(Hons) MSc* dis
                                300996
Stevens N S *BEng(Hons)* sq(w)
                                300996
Stringer A J *BA(Hons)*   300996
Swindells J E *BEng(Hons) MSc* dis sq(w)   300996
Tod J R *BEng(Hons) MA MSc* psc(J) dis sq(w)   300996
Walton I A *BSc* sq(w)   300996
Baker P C *MA* sq(w) †   300997
Bizley D J M *MSc* dis sq(w)   300997
Bosher P *BEng BEng(Hons)*   300997
Caleb N R N   300997
Carmichael T J *BEng BEng(Hons) MSc AMIEE AIL*   300997
Cole J J *BEng(Hons)* psc(J)   300997
Coleman M S *BSc* sq(w)   300997
Dooley M S   300997
ØFreely F J *MA*   300997
Gillespie J C *BSc(Hons) MSc* dis
                                300997
Hume G H AIS   300997
ØLapslie A D M *BSc(Hons)*   300997
Mannings K *BA(Hons)*   300997
Smart J L *BSc(Arch)*   300997
Stocker A B *BA PGDA MDA MDA*
                                300997
ØSunderland D A *BA(Hons)*   300997
Walker N A AIS   300997
Whichelo F E R *BEng BEng(Hons)* psc(J)   300997
Williamson S M *BEng(Hons)* ais
                                300997
Addley G N *BEng(Hons)*   300998
Allen T J S *BSc*   300998
Anderson G D sq   300998
Cameron A D E *BSc(Hons)*   300998
Cook C D *BA(Hons)*   300998
Cubbin P S AIS   300998
Drew P E J *MEng(Hons)*   300998
Ford C A *BEng(Hons)* psc(J)   300998
France S O   300998
Fraser J H *BSc MAPM* sq(w) 300998
Fraser N D *BSc(Hons) MSc* psc(J)
                                300998

141

Hunter I N *BEng(Hons) MSc* dis 300998
Makepeace N J *BSc(Hons) MSc* dis 300998
Mannings S R *BSc* 300998
ØMurdoch C E *BSc(Hons)* 300998
Smith P A *BSc(Hons) MSc* psc(J) dis 300998
Spiers S J P 300998
ØTomkins L V 300998
Turner P I *BA(Hons)* 300998
Whitehead C J 300998
Beecher N A 300999
Bever M R *BA(Hons) MSc* 300999
Cathro A D *BSc(Hons)* 300999
ØCopley S L *BSc(Hons)* 300999
Drinkall D *BEng* 300999
Fletcher G W *BEng(Hons)* 300999
Gaul D C *BSc* 300999
Gibson R S *AIS* 300999
Inglis G *BSc(Hons)* 300999
Langley J A G *BEng(Hons)* 300999
Long A *BSc(Hons)* 300999
Norris J M *BSc(Hons)* 300999
Parsons A J *BEng(Hons)* 300999
Percival A E *BSc(Hons)* 300999
Saddington A S *BEng(Hons) MSc* MESE 300999
Sharkey D M *BA(Hons)* 300999
Smith P R 300999
Spencer R J B 300999
Sutherland C R 300999
Sutton J E 300999
Urwin A R 300999
Alderson B *BEng(Hons) PGDip* 300900
Bennett G E *BEng(Hons)* 300900
Caesar J *BEng(Hons)* 300900
Clewlow A J 300900
Cooper C N *BEng(Hons)* 300900
Cornell M C *BEng(Hons)* 300900
ØDavies S L *BA(Hons) MPhil* 300900
ØDonovan S A *BSc(Hons)* 300900
Duggan D J *BSc(Hons)* 300900
Fallows A M 300900
Gray I C *BEng(Hons)* 300900
Hargreaves F E 300900
Hayden A L *BSc(Hons)* 300900
Knott A R *BA(Hons)* 300900
Mountford T M P *BSc(Hons)* 300900
ØNesmith S P M *BSc(Hons)* 300900
Parkinson D R 300900
ØRayner M J *BSocSc(Hons)* 300900
Talbot A E *BSc(Hons)* 300900
Townsend J P 300900
White A M *BSc(Hons) MBCS* ph 300900
Wood C M *BSc(Hons)* 300900
Wood T O *BSc(Hons)* 300900

Captains

Deans G *(A/Maj 120196)* 141291
Youngson S S M *MSc (A/Maj 040900)* 121293
Wilson D T 50394
Hanby M J 101294
Anderson J R *BA(Hons)* 10495
Churchill A M *BSc(Hons) MSc (A/Maj 290800)* 10495
Gunning J S 10495

King R H 10495
Mould A J *BA(Hons)* 10495
Shipley D M T *BEng(Hons)* 10495
Blower I A *BEng(Hons) (A/Maj 201100)* 240595
Abram P J *BEng(Hons)* 110895
Gillespie S T 110895
Kennedy J A 110895
Strawbridge R G *BEng(Hons)* 110895
ØBrown R M *BSc* 50995
ØDallyn E A *BA(CombHons)* 60995
Meadowcroft S N *BEM* 270995
Webb R J *BA(Hons) LLM* 141295
Lovett R J *BEng(Hons)* 151295
Peet N M 151295
Rumsey R D W 151295
Wilson G W *BSc(Hons)* 151295
Lucas A G 110396
McCole A S 130496
Smith M J *BSc(Hons)* AIMGT MISM *(A/Maj 040900)* 130496
Boyne S J *BA(Hons)* 270496
Range N H *(A/Maj 010900)* 80796
Bruce N C *BEng(Hons)* 70896
Hill J G 70896
Vaudin C M *BEng(Hons)* 70896
Anderton-Brown R J *BSc(Hons)* 270896
Crapper T N *BEng(Hons)* 270896
Graham M F *MA BA* 270896
ØMcColl J K 30996
Watts R J *BSc(Hons)* 60996
Chalmers R C ph 141296
Hargreaves I R *BEng(Hons)* MISM 141296
Marsh G E 141296
Worden D C *BSc(Hons)* 281296
ØBurrell L D *BSc(Hons)* 30197
Coulston A P J *BEng(Hons)* 100197
Harrington J H N *BEng(Hons)* 100197
Russell C I *(L/Maj 031000)* 170197
Moir R S *BEng(Hons)* 170197
Hazlewood J P *BEng(Hons)* 210297
Atkinson P G M *AIS* 110497
ØReynolds K A 110497
Brookes M C 240497
Abram S J *BEng(Hons)* AMIEE 80897
Craig R J 80897
Greenfield A 80897
Golley L 80897
Hawkes L J *BEng(Hons)* 80897
Massey N W 80897
O'Rourke L 80897
Merry P D *BEng* 141097
Hendricks L W *Tech(CEI)* 151197
Buxton G P J 121297
Mosby K N 121297
Shenow N R D 121297
Stokoe N M 121297
Aitken A R *LLB(Hons) DipLP* 120298
ØBosley H L *BSc(Hons)* 120298
Lamb G B *BSc(Hons)* 120298
Grierson M J *BEng(Hons)* 90498
ØBarnard S E G *BSc(Hons)* 160698
ØPriestnall F I *MA(Hons)* 160698
Seymour R J *BSc(Hons)* ph 160698
Arthurton A B *BSc(Hons)* 70898
Cooper D A *BEng(Hons)* 70898

Fawcett A R 70898
Fitch B J 70898
Johnson B G W 70898
Smith A J *BEng(Hons)* 70898
Carter R J *BEng(Hons)* 131098
ØMcAnulty K H *BA(Hons)* 131098
Torrell J J ph 231198
Kell C J *BA(Hons)* 111298
Sellwood R J 111298
Newson P G *BSc(Hons)* 100299
Wong M J *BA(Hons)* 100299
Collyer J R 90499
Warren E R 90499
Byfield R N 60899
Parfitt A J 290999
Hutton A S F 101299
Francis R L 90200
Griffiths J S 90200
White B G *BSc(Hons)* 90200
Quinsey R C *BEng(Hons)* 140400
Gough S 120800
ØWoodbridge C J 120800
ØStewart F A W *BSc(Hons)* 101000
ØAylward A C *BEng(Hons)* 80201
Higgs B Y *BEng(Hons)* 80201

Lieutenants

Brunton P J *BEng(Hons)* 120897
Grey T E 161297
Acton J R L 100298
Farragher D P 130498
ØSimmonds K P 130498
ØHughes H M *BEng(Hons)* 100898
Smith C P *BEng(Hons)* 100898
Ashton D J 141298
ØAstley K M *BA(HonsCantab)* 141298
Malcolm J 141298
Sherry D 141298
ØCochran K E 120499
Day T W 90899
Jones P D 90899
Haslewood D A 121200
Spencer D P 121200

2nd Lieutenants

ØBermingham K J 80996
ØCowling I N 60998
††Sultan F 60998
††Mash P W T 50999
††McGuckian D J 50999
†Russell S A 50999
Clarke G J 111299
Clements N S 111299
Endean G P 111299
Hodgkinson P A 111299
Jeffery B K 111299
Maskell-Pedersen E D L 111299
ØMilner K L 111299
Smith S M 111299
††Bennett S R 110900

Regular Category Late Entry Officers

Lieutenant Colonels

Ledwards M V sq 10198
Whitehead P W J 70499
Robertson A 50599
White W N *MBE* 300699
Walker D J *MBE* 271099

Turner A D 300600
Lumb D J 161200

Majors

Dudding I L 300992
Aspinall J *MBE* 300993
Daisey P J 300993
Dearman B T *MInstAM* sq 300993
Hickling A *MBE* sq 300994
Craven T R 300995
Gardner B P 300995
Gladwin R H sq 300995
Harwood G *MBE* 300995
Licence R A *MBE* 300995
Clark K E 300996
Davis M *MBE* 300996
Doherty P J *MBE* 300996
Hammett N J 300996
Stokoe A M 300996
Thomas G 300996
Britton H C 300997
Duncan G W 300997
Ellis D C A *IEng FIEIE* 300997
Kerr M A 300997
Maycock C A *MILT* 300997
O'Hara R T 300997
Oakes J W 300997
Pickersgill G sq 300997
Pilling L S *BEM* 300997
Poland M 300997
Sarginson A C sq(w) 300997
Young R C 300997
Bell K *MBE BSc(Hons)* 300998
Colville N H 300998
Dale E C 300998
Dalton B J 300998
Dean T A 300998
Doughty E 300998
Drake M L sq(w) 300998
Graham K J 300998
Heaney M 300998
Holmes D A O 300998
Jepson D H 300998
Langford T P 300998
Pawlak M E 300998
Whitehouse P 300998
Wright D *BEM BSc MSc* sq 300998
Allan R G *BSc MBCS MIMGT* sq(w) ais 300999
Barron P R *MBE* 300999
Bohanan M G P 300999
Connors P T 300999
Dolling D P *MBE* 300999
Douglas G *MBE* 300999
Drain W J 300999
Gaffney P 300999
Grist R P *BA BSc(Hons)* sq 300999
Kirkwood W R 300999
Leggate J M P 300999
Manning G F 300999
Mullender J E 300999
Pawlow D K 300999
Roberts A 300999
Boxall M J 300999
Burrows G R *QGM BEM•* 300900
Chrystal D *BEM BSc* 300900
Clarke S A *GM QGM•* 300900
Cory R C 300900
Gamble R C 300900
Parry I L 300900
Plumb C A 300900
Townsend K A *MBE* ais 300900

Waites T P *BSc(Hons) MSc IEng FIIEE F I E I E* dis 300900
Webb M G 300900
Whytock S J *MBE* 300900
Wyllie R B 300900

Captains

Barber G W *(A/Maj 010200)* 140294
Smith M *MBE (A/Maj 170400)* 80195
Marriott J E 10795
Parkinson R J *(A/Maj 021000)* 10795
Sykes J S T *(A/Maj 070200)* 10795
Brennan W J J *(A/Maj 050500)* 280795
Middleton A *MBE (A/Maj 050600)* 90895
Taylor R W *(A/Maj 030798)* 10995
Handibode P *(A/Maj 021000)* 250396
Smith D I 220496
Patrickson R *(A/Maj 121000)* 90596
Baldwin S J *BSc(Hons) PGDip* ais *(A/Maj 240700)* 10796
Boxhall D J H *MBE (A/Maj 170898)* 10796
Smith J J *(A/Maj 210699)* 80796
Roden S 160996
Mackay J W *(A/Maj 260100)* 51196
McCrindle G M 160197
Spiers B J pl(cfs) 190597
Baugh N E *MBE (A/Maj 011299)* 100697
Mactaggart D 300697
Ferris A P *MBE (A/Maj 200300)* 30797
Wilson D T H 30797
Standen J M *(A/Maj 030700)* 21297
Prince T J *IEng MICD FIEIE (A/Maj 181200)* 10198

Technical Officers in Communications

White J *MBE Lt Col 140497* 40385
Shawyer P D *IEng Maj 300991* 30985
Banks M *Maj 010494* 10486
Davey D R sq(w) *Maj 300994* 231087
Running F C *Maj 300994* 50288
Morley R *Lt Col 030400* 50888

Traffic Officers

Naylor N J H *MBE* sq(w) *Lt Col 300499* 171285
Baron P R *Lt Col 030698* 300187
Floyd J A B *Maj 190296* 190288
Gruncell D A sq(w) *Maj 300994* 190288
Greenwood B sq *Maj 300995* 30688
Storey C D G *Maj 300997* 71088
Calvert J F *Maj 300995* 121288

Traffic Officers (Radio)

Luckett D J sq(w) *Lt Col 010500* 280487

Weaver A *Maj 300994* 71088

Special Regular Officers Late Entry

Majors

Barnett D sq(w) ais 300999
Payet F S 300999
Rackham D K *MIMGT* 300999
Wood P F 300999

Captains

Gorse J D *(A/Maj 161000)* 240794
Blythe G E *(A/Maj 010200)* 11194
Brisco D A *(A/Maj 021000)* 10395
Sulivan A M 10795
Campbell M J *PC* 11295
Hailstone G C *(A/Maj 010999)* 10496
Grainger P H *(A/Maj 260600)* 240696
Knight G N F 10796
Abbott P R 161296
Hoensch A G R 160297
Wilson P *BEM IEng (A/Maj 160800)* 300697
Palfreyman S *(A/Maj 011100)* 291197
Hall T *(A/Maj 140800)* 151297
Wright-Jones M A 10298
Benson G L 10498
Blondel G 10498
Crosby T C 10498
Cullen N B 10498
Deegan D A 10498
Honeyman J A 10498
McElwee P J 10498
Morgan S J 10498
Purves M P 10498
Reith G G A 10498
Richards G L 10498
Stachini D M 10498
Stewart D A *BA BSc(Hons)* 10498
Stoddart P J 10498
Toms S M 10498
Williams J 10498
Wookey L A *BEM* 10498
Wright D A *MBE* 10498

Intermediate Regular Officers

Majors

Carter R J *MBE TD* sq 300991
Hill T 300997
Deans P 300999
Parsons A J E J 300999

Captains

Kenyon D F H 70490
Owen K A *BA(Hons) (A/Maj 151200)* 10495
Edwards R J G *BSc* 70995
ØMacgill R E *BSc(Hons)* ph 70596
ØWesterman L C *BA(Hons) MA* 110896
Barker K B A 51096
O'Kelly N J 141296
Purves M R 40597
Anderson W 70897
ØSpinney G M *BSc(Hons)* ph 141097
ØHarrild S J *BSc(Hons)* 141097
Wilson W D J 120598

Ballantyne I M *BEng* 160698
ØEvans J M *BA(Hons)* 160698
ØHarvey R M *MA(Hons)* 160698
Yardley N G C 160698
Garrett A H T 70898
Jennings J R *BA(Hons)* 100998
ØFarrimond R J *BA(Hons)* 131098
Scott S G 251098
Gray A J 101198
ØMaloney G J H ph 101198
Griffiths P R 111298
Holbrook W R *BSc(Hons)* 10299
Buck P A *LLB(Hons)* 100299
ØCaie C E *BA* 100299
Finnie O S *BSc(Hons)* 100299
Ingram G B *BSc(Hons)* 100299
Wilson R A *BSc(Hons)* 100299
Young P C *BSc(Hons)* 100299
Lambeth J O *B Sc (Hons)* 90499
Fraser J C 140699
ØPritchett N P M *BA(Hons)* 140699
Thomson-Smith C *MA* 140699
ØTyndale G C *BA* 140699
ØWarhurst E S *BSc* 140699
Crapper A K T *BA(Hons)* 170699
Short S J 60899
Bates I F K *BEng(Hons)* 121099
Crowther C P *BSc(Hons)* 121099
Jeeves K A *BA(Hons)* 121099
ØRae E *BSc(Hons)* 121099
Chambers M J *BSc(Hons)* 171199
Hutchinson S H 251299
Clixby A D *BA(Hons)* 90200
ØDownes T J *BSc(Hons)* 90200
Muir P R D *BSc(Hons)* 90200
ØStewart J C *BSc(Hons)* 90200
Nichols J P 30300
Morris N J 140400
Farrimond D R *MEng(Hons)* 130600
Crinnion M J *BA(Hons)* 130600
Hale P J 130600
ØHanlon M *BSc(Hons)* 130600
Morton M J *BSocSc(Hons)* 130600
Randell P N *BEng(Hons) MSc* 130600
Scott H J 130600
Biddulph C N *BEng(Hons)* 101000
ØHenderson L J *BSc(Hons)* 101000
Howarth B D D 101000
Reid F J *BA(Hons)* 101000

Lieutenants

Balfour J S 130498
Baker N D 100898
Barber J C *B Sc (Hons)* 90899
Norton D B *BEng(Hons)* 90899
Psaila B L *BEng(Hons) AMIEE* 90899
Whittley S W *(A/Capt 250600)* 90899
Wills G M A 131299
Foote A S 80800

2nd Lieutenants

ØLucas M L 291099
ØWootten C J H 111299
Davis S G 120800

Short Service Late Entry Officers

Majors

Coffey J 300995
Bailes M D 300996
Carr J D *BEM* 300996
Wood L *MBE* 300996
Hegarty G L 300998
Welch P J 300998
Greig C 300900

Captains

Gurung K 20493
Mayson J *MBE (A/Maj 240100)* 291095
Brown L F 60396
Bousfield R W 10498
Stratton G E 10498
Turnbull N 10498
Boyle J C 30498
Dobson I R *BSc(Hons)* 30498
Jones K A 30498
Yeomans G O *MBE* 30498
Shead C P *MBE* 90498
Brant S 240498
Keates T J 10598
Johnston S C *MBE BSc* 80598
Boyle M P 290598
Kendrick P 50698
Hiorns J S 100798
O'Brien D J 170798
Sacree D A 170798
Horton P A *BEM* 240798
McCreedy N 310798
Williams B 310798
Duckworth J B 40998
Roach K E 250998
Lifton R Q 21098
Patterson A 231098
Fitzpatrick K M 61198
Woodcock G 201198
Howell-Walmsley J 220199
ØNelson F 220199
Keech M *BEM* 10299
Alexander D S 10499
Clee E F 10499
Johnson G R 10499
Bain N J 160499
Gower P 160499
Schofield M A 230499
Cooper P J 70599
Whitaker D A 210599
Day P J *MBE* 40699
Ball D C 110699
Emmerson K E 110699
Milne M C 250699
Stapleton D 20799
Nicol R 90799
Laycock D C 140799
Large A J 300799
Shakespeare G 300799
Griffiths P J 170999
Moye C M 170999
Williams D J 291099
Woolaston A G A 31299
Crane T P 70100
Ashworth P D 30400
Coatsworth N R 30400
Malley T 30400
Montgomery C J 30400
Osborne J M 30400

Simpson W 30400
Cox A C 70400
Bowlby L G 100400
ØStonier S J 140400
Cutforth P A *MBE* 270400
Godwin M 280400
Stanton R J 280400
Haresign A M 50500
McKenna M J 190500
Anderson P A 90600
Keily L 90600
Edwards M R 300600
Lane R A 300600
Lowe P H 300600
Herbert A K 140700
Scott A 140700
McNelly I 280700
Steven S 10800
Hughes J C J 110800
Pardew G 220900
Fradley J 120101

Short Service Officers

Captains

Newhouse R J *BA(Hons)* 270896
Peden G 120298
ØBryan B H *BSc(Hons)* 100299
Roberts C D *BSc(Hons)* 260399
Alexander C S *BEng(Hons)* 121099
ØTaylor A M *BA* 121099
Connor P E *B Sc (Hons)* 90200
Jones R M *BEng* 90200
ØPedder S J *BA(Hons)* 90200
ØThirsk L J *BSc(Hons)* 90200
Toze J E *BA(Hons)* 90200
Wilson A S *BSc(Hons)* 90200
Oliver G J 140400
Jackson D A *BSc(Hons)* 280400
ØBruce E J 130600
Corkery A E A *BEng(Hons)* 130600
Preston C J *BA(Hons)* 130600
Francis-Mcgann N H A *BSc DipHE MISM* 100700
ØJames N E *BA(Hons)* 20900
Jones J S *BEng(Hons)* 30900
Dagless J W *BA(Hons)* 101000
Davis M W *BEng(Hons)* 101000
ØEvans C N C *BA(Hons)* 101000
ØFawcett E J *BSc(Hons)* 101000
Gardner O E R *BSc* 101000
Guthrie F D *BSc LIPD* 101000
Kemp G J 101000
ØMulholland I V I 101000
ØNoakes T M *BSc(Hons)* 101000
Coeshott S F 161200
ØCalderhead L J *BA(Hons)* 80201
Dinnis O R *BSc(Hons)* 80201
Hill A L *BA(Hons)* 80201
McTurk P S *BSc* 80201

Lieutenants

Hamilton R A *MA(Hons) (A/Capt 041200)* 120297
Simpson P J *BSc(Hons)* 120297
Rodger I G *MEng(Hons)* 160697
ØSouthern M A *MA(Hons)* 160697
Irwin G 80897
ØIrwin S E *BSc(Hons)* im 120897
ØHughes S V D *BA(Hons)* 131097

Davenport B P *BSc(Hons)*   141297
Booker M T *BSc(Hons)*   161297
Courage O T B *BSc(Hons)*   161297
ØCovey-Crump S J D *BSc(Hons)*
161297
Lyons J A *BSc(Hons)*   161297
Mayne J N   161297
Waddell P J *BEng*   161297
Johnson A S   *(A/Capt 301000)*
261297
Macdonald M S W *BEng(Hons)*
100298
Morris B W M *MSc*   100298
ØRichardson S Y *BA(Hons)*   100298
ØTacon H B *BSc(Hons)*   100298
Dickson E C   120398
ØKnightly Brown R *BSc(Hons)*
130498
ØPim L G *BA(Hons)*   130498
Stoter D M *BSc(Hons)*   130498
Lumley S C *BA*   210498
Noble J D   290598
ØMadgwick A S A *BA(Hons)*
140698
Orr D R *BSc(Hons)*   140698
Bristow S J *BSc(Hons)*   100898
Fayers M J *BA(Hons)*   100898
Hawkins J K R *BSc(Hons)*   100898
ØHebblethwaite H J P *BSc(Hons)*
100898
ØMcLellan E L *BA(Hons)*   100898

Wills G P *BSc(Hons)*   100898
Shakespeare A D   110998
ØStephens C H *MA(Hons)*   121098
ØStokoe J K *BEng(Hons)*   121098
Gladwin S J   131198
Lawson A J   101298
ØAllison S C   141298
Rickman L N *BSc(Hons)*   141298
ØWilliams E A *BSc(Hons)*   141298
ØMoore K   300399
Childs S P L *MSc BA(Hons)*   120499
Dixon C M *BSc(Hons)*   120499
Lowther I   120499
ØPittaway S E *BA(Hons)*   120499
Senneck A *BA(Hons)*   120499
ØCrawford M J *BSc(Hons)*   130699
Dawes J M *BA(Hons)*   130699
Docherty J W A *BSc(Hons)*   130699
Pritchard S A A *MEng(Hons)*
130699
Wilson R N *BA(Hons)*   130699
Clowes A C *B Sc (Hons)*   90899
ØGalloway V J *BA(Hons)*   90899
ØHenderson B J *BA(Hons)*   90899
ØJardine C L *BSc(Hons)*   90899
ØLabram A F *BSc*   90899
Parke M P   291099
Bosworth M A *BSc(Hons)*   131299
ØBrereton-Martin L J *BA(Econ)Hons*
131299
ØCairns H C *BSc(Hons)*   131299

ØCoslett D S *BSc(Hons)*   131299
Freemantle M *LLB(Hons)*   131299
ØGreenwood E J *BA(Hons)*   131299
Gunson S J W   131299
Higginson J C *BSc(Hons) PGCE*
Knight S M *BSc(Hons)*   131299
ØMetcalfe E *BA(Hons)*   131299
ØParkinson A J   131299
ØRobson E A *BSc(Hons)*   131299
Grice K J   110200
Croslegh J   130600
Holland C M   280900

2nd Lieutenants

Atkinson D R   170598
ØSmith L F   161099
Lord S R   181099
Keith F S   161199
Wadia J M   150400
ØClark L   120800
Kamara C S D   161200
Nicol J A   161200

Rec Res (RARO)

Lieutenants

Rimmer R J   130483

THE GUARDS DIVISION
GRENADIER GUARDS

The Queen's Colours:-

1st Battalion - Gules (crimson): In the centre The Crown; in base a Grenade fired proper

2nd Battalion - Gules (crimson): In the centre the Royal Cypher reversed and interlaced, or ensigned with the Crown. In base a Grenade fired proper; in the dexter canton the Union (Suspended animation. Colours now carried by Nijmegen Company, Grenadier Guards).

3rd Battalion - As for the 2nd Battalion, with, for difference, issuing from the Union in bend a pile wavy or (Suspended Animation)

The Regimental Colours:-

The Union: In the centre a company badge ensigned with The Crown; in base a Grenade fired proper. The 30 company badges are borne in rotation, one on the Regimental Colour of each of the Battalions.

The Battle Honours shown in heavy type below are borne upon the Queen's and Regimental Colours:

Tangier 1680, Namur 1695, Gibraltar 1704-5, Blenheim, Ramillies, Oudenarde, Malplaquet, Dettingen, Lincelles, Egmont-op-Zee, Corunna, Barrosa, Nive, Peninsula, Waterloo, Alma, Inkerman, Sevastopol, Tel-el-Kabir, Egypt 1882, Suakin 1885, Khartoum, Modder River, South Africa 1889-1902

*The Great War_* Mons, Retreat from Mons, **Marne 1914, Aisne 1914, Ypres 1914-17,** Langemark 1914, Gheluvelt, Nonne Bosschen, Neuve Chapelle, Aubers, Festubert 1915, **Loos, Somme 1916, 18,** Ginchy, Flers-Courcelette, Morval, Pilckem, Menin Road, Poelcappelle, Passchendaele, **Cambrai 1917, 18,** St Quentin, Bapaume 1918, **Arras 1918,** Lys, **Hazebrouck,** Albert 1918, Scarpe 1918, **Hindenburg Line,** Havrincourt, Canal du Nord, Selle, Sambre, **France and Flanders 1914-18**

*The Second World War_* Dyle, **Dunkirk 1940,** North Africa 1942-43, **Mareth, Medjez Plain, Salerno,** Volturno Crossing, **Monte Camino, Anzio,** Cagny, **Mont Pincon, Gothic Line, Nijmegen,** Battaglia, Reichswald, **Rhine,** Italy 1943-45, North-West Europe 1940, 44-45.

Gulf 1991, Wadi Al Batin

Regimental Marches

Quick March . . . .(i) The British Grenadiers (ii) The Grenadiers March
Slow March . . . .(i) March from Scipio (ii) The Duke of York's March

Agents . . : . . . . .Lloyds Bank plc, Cox's & King's Branch

Regimental Headquarters . . . . .Wellington Barracks, Birdcage Walk, London SW1E 6HQ (Tel: 020 7414-3280)

Alliances

Canadian Armed Forces . . . . .The Canadian Grenadier Guards
Australian Military Forces . . . . .1st Battalion The Royal Australian Regiment

Colonel in Chief . . . . .THE QUEEN
Colonel . . . . .Field Marshal *HRH The Prince* Philip *Duke of* Edinburgh
KG KT OM GBE AC QSO

Regimental Lieutenant Colonel . . . . . .Col E T Bolitho *OBE* 310700

Colonels	Norton G P R *MBE MA* psc(GE) 300600	Hatherley A G C *MA* psc psc(J) 300997
Aubrey-Fletcher R E H psc 300699	*Majors*	Hewitt C T D 300999
		Maundrell R T *BSc(Hons) MDA* 300999
	March Phillipps De Lisle H L R odc(FR) osc(FR) sq I 311279	Soskin S G *BA(Hons)* 300999
Lieutenant Colonels	Wiggin Bt Sir Charles psc 300982	Wrench J D M 300999
Drage M G A psc 300688	Jalland T W sq 300992	Denison-Smith G R 300900
Lesinski G F psc 300689	Levine J L J *MBE* psc(n) ais 300992	Frost J G R 300900
Scott-Clarke J S psc(n)† 300691	Bibby G K *MBE* psc 300993	James A F R *MA* 300900
Hargreaves J P *BSc(Hons)* psc† 300692	Reames R M T *BA(Hons)* odc(IT) sq 300993	*Captains*
Lloyd J S *MBE BA(Hons)* psc *(A/Col 110101)* 300692	Adams R G 300994	Griffiths M A 300493
Hutchison A D *MA* psc† *(A/Col 041200)* 300694	Hutchings M C J psc 300994	Wade S C E *BSc(Hons)* *(A/Maj 010400)* 110895
Bagnall A R K *MBE* sq 300699	Mills R H G *MA* psc† *(A/Lt Col 260900)* 300994	Bond-Gunning H J R *BA(Hons)* 131296
Hobbs E F psc 300699	Russell-Parsons D J C *MA(Hons)* psc(GE) 300995	Hunt-Davis J J R 141296
Maddan D J H *BSc* psc psc(J) 300699	Winstanley R D psc 300995	Barnes-Taylor T P 80897
		Cordle G J H *BSc(Hons)* 100299

Black T X V *BEng(Hons)*   90200

Regular Category Late Entry Officers

Majors

Kitchen C E *MBE*   300991
Tuck S *BEM* sq   300994
Harris P *MBE*   300995
Inglis B M P   300996
Phasey R A J *BEM*   300996
Marcham S D *MBE*   300999
Dehnel S H   300900

Special Regular Officers Late Entry

Majors

Beresford D   300900

Captains

Green A J   10498

Intermediate Regular Officers

Captains

David M P *(A/Maj 100599)*   110895

Hancock B C P *BA(Hons)*   120298
Harper R A *BSc(Hons)* ph   120298
Bowder J M H *BA(Hons)*   131098

2nd Lieutenants

†Leigh-Pemberton C D   100900

Short Service Late Entry Officers

Captains

Overton V J   70499

Short Service Officers

Captains

Youngman-Sullivan T T *BA (A/Maj 180900)*   100299
Holtby R C D *BSc(Hons)*   30699
Holland L R E *BA(Hons)*   140699
Oconnell J A *BA(Hons)*   121099
Lyon F J E *BA(Hons)*   90200
Cartwright A R G *BA(Hons)*   130600
Hender N J *BA(Hons)*   130600

Lieutenants

Cartwright F F A *MA(Hons)*   120897
Stacey S N J *BSc(Hons)*   161297
Paintin E J *BSc(Hons)*   100298
Broughton The Honourable *(A/Capt 041099)*   130498
Randell S *BA(Hons)*   130498
Elliot-Square M J G *(A/Capt 300999)*   100898
Alkin D J *BCom(Hons)*   121098
Collishaw J R A *BEng(Hons)*   90299
Griffith N J *BA(Hons)*   120499
Reynolds A M *BSc(Hons)*   120499
Lucas D M R   90899
Saxby O C G *BA(Hons)*   90899
Cecil J R   100400

2nd Lieutenants

Green J R   150400
Pinfold R J B *BCom BA*   161200

Rec Res (RARO)

Captains

Davies J L *BA(Hons)*   20496

COLDSTREAM GUARDS

'Nulli Secundus'

The Queen's Colours:-

1st Battalion - Gules (crimson): In the centre the Star of the Order proper, ensigned with The Crown; in base a Sphinx argent between two branches of laurel and tied with a riband vert; above a scroll or, the word 'Egypt' in black letters.

2nd Battalion - Gules (crimson): In the centre a star of eight points argent, within the Garter proper, ensigned with The Crown; in base the Sphinx superscribed 'Egypt' as for 1st Battalion; in the dexter canton the Union (Suspended Animation, but now carried by Number 7 Company Coldstream Guards).

3rd Battalion - As for the 1st Battalion, and, for difference, in the dexter canton, the Union, and issuing therefrom in bend a pile wavy or. (Suspended Animation)

The Regimental Colours:-

The Union: In the centre a company badge ensigned with The Crown; in base the Sphinx superscribed 'Egypt'. The 24 company badges are borne in rotation, 2 at a time, one on the Regimental Colour of both the 1st Battalion and Number 7 Company.

The Battle Honours shown in heavy type below are borne upon the Queen's and Regimental Colours:

Tangier 1680, Namur 1695, Gibraltar 1704-5, Oudenarde, Malplaquet, Dettingen, Lincelles, Talavera, Barrosa, Fuentes d'Onor, Salamanca, Nive, Peninsula, Waterloo, Alma, Inkerman, Sevastopol, Tel-el-Kabir, Egypt 1882, Suakin 1885, Modder River, South Africa 1899-1902

*The Great War_* Mons, **Retreat from Mons, Marne 1914, Aisne 1914, Ypres 1914, 17,** Langemark 1914, Gheluvelt, Nonne Bosschen, Givenchy 1914, Neuve Chapelle, Aubers, Festubert 1915, **Loos,** Mount Sorrel, **Somme 1916, 18,** Flers-Courcelette, Morval, Pilckem, Menin Road, Poelcappelle, Passchendaele, **Cambrai 1917, 18,** St Quentin, Bapaume 1918, **Arras 1918,** Lys, **Hazebrouck,** Albert 1918, Scarpe 1918, Drocourt-Queant, **Hindenburg Line,** Havrincourt, Canal du Nord, Selle, Sambre, France and Flanders 1914-18

*The Second World War_* Dyle, Defence of Escaut, **Dunkirk 1940,** Cagny, **Mont Pincon,** Quarry Hill, Estry, Heppen Nederrijn, Venraij, Meijel, Roer, **Rhineland,** Reichswald, Cleve, Goch, Moyland, Hochwald, Rhine, Lingen, Uelzen, **North-West Europe 1940, 44-45,** Egyptian Frontier 1940, **Sidi Barrani,** Halfaya 1941, **Tobruk 1941, 1942,** Msus, Knightsbridge, Defence of Alamein Line, Medenine, Mareth, Longstop Hill 1942, Sbiba, Steamroller Farm, **Tunis,** Hammam Lif, North Africa 1940-43, **Salerno,** Battipaglia, Cappezano, Volturno Crossing, Monte Camino, Calabritto, Garigliano Crossing, **Monte Ornito,** Monte Piccolo, Capture of Perugia, Arezzo, Advance to Florence, Monte Domini, Catarelto Ridge, Argenta Gap, **Italy 1943-45**

Gulf 1991

Regimental Marches

Quick March ....Regimental March of the Coldstream Guards 'Milanollo'
Slow March ....'Figaro'

Agents ....:...................Lloyds Bank plc, Cox's & King's Branch

Regimental Headquarters ....Wellington Barracks, Birdcage Walk, London SW1E 6HQ (Tel:020-7414-3246)

Alliances

Canadian Armed Forces ....Governor General's Foot Guards
Australian Military Forces ....2nd Battalion The Royal Australian Regiment

Colonel in Chief ....THE QUEEN

Colonel ....General *Sir* Michael Rose *KCB CBE DSO QGM*

Regimental Lieutenant Colonel ......Col E B L Armitstead *OBE* 010299

Colonels

Biggs A R *OBE* psc hcsc(J) 300693
Armitstead E B L *OBE* psc 300694
Williams P G *OBE MA MIL*
  ocds(AUS) psc I *(A/Brig 260201)*
      300695
Bucknall J J C *MBE* psc† 300699

———

Lieutenant Colonels

Emson N E (SL) *MC BA(Hons)* psc
      300688

Somervell M H (SL) *MBE* sq 300691
Boscawen H G R *BA(Hons)* psc
      300693
Bourne-May J J S psc jsdc 300696
Hingston P J sq jsdc ph 300696
Matheson A F Matheson Yr Of *BA*
  psc 300696
Vandeleur D D S A *BSc* psc† 300696
Toler D H *MBE* psc 300698

Majors

Mills P H *MIL* sq I 300981
Turner-Bridger J M sq 300983
Hicks P E D *JP* psc(CAN) 300986
Style W B sq 300987

Holborow S D *MBE* sq 300988
Windsor Clive O J sq 300990
Margesson Honourable *BA(Hons)*
  psc 300992
Vernon J M sq 300992
Blackett J W B sq 300995
Henderson N B *MA* psc † 300995
Tower W J sq 300995
Waters G C C *BSocSc(Hons)* psc(J)
      300996
Bagshaw J D *MA(Hons)* psc(J)
      300997
Gray T W 300997
Stoner C W E 300997
Yorke R W *QGM* 300999

148

Captains		
Pullen C M	*(A/Maj 221099)*	
		110895
Mayhead J R	*(A/Maj 170400)*	
		141296
Duckworth-Chad J A D	*BSc(Hons)*	
		120298
Newall J W G	*BA(Hons)*	120298
Edmunds N H		90498
Till T P O		90498
Rous J A E	*BA(Hons)*	100299

Lieutenants		
Thurstan C B	*BA(Hons)*	120297
Brinn J D		90299
Neill J H		90299
Jones N R	*BSc(Hons)*	90899

2nd Lieutenants		
†Pepper M E H		60998

Regular Category Late Entry Officers

Majors	
Winter L	300995
Lord A	300996
Manning M J	300996

Special Regular Officers Late Entry

Majors	
Barnes A	300999

Captains		
Howick R J		10498
McCormack R H	*MBE*	10498
Tester S		10498

Intermediate Regular Officers

Captains		
Philp C A H		110497
Sergeant R C N	*BSc(Hons)*	120298
Liddell A B D		131098
Selby G C	*BA(Hons)*	131098

Short Service Late Entry Officers

Captains	
Perry K	10498
Pears M	150299
Clarke G J	60400
Hall D P	60400

Short Service Officers

Captains		
Scott J L A	*BA(Hons)*	160698
Elliott H D L	*BSc(Hons)*	100299
Lissauer M G	*BA(Hons)*	100299
Hodder G M G	*BSc(Hons)*	140699
Barthorp R S A	*BSc(Hons)*	90200
Thurstan J H F	*BSc(Hons)*	90200
Scrope S H R	*BA(Hons)*	200700
Payne M R L	*BA(Hons)*	101000
De Borchgrave Daltena S G		
	BSc(Hons)	80201

Lieutenants		
Walker D H D	*BA*	160697
Freeland A R D	*BSc(Hons)*	120897
Hamilton B J	*BSc(Hons)*	120897
Weller-Poley G H	*BA(Hons)*	120897
McLean R C	*BA(Hons)*	100298
Luther W G L	*BA(Hons)*	100898
Stephens T C S	*BA(Hons)*	10199
D Apice C M J	*BA(Hons)*	90899
Beale M A G		131299
Rosen H W		131299

2nd Lieutenants		
Lloyd Owen T O M		120800

SCOTS GUARDS

The Queen's Colours:-

1st Battalion - Gules (crimson): In the centre Royal Arms of Scotland, ensigned with The Crown. Motto *'En Ferus Hostis'* in base the Sphinx superscribed "Egypt"

2nd Battalion - Gules (crimson): In the centre the Thistle and the Red and White Roses conjoined, issuant from the same stalk all proper, ensigned with The Crown. Motto *'Unita Fortior'*; in base the Sphinx superscribed 'Egypt'; in the dexter canton the Union (Suspended Animation, but now carried by F Company Scots Guards).

The Regimental Colours:-

The Union: In the centre a company badge ensigned with The Crown; in base the Sphinx superscribed 'Egypt'. The 24 company badges are borne in rotation, 2 at a time, one on the Regimental Colour of each of the two Battalions.

The Battle Honours shown in heavy type below are borne upon the Queen's and Regimental Colours:

Namur 1695, Dettingen, Lincelles, Talavera, Barrosa, Fuentes d'Onor, Salamanca, Nive, Peninsula, Waterloo, Alma, Inkerman, Sevastopol, Tel-el-Kabir, Egypt 1882, Suakin 1885, Modder River, South Africa 1889-1902

*The Great War_* **Retreat from Mons, Marne 1914, Aisne 1914, Ypres 1914-17,** Langemark 1914, Gheluvelt, Nonne Bosschen, Givenchy 1914, Neuve Chapelle, Aubers, **Festubert 1915, Loos, Somme 1916, 18,** Flers-Courcelette, Morval, Pilckem, Poelcappelle, Passchendaele, **Cambrai 1917, 18,** St Quentin, Albert 1918, Bapaume 1918, Arras 1918, Drocourt-Queant, **Hindenburg Line,** Havrincourt, Canal du Nord, Selle, Sambre, **France and Flanders 1914-18**

*The Second World War_* Stien, Norway 1940, Halfaya 1941, Sidi Suleiman, Tobruk 1941, **Gazala,** Knightsbridge, Defence of Alamein Line, Medenine, Tadjera Khir, Medjez Plain, Grich el Oued, **Djebel Bou Aoukaz 1943, I, North Africa 1941-3,** Salerno, Battipaglia, Volturno Crossing, Rocchetta e Croce, **Monte Camino, Anzio,** Campoleone, Carroceto, Trasimene Line, Advance to Florence, Monte San Michele, Catarelto Ridge, Argenta Gap, **Italy 1943-45,** Mont Pincon, **Quarry Hills,** Estry, Venlo Pocket, **Rhineland,** Reichswald, Cleve, Moyland, Hochwald, Rhine, Lingen, Uelzen, **North-West Europe 1944-45.**

Tumbledown Mountain, Falkland Islands 1982   Gulf 1991

Regimental Marches

Pipes and Drums   ·
Quick March . . . . .Heilan' Laddie
Slow March .The Garb of Old Gaul

Regimental Band
Quick March . . . . .Heilan' Laddie
Slow March .The Garb of Old Gaul

Agents . . . . .Lloyds Bank plc, Cox's & King's Branch

Regimental Headquarters . . . . .Wellington Barracks, Birdcage Walk, London SW1E 6HQ (Tel: 020 7414-3333)

Alliance

Australian Military Forces . . . . .3rd Battalion The Royal Australian Regiment

Colonel in Chief . . . . , ...THE QUEEN

Colonel . . . . .Field Marshal *HRH The Duke of* Kent *KG GCMG GCVO ADC* 090774

Regimental Lieutenant Colonel . . . . . .Maj Gen J T Holmes *OBE MC* 150201

	Majors	
	Dalzel-Job I E *BSc(Eng)* sq(w)	
		300980
	Woods E A sq	300981
Colonels	Price S A C psc(AUS)	300984
Fitzalan Howard T M *OBE*	Farrelly P J L *MBE* psc	300991
MA(Hons) rcds psc 300696	Hayward J R *BA(Hons)* sq	300991
Lancaster J A S *MBE* psc 300697	Bence-Trower M G *BA(Hons)*	
Miller-Bakewell A J psc aic 300698	osc(SP) sq	300992
————	Nickerson G H F S *MA GCGI* psc†	
	ph	300994
Lieutenant Colonels	Page C S T psc	300994
Cargill J J *OBE MA* psc 300686	Stuart J D *MA* psc psc(J) *(A/Lt Col*	
Gascoigne P E C *MBE* sq 300691	*160201)*	300994
Crowe J E M *OBE* psc 300696	Hancock J H T *BA(Hons)* psc(J)	
Turner M N D *MBE BSc MBA* psc		300995
	300696	Swinton W H C psc(J)	300995
Foster A W psc 300697	Copeland P M	300997
Mathewson A D *M A (Oxon)* psc†	Lindsay R H *BSc(Hons)* psc(J)	
	300699		300997

Macnamee R C	300997
Holling K B	300998
Jopp L P M *MC BA*	300998
Inglis W J *BA(Hons)*	300999
Speed A P *BA(Hons)*	300900
Captains	
Hutchison T M O	101294
Spencer R J *BA(Hons)*	120297
Bell C J	70897
Daly A C *MA(Hons)*	90200
Lawrie W K M *BA(Hons)*	90200
Maxwell-Stuart J F C *BA*	130600
Lieutenants	
Hughes J A *BA(Hons)* *(A/Capt*	
311000)	120897
Pitt J P T *MA(Hons)*	140698
Bassett Cross R J	90899

Regular Category Late Entry Officers

Majors

Wood D J — 300998
Walker R *MBE* — 300999

Special Regular Officers Late Entry

Captains

Crawford A J *MBE* — 10496
Spence J G — 10696
Gwynne I *BEM* — 10498

Intermediate Regular Officers

Majors

Kelly J R — 201196
Taylor G A P — 300998

Captains

French M A *BSc(Hons)* — 131296
Sinclair R H *BSc(Hons)* — 131296
Elmhirst C M R *BSc (A/Maj 011100)* — 120298
Howieson R M — 90499
Lindsay-German I J V *MBE* — 101299
Kitching R E C — 80201

Short Service Late Entry Officers

Captains

Hay A S — 60400

Short Service Officers

Captains

D'Apice H A C *BSc(Hons)* — 120298

Macrae C A *MA(Hons)* — 140699
Wilson A M *BSc(Hons)* — 90200
Snow J A *MA(Hons)* — 130600

Lieutenants

Mace W N — 160697
Dewhurst P M J *BA(Hons)* — 161297
Jungels C *MA(Hons)* — 100298
Shannon R M T *BSc(Hons)* — 100298
Wilson A J A *BA(Hons)* — 100898
Woodward D E T *MA(Hons)* — 90299
McEwan T N — 120499
Timpson L R J *(A/Capt 280101)* — 120499
Hickie M D J *BSc(Hons)* — 90899
Holroyd-Smith A J *BA(Hons)* — 90899
Ure A H B *BA(Hons)* — 90899

2nd Lieutenants

Dobson M J — 70899

IRISH GUARDS

The Queen's Colours:-
1st Battalion - Gules (crimson): In the centre the Royal Cypher or, within the Collar of the Order of St Patrick with badge appendant proper, ensigned with The Crown
2nd Battalion - Gules (crimson): In the centre the Star of the Order of St Patrick ensigned with The Crown; in the dexter canton the Union (Suspended Animation)

The Regimental Colours:-
The Union, in the centre a company badge ensigned with The Crown. The 22 company badges are borne in rotation
The Battle Honours shown in heavy type below are borne upon the Queen's and Regimental Colours:

*The Great War_* Mons, **Retreat from Mons, Marne 1914, Aisne 1914, Ypres 1914, 17,** Langemark 1914, Gheluvelt, Nonne Bosschen, **Festubert 1915, Loos, Somme 1916, 18,** Flers-Courcelette, Morval, Pilckem, Poelcappelle, Passchendaele, **Cambrai 1917, 18,** St Quentin, Lys, **Hazebrouck,** Albert 1918, Bapaume 1918, Arras 1918, Scarpe 1918, Drocourt-Queant, **Hindenburg Line,** Canal du Nord, Selle, Sambre, France and Flanders 1914-18

*The Second World War_* Pothus, **Norway 1940, Boulogne 1940,** Cagny, **Mont Pincon, Neerpelt, Nijmegen,** Aam, **Rhineland,** Hochwald, Rhine, Bentheim, **North-West Europe 1944-45,** Medjez Plain, **Djebel Bou Aoukaz 1943, North Africa 1943, Anzio,** Aprilla, Carroceto, Italy 1943-44.

Regimental Marches

Quick March . . . . .St Patrick's Day
Slow March . . . . .Let Erin Remember

Agents . . . . .Lloyds Bank plc, Cox's & King's Branch

Regimental Headquarters . . . . .Wellington Barracks, Birdcage Walk, London SW1E 6HQ (Tel:020 7414-3293)

Alliances

Australian Military Forces . . . . .4th Battalion The Royal Australian Regiment
Leeward Islands . . . . .Montserrat Defence Force

Colonel in Chief . . . . .THE QUEEN
Colonel . . . .*The Duke of* Abercorn *KG* 011100
Regimental Lieutenant Colonel . . . . . .Brig S J L Roberts 010799

Brigadiers
Roberts S J L *OBE MA* psc hcsc(J) 300699

Colonels
Langton C R *OBE AIL* psc 300694

Lieutenant Colonels
O'Gorman J B (SL) sq 300691
Pollock J H O'H *MBE* psc 300695
Cubitt W G *OBE BSc(Hons)* psc† 300696
Owen S P *MSc* psc† 300699

Majors
Macmullen T W J *BA(Hons)* sq 300984
Shaw R C O 300993
Stopford J R H psc 300993
Knaggs C P H psc 300994
Moriarty G M psc - 300994
Carleton-Smith M A P *MBE BA(Hons)* psc† 300995
Craig-Harvey C A cafs ph sq(w) 300995
Melotte E J F V psc(J) 300995
Segrave S O psc(J) 300996
Hannah D M *BA(Hons)* 300997
O'Dwyer M G C *BSc(Hons)* psc(J) 300997
Farrell B C *MBE BA* 300998

Holt H A B *BA(Hons)* 300998
Ghika C J *BA(Hons)* 300900
Walker C R V *BSc(Hons)* jssc 300900

Captains
Macmullen P C A 110895
Boanas E T *BA(Hons)* 141295
Wilson E K 130496
Orrell J B J 70897
Hymans N A *LLB* jssc 121297
Reddington J M *BA(Hons)* 140699

Lieutenants
Rous R W J 120897
Turner I A J *BA(Hons)* 161297
†Leavey P G *BSc(Hons)* 100898
Smythe B P 90299

2nd Lieutenants
Plummer R J 120800

Regular Category Late Entry Officers
Majors
Faloone J F P 300994

Special Regular Officers Late Entry
Captains
Cloney P J 10497

Intermediate Regular Officers
Captains
O'Reilly C *BBS* 120298
Roberts F A D L *BA(Hons)* 120298
Wilkinson D G L 111298
Light G C *BSc(Hons)* 100299
Collins M J *DipHE* 100200

Short Service Late Entry Officers
Majors
Knowles J C 300900

Captains
Windle L K 100894
Lumb G C 10498
Devitt S 10700

Short Service Officers
Captains
Lythe J E *BSc(Hons)* 131296
Stewart M R N *BA(Hons)* 140699
Grayson M P M *BA(Hons)* 90200
Hopkirk W J *BA(Hons)* 90200
Wills A J *BSc(Hons)* 90200
Keilthy P N 101000
Ormerod P M P *BA(Econ)Hons* 101000

Lieutenants

Gay N P T *BA(Hons)*	120897
Jones E N *BA(Hons)*	120897
Olsen T A L *BA(Hons)*	161297
Scott Kerr J W	161297
Roscoe W J F *BA(Hons)*	100298
Nunan M W	130498

Magan E W M	140698
Moulton J D *BA(Hons)*	140698
Brennan N P *BA*	100898
Cosby A J A *MEng(Hons) ACGI*	
	90299
Palmer J A E *BA(Hons)*	120499
Sincock C E W *BEng(Hons)*	90899

Townley J P F *BA(Hons)*	121299
Lance P C *BA(Hons)*	131299

2nd Lieutenants

Erasmus J V	100499
Dickinson H A H	161200

WELSH GUARDS

The Queen's Colours:-
1st Battalion - Gules (crimson): In the centre a Dragon passant or, underneath a scroll with motto 'Cymru Am Byth', the whole ensigned with The Crown
2nd Battalion - Gules (crimson): In the centre a leek or within the Garter, ensigned with The Crown, in the dexter canton the Union (Suspended animation).

The Regimental Colours:-
The Union. In the centre a company badge ensigned with The Crown.

The Battle Honours shown in heavy type below are borne upon the Queen's and Regimental Colours:

The Great War **Loos,** Somme 1916, 18, **Ginchy, Flers-Courcelette, Morval,** Ypres 1917, **Pilckem, Poelcappelle,** Passchendaele, **Cambrai 1917, 18, Bapaume 1918,** Arras 1918, Albert 1918, Drocourt-Queant, Hindenburg Line, Havrincourt, **Canal du Nord,** Selle, **Sambre,** France and Flanders 1915-18

The Second World War **Defence of Arras, Boulogne 1940,** St Omer-La Bassee, Bourguebus Ridge, Cagny, **Mont Pincon, Brussels, Hechtel,** Nederrijn, Rhineland, Lingen, North-West Europe 1940, 44-45, **Foundouk,** Djebel el Rhorab, Tunis, **Hammam Lif,** North Africa 1943, **Monte Ornito,** Liri Valley, **Monte Piccolo,** Capture of Perugia, Arezzo, Advance to Florence, Gothic Line, **Battaglia,** Italy 1944-45.

Falkland Islands 1982

Regimental Marches

Quick March	Rising of the Lark
Slow March	Men of Harlech
Agents	Lloyds Bank plc, Cox's & King's Branch
Regimental Headquarters	Wellington Barracks, Birdcage Walk, London SW1E 6HQ (Tel:020 7414-3288)

Alliance

Australian Military Forces	5th/7th Battalion The Royal Australian Regiment
	HMS Campbeltown

Colonel in Chief	THE QUEEN
Colonel	HRH *The Prince of* Wales *KG KT GCB AK QSO ADC*
Regimental Lieutenant Colonel	Maj Gen C R Watt *CBE* 010100

Harris G R *BA(Hons)*   100299

Lieutenant Colonels

Bonas T C S *BA(Hons)* psc   300694
Malcolm A J E *OBE* psc(AUS) psc(J)
 (A/Col 200101)   300695
Ford A C   sq jsdc   300698
Black C N *MBE MA MPhil(Cantab)*
psc   300600

Majors

Sayers J D G   sq   300986
Bodington R H W ST G *MBE* psc
  300993
Bathurst B J *BSc(Hons)* psc†
  300995
Talbot Rice R H *BA(Hons) MA*
 GCGI psc† *(A/Lt Col 311000)*
  300995
Stanford R J A   *MBE* psc(J)   300996
Treadgold S J N   300996
Macintosh G A J   300998
Bartle-Jones G   300999
Jenkins M B D   *BD*   300999
Thorneloe R S M   *BA(Hons)*   300999
Lloyd H R H   300900
Williams-Bulkeley R H   *BSc(Hons)*
  300900

Captains

Lewis G A G   151295
Legge-Bourke H R   121297

Lieutenants

Spry A R M   80800

2nd Lieutenants

†Smith T A   80996

Regular Category Late Entry Officers

Lieutenant Colonels

Evans D R   *MBE*   10197

Majors

Denman A L   300999
Harvey N   300999

Special Regular Officers Late Entry

Majors

Stacey K W   300999

Captains

Dyas I P   *(A/Maj 011297)*   100696
Oultram F K   150696
Powell A J   10497
Harford J W   *(A/Maj 290101)*
  10498

Intermediate Regular Officers

Captains

Bossi D L   *BA(Hons)*   *(A/Maj 080101)*   110896
Larkin R W C   *BA(Hons)*   120298
Stenner J D   *BEng(Hons)*   *(A/Maj 041200)*   120298
Pim R G B   *BA(Hons)*   90200
Ramsay B P N   *MA(Hons)*   90200
Stone G C G R   120800

Lieutenants

Charles T F   *(A/Capt 120499)*
  140497
Lorriman R E E A   *(A/Capt 261199)*
  130498

Short Service Late Entry Officers

Captains

Browne M E   *BEM*   280499
Miles M W   60400

Short Service Officers

Captains

Antelme C K   *BA(Hons)*   200499
Simpson P S   *BA*   140699
Gallimore R W   121099
Hearn E J W   *BSocSc(Hons)*   121099

154

Bevan D W N *BA(Hons)*	130600	
Bettinson H G C	200700	

Lieutenants

Marsh N A *BA(Hons)* *(A/Capt 081200)* 120897
Janes R G S *BA(Hons)* 161297

Hobrough J M *BSc(Hons)* 100898
Salusbury J D *BA* 100898
Birchall S E *BSc(Hons)* 141298
Burnett R C R *BA(Hons)* 141298
Mellish E J T *BA(Hons)* 141298
Eastman T A H 120499
Sargent C T *(A/Capt 190600)* 120499

Lewis M L *BSc(Hons)* 90899
Ulvert C N 90899

2nd Lieutenants

Basson D H 111299

THE SCOTTISH DIVISION

Comprising .The Royal Scots (The Royal Regiment) (1 Regular Battalion and Volunteer Company)

The Royal Highland Fusiliers (Princess Margaret's Own Glasgow and Ayrshire Regiment) (1 Regular Battalion and Volunteer Company)

The King's Own Scottish Borderers (1 Regular Battalion and Volunteer Company)

The Black Watch (Royal Highland Regiment) (1 Regular Battalion and Volunteer Company)

The Highlanders (Seaforth, Gordons and Camerons) (1 Regular Battalion and 2 Volunteer Companies)

The Argyll and Sutherland Highlanders (Princess Louise's) (1 Regular Battalion and 2 Volunteer Companies)

52nd Lowland Regiment (1 Volunteer Battalion)

51st Highland Regiment (1 Volunteer Battalion)

Divisional Officer . . . . .The Castle, Edinburgh EH1 2YT (Tel: 0131-310-5001 Fax: 0131-310-5075) and HQ Infantry Warminster BA12 0DJ (Tel: 01985-222674 Fax: 01985-222151)

Colonel Commandant . . . . .Lt Gen A S H Irwin *CBE* 010400

Divisional Lieutenant Colonel . . . . . . .Lt Col R M Riddell BW 150199

The origins of amalgamated Regiments now included in the Scottish Division are as follows:

THE ROYAL HIGHLAND FUSILIERS (PRINCESS MARGARET'S OWN GLASGOW AND AYRSHIRE REGIMENT)

On 20 January 1959

The Royal Scots Fusiliers (21) and

The Highland Light Infantry (City of Glasgow Regiment) (71 and 74) amalgamated to form:

The Royal Highland Fusiliers (Princess Margaret's Own Glasgow and Ayrshire Regiment) (21, 71 and 74)

THE HIGHLANDERS (SEAFORTH, GORDONS AND CAMERONS)

On 7 February 1961

Seaforth Highlanders (Ross-shire Buffs, The Duke of Albany's) (72 and 78) and

The Queen's Own Cameron Highlanders (79) amalgamated to form:

Queen's Own Highlanders (Seaforth and Camerons) (72, 78 and 79)

On 17 September 1994

Queen's Own Highlanders (Seaforth and Camerons) (72, 78 and 79) and

The Gordon Highlanders (75 and 92) amalgamated to form:

The Highlanders (Seaforth, Gordons and Camerons) (72, 75, 78, 79 and 92)

156

THE ROYAL SCOTS (THE ROYAL REGIMENT) (1)

The Royal Cypher within the Collar of the Order of the Thistle with the Badge appendant
In each of the four corners the Thistle within the Circle and motto of the Order, ensigned with The Crown,
The Sphinx, superscribed Egypt

Tangier 1680, Namur 1695, Blenheim, Ramillies, Oudenarde, Malplaquet, Louisburg, Havannah, Egmont-op-Zee, Egypt, St Lucia 1803, Corunna, Busaco, Salamanca, Vittoria, St Sebastian, Nive, Peninsula, Niagara, Waterloo, Nagpore, Maheidpoor, Ava, Alma, Inkerman, Sevastopol, Taku Forts, Pekin 1860, South Africa 1899-1902

*The Great War_* Mons, Le Cateau, Retreat from Mons, **Marne 1914 18**, Aisne 1914, La Bassee 1914, Neuve Chapelle, **Ypres 1915, 17, 18**, Gravenstafel, St Julien, Frezenburg, Bellewaarde, Aubers, Festubert 1915, **Loos, Somme 1916, 18**, Albert 1916, 18, Bazentin, Pozieres, Flers-Courcelette, Le Transloy, Ancre Heights, Ancre 1916, 18, **Arras 1917, 18**, Scarpe 1917, 18, Arleux, Pilckem, Langemarck 1917, Menin Road, Polygon Wood, Poelcappelle, Passchendaele, Cambrai 1917, St Quentin, Rosieres, **Lys**, Estaires, Messines 1918, Hazebrouck, Bailleul, Kemmel, Bethune, Soissonnais-Ourcq, Tardenois, Amiens, Bapaume 1918, Drocourt-Queant, Hindenburg Line, Canal du Nord, St Quentin Canal, Beaurevoir, Courtrai, Selle, Sambre, France and Flanders 1914-18, **Struma**, Macedonia 1915-18, Helles, Landing at Helles, Krithia, Suvla, Scimitar Hill, **Gallipoli 1915-16**, Rumani, Egypt 1915-16, Gaza, El Mughar, Nebi Samwil, Jaffa, **Palestine 1917-18**, Archangel 1918-19

*The Second World War_* Dyle, **Defence of Escaut**, St Omer-La-Bassee, **Odon**, Cheux, Defence of Rauray, Caen, Esquay, Mont Pincon, **Aart**, Nederrijn, Best, Scheldt, **Flushing**, Meijel, Venlo Pocket, Roer, Rhineland, Reichswald, Cleve, Goch, **Rhine**, Uelzen, Bremen, Artlenberg, **North-West Europe 1940, 44-45, Gothic Line**, Marradi, Monte Gamberaldi, **Italy 1944-45**, South East Asia 1941, Donbaik, **Kohima**, Relief of Kohima, Aradura, Shwebo, Mandalay, **Burma 1943-45**.

Gulf 1991, Wadi Al Batin

Regimental Marches

Pipes and Drums

Quick March	Dumbarton's Drums
Slow March	The Garb of Old Gaul

Military Band

Quick March	Dumbarton's Drums
Slow March	The Garb of Old Gaul

Agents .... Lloyds Bank plc, Cox's & King's Branch

Regimental Headquarters .... The Castle, Edinburgh EH1 2YT (Tel: 0131-310-5014 Fax: 0131-310-5019)

Alliances

Canadian Armed Forces .... The Canadian Scottish Regiment (Princess Mary's)
The Royal Newfoundland Regiment

Affiliated Regiment
Royal Gurkha Rifles

Colonel in Chief .... HRH THE PRINCESS ROYAL *KG KT GCVO QSO*

Colonel .... Maj Gen M J Strudwick *CBE* .... .201095

	Fraser-Hopewell P D *MBE* sq	Donovan J M *MA* psc(J)	300998
	300697	Douglas K P *BEd*	300900
	Telfer S F M *MBE MA* psc(CAN)	Moffat N A J *BEng(Hons)*	300900
	300699		
Brigadiers	Stevenson J I S *MBE* psc 300600	*Captains*	
Johnstone I A *OBE* psc† psc(n)		Bristow J D M *BA*	101094
hcsc(J) 300692	*Majors*	Lowder M *BA*	101294
	Rae G J *MSc DipM MAPM* aic sq(w)	Dobson D *MA*	170595
Colonels	300988	Henderson S J S	110895
Maclean F R J osc(ZIM) sq 300694	Smith D R R sq(w) † 300990	Bathgate D D C (*A/Maj 110900*)	
Scott-Bowden R L *MBE*	Bruce R B *MA(Hons) MSc* psc(J)		180696
BSc(Eng)Hons psc† 300699	G(ss) 300995	Strudwick P G B *BSc(SocSciENCE)*	
	Jack D T 300995		110896
	Lowder G E *MBE LLB MA* psc†	Winskill J D *BA(Hons)*	110896
Lieutenant Colonels	300995	Haston N J *BA(Hons)*	81096
	Onslow M P D *BA(Hons)* sq	Anderson J R *MA(Hons)* PC	
Blamire R G A (SL) sq 300691	300995		120297
McDowall A R M psc† psc ph	Wallace C P 300995	Keetley P A *BA(Hons)*	131098
300694	Richardson G S 300996	Bryce-Stafford R D *BEng(Hons)*	
Gillies K R *MBE* sq jsdc 311295	McLeod A R cafs sq(w) 300997		100299
De La Haye B G sq jsdc 300697	Walker R M *BSc(Hons)* 300997	Salmon D A B *BA(Hons)*	80201

157

Regular Category Late Entry Officers

Majors

Thomson W C 300998

Special Regular Officers Late Entry

Captains

Vevers G M 10498

Intermediate Regular Officers

Captains

Brodie A J P *BA(Hons)* 120298
Cruickshank J *BSc(Eng)Hons*
160698

Dougall I *BSc(Hons)* 121099
Hunter R G 121099
Bunney T J H *BSc/BA(Hons)*
90200

Short Service Late Entry Officers

Captains

Shanks C 130498
Wallace R H 70400

Short Service Officers

Captains

Tweedie G T H 140699
McLeish R N *BLE(Hons)* 130600
Lumley A D *MA(Hons)* 80201
Goodacre D A *BSc(Hons)* 80201

Lieutenants

Mouat S 180598
Sharwood-Smith P M *BSc(Hons)*
140698
Stark R D R *BSc(Hons)* 130699
Giles J F *BA(Hons)* 90899
Watt M A C *BTech* 90899
Dunn N S *BSc(Hons)* 131299
Wight-Boycott N M   *(A/Capt*
111200) 131299
Howard M J 210700

2nd Lieutenants

Bolas D G H 120800

158

THE ROYAL HIGHLAND FUSILIERS (PRINCESS MARGARET'S OWN GLASGOW AND AYRSHIRE REGIMENT) (21, 71 and 74)

The monogram H.L.I. surmounted by The Crown upon a grenade, with the motto,
Nemo Nos Impune Lacessit.

The Royal Cypher surmounted by The Crown. The Castle and Key superscribed "Gibraltar, 1780-83", and with the motto *"Montis Insignia Calpe"*. An Elephant superscribed Assaye

Blenheim, Ramillies, Oudenarde, Malplaquet, Dettingen, Belleisle, Carnatic, Hindoostan, Sholinghur, Mysore, Martinique 1794, Seringapatam, Cape of Good Hope 1806, Rolica, Vimiera, Corunna, Busaco, Fuentes D'Onor, Almaraz, Ciudad Rodrigo, Badajoz, Salamanca, Vittoria, Pyrenees, Nivelle, Nive, Orthes, Toulouse, Peninsula, Bladensburg, Waterloo, South Africa 1851-53, Alma, Inkerman, Sevastopol, Central India, South Africa 1879, Tel-el-Kabir, Egypt 1882, Burma 1885-87, Tirah, Modder River, Relief of Ladysmith, South Africa 1899-1902, Gibraltar 1780-83, Assaye

*The Great War_* **Mons,** Le Cateau, Retreat from Mons, **Marne 1914,** Aisne 1914, La Bassee 1914, **Ypres 1914, 15, 17, 18,** Langemarck 1914, 17, Gheluvelt, Nonne Bosschen, Givenchy 1914, Neuve Chapelle, St Julien, Aubers, Festubert 1915, **Loos, Somme 1916, 18,** Albert 1916, 18, Bazentin, Delville Wood, Pozieres, Flers-Courcelette, La Transloy, Ancre Heights, Ancre 1916, 18, **Arras 1917, 18,** Vimy 1917, **Scarpe 1917,** 18, Arleux, Messines 1917, 18, Pilckem, Menin Road, Polygon Wood, Passchendaele, Cambrai 1917-18, St Quentin, Baupaume 1918, Rosieres, Lys, Estaires, Hazebroucke, Bailleul, Kemmel, Bethune, Scherpenberg, Amiens, Queant, **Hindenburg Line,** Havrincourt, Canal du Nord, St Quentin Canal, Beaurevoir, Courtrai, Selle, Sambre, France and Flanders 1914-18, **Doiran 1917, 18,** Macedonia 1916-18, Helles, **Gallipoli 1915-16,** Rumani, Egypt 1916-17, Gaza, El Mughar, Nebi Samwil, Jerusalem, Jaffa, Tell' Asur, **Palestine 1917-18,** Tigris 1916, Kut Al Amara 1917, Sharqat, **Mesopotamia 1916-18**

*The Second World War_*Defence of Arras, **Ypres-Comines Canal,** Somme 1940, Withdrawal to Seine, Withdrawal to Cherbourg, **Odon,** Fontenay Le Pesnil, Cheux, Defence of Rauray, Esquay, Mont Pincon, Quarry Hill, Estry, **Falaise,** Le Vie Crossing, La Touques Crossing, Seine 1944, Asrt, Nederrijn, Best, Le Havre, Antwerp-Turnhout Canal, **Scheldt,** South Beveland, **Walcheren,** Lower Maas, Meijel, Venlo Pocket, Roer, Ourthe, Rhineland, **Reichswald,** Cleve, Goch, Moyland Wood, Weeze, **Rhine,** Ibbenburen, Dreirwalde, Aller, Ulzen, **Bremen,** Artlenberg, **North-West Europe 1940, 44-45,** Jebel Shiba, Barentu, **Keren,** Massawa, Abyssinia 1941, Gazala, **Cauldron,** Mersa Matruh, Fuka, North Africa 1940-42, **Landing in Sicily,** Sangro, **Garigliano Crossing,** Minturno, Anzio, Advance to Tiber, Italy 1943, 44, 45, Madagascar, Adriatic, Middle East 1942, 44, Athens, **Greece 1944-45, North Arakan,** Razabil, **Pinwe,** Shweli, Mandalay, Burma 1944-45.

Gulf 1991

Regimental Marches

Pipes and Drums

Quick Marches . . . .(i) Heilan Laddie (ii) Blue Bonnets are over the Border
Slow March .My Home

Military Band

Quick Marches . . . .(i) British Grenadiers (ii) Whistle o'er the Lave o't
Slow Marches . . . .(i) The Garb of Old Gaul (ii) March of the 21st Regiment

Agents . . . . .Holt's Branch, Royal Bank of Scotland plc, Lawrie House, Farnborough, Hants GU14 7NR

Regimental Headquarters . . . . .518 Sauchiehall Street, Glasgow G2 3LW
(Tel: 0141-332-0961/5639. Fax: 0141-353-1493)

Alliances

Canadian Armed Forces . . . . .The Royal Highland Fusiliers of Canada
New Zealand Army . . . . .1st Battalion The Royal New Zealand Infantry Regiment
Pakistan Army . . . . .11th Battalion The Baloch Regiment
South African Defence Force . . . . .Prince Alfred's Guard

Colonel in Chief . . . . .HRH The Princess Margaret Countess of Snowdon *CI GCVO*

Colonel . . . . .Maj Gen A I Ramsay *CBE DSO* 011297

		Roberts A J psc odc(KEN) 300600		Pickard I D R *BA(Hons)* psc(PAK)
		———		300699
Brigadiers				Cartwright P A S *BA(Hons) MA MSc*
Loudon W E B *OBE* psc hcsc(J)				psc†	300600
	300699	*Lieutenant Colonels*		Johnston A D *MBE BSc* psc 300600
		Allison C G *MBE* psc jsdc	300696	
Colonels		Campbell N T psc	300696	*Majors*
		Kirk D C *MBE* psc† psc psc(J)		Harvey A C H sq	300679
Edwardes J S M *OBE* psc(n)†			300698	Archibald N A *MBE BD* psc 300985
	300699			

Miln H M *MSc* psc† 300987
Common W A *MA* nadc sq jsdc
        300988
Middleton A D *MBE* sq 300989
Whitmore A C   sq sq(w) ais 300989
Garven J *MBE* sq 300990
Whitelaw A C B   psc(PAK) 300991
Campbell N B V *BA(Hons)* 300994
Channer N H D R *BA(Hons) MA*
  psc† 300995
Marlow E H R *BA* osc(US) 300995
Steel D G   psc(J) 300996
Mack D N M   psc(J) 300997
Richmond D C   psc(J) 300997
Cartwright S J *BSc* 300998
Borton N R M *BA* 300999
Fenton E A *MA(Hons)* 300999
Herbert C L G 300999
Masson D C 300999
Montgomery B S 300999
Whitehead P 300999
Rule A T 300900

Captains

Hutt P 10495
Baxter G J *BSc(Hons) (A/Maj*
  011100) 90695
Taylor C C J W 271295
Cherrington C *BA(Hons) (A/Maj*
  161000) 60296
Fitzpatrick A J   *(A/Maj 140200)*
        130496
Holme E M N *BEng(Hons)* 100299

Lieutenants

Ling D P *BA(Hons)* 120897
Abram N D E *MA(Hons)* 131097
Duff J R *BA(Hons)* 131098

Regular Category Late Entry Officers

Majors

McGarva H M *MBE* 300993
McAulay H M 300997
Connelly G J *MBE BSc(Hons)*
  MIMGT 300999

Special Regular Officers Late Entry

Captains

Frew J 30497
Roy H 10498

Intermediate Regular Officers

Captains

Ross G D   ph 80897
Cave-Gibbs T J *BA(Hons)* 170699

Lieutenants

Feaver S R *BSc(Hons) (A/Capt*
  040800) 141096
Luckyn-Malone M P S   *(A/Capt*
  100898) 100898

Barber N G   *(A/Capt 070699)*
        141298
Joyce P A   *(A/Capt 260700)* 141298

Short Service Late Entry Officers

Majors

Stoddart G N M *MBE BEM* 300998

Captains

Kerr C 10898
Fyfe D   *(L/Maj 130700)* 60499
Kerr J E B 80201

Short Service Officers

Captains

Thomson K C *BA* 121099
Channer T H C D *BA(Hons)* 130600

Lieutenants

Luckyn-Malone F A L *MA(Hons)*
        100298
Greene K *BA* 90299
Winfield T A 90899
Brown N J L 121199
Kindness N J 100400

2nd Lieutenants

Bridle N P 161200

THE KING'S OWN SCOTTISH BORDERERS (25)

The Castle of Edinburgh. *'Nisi Dominus frustra'*
In the first and fourth corners the Royal Crest, with the motto *'In Veritate Religionis confido'*
In the second and third corners the White Horse with the motto *'Nec aspera terrent'*
The Sphinx, superscribed Egypt

Namur 1695, Minden, Egmont-op-Zee, Martinique 1809, Afghanistan 1878-80 Chitral, Tirah, Paardeberg, South Africa 1900-02

*The Great War_* **Mons,** Le Cateau, Retreat from Mons, Marne 1914, 18, **Aisne 1914,** La Bassee 1914, Messines 1914, **Ypres 1914, 15, 17, 18,** Nonne Bosschen, Hill 60, Gravenstafel, St Julien, Frezenberg, Bellewaarde, **Loos, Somme 1916, 18,** Albert 1916, 18, Bazentin, Delville Wood, Pozieres, Guillemont, Flers-Courcelette, Morval, Le Transloy, Ancre Heights, **Arras 1917, 18,** Vimy 1917, Scarpe 1917, 18, Arleux, Pilckem, Langemarck,1917, Menin Road, Polygon Wood, Broodseinde, Poelcappelle, Passchendaele, Cambrai 1917-18, St Quentin, Lys, Estaires, Hazebrouck, Kemmel, **Soissonnais-Ourcq,** Bapaume 1918, Drocourt-Queant, **Hindenburg Line,** Epehy, Canal du Nord, Courtrai, Selle, Sambre, France and Flanders 1914-18, Italy 1917-18, Helles, Landing at Helles, Krithia, Suvla, Scimitar Hill, **Gallipoli 1915-16,** Rumani, Egypt 1916, **Gaza, El Mughar, Nebi Samwil, Jaffa, Palestine 1917-18.**

*The Second World War_* **Dunkirk 1940,** Cambes, **Odon,** Cheux, Defence of Rauray, **Caen,** Esquay, Troarn, Mont Pincon, Estry, Aart, Nederrijn, **Arnhem 1944,** Best, Scheldt, **Flushing,** Venraij, Meijel, Venlo Pocket, Roer, Rhineland, Reichswald, Cleve, Goch, **Rhine,** Ibbenburen, Lingen, Dreirwalde, Uelzen, **Bremen,** Artlenberg, North-West Europe 1940, 44-45, North Arakan, Buthidaung, **Ngakyedauk Pass, Imphal,** Kanglatongbi, Ukhrul, Meiktila, **Irrawaddy, Kama, Burma 1943, 45.**

Kowang-San, Maryang-San, **Korea 1951-52, Gulf 1991**

Regimental Marches

Pipes and Drums

Quick March . . . . .Blue Bonnets are over the Border
Slow March .The Borderers

Military Band

Quick March . . . . .Blue Bonnets are over the Border
Slow March .The Garb of Old Gaul

Agents . . . . .Lloyds Bank plc Cox's & King's Branch

Regimental Headquarters . . . . .The Barracks, Berwick-on-Tweed, Northumberland TD15 1DG
(Tel: 01289-307426 Fax: 01289-331928)

Alliances

Canadian Armed Forces . . . . .1st Battalion The Royal New Brunswick Regiment (Carleton and York)
Australian Military Forces . . . . .25th/49th The Royal Queensland Regiment
Malaysian Armed Forces . . . . .5th Battalion The Royal Malay Regiment
South African Defence Force . . . . . . .The Witwatersrand Rifles

Colonel in Chief . . . .*HRH Princess* Alice *Duchess of* Gloucester *GCB CI GCVO GBE*
Colonel . . . . .Brig J Cooper *DSO MBE* 090201

Brigadiers	Majors		Captains	
			Addinell I W *BA(Hons)*	10495
	Orr I A *MBE* sq	300989	Tweedie J G *BA(Econ)Hons*	81095
Cooper J *DSO MBE* psc hcsc(J)	Linaker M A C *BA(Hons)* psc		Ramsay C A	151295
300699		300990	Irvine S J *(A/Maj 080301)*	110497
	Combe R S *MBE* sq	300991	Connolly R J *BSc* P	120298
Colonels	Macmillan-Scott A H C *MBE*		Rennie A M	90499
	BA(Hons) sq	300992	Little P M	101299
Kirkwood J A *OBE* rcds psc 300695	Craig J M R psc	300993	Eydes D R P *BSc(Hons)*	130600
Jackson A C psc ph 300699	McCutcheon P *LLB* sq(w) †	300994	Douglas A S J	300700
————	Jefferies R *BSc(Hons)* sq	300995		
	Ingram T A W *BA(Hons)* psc(J)		Lieutenants	
Lieutenant Colonels		200997		
	Platt C E psc(J)	300997	Forsyth A R *BA(Hons)*	131097
Middlemiss P W psc 300690	Hill T A S *MBE*	300998		
Legg R A E (SL) sq 300692	Busby A R *BA(Hons)*	300999		
Walker J S M sq 300692	Cochran D J S	300900	**Regular Category Late Entry**	
Rennie P J *MBE* psc 300695	Edlmann R H *MA(Hons)*	300900	**Officers**	
Mackay A D *MBE* psc 300696	Frazer C D	300900		
McCurdy J A M psc jsdc 300697	Glendinning M P S C	300900	*Majors*	
Moynan G M psc 300698	Lenthall G H *BA(Hons)* cafs 300900		Hogg P D	300992
Stanton J R M *BA(Hons)* psc†			Currie J A *MBE*	300994
300600				

Morton F R	300998
Preacher A J	300998

Special Regular Officers Late Entry

Captains

Gregson D T	10498
McKay J *MBE*	10498
Mahony E	140498

Intermediate Regular Officers

Majors

Murphy E J A *MA*	300900

Captains

Angus R T A	40197
Tait A G *BA(Hons)*	100299
Christie J M	101299
Blamire J R *BA(Hons)*	90200

Litster K	80201

Lieutenants

Loudoun J D *BSc(Hons)*	120297
Baxter J B M *(A/Capt 010100)*	130498
Drummond L J *(A/Capt 061100)*	141298
Russell E J *(A/Capt 070600)*	141298
Chestnutt J E A	131299

Short Service Late Entry Officers

Captains

Campbell K	10499
Cann A	70400
Hunter D A	51000

Macgregor N C	50201

Short Service Officers

Captains

Brown R S *BSc*	130600

Lieutenants

Patterson G W H *LLB(Hons)* *(A/Capt 060300)*	140497
Stanley S J	130498
Logan D C *BSc(Hons)*	140698
Tweedie J R *BSc(Hons)*	100898
Holmes N J J *BA(Hons)*	141298
Marshall P V *BA(Hons)*	130699

2nd Lieutenants

McNay G J	70300
Birkbeck B G	120800

162

THE BLACK WATCH (ROYAL HIGHLAND REGIMENT) (42 and 73)

The Royal Cypher Within The Garter, the badge and motto of the Order of the Thistle
In each of the four corners the Royal Cypher ensigned with Crown
The Sphinx, superscribed Egypt

Guadaloupe 1759, Martinique 1762, Havannah, North America 1763-64, Mangalore, Mysore, Seringapatam, Corunna, Busaco, Fuentes d'Onor, Salamanca, Pyrenees, Nivelle, Nive, Orthes, Toulouse, Peninsula, Waterloo, South Africa 1846-7, 1851-2-3, Alma, Sevastopol, Lucknow, Ashantee 1873-4, Tel-el-Kebir, Egypt 1882, 1884, Kirbekan, Nile 1884-85, Paardeberg, South Africa 1899-1902

*The Great War_* Retreat from Mons, **Marne 1914**, Aisne 1914, La Bassee 1914, **Ypres 1914, 17, 18**, Langemarck 1914, Gheluvelt, Nonne Bosschen, Givenchy 1914, Neuve Chapelle, Aubers, Festubert 1915, **Loos, Somme 1916, 18**, Albert 1916, Bazentin, Delville Wood, Pozieres, Flers-Courcelette, Morval, Thiepval, Le Ancre Heights, Ancre 1916, **Arras 1917, 18**, Vimy 1917, Scarpe 1917, 18, Arleux, Pilckem, Menin Road, Polygon Wood, Poelcappelle, Passchendaele, Cambrai 1917, 18, St Quentin, Bapaume 1918, Rosieres, **Lys**, Estaires, Messines 1918, Hazebrouck, Kemmel, Bethune, Scherpenberg, Soissonnais-Ourcq, Tardenois, Drocourt-Queant, **Hindenburg Line,** Epehy, St Quentin Canal, Beaurevoir, Courtrai, Selle, Sambre, France and Flanders 1914-18, **Doiran 1917,** Macedonia 1915-18, Egypt 1916, Gaza, Jerusalem, Tell'Asur, **Megiddo,** Sharon, Damascus, Palestine 1917-18, Tigris 1916, **Kut al Amara 1917,** Baghdad, Mesopotamia 1915-17.

*The Second World War_* Defence of Arras, Ypres-Comines Canal, Dunkirk 1940, Somme 1940, St Valery-en-Caux, Saar, Breville, Odon, Fontenay le Pesnil, Defence of Rauray, Caen, Falaise, **Falaise Road,** La Vie Crossing, Le Havre, Lower Maas, Venlo Pocket, Ourthe, Rhineland, Reichswald, Goch, **Rhine,** North-West Europe 1940, 44-45, Barkasan, British Somaliland 1940, **Tobruk 1941,** Tobruk Sortie, **El Alamein,** Advance on Tripoli, Medenine, Zemlet el Lebene, Mareth, **Akarit,** Wadi Akarit East, Djebel Roumana, Medjez Plain, Si Mediene, **Tunis,** North Africa 1941-43, Landing in Sicily, Vizzini, Sferro, Gerbini, Adrano, Sferro Hills, **Sicily 1943, Cassino II,** Liri Valley, Advance to Florence, Monte Scalari, Casa Fortis, Rimini Line, Casa Fabbri Ridge, Savio Bridgehead, Italy 1944-45, Athens, Greece 1944-45, **Crete,** Heraklion, Middle East 1941, Chindits 1944, Burma 1944.

The Hook 1952, Korea 1952-53

Regimental Marches

Pipes and Drums

Quick March .Hielan' Laddie
Slow Marches . . . .(i) My Home (ii) Highland Cradle Song

Military Band

Quick March .All The Blue Bonnets are over the Border
Slow March .The Garb of Old Gaul

Agents . . . . .Lloyds Bank plc Cox's & King's Branch

Regimental Headquarters . . . . .Balhousie Castle, Perth PH1 5HR
(Tel: 0131-310-8530. Fax: 01738 643245)

Alliances

Canadian Armed Forces . . . . .The Prince Edward Island Regiment
The Black Watch (Royal Highland Regiment) of Canada
The Lanark and Renfrew Scottish Regiment
Australian Military Forces . . . . .The Royal Queensland Regiment
The Royal New South Wales Regiment
New Zealand Army . . . . .1st and 2nd Squadron New Zealand Scottish, RNZAC
South African Defence Force . . . . . . .Transvaal Scottish

Colonel in Chief . . . .*HM* QUEEN ELIZABETH THE QUEEN MOTHER
Colonel . . . . .Brig G C Barnett *OBE* 280992

Lieutenant Colonels

Gilchrist R A L psc   300690
Ogilvy-Wedderburn Bt Sir Andrew
sq jsdc   300692
Loudon A W B *OBE BA(Hons)* psc
300694
Riddell R M   sq jsdc   300696
Bradford R J K *BSc(For)* psc†
300697
Riddell-Webster M L *BSc* psc†
300698

Brigadiers

Wilson D R   rcds psc†   300697

Colonels

Lithgow N C D   psc psc(PAK)
300695
Thornycroft D C *OBE MA(Hons)*
MDA MCGI psc† psc(PAK) aic
300698

Majors

Macduff-Duncan S C *MBE* sq
300985
Monteith J D *MBE MBA* sq   300986
Coles T A *MBE* sq *(A/Lt Col 041200)*
300988
Erskine J M K *MBE* sq   300989
Macdonald A A S *MBE* psc *(A/Lt Col
190101)*   300990
Carmichael T J O   osc(FR) sq *(L/Lt
Col 061299)*   300991
Forrest R A *MBE* psc† psc sq
300993

163

Cole-Mackintosh R C *BA(Hons)* sq
    300994
Denholm D W M *MA MSc* dis sq(w)
    300994
Cowan J M *MBE BA(Oxon)*
  MA(Hons) psc   300995
Orr Ewing D R   CAFS sq(w)
    300995
Macduff L R *BA(Hons)*   300996
Ewing M J F *MA(Hons)*   300998
Jones E G *BA(Hons)*   300998
Aitken A J   300999
Kemmis-Betty D E J   300900
Macgillivray A D   300900

Captains

Houghton J W *BA(Hons)* 111095
Elliott T R *BSc(Hons)* 241195
Brown C J M *BA(HonsCantab)*
  MA(Cantab) 141295
Wrench B M A *MA(Hons)* 60296
Roddis J C *BA(Hons)* 110896
Lindsay R R E *BSc(Hons)* 120298
Ord N E *BA(Hons)* 100299
Philp A M *BA(Hons)* 121099
Rennie P D L *MA(Hons)* 90200

Lieutenants

Prowse J S *BSc(Hons)* 90299
Riddell A J M *BEng(Hons)* 90299

Regular Category Late Entry Officers

Lieutenant Colonels

Smith M *MBE* 231200

Majors

Williamson J S *MBE* 300996
Menzies J A 300998

Special Regular Officers Late Entry

Majors

Stewart A M *BEM* 300900

Captains

Gray C 10498

Intermediate Regular Officers

Captains

Cole S O *BA(Hons)* 120298
Ferguson A H *BA(Hons)* 120298
Fraser A J M *BA(Hons)* 131098
Bushby A R P *BSc(Hons)* 140699
Percy M A *BSc(Hons)* 140699
Thirkill J D *BSc(Econ)Hons* 90200

Lieutenants

Tomlin N K G *BA(Hons)* *(A/Capt 271100)* 120897

Short Service Late Entry Officers

Captains

McEwen A G 191098
Stevenson J R 220500

Short Service Officers

Captains

Walker R W J 180197
Lockett G C T *BA(Hons)* 140699
McElhinney J R 120400

Lieutenants

Sheldrick D M *BA(Hons)* 140698
Williamson M A N *BA(Hons)* 100898
Close D C *B Sc (Hons)* 90299
Petransky T J *BA(Hons)* 120499
Watson A R W *BEng(Hons)* 120699
Hedderwick R S J *BA(Hons)* 90899

2nd Lieutenants

Sinclair I J 111299

164

THE HIGHLANDERS
(SEAFORTH, GORDONS AND CAMERONS) (72, 75, 78, 79 and 92)

A stag's head caboshed, between the attires the Thistle ensigned with the Crown
The Cypher of Queen Victoria within the Garter. The Cypher of the Duke of York and Albany. The Cypher of the Duke of Edinburgh. The Sphinx, superscribed Egypt. The Elephant, superscribed Assaye. The Royal Tiger, superscribed India.
"Cuidich 'n Righ"

Carnatic, Hindoostan, Mysore, Seringapatam, Egmont-op-Zee, Mandora, Cape of Good Hope 1806, Maida, Corunna, Busaco, Fuentes d'Onor, Java, Almaraz, Salamanca, Vittoria, Pyrenees, Nivelle, Nive, Orthes, Toulouse, Peninsula, Waterloo, South Africa 1835, Alma, Sevastopol, Koosh-ab, Persia, Delhi 1857, Lucknow, Central India, Peiwar Kotal, Charasiah, Kabul 1879, Kandahar 1880, Afghanistan 1878-80, Tel-El-Kebir, Egypt 1882-84, Nile 1884-85, Chitral, Tirah, Atbara, Khartoum, Defence of Ladysmith, Paardeberg, South Africa 1899-1902.

The Great War _ **Mons, Le Cateau,** Retreat from Mons, **Marne 1914-18, Aisne 1914,** La Bassee 1914, Armentieres 1914, Messines 1914, **Ypres 1914, 15, 17, 18,** Langemark 1914, Gheluvelt, Nonne Bosschen, Festubert 1914, 15, Givenchy 1914, **Neuve Chapelle,** Hill 60, Gravenstafel, St Julian, Frezenberg, Bellewaarde, Aubers, Hooge 1915, **Loos, Somme 1916, 18,** Albert 1916, 18, Bazentin, **Delville Wood,** Pozieres, Guillemont, Flers-Courcelette, Morval, Le Transloy, Ancre Heights, **Ancre 1916, Arras 1917, 18, Vimy 1917,** Scarpe 1917, 18, Arleux, Bullecourt, Pilckem, Menin Road, Polygon Wood, Broodseinde, Poelcapelle, Passchendaele, **Cambrai 1917, 18,** St Quentin, Bapaume 1918, Rosieres, Lys, Estaires, Messines 1918, Hazebrouck, Bailleul, Kemmel, Bethune, Soissonais-Ourcq, Tardenois, Drocourt-Queant, Hindenburg Line, Epehy, Canal du Nord, St Quentin Canal, Courtai, Selle, **Valenciennes, Sambre,** France and Flanders 1914-18, Piave, **Vittoria Veneto,** Italy 1917-18, Struma, **Macedonia 1915-18,** Megiddo, Sharon, **Palestine 1918,** Tigris 1916, Kut Al Amara 1917, **Baghdad,** Mesopotamia 1915-18

The Second World War _ Withdrawal to Escaut, Defence of Escaut, **St Omer-La-Bassee,** Ypres-Comines Canal, Dunkirk 1940, Somme 1940, Withdrawal to Seine, **St Valery-en-Caux, Odon,** Cheux, **Caen,** Troarn, Mont Pincon, Quarry Hill, Falaise, Falaise Road, Dives Crossing, La Vie Crossing, Lisieux, Nederrijn, Best, Le Havre, Lower Maas, Meijel, Venlo Pocket, Ourthe, **Rhineland, Reichswald,** Cleve, **Goch,** Moyland, **Rhine,** Uelzen, Artlenberg, **North-West Europe 1940, 44-45,** Agordat, **Keren,** Abyssinia 1941, **Sidi Barrani,** Tobruk 1941, 42, Gubi ii, Carmusa, Gazala, **El Alamein,** Advance on Tripoli, **Mareth,** Wadi Zigzaou, Akarit, Djebel Roumana, Medjez Plain, **North Africa 1940-43,** Landing in Sicily, Augusta, Francofonte, **Sferro,** Adrano, Sferro Hills, **Sicily 1943,** Garigliano Crossing, Cassino, **Anzio,** Rome, Poggio del Grillo, **Gothic Line,** Tavoleto, Coriano, Pian di Castello, Rimini Line, San Marino, Monte Reggiano, Italy 1943-45, **Madagascar,** Middle East 1942, **Imphal,** Shenam Pass, Litan, **Kohima,** Relief of Kohima, Naga Village, Aradura, Tengnoupal, Shwebo, **Mandalay,** Ava, Irrawaddy, Mt Popa, **Burma 1942-45, Gulf 1991.**

Regimental Marches
Pipes and Drums

Quick Marches	Pibroch of Donuil Dubh
	Cock o' the North
March Past	The Wee Highland Laddie
Slow March	The Highlanders Slow March

Military Band

Quick March	The Wee Highland Laddie
Slow March	The Garb of Old Gaul
Agents	The Royal Bank of Scotland, Harbour Road, Inverness
Regimental Headquarters	Cameron Barracks, Inverness IV2 3XD Scotland (Tel: Civ 01463-224380 Mil Inverness Ext 8136 Fax: 0131-310-8172)
Out Station	St Lukes,Viewfield Road, Aberdeen AB15 7XH (Tel: Civ 01224-318174 Mil Aberdeen Ext 4554 Fax: 01224-208652)

Alliances

Canadian Armed Forces	The Cameron Highlanders of Ottawa
	48th Highlanders of Canada
	The Queen's Own Cameron Highlanders of Canada
	The Seaforth Highlanders of Canada
	The Toronto Scottish Regiment
Australian Armed Forces	5th/7th Battalion The Royal Australian Regiment
	The Royal South Australia Regiment
	The Royal Western Australia Regiment
	5th/6th Battalion The Royal Victoria Regiment
New Zealand Army	4th Battalion (Otago and Southland) Royal New Zealand Infantry Regiment
	7th Battalion (Wellington (City of Wellington's Own) and Hawkes Bay) Royal New Zealand Infantry Regiment
South African Armed Forces	The Cape Town Highlanders
Colonel in Chief	Field Marshal *HRH The Prince* Philip *Duke of* Edinburgh *KG KT OM GBE AC QSO*

Deputy Colonel in Chief . . . . .Maj Gen *HRH The Prince of* Wales *Duke of* Rothesay
KG KT GCB AK QSO ADC

Colonel . . . . .Gen *Sir* Jeremy Mackenzie *GCB OBE* 170994

Brigadiers

Monro S H R H *CBE ADC*
odc(AUS) psc psc(CAN) hcsc(J)
                    300693
Lamb G C M *OBE* psc psc(J) hcsc(J)
jsdc   300696
Durcan A J M *LLB MA* psc psc(IND)
                    300697
Grant C S *OBE CGIA* psc† 300697
Monro H B H E *MBE* psc 300699

Colonels

Price C E psc jsdc 300692
Campbell The Hon Ajc *BA(Hons)*
psc   300699

Lieutenant Colonels

Gilmour C E (SL) sq aic sq(w)
                    300689
Chant-Sempill *The Hon* I D W sq
jsdc   300692
Stewart D N F *BSc(Hons) MBA* psc†
                    300695
Dodson M P *MBE* psc 300697
Hall R P *LLB(Hons)* psc 300697
Broadfoot D N *MBE* sq 300698
Maitland-Makgill-Crichton A J sq
                    311298

Majors

Alderson A *MBE BSc(Hons) MA*
psc†   300600
Miller R D J *MBA BA* psc 300600
Maitland-Makgill-Crichton D E sq
                    300986
Torp-Petersen K sq 300986
Irvine-Fortescue G A sq 300987
Wimberley M C sq 300987
Braithwaite-Exley M sq 300988
Cole R *FRGS* sq sq(w) *(A/Lt Col
271100)*   300988
Macnair H P A psc 300988
Robertson W A S *BSc(Econ)Hons)
MBA* psc jsdc *(A/Lt Col 111200)*
                    300989
Barron D C N psc(CAN) 300991
Bird P R C *BSc* sq(w) † 300991
Philip F M psc 300991
Cruickshank P M psc† 300995
Harkness P K *MThEOL(Hons) MA*
psc(J)   300995
Hopkinson J M R *MA(Hons)*
psc(AUS)   300995

McArthur R odc(AUS) 300995
Niekirk W D *BSc* sq(w) ais 300995
Potts K M psc(J) 300995
Tootal S J C *BA(Hons) MPhil* psc(J)
                    300995
Wells M R 300995
West S R psc† 300995
Eaton H R A *MBE* psc(J) 300996
Hay D W 300996
Bremner C A *BSc(Hons)* psc(J)
                    300997
Campbell J *BA(Hons)* psc(J) 300997
Deere R E J *BA(Hons)* 300997
Gray A I *BSc* 300997
Tink J D 300997
Calder J A J 300999
Fairrie A H *BSc* 300900

Captains

Coutts R L 10495
Crane S J *MA(Hons)* *(A/Maj
271100)*   10495
Irving C J E *MA(Hons)* 60296
Lane C A M 60296
White P J *BSc(Hons)* 120496
Humphries C M 110497
Reilly A P 121297
Hutton A G S *BEng(Hons)* 121099
Cross J E S *BA(Hons)* 90200

Lieutenants

Williams R A D 80800

2nd Lieutenants

††Dobbie W A C 50999
Charteris J N R 150400

Regular Category Late Entry Officers

Lieutenant Colonels

Towns R J *MBE* 90400

Majors

Munro D R 300997
Duncan D A 300998
Birnie R 300999
Knowles R B 300900

Special Regular Officers Late Entry

Majors

Ross B M 300900

Captains

Gray J K *BEM* 71195
Archibald J M *MBE* 10496
Cameron I K *BSc* 50597
Wood K 10498

Intermediate Regular Officers

Captains

Hay A G P *(A/Maj 280998)*
                    190493
Quinn C J M 121297
Christie T S B *MA* 120298
Cox A T *BSc(Hons)* 100299
McMaster B C *BA* 100299
Fieldhouse J G *BSc* 121099

Lieutenants

Cameron I R *(A/Capt 011200)*
                    190799

Short Service Late Entry Officers

Captains

Mackay A J *MBE* 10499
Wemyss S G 120499
Payne S *MBE* 10900

Short Service Officers

Captains

Macaulay S K G *BSc* 140699
Macleod A C R *MA(Hons)* 121099
Gordon J B *BSc(Hons)* 90200
Gollan G R *MA(Hons)* 220201

Lieutenants

Angella G J A *BSc(Hons)* 160697
Lister-Kaye J W N 130498
Macintyre D I *BSc* 121098
Walker T A V *BSc* 141298

2nd Lieutenants

Clayton B G 150400
Hawkins T W 150400
Logie A G A 161200

THE ARGYLL AND SUTHERLAND HIGHLANDERS
(PRINCESS LOUISE'S) (91 and 93)

The Princess Louise's Cypher and Coronet. A boar's head, with the motto *No obliviscaris,* within a wreath of myrtle, and a cat, with the motto *"Sans Peur"* within a wreath of broom, over all the label as represented in the Arms of the Princess Louise and surmounted with Her Royal Highness's Coronet.

Cape of Good Hope 1806, Rolica, Vimiera, Corunna, Pyrenees, Nivelle, Nive, Orthers, Toulouse, Peninsula, South Africa 1846-7, 1851-2-3, Alma, Balaklava, Sevastopol, Lucknow, South Africa 1879, Modder River, Paardeberg, South Africa 1899-1902.

The Great War: - **Mons, Le Cateau,** Retreat from Mons, **Marne 1914, 18,** Aisne 1914, La Bassee 1914, Messines 1914, 18, Armentieres 1914, **Ypres 1915, 17, 18,** Gravenstafel, St Julien, Frezenberg, Bellewaarde, Festubert 1915, **Loos, Somme 1916, 18,** Albert 1916, 18, Bazentin, Delville Wood, Pozieres, Flers-Courcelette, Morval, Le Transloy, Ancre Heights, Ancre 1916, **Arras 1917, 18,** Scarpe 1917, 18, Arleux, Pilckem, Menin Road, Polygon Wood, Broodseinde, Poelcappelle, Passchendaele, **Cambrai 1917, 18,** St Quentin, Bapaume 1918, Rosieres Lys, Estaires, Hazebrouck, Bailleul, Kemmel, Bethune, Soissonnais-Ourcq, Tardenois, Amiens, Hindenburg Line, Epehy, Canal du Nord, St Quentin Canal, Beaurevoir, Courtrai, Selle, Sambre, France and Flanders 1914-18, Italy 1917-18, Struma, **Doiran 1917, 18,** Macedonia 1915-18, Gallipoli 1915-16, Rumani, Egypt 1916, Gaza, El Mughar, Nebi Samwil, Jaffa, Palestine 1917-18.

The Second World War: - Somme 1940, **Odon,** Tourmauville Bridge, Caen, Esquay, Mont Pincon, Quarry Hill, Estry, Falaise, Dives Crossing, Aart, Lower Maas, Meijel, Venlo Pocket, Ourthe, Rhineland, Reichswald, **Rhine,** Uelzen, Artlenberg, North-West Europe 1940, 44-45, Abyssinia 1941, **Sidi Barrani, El Alamein,** Medenine, **Akarit,** Diebel Azzag 1942, Kef Ouiba Pass, Mine de Sedjienane, Medjez Plain, **Longstop Hill 1943,** North Africa 1940-43, Landing in Sicily, Gerbini, Adrano, Centuripe, Sicily 1943, Termoli, Snagro, Cassino II, Liri Valley, Aquino, Monte Casalino, Monte Spaduro, Monte Grande, Senio, Santerno Crossing, Argenta Gap, **Italy 1943-45, Crete,** Heraklion, Middle East 1941, North Malaya, **Grik Road,** Central Malaya, Ipoh, Slim River, Singapore Island, **Malaya 1941-42.**

Pakchon, Korea 1950-51

Regimental Marches

Pipes and Drums

Quick Marches . . . .(i) Campbells are Coming (ii) Hielan' Laddie
Slow March .Skye Boat Song

Military Band

Quick March .The Thin Red Line
Slow March .The Garb of Old Gaul

Agents . . . . .Royal Bank of Scotland, Stirling Branch
Regimental Headquarters . . . . .The Castle, Stirling, Scotland FK8 1EH (Tel: 01786-475165)

Alliances

Canadian Armed Forces . . . . .The Argyll and Sutherland Highlanders of Canada (Princess Louise's)
The Calgary Highlanders
Australian Military Forces . . . . .The Royal New South Wales Regiment
Pakistan Army . . . . .1st Battalion (SCINDE) The Frontier Force Regiment

Colonel in Chief . . . . .THE QUEEN

Colonel . . . . .Brig A J N Graham *MBE* 010800

	Wade R N H A D V *OBE MDA* psc		Wills M *BA(Hons)*	300998
	MDA	300697	Graham D S G *BA*	300999
	Boswell A L S psc	300698	Hay M P	300999
	Gray J D psc	300699	Eason A J	300900
Brigadiers	Macnaughton A M *LLB(Hons)* psc†		Wright N A P *BA(Hons)*	300900
Graham A J N *MBE BA(Hons)* psc		300699		
hcsc(J)	300699	Russell B W O *MBE BSc(Hons)* psc†		*Captains*
		300699		
Colonels			Clark H I M	130495
Miller A K M *OBE BA* odc(US) psc	*Majors*		Den-Mckay N A *BEng(Hons)*	
	300699	McAlister I R *MBE* psc	300992		120297
Campbell A P W *BD* psc†	300600	Shirras J D *BA(Hons) MDA* psc		Spinner D C	110497
Douglas G A *OBE* psc	300600		300995	Miles C R *BA(Hons)*	100299
———		Storey N J psc†	300995	Graham M J	140699
		Wilson G C psc(J)	300995		
Lieutenant Colonels	Scott J A *BSc(Hons) MSc* psc(J) dis			*Lieutenants*
Macgregor-Smith D N psc	300691		300997		
Salisbury N J N *BA* sq jsdc	300696	Orr S A *BA(Hons)*	300998	Steele A F L *BCom(Hons)*	160697

Regular Category Late Entry Officers

Captains

McAulay D 200894

Special Regular Officers Late Entry

Majors

Macfarlane C M 300900

Captains

Elliot R *BEM* 10395
Webb C J 70697
Ballantyne H 10498
Haughie J J 110998

Intermediate Regular Officers

Majors

Linney G K R *MIAS MIBC* sq
300995

Captains

Whitelegge R S B *(A/Maj 040101)*
130496
Thomas C A 121297

Radford B W 130698
Clark H J L *BA(Hons)* 160698
Roan A R F *BSc(Hons)* 100299
Charlesworth P M *BSc(Hons)*
121099

Lieutenants

Calder N G *(A/Capt 051099)*
120897
Horridge W A *(A/Capt 180201)*
180898
Gibson M T A *(A/Capt 210800)*
141298

Short Service Late Entry Officers

Captains

Mackinnon N 70400

Short Service Officers

Captains

Sennett D A *BCom* 121099
Macgregor N D *BA(Hons)* 280400
James W L G *MA(Hons)* 101000
Philp I J *BSc(Hons)* 101000
†Lucas S A 50101
Barry J F *BSc(Hons)* 80201

Lieutenants

Richards A P *BA(Hons)* 110897
Rasor D J G *BSc(Hons)* 120897
Gibbs J E G *BSc(Hons)* 130498
Adamson G K 140698
Petrie B E *(A/Capt 270700)*
100898
Thirde G A M *BSc* 141298
Sefton G J *BSc(Hons)* 130699
Barclay C A O *B Sc (Hons)* 90899
Connelly M 11299

2nd Lieutenants

Rodgers A J S 161200

Rec Res (RARO)

Captains

Hunter I E 201190

Short Service Volunteer Officers

Lieutenants

Balfour E S C 180697

168
THE QUEEN'S DIVISION

Comprising ....The Princess of Wales's Royal Regiment (Queen's and Royal Hampshires)
(2 Regular Battalions, 1 Volunteer Battalion, 2 Volunteer Companies)
The Royal Regiment of Fusiliers (2 Regular Battalions, 4 Volunteer Companies)
The Royal Anglian Regiment (2 Regular Battalions, 4 Volunteer Companies)
The London Regiment (Volunteers)

Divisional Headquarters ....c/o Headquarters Infantry (Tel: 01985-222363/222466)

Colonel Commandant ....Maj Gen J C B Sutherell *CBE* 160100

Divisional Lieutenant Colonel ......Lt Col P D McLelland *OBE* PWRR 150500

The origins of amalgamated Regiments now included in The Queen's Division are as follows:

THE PRINCESS OF WALES'S ROYAL REGIMENT
(QUEEN'S AND ROYAL HAMPSHIRES)

On 14 October 1959
The Queen's Royal Regiment (West Surrey)(2) and
The East Surrey Regiment (31 and 70) amalgamated to form:
The Queen's Royal Surrey Regiment

On 1 March 1961
The Buffs (Royal East Kent Regiment) (3) and
The Queen's Own Royal West Kent Regiment (50 and 97) amalgamated to form:
The Queen's Own Buffs, The Royal Kent Regiment

On 31 December 1966
The Queen's Royal Surrey Regiment
The Queen's Own Buffs, The Royal Kent Regiment
The Royal Sussex Regiment (35 and 107) and
The Middlesex Regiment (Duke of Cambridge's Own) (57 and 77) amalgamated to form:
The Queen's Regiment

On 9 September 1992
The Queen's Regiment (2, 3, 35, 50, 57, 70, 77, 97 and 107) and
The Royal Hampshire Regiment (37 and 67) amalgamated to form:
The Princess of Wales's Royal Regiment (Queen's and Royal Hampshires)

THE ROYAL REGIMENT OF FUSILIERS

On 23 April 1968
The Royal Northumberland Fusiliers (5)
The Royal Warwickshire Fusiliers (6)
The Royal Fusiliers (City of London Regiment) (7) and
The Lancashire Fusiliers (20) amalgamated to form:
The Royal Regiment of Fusiliers

THE ROYAL ANGLIAN REGIMENT

On 2 June 1958

    The Bedfordshire and Hertfordshire Regiment (16) and
    The Essex Regiment (44 and 56) amalgamated to form:
    The 3rd East Anglian Regiment (16th/44th Foot)

On 29 August 1959

    The Royal Norfolk Regiment (9) and
    The Suffolk Regiment (12) amalgamated to form:
    The 1st East Anglian Regiment (Royal Norfolk and Suffolk)

On 1 June 1960

    The Royal Lincolnshire Regiment (10) and
    The Northamptonshire Regiment (48 and 58) amalgamated to form:
    The 2nd East Anglian Regiment (Duchess of Gloucester's Own Royal Lincolnshire and Northamptonshire)

On 1 September 1964

    1st East Anglian Regiment (Royal Norfolk and Suffolk)
    2nd East Anglian Regiment (Duchess of Gloucester's Own Royal Lincolnshire and Northamptonshire)
    3rd East Anglian Regiment (16th/44th Foot) and
    The Royal Leicestershire Regiment (17) amalgamated to form:
    The Royal Anglian Regiment

170

THE PRINCESS OF WALES'S ROYAL REGIMENT
(QUEEN'S AND ROYAL HAMPSHIRES)
(2, 3, 31, 35, 37, 50, 57, 67, 70, 77, 97 and 107)

A Dragon upon a mount with a double red rose fimbriated gold below within the Garter. Above the Dragon and superimposed on the Garter the Plume of the Prince of Wales.

A Paschal Lamb upon an eight pointed Star ensigned with The Crown. A White Horse rampant above a scroll inscribed Invicta. The Star of the Order of the Garter over the Roussillon Plume. A Naval Crown superscribed 1st June 1794. The Sphinx superscribed Egypt. The Royal Tiger, superscribed India. The Cypher of Queen Catherine.

Tangier 1662-80, Namur 1695, Gibraltar 1704-5, Blenheim, Ramillies, Oudenarde, Malplaquet, Dettingen, Minden, Louisburg, Guadaloupe 1759, Quebec 1759, Belleisle, Tournay, Barrosa, Martinique 1762, Havannah, St Lucia 1778, Mysore, Martinique 1794, Seringapatam, Maida, Vimiera, Corunna, Douro, Talavera, Guadaloupe 1810, Allbuhera, Almaraz, Cuidad Rodrigo, Badajoz, Salamanca, Vittoria, Pyrenees, Nivelle Nive, Orthes, Toulouse, Peninsula, Ghuznee 1839, Khelat, Afghanistan 1839, Cabool 1842, Punniar, Moodkee, Ferezoshah, Aliwal, Sobraon, South Africa 1851-53, Alma, Inkerman, Sevastopol, Lucknow, Taku Forts, Pekin 1860, New Zealand, Charasiah, Afghanistan 1879-80, South Africa 1879, Kabul 1879, Egypt 1882, Abu Klea, Nile 1884-85, Suakin 1885, Burma 1885-87, Chitral, Tirah, Relief of Ladysmith, Relief of Kimberley, Paardeberg, South Africa 1899-1902.

The Great War - Mons, Le Cateau, Retreat from Mons, Marne 1914, 18, Aisne 1914, La Bassee 1914, Messines 1914, 17, 18, Armentieres 1914, Ypres 1914, 15, 17, 18, Langemarck 1914, 17, Gheluvelt, Nonne Boschen, Givenchy 1914, Neuve Chappelle, Hill 60, Gravenstafel, St Julien, Frezenberg, Bellewaarde, Aubers, Festubert 1915, Hooge 1915, Loos, Somme 1916, 18, Albert 1916, 18, Bazentine, Delville Wood, Pozieres, Guillemont, Ginchy, Flers-Courcelette, Morval, Thiepval, Le Transloy, Ancre Heights, Ancre 1916, 18, Bapaume 1917, 18, Arras 1917, 18, Vimy 1917, Scarpe 1917, 18, Messines 1917, Langemark 1917, Arleux, Oppy, Bullecourt, Pilcken, Menin Road, Polygon Wood, Broodseinde, Poelcappelle, Passchendaele, Cambrai 1917, 18, St Quentin, Bapaume 1918, Rosieres, Avre, Villers Bretonneux, Lys, Estaires, Hazelbrouck, Bailleul, Kemmel, Bethune, Tardenois, Scherpenberg, Soissonnais-Ourcq, Amiens, Drocourt-Queant, Hindenburg Line, Havrincourt, Epehy, Canal du Nord, St Quentin Canal, Beaurevoir, Courtrai, Selle, Valenciennes, Sambre, France and Flanders 1914-18, Piave, Vittorio Veneto, Italy 1917-18, Kosturino, Struma, Doiran 1917-1918, Macedonia 1915-18, Helles, Landing at Helles, Krithia, Suvla, Landing at Suvla, Sari Bair, Scimitar Hill, Gallipoli 1915-16, Rumani, Egypt 1915-17, Gaza, El Mughar, Nebi Samwil, Jerusalem, Jaffa, Jericho, Jordan, Tell' Asur, Megiddo, Sharon, Palestine 1917-18, Aden, Shaiba, Defence of Kut al Amara, Kut al Amara 1915, 17, Tigris 1916, Bagdad, Khan Baghdadi, Sharqat, Mesopotamia 1915-18, North-West Frontier India 1915, 1916-17, Murman 1918-19, Dukhovskaya, Siberia 1918-19, Persia 1918-19, Archangel 1919, Afghanistan 1919.

The Second World War – Dyle, Defence of Escaut, Amiens 1940, St Omer-La-Bassee, Foret de Nieppe Ypres-Comines Canal, Dunkirk 1940, Withdrawal to Seine, Normandy Landing, Tilly sur Seulles, Cambes, Breville, Villers Bocage, Odon, Caen, Orne Hill 112, Bourgebus Ridge, Troarn, Mont Pincon, Jurques, St Pierre, Falaise, Seine 1944, Nederrijn, Le Havre, Lower Maas, Venraij, Meijel, Geilenkirchen, Venlo Pocket, Roer, Rhineland, Reichswald, Goch, Rhine, Lingen, Brinkum, Bremen, North-West Europe 1940, 44-45, Karora-Marsa Tacai, Cubcub, Mescelit Pass, Keren, Mt Englehat Massawa, Abyssinia 1941, Syria 1941, Sidi Barrani, Sidi Suleiman, Tobruk 1941, Tobruk Sortie, Omars, Alem Hamza Benghazi, Alem el Halfa, Deir El Munassib, El Alamein, El Aghelia, Advance on Tripoli, Medenine, Mareth, Tebaga Gap, El Hamma, Akarit, Djebel el Meida, Djebel Roumana, Djebel Abiod, Tebourba, Tebourba Gap, Sidi Nsir, Hunt's Gap, Montagne Farm, Fondouk, Pichon, El Kourzia, Ber Rabal, Djebel Assag 1942, 43 Robas Valley, Fort McGregor, Oued Zarga, Djjebel Bech Chekaoui, Djebel Ang, Heidous, Djebel Diaffa Pass, Medjez Plain, Longstop Hill 1943, Si Abdallah, Tunis, Montarnaud, North Africa 1940-43, Francofonte, Sferro, Adrano, Sferro Hills, Centuripe, Monte Rivoglia, Landing in Sicily, Regalbuto, Sicily 1943, Termoli, Trigno, San Salvo, Landing at Porto san Venere, Sangro Romagnoli, Impossible Bridge, Villa Grande, Salerno, Monte Stella, Salerno Hills, Battipaglia, Cava di Tirreni, Scafati Bridge, Volurno Crossing, Monte Camino, Garigliano Crossing, Damiano, Monte Ornito, Cerasola, Anzio, Carroceto, Cassino, Monastery Hill, Castle Hill, Cassino II, Liri Valley, Aquino, Piedimonte Hill, Rome, Massa Vertecchi, Trasimene Line, Arezzo, Advance to Florence, Monte Scalari, Gothic Line, Monte Gridolfo, Montegaudio, Coriano, Montigallo, Pian di Castello, Gemmano Ridge, Monte Reggiano, Capture of Forli, Cosina Canal Crossing, Lamone Crossing, Pideura, Cassa Fortis, Senio Pocket, Senio Floodbank, Rimini Line, Casa Fabbri Ridge, Savio Bridgehead, Monte Pianoereno, Monte Spaduro, Monte Grande, Senio, Menate, Filo, Argenta Gap, Montescudo, Frisoni, Italy 1943-45, Athens, Greece 1944-45, Leros, Middle East 1943, Malta 1940-42, Kampar, Malaya 1941-42, Hong Kong, South East Asia 1941, North Arakan, Razabil, Mayu Tunnels, Kohima, Defence of Kohima, Pinwe, Pinwe, Shweli, Myitson, Taungtha, Yenangyaung 1945, Sittang 1945, Chindits 1944, Burma 1943-45.

Naktong Bridgehead, Chongiu, Chongchon II, Chaum-Ni, Kapyong-chon, Kapyong, Korea 1950-51

Regimental Marches

Quick March	The Farmers Boy, leading into The Soldiers of the Queen
Slow March	The Minden Rose
Agents	Lloyds Bank plc Cox's & King's Branch
Regimental Headquarters	Howe Barracks, Canterbury, Kent CT1 1JY (Tel: 01227-818095/818050)
Western Headquarters	Serle's House, Southgate Street, Winchester, Hants SO23 9EG (Tel: 01962-863658)

Alliances

Canadian Armed Forces . . . . .The Queen's York Rangers (1st American Regiment) (RCAC)
The South Alberta Light Horse (RCAC)
The Queen's Own Rifles of Canada
The Hastings and Prince Edward Regiment
1st Battalion The Royal New Brunswick Regiment (Carleton and York)
The Essex and Kent Scottish
49th (Sault Ste Marie) Field Artillery Regiment RCA
Australian Military Forces . . . . .The Royal New South Wales Regiment
The Royal Western Australia Regiment
The University of New South Wales Regiment
New Zealand Army . . . . .2nd Battalion (Canterbury, Nelson, Marlborough and West Coast)
The Royal New Zealand Infantry Regiment
5th Battalion (Wellington, West Coast and Taranaki)
The Royal New Zealand Infantry Regiment
Pakistan Army . . . . .12th, 14th, 15th and 17th Battalions The Punjab Regiment

Colonel in Chief . . . .*Her Majesty* Queen Margrethe II of Denmark

Colonel . . . . .Brig E R Holmes *CBE TD JP* 090999

Deputy Colonels . . . . .Col A C Mieville *OBE* 020494
Brig P R Newton 010998
Col M J Ball 160594
Col R W Dennis 010101

Brigadiers

Newton P R *MPhil* psc hcsc(J)
300600

Colonels

Ball M J osc(ZIM) sq	300691
Davis P A *CBE* psc	300693
Mieville A C *OBE BSc(Eng)Hons* psc†	300694
Beattie A A A psc(IND) jsdc 300699	

Lieutenant Colonels

Dewar J G T (SL) odc(US) psc	300688
Hughes P W L (SL) *MBE* sq	300688
Jelf A M F sq jsdc	300689
McLelland P D (SL) *OBE* psc	300690
Swanson P R P (SL) *MBE* sq jsdc	300691
Russell J D K *MBE BA(Hons)* psc	300692
Russell R P *BA(Hons)* psc jsdc	300693
Rayner M P psc	300694
Harcus J M (SL) sq	300695
Knight R J *MBE BSc(Hons)* sq jdsc	300695
Dennis R W *MBA* psc *(A/Col 011200)*	300696
Hurley T J *MBE* psc	300696
Pryce A H psc† aic	300696
Steevenson N T R odc(US) sq	300696
Jones P P psc jsdc	300697
Kilpatrick S P B *BA(Hons)* psc†	300697
Sim N A *MBE* psc	300697
Deakin S F *BSc(Econ)Hons* psc†	300698
Mans L S P *MBE* sq	300698
Ashton J V *MSc* psc†	300699
Cameron J E psc	300699

Cross G W *BSc(Hons)* psc	300699
Newell C A CAFS sq(w)	300699
Newman M A D *MBE* psc	300600
Watson D V *MBE* psc	300600

Majors

Acworth J C sq	300980
McGill P M H psc	300980
Warren R H sq	300980
Mills J P S sq	300981
Myles J N C sq	300982
Quinn M S sq	300983
Russell A W *MBE* psc	300984
Bulleid C A sq	300988
Lambert C G *MBE* sq	300988
Macdonald A R psc aic	300988
Maltman J C *BA(Hons)* sq(w) †	300988
Martin G J *BA* sq(w) ais	300988
Bourne G F sq	300989
Peckham N M *BSc(Hons)* sq	300989
Emery P W sq	300990
Corden P R *BA(Hons) GCGI* psc† I*	300992
Crowley P T psc	300992
Powell J R J psc	300992
Strutt D G *BA(Hons)* psc	300992
Prior A M *BA* sq	300993
Scott M G *BSc(Hons) MA GCGI* psc(n) †	300993
Williams M J *BSc(Hons)*	300993
Dewar J G *BSc(Eng)* CAFS sq(w)	300994
Fotheringham G I sq	300994
Dyer J F *BSc(Econ)*	300995
Edmunds A J psc	300995
Hanscomb M R psc	300995
Jones G P	300995
Luckham C A *MBE* sq	300995
Maer M P *MBE BSc(Hons)* psc†	300995
Sibeth P A	300995
Wright J P S *MA* psc†	300995
Hutchinson W N E *BSc(Hons)* ph	300996
Laidlaw A N	300996
Walch R T	300996

Bell H R *BA(Hons)* psc(J)	300997
Jones S R sq(w)	300997
Long H B *BA(Hons)*	300997
Taylor R M sq(w)	300997
Craig J P	300998
Graham R I	300998
Johns S J	300998
Parker C J	300998
Smith A G *BA(Hons)*	300998
Thomsett S C psc psc(J)	300998
Clapp G B	300999
Lloyd-Davis S G *BSc(Hons)*	300999
Saunders G D M	300999
Bradley D J *BA(Hons)*	300900
Denny N M *BA(Hons)*	300900
Scott L M	300900
Taylor S J *BSc(Hons)*	300900

Captains

Churcher G P *(A/Maj 080101)*	10495
Crawley A J *BA(Hons)*	110895
Young L D	130496
Carre A P *(A/Maj 011299)*	70896
Minton G E	70896
Coote J C *BEng(Hons)*	110896
Rout A J *BA(Hons)*	110896
James C A S *MBE*	290896
Houghton S P *BSc*	131296
Featherstone J B	141296
Francke G R *BSc(Hons)*	121297
Martin J R *BA(Hons)*	100299
Simmons D B *BA(Hons)*	100299
Nooney M A P *BA(Hons)*	90200
Swanson A P R *BA(Hons)*	80201

Lieutenants

Allen D R *MEng(Hons)*	160697

Regular Category Late Entry Officers

Lieutenant Colonels

Burke J F sq	11097

Majors

Bream S R *QGM*	300994
Lane M G P	300994
Abbott M J	300995
Daw T M *MBE*	300997
Farrow T R *MBE*	300997
Mears P R C	300998
Hilton B D *BEM*	300999

Special Regular Officers Late Entry

Majors

Eke W H *MBE*	300900

Captains

Young P A	40796
McCreadie K E	140897
Morrow G D	10498
Tidey P K *MBE*	10498

Intermediate Regular Officers

Captains

Baynham J L	70896
Chambers N G A *BEng(Hons)*	110896
Mott R O	80897
Thompson L D	80897

Baker B G *BA(Hons)*	160698
Dommett M N *BSc(Hons)*	160698
Betts A F J *BSc(Hons)*	131098
Bedford L J *BA(Hons)*	100299
Driscoll J J M *BA(Hons)*	100299
Curry C A *BA(Hons)*	140699
Stokes O W *BSc(Hons)*	140699
Melling R I	101299
Hickman M E *BA(Hons)*	90200
Birkett-Wendes P C T	140400
Josselin M C *BSc(Hons)*	101000
Mackenzie R C T *BEng(Hons)*	101000

Lieutenants

Myles M P C (A/Capt 050100)	130498
Flay A J (A/Capt 310100)	141298
Hanson S T *BEng(Hons)*	90899
Smith G M *BSc(Hons)*	90899
Noott R H	131299

Short Service Late Entry Officers

Captains

Hall I L	10498
Felstead I P	110299
Wright D J	10499
McDonald M R	120499

Garcia R	70400

Short Service Officers

Captains

Ramsey N S *BSc(Hons)*	131296
Johnson S A *BSc(Hons)*	130600
Tuitt A P *BSc(Hons)*	130600
Armstrong B J *BSc(Hons)*	101000
Hibbert K D *BA(Hons)*	101000
Hodgetts A R L *LLB(Hons)*	101000
Wallace R H	161200

Lieutenants

Thuilliez N P *BSc(Hons)*	70296
Sweny D M H *BA(Hons)*	161297
Devitt M R *BA(Hons)*	100298
Jardine D I *BSc(Hons)*	130498
Bagnold R A *BA(Hons)*	141298
Hooker P S	100399
Whiting J B *BSc(Hons)*	120499
Heal D J R	80800
Barley N D	90201

2nd Lieutenants

Brooks S	111299
Doyle S J	111299
Shepherd B	150400
Jones R M	161200

THE ROYAL REGIMENT OF FUSILIERS (5, 6, 7 and 20)

St George and the Dragon within the Garter

Honi Soit Qui Mal Y Pense

The United Red and White Rose slipped ensigned with the Royal Crest. An Antelope, gorged with a ducal coronet with rope reflexed over back. The White Horse of Hanover. The Red Rose of Lancaster. The Sphinx superscribed Egypt.

Namur 1695, Dettingen, Minden, Wilhelmstahl, St Lucia 1778, Martinique 1794, 1809, Egmont-op-Zee, Maida, Rolica, Vimiera, Corunna, Talavera, Busaco, Ciudad Rodrigo, Badajoz, Albuhera, Salamanca, Vittoria, Pyrenees, Nivelle, Orthes, Toulouse, Peninsula, Niagara, South Africa 1846-47, 1851, 2, 3, Alma, Inkerman, Sevastopol, Lucknow, Kandahar 1880, Afghanistan 1878-80, Atbara, Khartoum, Modder River, Relief of Ladysmith, South Africa 1899-1902.

The Great War – **Mons,** Le Cateau, Retreat from Mons, **Marne 1914, Aisne 1914, 18,** La Bassee 1914, Messines 1914, 17, 18 Armentieres 1914, **Ypres 1914, 15, 17, 18,** Langemarck 1914, 17, Gheluvelt, Nonne Bosschen, Neuve Chapelle, Gravenstafel, **St Julien,** Frezenburg, Bellewaarde, Hooge 1915, Aubers, Festubert 1915, Loos, **Somme 1916, 18,** Albert 1916, 18, Bazentin, Delville Wood, Pozieres, Guillemont, Ginchy, Flers-Courcelette, Morval, Thiepval, Le Transloy, Ancre Heights, Ancre 1916, 18, **Arras 1917, 18,** Vimy 1917, Scarpe 1917, 18, Arleux, Bullecourt, Oppy, Pilckem, Menin Road, Polygon Wood, Broodseinde, Poelcappelle, **Passchendaele, Cambrai 1917, 18,** St Quentin, Bepaume 1918, Rosieres, Avre, Villers Bretonneux, Lys, Estaires, Hazebrouck, Bailleul, Kemmel, Bethune, Scherpenberg, Amiens, Drocourt-Queant, **Hindenburg Line,** Havrincourt, Epehy, Canal du Nord, St Quentin Canal, Beaurevoir, Courtrai, Selle, Valenciennes, Sambre, France and Flanders 1914-18, **Piave,** Vittorio Veneto, Italy 1917-18, **Struma,** Doiran 1917, **Macedonia 1915-18,** Helles, **Landing at Helles,** Krithia, **Suvla, Sari Bair,** Landing at Suvla, Scimitar Hill, **Gallipoli 1915-16,** Rumani, **Egypt 1915-17,** Megiddo, Nablus, Palestine 1918, Tigris 1916, Kut al Amara 1917, **Baghdad,** Mesopotamia 1916-18, Baku, Persia 1918, Troitsa, Archangel 1919, Kilimanjaro, Behobeho, Nyangao, East Africa 1915-17.

The Second World War – **Defence of Escaut,** Arras counter attack, St Omer-La Bassee, Wormhoudt, Ypres-Comines Canal, **Dunkirk 1940, Normandy Landing,** Odon, **Caen,** Bourgebus Ridge, Cagny, Mount Pincon, Falaise, Nederrijn, Venraji, **Rhineland,** Lingen, Brinkum, **Bremen, North-West Europe 1940, 44-45,** Agordat, **Keren,** Syria 1941, Sidi Barrani, **Defence of Tobruk,** Tobruk 1941, Belhamed, Cauldron, Ruweisat Ridge, El Alamein, Advance on Tripoli, Medenine, Djebel Tebaga, **Medjez el Bab,** Oued Zarga, Peter's Corner, **North Africa 1940-43,** Adrano, Sicily 1943, Termoli, Trigno, **Sangro, Mozzagrogna,** Caldari, **Salerno,** St Lucia, Battipaglia, Teano, Volturno Crossing, Monte Camino, Garigliano Crossing, Damiano, **Anzio, Cassino II,** Ripa Ridge, Trasimene Line, Gabbiano, Advance to Florence, Monte Scalari, **Gothic Line,** Coriano, Croce, Monte Ceco, Casa Fortis, Monte Spaduro, Savio Bridgehead, Vali di Comacchio, Senio, Argenta Gap, Italy 1943-45, Athens, Greece 1944-45, **Malta 1941-42,** Singapore Island, Rathedaung, Htizwe, **Kohima,** Naga Village, Chindits 1944, **Burma 1943-45.**

Seoul, **Imjin,** Kowang-San, **Korea 1950-53, Gulf 1991,** Wadi Al Batin

Regimental Marches

Quick March .The British Grenadiers
Slow Marches . . . . Rule Britannia, De Normandie
          (i) St George (Northumberland)
          (ii) Macbean's Slow March (Warwickshire)
          (iii) De Normandie (London)
          (iv) The former Lancashire Fusiliers' Slow March

Agents . . . . .Lloyds Bank plc Cox's & King's Branch

Regimental Headquarters . . . . .HM Tower of London, Tower Hill, London, EC3N 4AB
          (Tel: 0207-488-5609)
          e-mail: rhq@thefusiliers.org website: www.thefusiliers.org

Alliances

Canadian Armed Forces . . . . .The Royal Canadian Regiment
          The Lorne Scots (Peel, Dufferin and Halton Regiment)
          31 Combat Engineer Regiment (The Elgins)
          Les Fusiliers du St Laurent
          The Royal Westminster Regiment
Australian Military Forces . . . . .5th/6th Battalion The Royal Victoria Regiment
New Zealand Army . . . . The Hauraki Regiment

Colonel in Chief . . . . .Field Marshal *HRH The Duke of* Kent *KG GCMG GCVO ADC*

Colonel . . . . .Brig R M Wilde *CBE* 010501

Deputy Colonels
  Northumberland. . . . . Brig T J Minter *OBE* 220496
  Warwickshire. . . . . Col R L Cariss *MBE TD*. 070196
  London . . . . Col P J Mostyn. 130401
  Lancashire . . . . Col B M Gorski 280999

Brigadiers

Wilde R M *CBE* rcds psc† osc(ZIM) hcsc(J) 300696
Minter T J *OBE BA(Hons)* psc hcsc(J) 300699

Colonels

Merritt T V *OBE* sq 300694
Mostyn P J *BA(Hons) MCGI* psc† hcsc(J) 300698
Bain A G *MBE BA(HonsCantab) MA(Cantab)* psc(a)† 300600
Gorski B M *MBE MSc* dis sq(w) † 300600

———

Lieutenant Colonels

Cleveland S C H (SL) *MBE* psc jsdc 300688
Henderson G W *MSc* psc† 300689
Porter J K R *BA(Hons)* psc 300690
Sanderson S H P *OBE* psc(a)† 300691
Beswick N W *MA* psc† jsdc 300693
Brazier I A psc 300693
Whistler A J *DSO MBE* psc† 300693
Kiddie K W *MA* psc 300694
Cass G P *OBE* psc 300695
O'Brien T C *MBE* psc† jsdc 300696
Bottomley D R sq 300697
Cross P T psc 300697
Diggins S L C *BA(Hons)* psc psc(J) 300697
Hiskett M W *MSc CGIA* psc† 300698
Marriott A G *MBE* psc(PAK) 300698
Murray-Playfair J L *MBE BA(Hons)* psc† 300698
Paterson D J *BSc* psc† 300698
Stack P A *MBE BA(Hons) MPhil* psc† 300698
Denny J W *MBE BA(Hons) MA* psc† psc(J) 300699
John T *BSc(Hons) MSc* psc† dis 300699
Clover J P *MBE BA(Hons)* psc† 300600

Majors

Molyneux-Carter K B *MBE* sq 300679
Seed D *MBE* psc 300980
Wolfenden R C *MBE* sq 300984
Greenwood A G psc 300985
Robertson B D *MA* sq(w) † 300988
Sturtivant P A psc 300988
Harward R B psc 300989
Oliver G G sq 300989
Bishop C N *BSc(Hons)* sq(w) † 300990
Longley P M *MA* psc† 300990
Welch A L psc *(A/Lt Col 101100)* 300990
Sayer J M R osc(P) sq 300991
Claridge C R psc† *(A/Lt Col 151200)* 300992
Macey P J *MBE* psc 300992
Aldridge W N *MBE MA(Cantab)* psc *(A/Lt Col 120101)* 300993
Coates E G psc 300993
Harnby G R 300993

Kippen I R *BA(Hons) BSc* sq(w) 300993
Thompson I M *BA MSc* psc† 300993
Cartwright A I psc† psc 00994
Eastwood C C *BA(Hons)* sq(w) † 300994
Whitehouse J G *BA(Hons)* sq 300994
Collicutt R J *BA(Hons) MA* osc(US) 300995
Evans H S psc 300995
Johnstone I R F *MSc* psc(J) 300995
Marr S R D psc 300995
Merriman P W *MBE MA* psc(J) 300995
Milo D N M *MA* psc† 300995
Moncur G D 300995
Whitwam J C E *MBE BA(Hons) MA* psc† 300995
Landon J 300996
Nanson P A E odc(AUST) psc(J) 300996
Thompson R P D psc(J) 300996
Whelan A M 300996
Travers M P M 300997
Hallam I M 300998
Turner C J 300998
Cartwright G G *MA* ifp 300999
Flute E J P *BA(Hons)* 300999
Matthews J A *BSc* 300999
Steemson P *BSc(Hons)* 300999
Thomas S J 300999
Flavell P R 300900
Mace K N *BSc(Hons)* 300900
McSporran D R *BSc(Hons)* 300900
Thorp M C R *BSc(Hons)* 300900

Captains

McDermott R P *BA(Hons)* 10495
Stott J R 110895
Robinson J P C 130496
Butterwick M R *BA(Hons)* 110896
Laws J M *BA(Hons)* 131296
Nicholson S F *BA(Hons)* 120298
Fulford-Talbot J L 90498
Gawthorpe A S *LLB(Hons)* 160698
Swift J *BSc(Hons)* 160698
Higgs A R A 111298
Canning M B *BA(Hons)* 100299
Taylor J W *BA(Hons)* 100299
Wilcox N J 90499
Coates R M *BA(Hons)* 90200
McCutcheon L C 130600
Frisby C D H *BA* 20900
Sutthery E P 161200

Lieutenants

Pavey R G *BA(Hons)* 120297
Lamb J *BEng(Hons)* 120897
Lawrence R C *BSc(Hons)* 90899
Franklin R J *(A/Capt 140200)* 131299

Regular Category Late Entry Officers

Lieutenant Colonels

Jones A T sq 10198
Moran M S *QGM* 61299

Majors

Hunt J R *BEM* 300992
Gorton P *MILT* 300996
Johnson N 300997
Richardson N J 300998

Special Regular Officers Late Entry

Captains

Meades A 110396
Leyland M R 10498

Intermediate Regular Officers

Captains

Hopkin C R *BSc(Hons)* 101294
Murphy T G M 10495
Rampe G 151295
Newell A W 40796
Stitt P B *BA(Hons)* 120298
Boyd A 10498
Freeman R W *BEng(Hons)* 160698
Ing S J F *BEng(Hons)* 140699
Morris T P D *BA(Hons)* 121099
Gentle E F *BEng(Hons)* 90200
Cornwell M D *BA(Hons)* 130600
Cooke M J *BSc* 80201

Lieutenants

Pugh E R *BA(Hons)* 120297
Austin J S 131299

2nd Lieutenants

†Ribbans A M 100900

Short Service Late Entry Officers

Captains

Hill J H 10498
Taylor D J 10498
Jones G B 10499
Stacey M A M 140200
Currie D P 30400
McCarthy M 30400

Short Service Officers

Captains

Summerfield G C D *BA(Hons)* 121099
Boyd G J 101299
Butterfill J *BA(Hons)* 130600
Orpin D J *BA(Hons)* 130600
Wilson J A J *BSc(Hons)* 130600
Murphy G A *BSc* 20900
Cranston N J *BA(Hons)* 101000
Macpherson H I 161200
Crighton J S *BA(Hons)* 80201

Lieutenants

Taylor C A 130498
Lowe J A *BSc(Hons)* 141298
Thomas D J *BA(Hons)* 141298
Wilson L P 90299
Skelton J S *BSc(Hons)* 120499
Speakman Z *BA(Hons)* 120499
Walters B *BA(Hons)* 120499
Jackson B A L *BA(Hons)* 30599
Weston B D *BA(Hons)* 130699

Anabtawi N *BEng(Hons)*	90899	Wilson D R	10999	Woodward M E	80800
Bird J M *B Sc (Hons)*	90899	Donnini J M	240999		
Dowling J T *LLB(Hons)*	90899			*2nd Lieutenants*	
Maltby J F J *BSc(Hons)*	90899	Campbell C O *BA(Hons)*	131299	Gibson A C	70899

176

THE ROYAL ANGLIAN REGIMENT (9, 10, 12, 16, 17, 44, 48, 56, 58)

The Castle and Key of Gibraltar upon an eight pointed Star

The figure of Britannia. The Sphinx superscribed Egypt. The Castle and Key superscribed Gibraltar, 1779-83 and with the motto *Montis Insignia Calpe* underneath. The Royal Tiger superscribed Hindoostan. An Eagle within the Garter.

Namur 1695, Blenheim, Ramillies, Oudenarde, Malplaquet, Dettingen, Louisburg, Minden, Quebec 1759, Belleisle, **Martinique 1762, 1794,** Moro, **Havannah,** India, **Seringapatan,** Surinam, Maida, Rolica, Vimiera, **Peninsula, Corunna,** Douro, **Talavera,** Busaca, **Albuhera, Badajoz, Salamanca, Vittoria,** Pyrenees, St Sebastian, Nivelle, Nive, Orthes, Toulouse, **Bladensburg,** Waterloo, Ava, Afghanistan 1839, **Ghuznee 1839, Khelat, Cabool 1842, 79, Moodkee, Ferozeshah, Sobraon, New Zealand,** Mooltan, **Goojerat, Punjaub, South Africa 1851-53,** Alma, **Inkerman, Sevastopol, Lucknow, Taku Forts,** South Africa 1879, **Afghanistan 1878-80,** Ali Masjid, **Nile 1884-85,** Chitral, **Tirah, Atbara, Khartoum, South Africa 1899-1902.** Modder River, Relief of Kimberley, **Paardeburg, Defence of Ladysmith.**

The Great War – **Mons, Le Cateau,** Retreat from Mons, **Marne 1914, Aisne 1914, 18,** La Bassee 1914, Messines 1914, 17, 18, Armentieres 1914, Givenchy 1914, **Ypres 1914, 15, 17, 18,** Langemarck 14, 17, Gheluvelt, Nonne Bosschen, Festubert 1914, 15, **Neuve Chapelle,** Hill 60, Gravenstafel, St Julien, Frezenberg, Bellewaarde, Aubers, Hooge 1915, **Loos, Somme 1916, 18,** Albert 1916, 18, Bazentin, Delville Wood, Pozieres, Guillemont, Flers-Courcelette, Morval, Thiepval, Le Transloy, Ancre Heights, Ancre 1916, 18, Bapaume 1917, 18, **Arras 1917, 18,** Vimy 1917, Scarpe 1917, 18, Arleux, Oppy, Pilckem, Menin Road, Polygon Wood, Broodseinde, Poelcappelle, Passchendaele, **Cambrai 1917, 18,** St Quentin, Rosieres, Avre, Villers Bretonneux, Lys, Estaires, Hazebrouck, Bailleul, Kemmel, Bethune, Scherpenberg, Amiens, Drocourt-Queant, Hindenburg Line, Havrincourt, Epehy, Canal du Nord, St Quentin Canal, Beaurevoir, Courtrai, Selle, Valenciennes, Sambre, **France and Flanders 1914-18,** Italy 1917-18, Helles, Landing at Helles, Struma, Doiran 1918, **Macedonia 1915-18,** Krithia, Suvla, Landing at Suvla, Scimitar Hill, **Gallipoli 1915-16,** Rumani, Egypt 1915-17, **Gaza,** El Mughar, Nebi Samwil, Jerusalem, **Jaffa,** Tell' Asur, Megiddo, Sharon, Damascus, **Palestine 1917-18,** Tigris 1916, **Shaiba,** Kut al Amara 1915, 17, Ctesiphon, Defence of Kut al Amara, Baghdad, **Mesopotamia 1914-18.**

The Second World War – Vist, Norway 1940, Defence of Escaut, **St Omar-la Basse,** Defence of Arras, Ypres-Comines Canal, **Dunkirk 1940,** St Valery-en-Caux, **Normandy Landing,** Cambes, Tilly sur Seulles, Fontenay le Pesnil, Odon, Defence of Rauray, Caen, Orne, Bourguebus Ridge, Troarn, Le Perier Ridge, **Brieux Bridgehead,** Falaise, Nederrijn, Le Havre, Antwerp-Turnhout Canal, Schmidt, **Venraij,** Venlo Pocket, Zetten, Rhineland, Hochwald, Lingen, Brinkum, Bremen, Arnhem 1945, **North-West Europe 1940, 44-45,** Abyssinia 1940, Falluja, Tobruk Sortie, Belhamed, Baghdad 1941, Iraq 1941, Palmyra, Jebel Mazar, Syria 1941, Sidi Barrani, **Tobruk 1941,** Tobruk Sortie, Belhamed, Mersa Matruh, **Defence of Alamein Line,** Deir El Shein, Ruweisat, Ruweisat Ridge, El Alamein, Matmata Hills, Akarit, Enfidaville, Djebel Garci, Djedeida, Djebel Djaffa, Montagne Farm, Sedjenane 1, Mine de Sedjenane, Oued Zargo, Djebel Tanngoucha, Argoub Tanngoucha, Argoub Sellah, Sidi Ahmed, Tunis, Ragoubet Souissi, **North Africa 1940-43,** Landing in Sicily, Adrano, Sicily 1943, Trigno, Sangro, **Villa Grande, Salerno,** Vietri Pass, Capture of Naples, Cava di Tirreni, Volturno Crossing, Calabritto, Garigliano Crossing, Monte Tuga, **Anzio, Cassino i-ii,** Castle Hill, Hangman's Hill, Monte Gaddione, Trasimene Line, **Gothic Line,** Monte Gridolfo, Gemmano Ridge, Lamone Crossing, Monte Columbo, San Marino, Monte La Pieve, Argenta Gap, **Italy 1943-45,** Athens, Greece 1944-45, **Crete,** Heraklion, Madagascar, Kampar, Johore, Muar, Batu Pahat, **Singapore Island, Malaya 1941-42,** Donbaik, Point 201 (Arakan), **Yu,** North Arakan, Buthidaung, **Ngakyedauk Pass, Imphal,** Tamu Road, Bishenpur, **Kohima,** Aradura, Monywa 1945, Mandalay, Myinmu Bridgehead, Irrawaddy, Ramree, **Chindits 1944, Burma 1943-45.**

Maryang-San, **Korea 1951-53**

Regimental Marches

Quick March	Rule Britannia and Speed the Plough
Slow March	The Slow March of The Northamptonshire Regiment
Agents	Holts Branch, Royal Bank of Scotland plc, Lawrie House, Farnborough, Hants.
Regimental Headquarters	The Keep, Gibraltar Barracks, Bury St Edmunds, Suffolk, IP33 3RN (Tel: 01284-752394 Ext: 5124)

Alliances

Canadian Armed Forces	Sherbrooke Hussars
	The Lincoln and Welland Regiment
	The Essex and Kent Scottish
	The Lake Superior Scottish Regiment
Australian Military Forces	The Royal Tasmania Regiment
New Zealand Army	3rd Battalion (Auckland (Countess of Ranfurly's Own) and Northland) Royal New Zealand Infantry Regiment
Pakistan Army	5th Battalion The Frontier Force Regiment
Malaysian Armed Forces	1st Battalion The Royal Malay Regiment
Barbados	The Barbados Regiment
South African Defence Forces	Regiment de la Rey First City Regiment
Colonial Forces	The Bermuda Regiment
	The Royal Gibraltar Regiment
	The Belize Defence Force

Colonel in Chief . . . .*HM* QUEEN ELIZABETH THE QUEEN MOTHER
Deputy Colonels in Chief . . . .*HRH* The Princess Margaret *Countess of* Snowdon *CI GCVO*
                                HRH Princess Alice *Duchess of* Gloucester *GCBCL GCVO GBE*
Colonel . . . . .Gen *Sir* Michael Walker *GCB CMG CBE ADC Gen*
Deputy Colonels . . . . .Maj Gen J C B Sutherell *CBE*
                                Maj Gen J C McColl *CBE*
                                Col N H Kelsey *OBE TD*

Brigadiers	Gregory D J *BA(Hons)* sq	300994	Inch J D	60999

Brigadiers

Deed A P *OBE MSc* psc(IND) 300697
Brunt R M *CBE MA* rcds psc hcsc(J) 311297

Colonels

Lacey J D *CBE* psc jsdc 300692
Clements D J *MBE BSc(Hons) FRGS* rcds psc† 300697
Cocker C A *OBE* odc(US) osc(US) 300698
Chisnall R M *OBE* psc 300699
Harrold R E *OBE* psc psc(J) 300600
———

Lieutenant Colonels

Dixon P R C (SL) *OBE* psc† *(L/Col 020192)* 300687
Haes R E (SL) *OBE* psc 300687
Stallard C G psc 300690
Duthoit G D sq jsdc 300691
Baylis D J W *OBE BA(Hons) MSc* psc(IND) OSC(KU) jsdc 300692
Chambers M D (SL) psc 300693
Porter S L psc *(A/Col 110900)* 300695
Holme P M sq 300696
Kemp R J *MBE* psc 300697
Jones P D *MBE* psc 300698
Wild A J C *MBE BA(Hons) MSc* dis psc(AUS)† 300698
Ladley R J *MBE BEng(Hons) MSc* psc† 300699
Bacon S J sq 300600
Beard M J sq 300600
Blyth S P M sq 300600

Majors

Ferrary P M L aic I* I sq(w) 300981
Gould R C sq 300982
Hall I R M sq 300986
Borthwick J A B psc 300987
Pearce C J sq 300987
Lucas R H C osc(MAL) sq 300988
Macdonald J F sq(w) 300988
Napier D C psc 300988
Hare R J psc 300989
Willmott W A sq 300989
Brunt S B sq 300991
Clements R J *JP* sq 300991
Goodin R C J *BA* sq 300991
Gaskin P H *BA(Hons) MSc MA* psc(IND) † 300992
Wadman A J sq 300992
Wenham M H sq 300992
Andrews S T H *BSc MA* psc† 300993
Knox R A psc 300993

Gregory D J *BA(Hons)* sq 300994
Pattison R W T *BSc(Hons)* sq(w) 300994
Wylie A M *BSc(Hons)* sq(w) 300994
Etherington S D *MA* psc(J) 300995
Harris J E *MA* psc† 300995
Hunter D G H *MSc* sq(w) 300995
O'Driscoll D P *BA(Hons)* psc psc(J) 300995
Saunders W J 300995
Thorne E E C *BSc(Hons) MA* psc† 300995
Vincent D G sq 300995
Eaton A E *BSc(Hons) Dis MSc* psc(J) dis 300996
Gosling A psc(J) 300996
Hart J J W *BA(Hons)* 300996
Latham R J *MA* psc(J) 300996
Nottingham N F C *BA(Hons)* 300996
Price A W *BA(Hons)* 300996
Browne S J R *MA BA(Hons)* psc(J) 300997
Carver S W *BA(Hons)* psc(J) 300997
Heap J M H *BA(Hons)* 300997
Marinos A C E *BA(Hons)* 300997
Woodham J M 300998
Down B M 300999
England D A 300999
Wright J C J *BSc(Hons)* 300999
York J A *BA(Hons)* 300999
Bailey P D *BA(Hons)* 300900
Beart A B 300900
Calder C S 300900
Morris G *BA(Hons)* 300900
O'Driscoll T E *BSc(Hons)* 300900
Wooddisse R W *BA(Hons)* 300900

Captains

Couch J *BA(Hons)* 10495
Grinonneau A G 110895
Grounds F J R *BSc(Hons)* 110895
Johnson N A 110895
McGrath L S F *BA(Hons)* 110895
Borgnis A H C *BA(Hons)* 110896
Smith S R *BSc(Hons)* 120298
Powell M G *BSc(Hons)* 131098
Romilly S W *BA(Hons)* 131098
Worthy S C *BA(Hons)* 131098
Biddick D S J 221099
Brown O C C *BSc(Econ)Hons* 130600
Muncey P A *B Sc (Hons)* 130600

Lieutenants

Wilson S D *BA(Hons)* *(A/Capt 231000)* 120897
Whitham R H *BA(Hons)* 131097

2nd Lieutenants

†Adams J J 220997
James-Roll D H 100499

Inch J D 60999

Regular Category Late Entry Officers

Majors

Potter R W *MBE* 300995
Jones A 300996
McCrum D *MBE* 300997
Brown R J 300999

Special Regular Officers Late Entry

Majors

Todd A E 300900

Captains

Grenfell R P 140796
Nye S J *MBE* 10498
Pallant S N 10498

Intermediate Regular Officers

Majors

Leslie P S *MA(Cantab)* 300900
Lyne R F L 300900

Captains

Dicker M B *(A/Maj 090499)* 141291
Aston M P 311295
Elphee M L *BEng(Hons)* 110896
Birch P M *MA(Cantab)* 131296
Bowman A P R *BA(Hons)* 131296
Smith P M 141297
Carnegie J D 90298
Paden E L *BSc(Hons)* 131098
Allen B M *BA(Hons)* 100299
Chance I M *BSc(Hons)* 100299
Faint N F *BA(Hons)* 140699
Mellar T B 60899
Moss D J 60899
Barry C B K *MA(Hons)* 121099
Hawley A F 90200
Messenger P J *BEng(Hons)* 130600
†Ives L M 11200

Lieutenants

Evans M R *BSc(Hons)* *(L/Capt 240400)* 120897
Woodeson M S *BA(Hons)* *(L/Capt 070600)* 120897
Davies C D *(A/Capt 140199)* 161297
Charlwood N D B *(A/Capt 050600)* 100898
Dingle M A *(A/Capt 020800)* 100898

2nd Lieutenants

Swallow C	100499
††Osborne G E	100900
Hartley O E	161200

Short Service Late Entry Officers

Captains

Hoyles C D	10498
Stefanetti D J	10299
Ralph F A *MBE*	10499
Beighton T P	70400

Short Service Officers

Captains

Holton P A	131296
Worthington P C *MA BA*	121099

Hughes J D	30300
Otter S T G *BA(Hons)*	130600
Rayment B J	130600

Lieutenants

Delf J P *BA(Hons)*	200797
Belderbos E J *BA(Hons) (A/Capt 300900)*	120897
James R J *BA(Hons)*	100298
Biggs A *BSc(Hons)*	130498
Hancock J *BSc(Hons)*	130498
Allen G L *BEng(Hons)*	100898
Foden G B *BA(Hons)*	100898
Haden N J *(A/Capt 100599)*	100898
Hitching R M *BA(Soc)Hons*	100898
Newmarch R H *BA(Hons)*	100898
Nicholas M A *BA(Hons)*	100898
Wolfe A P *BA(Hons)*	100898
Gregory T W *BSocSc(Hons)*	90299

Moxey P C *BSc(Hons)*	90299
Roberts S F *BA(Hons)*	120499
Dobbin A S *BSc(Hons)*	90899
Harris P A *BA(Econ)Hons*	90899
McNeil R J *BA(Hons)*	90899
Connolly P D *BSc*	131299
Teare J C J R *BSc(Econ)Hons*	131299

2nd Lieutenants

Melia M C	70899
Downes J P	150400

Short Service Volunteer Officers

Lieutenants

Bell R S C	30899

THE KING'S DIVISION

Comprising .The King's Own Royal Border Regiment (1 Regular Battalion, 2 Volunteer Companies)

The King's Regiment (1 Regular Battalion, 2 Volunteer Companies)

The Prince of Wales's Own Regiment of Yorkshire (1 Regular Battalion, 2 Volunteer Companies)

The Green Howards (Alexandra, Princess of Wales's Own Yorkshire Regiment) (1 Regular Battalion, 2 Volunteer Companies)

The Queen's Lancashire Regiment (1 Regular Battalion, 2 Volunteer Companies)

The Duke of Wellington's Regiment (West Riding) (1 Regular Battalion, 2 Volunteer Companies)

Divisional Office . . . . .Headquarters Infantry, Warminster, Wilts BA12 0DJ (Tel: 01985-222402)

Colonel Commandant . . . . .Lt Gen *Sir* Scott Grant *KCB* 010297

Divisional Colonel . . . . .Lt Col N J Rynn *BA(Hons)* psc 060599

The origins of amalgamated Regiments now included in The King's Division are as follows:

THE KING'S OWN ROYAL BORDER REGIMENT

On 1 October 1959

The King's Own Royal Regiment (Lancaster) and

The Border Regiment (34 and 55) amalgamated to form:

The King's Own Royal Border Regiment

THE KING'S REGIMENT

On 1 September 1958

The King's Regiment (Liverpool) (8) and

The Manchester Regiment (63 and 96) amalgamated to form:

The King's Regiment (Manchester and Liverpool) (8, 63 and 96)

On 13 December 1968 the Regiment was redesignated

The King's Regiment

THE PRINCE OF WALES'S OWN REGIMENT OF YORKSHIRE

On 24 April 1958

The West Yorkshire Regiment (The Prince of Wales's Own) (14) and

The East Yorkshire Regiment (Duke of York's Own) (15) amalgamated to form:

The Prince of Wales's Own Regiment of Yorkshire

180

THE QUEEN'S LANCASHIRE REGIMENT

On 1 July 1958
The East Lancashire Regiment (30 and 59) and
The South Lancashire Regiment (The Prince of Wales's Volunteers) (40 and 82) amalgamated to form:
The Lancashire Regiment (Prince of Wales's Volunteers)

On 25 March 1970
The Lancashire Regiment (Prince of Wales's Volunteers) (30, 40, 59 and 82) and
The Loyal Regiment (North Lancashire) (47 and 81) amalgamated to form:
The Queen's Lancashire Regiment

THE DUKE OF WELLINGTON'S REGIMENT

On 1 July 1881
The Duke of Wellington's Regiment (33) and
The 76th Regiment of Foot (76(amalgamated to form:
The Halifax Regiment which was subsequently renamed
The Duke of Wellington's Regiment

THE KING'S OWN ROYAL BORDER REGIMENT (4, 34 and 55)

The Royal Cypher within the garter all within a wreath of laurel. The Lion of England in each corner, Dragon Superscribed China

Namur 1695, Gibraltar 1704-5, Guadaloupe 1759, Havannah, St Lucia 1778, Corunna, Albuhera, Arroyo Dos Molinos, Badajoz, Salamanca, Vittoria, St Sebastian, Pyrenees, Nivelle, Nive, Orthes, Peninsula, Bladensburg, Waterloo, Alma, Inkerman, Sevastopol, Lucknow, Abyssinia, South Africa 1879, Relief of Ladysmith, South Africa 1899-1902.

The Great War – Le Cateau, Retreat from Mons, **Marne 1914**, Aisne 1914, Armentieres 1914, **Ypres 1914, 15, 17, 18**, **Langemarck 1914, 17**, Gheluvelt, Neuve Chappelle, Gravenstafel, St Julien, Frezenberg, Bellewaarde, Aubers, Festubert 1915, Loos, **Somme 1916, 18**, Albert 1916, 18, Bazentin, Delville Wood, Pozieres, Guillemont, Ginchy, Flers-Courcelette, Morval, Thiepval, Le Transloy, Ancre Heights, Ancre 1916, **Arras 1917, 18**, Scarpe 1917, 18, Arleux, Bullecourt, **Messines 1917, 18**, Pilckem, Menin Road, Polygon Wood, Broodseinde, Poelcappelle, Passchendaele, **Cambrai, 1917, 18**, St Quentin, Rosieres, **Lys**, Estaires, Hazebrouck, Bailleul, Kemmel, Bethune, Scherpenberg, Aisne 1918, Amiens, Bapaume 1918, Drocourt-Queant, Hindenburg Line, Epehy, Canal du Nord, St Quentin Canal, Beaurevoir, Courtrai, Selle, Valenciennes, Sambre, **France and Flanders 1914-18**, Piave, **Vittorio Veneto**, Italy 1917-18, Struma, Doiran 1917, 18, **Macedonia 1915-18**, Helles, Landing at Helles, Krithia, Suvla, Sari Bair, Landing at Suvla, Scimitar Hill, **Gallipoli 1915-16**, Egypt 1916, Tigris 1916, Kut al Amara 1917, Baghdad, **Mesopotamia 1916-18**, North-West Frontier India 1916-17, Afghanistan 1919.

The Second World War - Defence of Escaut, St Omer-La Bassee, **Dunkirk 1940**, Somme 1940, **Arnhem 1944**, **North-West Europe 1940, 44**, **Defence of Habbaniya**, Falluja, Iraq 1941, **Merjayum**, Jebel Mazar, Syria 1941, **Tobruk 1941**, **Tobruk Sortie**, North Africa 1940-42, **Landing in Sicily**, Montone, Citta di Castello, San Martino, Sogliano, **Lamone Bridgehead**, Italy 1944-45, **Malta 1941-42**, **Imphal**, Sakawng, Tamu Road, Shenam Pass, Kohima, Ukhrul, Mandalay, **Myinmu Bridgehead**, **Meiktila**, Rangoon Road, Pyawbwe, Sittang 1945, **Chindits 1944**, **Burma 1943-45**.

Regimental Marches

Quick March	Arrangement of 'John Peel' and 'Corn Rigs are Bonnie'
Slow March	Trelawny
Regimental Headquarters	The Castle, Carlisle, Cumbria, CA3 8UR (Tel: 01228-521275)

Alliances

Canadian Armed Forces	The King's Own Calgary Regiment
Australian Military Forces	The Royal Queensland Regiment
Pakistan Army	15th Battalion The Frontier Force Regiment
Colonel in Chief	*HRH Princess* Alexandra *Hon Lady* Ogilvy *GCVO*
Colonel	Maj Gen R J Hodges *CB OBE* 160588

Colonels

Westlake J R *OBE MSc* psc	300692
Davidson A F *MBE* psc	300694

Lieutenant Colonels

Jarvis-Bicknell T C *MBE* psc jsdc *(A/Col 010101)*	300689
Strickland S W L *OBE* psc	300690
Schumacher A *MBE* psc	300694
Iron R M *OBE MA* psc†	300696
Barrett T R *MBE* sq	270197
Griffiths M T *BSc(Hons)* psc†	300698

Majors

Welsh J R K sq	300980
Longhurst A R sq	300982
Allardice D H psc†	300984
Mawdsley S D *MA* psc(GE) I* I	300986
Hanna T J sq(w) †	300987
Gray C H W sq	300988
Perkin M S *MBE* sq	300990

Hewitt G M *BA* sq(w)	300993
Dennis A *BSc(Hons)* psc	300994
Sharpe J M A sq	300994
Watkins M J G *BA MBA MDA FRSA*	300994
Gardner J A	300995
Moss G P *OBE BSocSc(Hons) MA* psc†	300995
Pritchard H W *MBE MA MA(Hons)* psc† †	300995
Urquhart I A N *BA(Hons) MA* psc† †	300995
Rose R J J *BSc(Hons) MSc* dis	300997
Kennedy A P *BA(Hons)*	300998
Westbrooke J C	300998
Hartley J C *BA(Hons)*	300999
Davidson A J W *BSc* cafs	300900
Wood N I *BA(Hons)* *(A/Maj 090799)*	110895

Captains

Unsworth N	211295
Blakesley P J *BSc(Hons) MSc*	110896
Chaffer J B	110497
Crook J A *BA(Hons)*	120298
Nathan P R *BA(Hons)*	160698

Maund G A *BA(Hons)*	100299
Serle N *BA(Hons)*	130600

Lieutenants

Flynn J M *BA(Hons)*	90299

2nd Lieutenants

††Westcott B J	60998

Regular Category Late Entry Officers

Majors

Hopton R	300993
Parsonage D	300993

Special Regular Officers Late Entry

Captains

Firth S G *MBE*	210593

Intermediate Regular Officers

Majors

Hely T M H M	300998

Captains

Candlish G G   180196
Simpson J A *BSc*   110896
Allison-Green D M   141296
Welsh A M   20397
Cormack H G G *BA(Hons)*   131098
Hennessy-Barrett W J P *BA(Hons)*
                                 131098
Walker M P M *BSc(Hons)*   100299
Maskell A J *LLB(Hons) DipLP*
                                 140699

Lieutenants

Graves D C   121200

Short Service Late Entry Officers

Captains

Preston G H   10498

Sheehan C   100699
Graham M   70200

Short Service Officers

Captains

Smith T P *BSc(Hons)* ph   141295
Green J *BSc(Hons)*   100299
Johnson A G *BSc(Hons)*   90200
Darwent C I *BSc(Hons)*   130600
Picton E T   120700
Fry J I *BSc(Hons)*   101000
Tingey P J *BSc(Hons)*   101000
Watson J C A *BSc(Hons)*   101000

Lieutenants

Mackenzie N P *BA(Hons)*   120297
Porter J G A *BA(Hons)*   120297
Braithwaite C E *BSc(Hons)*   120897

Bullock R G *BSc(Hons)*   130498
Lowe J J *BSc(Hons)*   100898
Oakes R A *MA BA(Hons)*   100898
Morrison M R *BSc(Hons)*   131299
Singleton R J *BA(Hons)*   131299
Perschke J W C   80800

2nd Lieutenants

Locke N A *PGDA*   150399

Short Service Volunteer Officers

2nd Lieutenants

De Silva R D P   10899

Lieutenant Colonels

Castle J M   psc   260596

THE KING'S REGIMENT (8, 63 and 96)

The white horse of Hanover superimposed upon a yellow fleur-de-lys. The Royal Cypher surmounted by the Crown.
The Sphinx superscribed Egypt

Blenheim, Ramillies, Oudenarde, Malplaquet, Dettingen, Guadaloupe 1759, Egmont-op-Zee, Peninsula, Martinique 1809, Guadaloupe 1810, Niagara, New Zealand, Alma, Inkerman, Sevastopol, Delhi 1857, Lucknow, Peiwar Kotal, Afghanistan 1878-80, Egypt 1882, Burma 1885-87, Defence of Ladysmith, South Africa 1899-1902.

The Great War – **Mons**, Le Cateau, **Retreat from Mons, Marne 1914, Aisne 1914,** La Bassee 1914, Armentieres 1914, **Ypres 1914, 15, 17, 18,** Langemarck 1914, 17, Gheluvelt, Nonne Bosschen, **Givenchy 1914**, Neuve Chapelle, Gravenstafel, St Julien, Frezenberg, Bellewaarde, Aubers, Festubert 1915, **Loos, Somme 1916, 18,** Albert 1916, 18, Bazentin, Delville Wood, Guillemont, Ginchy, Flers-Courcellete, Morval, Thiepval, Le Transloy, Ancre 1916, 18, Bapaume 1917, 18, **Arras 1917-18,** Scarpe 1917, 18, Arleux, Bullecourt, Messines 1917, 18, Pilckem, Menin Road, Polygon Wood, Broodseinde, Poelcappelle, Passchendaele, **Cambrai 1917, 18,** St Quentin, Rosieres, Avre, Lys, Estaires, Bailleul, Kemmel, Bethune, Amiens, Scherpenberg, Drocourt-Queant, **Hindenburg Line,** Epehy, Canal du Nord, St Quentin Canal, Beaurevoir, Courtrai, Selle, Sambre, France and Flanders 1914-18, **Piave,** Vittorio Veneto, Italy 1917-18, Doiran 1917, **Macedonia 1915-18,** Helles, Krithia, Suvla, Landing at Suvla, Scimitar Hill, **Gallipoli 1915,** Rumani, Egypt 1915-17, **Megiddo,** Sharon, Palestine 1918, Tigris 1916, Kut al Amara 1917, **Baghdad,** Mesopotamia 1916-18, North-West Frontier India 1915.

Archangel 1918-19, Afghanistan 1919

The Second World War – **Dyle,** Withdrawal to Escaut, Defence of Escaut, **Defence of Arras,** St Omer-la-Basseem, Ypres-Comines Canal, **Normandy Landing, Caen,** Esquay, Falaise, Nederrijn, **Scheldt,** Walcharen Causeway, Flushing, **Lower Maas.** Venlo Pocket, **Roer,** Ourthe, Rhineland, **Reichswald,** Goch, Weeze, Rhine, Ibbenburen, Dreirwalde, Aller, Bremen, North-West Europe 1940, 44-45, **Cassino II, Trasimene Line, Tuori, Gothic Line,** Monte Gridolfo, Coriano, San Clemente, Gemmano Ridge, Montilgallo, **Capture of Forli,** Lamone Crossing, Defence of Lamone Bridgehead, **Rimini Line,** Montescudo, Cesena, Italy 1944-45, **Malta 1940, Athens,** Greece 1944-45, Singapore Island, Malaya 1941-42, North Arakan, **Kohima,** Pinwe, Schwebo, Myinmu Bridgehead, Irrawaddy, **Chindits 1943, Chindits 1944,** Burma 1943-45.

The Hook 1953, Korea 1952-53

Regimental Marches

Quick March .The Kingsman
Slow March .Lord Ferrars March

Agents . . . . .Barclays Bank, 4 Water Street, Liverpool, L69 2DU

Regimental Headquarters . . . . .New Zealand House, Water Street, Liverpool L2 8TD
(Tel: Civil: 0151-236-6363 Mil: 94552-2417)

Regimental Headquarters (Increment) .TA Centre, Ardwick Green, Manchester, M12 6HD
(Tel: Civil: 0161-273-6191 Mil: 94571-3250)

Alliances

Canadian Armed Forces . . . . .The Royal Regiment of Canada
Australian Military Forces . . . . .10th/27th Battalion The Royal South Australia Regiment
New Zealand Army . . . . .The Otago and Southland Regiment
Pakistan Army . . . . .1st Battalion (Scinde) The Frontier Force Regiment
Indian Army .5th Battalion The Sikh Regiment

Colonel in Chief . . . .*HM* QUEEN ELIZABETH THE QUEEN MOTHER

Colonel . . . . .Brig J J Gaskell *OBE* 210194

Colonels

Hodges C O *MBE BA(Hons)* psc
300699
Parish M C *OBE BA(Hons)* psc
300600

Lieutenant Colonels

Hodges R E L psc   300691
Horsford I T (SL) sq   300694
Barnes R W *MBE* psc   300696
Owen C W *BSc(Hons)* psc(a)†
300696

Majors

Turley J F *BA* sq	300985
Hammond S A *MBE* psc	300989
Storr J P *BSc(Eng)Hons MSc ACGI* psc†	300992
Cain T D *BA(Hons)* sq	300993
Nicholls M *MA* psc† †	300993
Griffin C M *MA* psc†	300994
Barnett S N psc(J)	300995
Docherty A J psc†	300995
Hutchinson S D *MBE* psc	300995
Rafferty P S *BSc MA* psc(a) osc(US)	300995
Simpson R M osc(MAL) sq	300995
Smith N D S psc	300995
Farrell D T *BSc(Hons) MDA*	300996

Lettin G D *BA(Hons)*	300996
Pullan A M *MDA* odc(US) MDA	300996
Deakin G C	300998
Cheetham N J *BSc(Hons)*	300999
Lee M R	300999
Routledge S J *BSc(Hons)*	300900
White D L	300900

Captains

Cowell E W J *BSc(Econ)Hons*	10495
Hollister J B W *BA(Hons)*	110895
Roffey S N J *BA(Hons)*	100696
Hughes A M	121297
Holmes D W *BA(Hons)*	100299

184

Lieutenants		
Hunt D M		141298
Hill C J E M *BEng(Hons)*		90899

Regular Category Late Entry Officers

Lieutenant Colonels

Hollingsworth A *MBE* 90300

Majors

Attwood D T *MBE*	300998
Cunningham D J *BSc(Hons)*	300998
Meacock T W	300900

Special Regular Officers Late Entry

Captains

Johnson K G *(A/Maj 060197)*	
	311295
Singh J	170196

Piercy S J 10496

Intermediate Regular Officers

Captains

Metcalf I P	300596
Job C J T	141296
Russell J S *BSc(Agr)*	131098
Rideout M W H *BSc(Hons)*	140699
Yates M *BSc(Hons)*	90200
Driver P R	141000
Hendry-Adams I A	161200

Lieutenants

Coleman C P	100898
McGuire I	90899

Short Service Late Entry Officers

Captains

Hunt M R	10498
Bell M	300499
Davies R A	300499

Short Service Officers

Captains

Stringer G H P *BA*	160698
Bell R	121099
Deuchar M R N	101000

Lieutenants

Barry G M *BEng(Hons)*	160697
Henebury E J *BA(Hons)*	100898
Spencer D J *BA(Hons)*	100898
Pratt M F *BA(Hons)*	141298
Adams M B	90899
Brown R D	90899
Hughes R *LLB(Hons)*	90899
Ayo L P	131299

Short Service Volunteer Officers

Majors

David J T *MILOG* 61181

185

THE PRINCE OF WALES'S OWN REGIMENT OF YORKSHIRE (14 and 15)

The White Rose of York superimposed upon an eight-pointed star
The Prince of Wales's Plume. The White Horse of Hanover with motto *"Nec aspera terrent"*
The Royal Tiger superscribed India

Namur 1695, Blenheim, Ramillies, Oudenarde, Malplaquet, Louisburg, Quebec 1759, Martinique 1762, Havannah, St Lucia 1778, Martinique 1794, 1809, Tournay, Corunna, Guadaloupe 1810, Java, Waterloo, Bhurtpore, Sevastopol, New Zealand, Afghanistan 1879-80, Relief of Ladysmith, South Africa 1899-1902.

The Great War – Aisne 1914, 18, Armentieres 1914, Neuve Chapelle, Ypres 1915, 17, 18, Gravenstafel, St Julien, Frezenberg, Bellewaarde, Aubers, Hooge 1915, Loos, Somme 1916, 18, Albert 1916, 18, Bazentin, Delville Wood, Pozieres, Flers-Courcellete, Morval, Thiepval, Le Transloy, Ancre Heights, Ancre 1916, Arras 1917, 18, Scarpe 1917, 18, Arleux, Oppy, Bullecourt, Hill 70, Messines 1917, 18, Pilckem, Langemarck 1917, Menin Road, Polygon Wood, Broodseinde, Poelcappelle, Passchendaele, Cambrai 1917, 18, St Quentin, Bapaume 1918, Rosieres, Villers Bretonneux, Lys, Estaires, Hazebrouck, Bailleul, Kemmel, Scherpenberg, Marne 1918, Tardenois, Amiens, Drocourt-Queant, Hindenburg Line, Havrincourt, Epehy, Canal du Nord, St Quentin Canal, Selle, Valenciennes, Sambre, France and Flanders, 1914-18, Piave, Vittorio Veneto, Italy 1917-18, Struma, Doiran 1917, Macedonia 1915-18, Suvla, Landing at Suvla, Scimitar Hill, Gallipoli 1915, Egypt 1915-16.

The Second World War – Withdrawal to Escaut, Defence of Escaut, Defence of Arras, French Frontier 1940, Ypres-Comines Canal, Dunkirk 1940, Normandy Landing, Tilly sur Seulles, Odon, Caen, Bourguebus Ridge, Troarn, Mont Pincon, St Pierre la Vielle, Gheel, Nederrijn, Aam, Venraig, Rhineland, Schaddenhof, Brinkum, Bremen, North-West Europe 1940, 44-45, Jebel Dafeis, Keren, Ad Teclescan, Abyssinia 1940-41, Gazala, Cauldron, Mersa Matruh, Defence of Alamein Line, El Alamein, Mareth, Wadi Zigraou, Akarit, North Africa 1940-43, Primosole Bridge, Sicily 1943, Pegu 1942, Yenamgyaung 1942, North Arakan, Maungdaw, Defence of Sinzweya, Imphal, Bishenpur, Kanglatonghi, Meiktila, Capture of Meiktila, Defence of Meiktila, Rangdon Road, Pyawbwe, Sittang 1945, Burma 1942-45.

Honorary Distinction

The Leeds Rifles – A Badge of the Royal Tank Regiment, with year-dates 1942-45 and two scrolls:
North Africa, Italy

Regimental Marches

Quick Marches . . . .(i) Ca Ira (ii) The Yorkshire Lass (The March of the Prince of Wales's Own Regiment of Yorkshire)

Slow Marches . . . .(i) God Bless the Prince of Wales (Slow March of the West Yorks Regiment)
(ii) March of the XV Regiment (Slow March of The East Yorks Regiment)

Agents . . . . .Lloyds Bank plc Cox's & King's Branch

Regimental Headquarters . . . . .3 Tower Street, York, YO1 9SB
(Tel: 01904 662790)

Alliances

Canadian Armed Forces . . . . .Les Voltigeurs de Quebec
1st Battalion The Royal New Brunswick Regiment (Carleton and York)
The Royal Montreal Regiment

Falkland Islands . . . . .The Falkland Islands Defence Force

Colonel in Chief . . . . .Hon Maj Gen *HRH The Duchess of* Kent *GCVO* .070585

Colonel . . . . .Maj Gen E H A Beckett *CB MBE* 220696

Designate . . . . .Brig A D A Duncan *DSO OBE* 250601

	Barley D A *BA(Hons)* psc†	300696	Hancock D S *BA(Hons) MSc* sq	
	Watson R J sq jsdc	300697		300994
Brigadiers	Caley S R psc	300698	Sawtell R F *MA* psc psc(J)	300994
	Hill D A *MBE* sq	300699	Germain P S *BA(Hons)* psc†	300995
Duncan A D A *DSO OBE* rcds psc†	Padgett S psc	300699	Jackson A T *BA(Hons) MA* psc(J)	
hcsc(J) 300695	Jones P D sq	300600		300995
King J C L *MBE* ocds(US) psc			Bower M W *QGM* sq	300996
300697	*Majors*		Wagstaff T E	300996
Binns G J *MBE MC* psc(CAN)			Newson H *BSc(Hons) MSc*	300998
300600	Knopp J F *MBE* sq	300981	Astley I W K *BA(Hons)*	300999
	Watson M J *MBE* sq	300981	Fyfe A P W psc(J)	300999
Colonels	Allbeury N LE B *MBE* psc	300982	Crowley I G	300900
	Thurlow M R C sq sq(w) ais		McNicholas P	300900
Le Brun C G psc 300600		300988		
	Tracy E P *MBE* sq	300989	*Captains*	
———	Parker N R M psc(a) sq †	300991		
Lieutenant Colonels	Schofield C J sq	300991	Mulholland L M *BSc*	10495
Potter A C L psc†	300689	Bruce R M *BA(Hons)* sq	300993	Reeve B J *BSc(Hons)*	10495
Blanch A C G sq	300690			

Boothby A J W *BA(Hons)* 110895
Bradbury D S *LLB(Hons)* 110896

Regular Category Late Entry Officers

Majors

Sullivan M L 300991
Cawkwell B 300998
Haynes M T 300998
Stainthorpe P A 300999

Special Regular Officers Late Entry

Captains

Adair A 30297
Cantrell R F 10498

Intermediate Regular Officers

Majors

Bradley H 300900
Cowen A B 300900

Elischer W K *BEC* 300900
Lockwood R 300900
Ratcliffe C J *BA(Hons)* 300900

Captains

Reeves A J *BA(Hons)* 141097
Wilson T *BA(Hons)* 120298
Lees S F *(A/Maj 131299)* 90498
Wolfenden G R *BA(Hons) (A/Maj 040900)* 131098
Graham G R 60899
Marshall M I *BA(Hons)* 121099
Lord R R *BA(Hons)* 90200

Short Service Late Entry Officers

Captains

Wright A *(A/Maj 011096)* 130995
Burton A J 10498
Emerson S W 130998
Melbourne F P 200500

Short Service Officers

Captains

Whiter D P *BA* 140699
Powers C P A *BA(Hons)* 90200
Hall J A *BEng(Hons)* 101000
Castle J H *BA(Hons)* 80201

Lieutenants

Thirsk A D *BSc(Hons)* 120297
Manwaring P S *BA(Hons)* 120897
Richards B E H *BSc(Hons)* 131097
Baker N P *LLB(Hons)* 161297
Townend A A R *BA(Hons)* 161297
Harrison M P *BA(Hons)* 130699
Grieve R W *BA(Hons)* 131299
Smith K A *BSc(Hons)* 131299

Short Service Volunteers Officers

Lieutenants

Dyson I A 11299

THE GREEN HOWARDS (ALEXANDRA, PRINCESS OF WALES'S OWN YORKSHIRE REGIMENT) (19)

The Cypher of HRH Alexandra, Princess of Wales, interlaced with the Dannebrog inscribed with the date 1875, the Roman numerals XIX below and the whole surmounted by the Coronet of the Princess.

Malplaquet, Belle Isle, Alma, Inkerman, Sevastopol, Tirah, Relief of Kimberley, Paardeberg, South Africa 1899-1902.

The Great War – **Ypres 1914, 15, 17,** Langemarck 1914, 17, Gheluvelt, Neuve Chappelle, St Julien, Frezenberg, Bellewaarde, Aubers, Festubert 1915, **Loos, Somme 1916, 18,** Albert 1916, Bazentin, Pozieres, Flers-Courcelette, Morval, Thiepval, Le Transloy, Ancre Heights, Ancre 1916, **Arras 1917, 18,** Scarpe 1917, 18, **Messines 1917, 18,** Pilckem, Menin Road, Polygon Wood, Broodseinde, Poelcappelle, Passchendaele, Cambrai 1917, 18, St Quentin, Hindenburg Line, Canal du Nord, Beaurevoir, Selle, **Valenciennes, Sambre, France and Flanders 1914-18,** Piave, **Vittorio Veneto,** Italy 1917-18, **Suvla,** Landing at Suvla, Scimitar Hill, Gallipoli 1915, Egypt 1916, Archangel 1918.

Afghanistan 1919

The Second World War – Otta, **Norway 1940,** Defence of Arras, Dunkirk 1940, **Normandy Landing,** Tilly sur Seulles, St Pierre La Vielle, Gheel, Nederrijn, **North-West Europe 1940, 44-45** Gazala, Defence of Alamein Line, **El Alamein, Mareth, Akarit,** North Africa 1942-43, Landing in Sicily, Lentini, **Sicily 1943, Minturno, Anzio,** Italy 1943-44, Arakan Beaches, Burma 1945.

Regimental Marches

Quick March . . . . .Bonnie English Rose
Slow March . . . . .Maria Theresa
Regimental Headquarters . . . . .Trinity Church Square, The Market Place, Richmond, North Yorkshire, DL10 4QN
Tel: 01748-822133 Fax: 01748-826561)

Alliances

Canadian Armed Forces . . . . .The Rocky Mountain Rangers
The Queen's York Rangers (1st American Regiment) RCAC
Colonel in Chief . . . .(Hon) Gen *His Majesty* Harald V, *King of* Norway *GCVO* 060292
Colonel . . . . .Maj Gen F R Dannatt *CBE MC* 011294

Brigadiers	Barker R C sq AIS	300992
Houghton J N R *CBE MA BA(Hons)*	Denison J N psc	300992
psc† hcsc(J) 311297	Buchanan I A *BA(Hons)* cafs sq(w)	300994
Farquhar A P *MBE BEng(Hons)* psc†		300994
300600	Fenton J A G *MBE* sq	300994
	O'Kelly D R E *BA(Hons) MA* psc†	300994
Colonels	Perks J P B *MBE MA* psc†	300994
Kirkland R L *OBE* psc 300600	Fovargue S G *MBE BA(Hons) MDA*	
	DipM psc(J) MDA	300995
	Hinde M G sq(w) †	300995
Lieutenant Colonels	Willis J M G *MBE* psc	300995
Mantell R C *MBE* sq jsdc *(L/Col*	Brasher J J	300997
010100) 300688	Wright J K *BSc(Hons)*	300997
Robey G T (SL) *OBE* odc(AUST)	Coleman M L *BEng(Hons)*	300998
psc(CAN) 300690	Colthup E D	300998
Best K psc 300693	Price J C *BSc(Hons)*	300999
Roberts P T *MBE* psc 300696		
Rynn N J *BA(Hons)* psc 300696	**Captains**	
Gallier N P *MBE MA MSc* psc† gw	Mackenzie J A *BA(Hons)* cafs	
300697		60894
Tovey M W *CertEd* psc† 300698	Rodber T A K *BSc*	10495
Watt J N *MA* psc† 300699	Little P A *BA*	110895
	Wood I T *BA(Hons) (A/Maj 011000)*	
Majors		110895
Cooper G M sq 300981	Aisbitt J P *(A/Maj 241100)*	120496
Green G N sq 241089	Cunningham J E *BA(Hons)*	120496
Panton J F sq 300990	Roe A M	110497
Leighton P J *MBE* sq 300991	Greville T M *BA(Hons)*	70897
Rose D J *BA(Hons) MSc* psc(IND)	Phillips C J R *(A/Maj 011200)*	
300991		121297
	Stenning Z R *BA(Hons)*	160398
	Wright S N *BSc(Hons)*	160698
	Griffin G W *BA(Hons)*	90200

Lieutenants		
Johnson A T *BSc(Hons)*	120297	
Regular Category Late Entry Officers		
Majors		
O'Dea B F	300994	
Warriner A	300998	
Helmn R C *BEM*	300900	
Special Regular Officers Late Entry		
Captains		
Gregson J C	150695	
Mincher S	230197	
Ross P	10498	
Intermediate Regular Officers		
Captains		
Harrison C G	151295	
Snaith D R	10596	
Little J A *BA(Hons)*	120298	
Terry B F S *BA(Hons)*	100299	
James T P	130300	
Short Service Late Entry Officers		
Captains		
Siddle P	10498	
O'Connor A T	11299	

Short Service Officers

Captains

Searle P J *BA(Hons)*	130600
Pittman M E P *BA(Hons)*	101000

Lieutenants

Thom N G D *BA(Hons)*	100298
Pile O A E *BA(Hons)*	130498
Levey N R *BA(Hons)*	141298
Knox B J	131299
Lord P S	131299

Thomas R T *BSc(Hons)*	131299

Short Service Volunteer Officers

Captains

Porter J G	80997

THE QUEEN'S LANCASHIRE REGIMENT (30, 40, 47, 59, 81 and 82)

The Red Rose of Lancaster

The Red Rose of Lancaster ensigned with the Plume of the Prince of Wales. The Red Rose ensigned with the Sphinx subscribed Egypt. A Sphinx superscribed Egypt ensigned with the Plume of the Prince of Wales

The Red Rose ensigned with the Royal Crest

A Sphinx Superscribed Egypt

Loyally I Serve

Gibraltar 1704-5, Louisburg, Quebec 1759, Bellisle, Martinique 1762, **Havannah,** St Lucia 1778, **Cape of Good Hope 1806, Maida, Monte Video,** Rolica, **Vimiera, Corunna, Talavera, Java, Tarifa, Badajoz, Salamanca, Vittoria, St Sebastian, Pyrenees, Nivelle, Nive, Orthes, Toulouse,** Peninsula, **Niagara, Waterloo, Ava, Bhurtpore, Candahar 1842, Ghuznee 1842, Cabool 1842, Maharajpore, Alma, Inkerman, Sevastopol, Lucknow, Canton, New Zealand, Ali Masjid, Ahmed Khel,** Afghanistan 1878-80, **Chitral, Defence of Kimberley, Relief of Ladysmith,** South Africa 1899-1902.

The Great War – **Mons,** Le Cateau, **Retreat from Mons, Marne 1914-18,** Aisne 1914, 18, La Bassee 1914, **Messines 1914, 17, 18,** Armentieres 1914, **Ypres 1914, 15, 17, 18,** Langemarck 1914, 17, Gheluvelt, Nonne Bosschen, Givenchy 1914, **Neuve Chapelle,** St Julien, Frezenberg, Bellewaarde, Aubers, Festubert 1915, Loos, **Somme 1916, 18,** Albert 1916, 18, Bazentin, Pozieres, Guillemont, Ginchy, Flers-Courcelette, Morval, Le Transloy, Ancre Heights, Ancre 1916, 18, **Arras 1917, 18,** Vimy 1917, Scarpe 1917, 18, Arleux, Oppy, Pilckem, Menin Road, Polygon Wood, Broodseinde, Poelcappelle, Passchendaele, Cambrai 1917, 18, St Quentin, Bapaume 1918, Rosieres, Villers-Bretonneux, Lys, Estaires, Hazebrouck, Baillleul, Kemmel, Bethune, Scherpenberg, Soissonnais-Ourcq, Drocourt-Queant, **Hindenburg Line,** Epehy, Canal du Nord, St Quentin Canal, Courtrai, Selle, Valenciennes, Sambre, France and Flanders 1914-18, Kosturino, **Doiran 1917, 18,** Macedonia 1915-18, **Helles,** Krithia, **Suvla, Sari Bair,** Gallipoli 1915, Rumani, Egypt 1915-17, **Gaza,** Nebi Samwil, Jerusalem, Jaffa, Tell' Asur, Palestine 1917-18, Tigris 1916, **Kut al Amara 1917, Baghdad,** Mesopotamia 1916-18, **Kilimanjaro,** East Africa 1914-16, **Baluchistan 1918.**

Afghanistan 1919

The Second World War – Defence of Escaut, **Dunkirk 1940, Normandy Landing,** Odon, Caen, **Bourguebus Ridge,** Troarn, **Falaise,** Nederrijn, **Lower Maas,** Venraig, **Ourthe, Rhineland, Reichswald,** Weeze, Hochwald, Rhine, Ibbenburen, **Aller,** Bremen, North-West Europe 1940, 44-45, Banana Ridge, **Djebel Kesskiss,** Medjez Plain, **Gueriat El Atach Ridge,** Gab Gab Gap, Djebel Bou Aoukaz 1943, North Africa 1943, **Anzio,** Rome, **Fiesole,** Gothic Line, Monte Gamberaldi, Monte Ceco, **Monte Grande,** Italy 1944-45, **Madagascar,** Middle East 1942, **Johore,** Batu Pahat, **Singapore Island,** Malaya 1941-42, **North Arakan,** Mayu Tunnels, **Kohima,** Pinwe, Meiktila, **Nyamgu Bridgehead,** Letse, Irrawaddy, Burma 1943-45.

Regimental Marches

Quick March . . . . .L'Attaque – The Red Rose
Slow March . . . . .Long Live Elizabeth (from Selection No 2 Merrie England)
Regimental Headquarters . . . . .Fulwood Barracks, Preston, PR2 8AA (Tel: 01772-716543 Ext: 2362)

Alliances

Canadian Armed Forces . . . . .The Princess of Wales's Own Regiment
The West Nova Scotia Regiment
The Loyal Edmonton Regiment (4th Battalion Princess Patricia's Canadian Light Infantry)
Australian Military Forces . . . . .The Royal Tasmania Regiment
New Zealand Army . . . . .7th Battalion (Wellington (City of Wellington's Own) and Hawkes Bay) Royal New Zealand Infantry Regiment
Pakistan Army . . . . .8th Battalion The Punjab Regiment
14th Battalion The Punjab Regiment
Malaysian Armed Forces . . . . .2nd Battalion The Royal Malay Regiment
South African Defence Forces . . . . . . .Kimberley Regiment
Colonel in Chief . . . . .THE QUEEN
Colonel . . . . .Brig A F Birtwistle *OBE ADC* 130299

Colonels

Sheldon J A *BA(Hons) FRGS* psc(GE) I   300698

Brigadiers

Birtwistle A F *OBE MA* psc jsdc   300699
Sheldon G P *MA* rcds ocds(IND) psc†   300699

Lieutenant Colonels

Aldis R C (SL) psc aic   300689
Guest G E (SL) *MIPD* sq   300696

James D C *OBE MA MA(Cantab)*
CGIA psc(n)†   300696
Shearman M J *BSc(Hons)* psc† jsdc   300696
Davies S *MBE* psc   300699
Sanderson D J *MBE MBA FRGS* psc   300699
Mendonca J E *MBE BA(Econ)Hons MA* psc†   300600

Majors

Cummings D F J sq	300980
Upton H C sq	300984
Brown K G *BSc* sq(w) † ais	300987
Wright G R aicʳsq(w)	300988
Courteney-Harris R J *BA(Hons) MBA DipM MCIM* sq	300989
D'Apice M H R *MBE BSc(Hons)* sq	300989
Kent-Payne V R psc	300990
Janes J R E *MSc* cafs jssc dis	300992
Bostock S E *LLB(Hons)* psc(J)	300994
Loynds I A cafs sq(w)	300994
Rix A C *BSc(Hons)* cafs sq(w)	300994
Beatson R J *MA* psc† †	300995
Brown R D I psc†	300995
Howcroft D J B *MBE* sq	300995
Jefferies R A *MBE BSocSc(Hons)* psc†	300995
Shorrock A C	300995
Cottrell J A *BA(HonsCantab) MA*	300996
Downey S J *BA(Hons)* psc(J)	300996
Suss-Francksen C M *BSc*	300996
Kenyon M P *BA(Hons)* psc(J)	300997
Lighten J G *MBE BA(Hons) PGCE* psc(J)	300997
Englefield R J	300998
Davis P V *BSc(Hons)*	300999
Hemesley E J	300900
Park B W	300900

Captains

Jackson S D *BSc(Hons)* *(A/Maj 191199)*	70896

Driver J E S	80897
Reeves I D	80897
Cronin S	101000

Lieutenants

Sweeney A K *MA(Hons)*	160697
Seaman J E *(A/Capt 160800)*	161297
Moutarde M J *(A/Capt 100100)*	100898

Regular Category Late Entry Officers

Majors

Barnes B K	300999
Hardman D J	300900

Special Regular Officers Late Entry

Captains

Greenwood S	10497
Darlington S J	10498
Lowton E J *MBE*	10498

Intermediate Regular Officers

Majors

McQueenie S S	300999

Captains

Cartwright R	10495
Peters A	70896
Royce A A D *BEng(Hons)*	110896
Dewar S P	80897
Brooks E G *BSc(Hons)*	141097
Mitchell C P *BA(Hons)*	160698

Peebles M E *BSc(Hons)*	160698
Farnon L D	111298
McIntyre C J *(L/Maj 131299)*	100299
Newman D M	90499

Short Service Late Entry Officers

Captains

Jolley S	10499
Goodenough A M	60400

Short Service Officers

Captains

Seeds G J	140998
Firth M R *BSc(Hons)*	100299
Guthrie W D *MA*	101000
Smith A J E *BSc*	101000

Lieutenants

Osborne R C A *LLB(Hons)*	161297
Wakefield J T *MA(Hons)*	100298
Salt S N *(A/Capt 131099)*	130498
McGrory C F *BSc(Hons)*	141298
Elliott M J *(L/Capt 181199)*	90899

2nd Lieutenants

Tortoishell D	150399
McMahon J D	100499
Morris D L	70899

Short Service Volunteer Officers

Captains

Barratt S M *BSc(Hons)*	10899

191

THE DUKE OF WELLINGTON'S REGIMENT (WEST RIDING) (33 and 76)

The Duke of Wellington's Crest, with the motto Virtutis fortuna comes
An Elephant, with howdah and mahout, circumscribed Hindoostan, ensigned with The Crown

Dettingen, Mysore, Seringapatam, Ally Ghur, Delhi 1803, Leswarree, Deig, Corunna, Nive, Peninsula, Waterloo, Alma Inkerman, Sevastopol, Abyssinia, Relief of Kimberley, Paardeberg, South Africa 1900-02.

The Great War – **Mons,** Le Cateau, Retreat from Mons, **Marne 1914, 18,** Aisne 1914, La Bassee 1914, **Ypres 1914, 15, 17,** Nonne Bosschen, **Hill 60,** Gravenstafel, St Julien, Aubers, **Somme 1916, 18,** Albert 1916, Bazentin, Delville Wood, Pozieres, Flers-Courcelette, Morval, Thiepval, Le Transloy, Ancre Heights, **Arras 1917, 18,** Scarpe 1917, 18, Arieux, Bullecourt, Messines 1917, 18, Langemarck 1917, Menin Road, Polygon Wood, Broodseinde, Poelcappelle, Passchendaele, **Cambrai 1917, 18,** St Quentin, Ancre 1918, Lys, Estaires, Hazebrouck, Bailleul, Kemmel, Bethune, Scherpenberg, Tardenois, Amiens, Bapaume 1918, Drocourt-Queant, Hindenburg Line, Havrincourt, Epehy, Canal du Nord, Selle, Valenciennes, Sambre, France and Flanders 1914-18, **Piave,** Vittorio Veneto, Italy 1917-18, Suvla, **Landing at Suvla,** Scimitar Hill, Gallipoli 1915, Egypt 1916.

Afghanistan 1919

The Second World War – **Dunkirk 1940,** St Valery-en-Caux, Tilly sur Seulles, Odon, **Fontenay Le Pesnil, North-West Europe 1940, 44-45,** Banana Ridge, Mediez Plain, Gueriat el Atach Ridge, Tunis, **Djebel Bou Aoukaz 1943,** North Africa 1943, **Anzio,** Campoleone, Rome, **Monte Ceco,** Italy 1943-45, **Sittang 1942,** Paungde, Kohima, **Chindits 1944, Burma 1942-44.**

The Hook 1953, Korea 1952-53

Regimental March

Quick March . . . . .The Wellesley

Agents . . . . .Lloyds Bank plc Halifax Branch

Regimental Headquarters . . . . .Wellesley Park, Halifax, Yorkshire, HX2 0BA (Tel: 01422-361671/York Mil 8770)

Alliances

Canadian Armed Forces . . . . .Les Voltigeurs de Quebec
Pakistan Army . . . . .10th Battalion The Baloch Regiment

Colonel in Chief . . . . .Col (Hon Brig) *The Duke of* Wellington *KG LVO OBE MC DL* ret pay . . .230174
Colonel . . . . .Maj Gen *Sir* Evelyn Webb-Carter *KCVO OBE* psc hcsc 180699

Brigadiers

Meek A D   rcds psc(AUS)   300600

Colonels

Santa-Olalla D M   *DSO MC MA* psc
  hcsc(J)   300697
Hall N ST J   *BA(Hons) AKC* psc   300698
Stone M J   *BA(Hons) MBA MSc* psc
  dis *(A/Brig 111200)*   300699

Lieutenant Colonels

Drake A H S   *MBE* sq   300695
Newton S C   *MBE* sq jsdc   300695
Kilburn G A   *MBE* odc(FR) sq   300697
Richardson D I   *MBE* sq jsdc 300697
Borwell N G   psc osc(MAL) 300698
Bruce D S   *MBE* psc   300600
Shuttleworth G D   psc   300600

Majors

Morgan P J   sq   300980
Sherlock M S   sq   300981
Grieve C F   *MBE* psc   300983

Bailey P R S   sq   300987
Lehmann C S T   *BSc* sq(w) †   300991
Bailey J C   *BA(Hons) MDA MSc* sq
  MDA   300994
Lewis P M   sq   300994
Goodwin R N   *BA(HonsCantab)
  MA(Cantab)* psc(J)   300995
Holroyd R C   *BA(Hons)* sq   300995
Chadwick R N   300996
Norman M D   *BEd(Hons)*   300996
Adams A J   300997
Monteith D P   *BA(Hons)*   300997
Faithfull B J T   *BA(Hons)*   300999
Fox P R   *BA(Hons)*   300999
Vallings T G   300999
O'Connor R C   *BA(Hons)*   300900
Wood N M B   300900

Captains

Purcell J H   *BA*   120492
Rhodes N P   *(A/Maj 010500)*
  70896
Bryden J R   *BA(Hons)*   110896
Liddle A J M   *BSc(Hons) (A/Maj
  140400)*   110896
Garner A S   190599

2nd Lieutenants

††Smart T E J   60998

**Regular Category Late Entry
Officers**

Majors

Sykes B W   *MBE*   300995
Ennis P M   300999

Special Regular Officers Late Entry

Majors

Pierce R M   300900

Captains

Jackson A L   10498
Smith M   10498

Intermediate Regular Officers

Captains

Mayo J C   101294
Townhill J E   *BSc*   80396
Wilson P J   *BA(Hons)*   141097
Kirk D J J   *BSc(Hons)*   120298
Richardson S   *BSc(Hons) PGCE*
  120298
Cowell P M J   *BA(Hons)*   100299
Harford R A   *BA(Hons)*   140699
McCormick L R   *BSc(Hons)*   140699
Robinson M   *BA*   140699
Smith K D   *BSc(Hons)*   90200

Sutcliffe R M *BSc(Hons)*	90200	Frear J	290100	Kennedy J A *BSc(Hons)*	130498
Tetley M C *BA(Hons)*	91000	Mitchell P	60400	Lee P *BSc(Hons)*	140698
Johnston A J *LLB(Hons)*	101000	Pigg A G *MBE*	60400	Peters W J W *MA(Hons)*	140698
				Pawson D J *BA(Hons)*	141298
Lieutenants		**Short Service Officers**		Williams G P *BA*	141298
Glossop J A *BSc(Hons)*	120897			Adair C D *LLB(Hons)*	90899
Stear M M D *(A/Capt 010900)*		*Captains*		Colver E R H *BSc(Hons)*	90899
	120499	Hinchliffe J P	180900	Dick S J *BA(Hons)*	90899
Hall R J *(A/Capt 070500)*	131299	Palmer M C A *BSc(Hons)*	101000	Ogilvie D J *BA(Hons)*	90899
		Bibby F *BSc(Hons)*	80201	Price K M	10800
		Humphris S L *BA(Hons)*	80201		
Short Service Late Entry Officers		Payne R B *BSc(Hons)*	80201		
				2nd Lieutenants	
Captains		*Lieutenants*		Scothern R R G	70899
Sutcliffe A J	10498	Palfrey R J *BSc(Hons) (A/Capt*		Pearce J L	120800
Thomas B J *BEM*	10498	*180900)*	161297	Cataldo M H	161200

THE PRINCE OF WALES'S DIVISION

Comprising ....The Devonshire and Dorset Regiment (1 Regular Battalion, 2 Volunteer
Companies)

The Cheshire Regiment (1 Regular Battalion, 2 Volunteer Companies)

The Royal Welch Fusiliers (1Regular Battalion, 2 Volunteer Companies)

The Royal Regiment of Wales (24th/41st Foot) (1 Regular Battalion,
2 Volunteer Companies)

The Royal Gloucestershire, Berkshire and Wiltshire Regiment
(1 Regular Battalion, 2 Volunteer Companies)

The Worcestershire and Sherwood Foresters Regiment (29th/45th Foot)
(1 Regular Battalion, 2 Volunteer Companies)

The Staffordshire Regiment (The Prince of Wales's) (1 Regular Battalion,
2 Volunteer Companies)

Divisional Headquarters ....Headquarters Infantry, Warminster Training Centre, Warminster, Wilts BA12 0DJ
(Tel: Warminster Mil (94381) Extn 2235 Fax: 2151)

Colonel Commandant ....Maj Gen C H Elliott *CBE* 010299

Divisinal Lieutenant Colonel ....Lt Col P E W Smith 090999

The origins of amalgamated Regiments now included in The Prince of Wales's Division are as follows:

THE DEVONSHIRE AND DORSET REGIMENT

On 17 May 1958
The Devonshire Regiment (11) and
The Dorset Regiment (39 and 54) amalgamated to form:
The Devonshire and Dorset Regiment

THE ROYAL REGIMENT OF WALES (24th/41st FOOT)

On 11 June 1969
The South Wales Borderers (24) and
The Welch Regiment (41 and 69) amalgamated to form:
The Royal Regiment of Wales (24th/41st Foot)

THE ROYAL GLOUCESTERSHIRE, BERKSHIRE AND WILTSHIRE REGIMENT

On 9 June 1959
The Royal Berkshire Regiment (Princess Charlotte of Wales's) (49 and 66) and
The Wiltshire Regiment (Duke of Edinburgh's) (62 and 99) amalgamated to form:
The Duke of Edinburgh's Royal Regiment (Berkshire and Wiltshire)

On 27 April 1994
The Goucestershire Regiment (28 and 61) and
The Duke of Edinburgh's Royal Regiment (Berkshire and Wiltshire) amalgamated to form:
The Royal Gloucestershire, Berkshire and Wiltshire Regiment

On 1 October 1995
The 1st Battalion The Wessex Regiment (Rifle Volunteers) and
The 2nd Battalion, The Wessex Regiment (Volunteers) amalgamated to form:
The 2nd (Volunteer) Battalion, The Royal Gloucestershire, Berkshire and Wiltshire Regiment

THE WORCESTERSHIRE AND SHERWOOD FORESTERS REGIMENT (29th/45th FOOT)

On 28 February 1970
The Worcestershire Regiment (29 and 36) and
The Sherwood Foresters (Nottinghamshire and Derbyshire Regiment) (45 and 95) amalgamated to form:
The Worcestershire and Sherwood Foresters Regiment (29th/45th Foot)

THE STAFFORDSHIRE REGIMENT (THE PRINCE OF WALES'S)

On 31 January 1959
The South Staffordshire Regiment (38 and 80) and
The North Staffordshire Regiment (The Prince of Wales's) 64 and 98) amalgamated to form:
The Staffordshire Regiment (The Prince of Wales's)

THE DEVONSHIRE AND DORSET REGIMENT (11, 39 and 54)

The Sphinx superimposed upon the Castle of Exeter

The Castle and Key superscribed Gibraltar, 1779-83 and with the motto *Montis Insignia Calpe*

The Sphinx superscribed *Semper Fidelis Primus in Indis*

Dettingen, Plassey, Martinique 1794, Marabout, Albuhera, Salamanca, Vittoria, Pyrenees, Nivelle, Nive, Orthes, Toulouse, Peninsula, Ava, Maharajpore, Afghanistan 1879-80, Tirah, Defence of Ladysmith, Relief of Ladysmith, South Africa 1899-1902.

The Great War – **Mons**, Le Cateau, Retreat from Mons, **Marne 1914**, Aisne 1914, 18, **La Bassee 1914**, Armentieres 1914, Neuve Chapelle, Hill 60, **Ypres 1915**, 17, Gravenstafel, St Julien, Frezenberg, Bellewaarde, Aubers, **Loos, Somme 1916, 18**, Albert 1916, 18, Bazentin, Delville Wood, Guillemont, Flers-Courcelette, Morval, Thiepval, Ancre 1916, 18, Arras 1917, Vimy 1917, Scarpe 1917, Bullecourt, Messines 1917, Pilckem, Langemarck 1917, Polygon Wood, Broodseinde, Poelcappelle, Passchendaele, St Quentin, Rosiers, Villers Bretonneux, Lys, Hazebrouck, **Bois des Buttes**, Marne 1918, Tardenois, Amiens, Bapaume 1918, **Hindenburg Line**, Havrincourt, Epehy, Canal du Nord, St Quentin Canal, Beaurevoir, Cambrai 1918, Selle, **Sambre**, France and Flanders 1914-18, Piave, **Vittorio Veneto**, Italy 1917-18, **Doiran 1917, 18**, Macedonia 1915-18, **Suvla**, Landing at Suvla, Scimitar Hill, Gallipoli 1915, Egypt 1916-17, **Gaza**, El Mughar, Nebi Samwil, Jerusalem, Tell' Asur, Megiddo, Sharon, **Palestine 1917-18**, Basra, **Shaiba**, Kut al Amara 1915, 17, **Ctesiphon**, Defence of Kut al Amara, Tigris 1916, Baghdad, **Khan Baghdadi, Mesopotamia 1916-18.**

The Second World War – **St Omer-La Bassee, Normandy Landing**, Port en Bessin, Villiers Bocage, Tilly sur Suelles, **Caen**, Mont Pincon, St Pierre La Vielle, Nederrijn, **Arnhem 1944, Aam, Gellenkirchen**, Roer, Goch, **Rhine**, Ibbenburen, Twente Canal, **North-West Europe 1940, 44-45, Landing in Sicily**, Agira, **Regalbuto**, Sicily 1943, Landing at Porto San Venere, Italy 1943, **Malta 1940-42, Imphal**, Tamu Road, Shenam Pass, **Kohima**, Ukhrul, **Mandalay, Myinmu Bridgehead**, Kyaukse 1945, Mt Popa, **Burma 1943-45.**

Regimental Marches

Quick March . . . . Arrangement of 'Widecombe Fair', 'We've Lived and Loved Together' & 'The Maid of Glenconnel'

Regimental Headquarters . . . . Wyvern Barracks, Exeter, Devon
(Tel: Civil: 01392 492436, Mil: Exeter Mil Ext 2434, 2435, 2436)

Alliances

Canadian Armed Forces . . . . Les Fusiliers de Sherbrooke
Australian Military Forces . . . . The Royal New South Wales Regiment
Malaysian Armed Forces . . . . 6th Battalion The Royal Malay Regiment

Bonds of Friendship

Le Deuxienne Regiment Etrange D'Infantrie
5th Battalion The South African Infantry

Colonel in Chief . . . . Field Marshall *HRH The Duke of* Kent *KG GCMG GCVO ADC*

Colonel . . . . Maj Gen B H Dutton *CB CBE* 010198

Toomey R H D *MBE* psc psc(J)	300699
Storrie A J S *MBE MA MA(Hons)* psc	300600

Brigadiers

Young S D *CBE* rcds psc sq	00696
Cook J R *OBE MC* psc hcsc(J)	300699
————	

Lieutenant Colonels

Richardson M F psc jsdc	300691
Thornburn A W *MBE* sq jsdc sq(w)	300692
Edwards A J B psc	300695
Steevenson D M M *MBE* sq jsdc	300696
King M P *MBE* psc(CAN)	300697
Watson J F *MBE MA* psc†	300697
Nicholls G S sq	300698
Harrison D J *BA* nadc psc	300699
Sharpe W M *MBE BA(Hons)* psc	300699

Majors

Trevis A J sq	300987
Saunders T J J *MBE* sq	300988
Underhill P F C sq(w)	300989
Blewett I P sq	300991
Messervy P S *MA(Hons)* psc†	300994
Beattie C J *MA GCGI* psc(J)	300995
Field D C E psc(AUS)	300995
House T W osc(MAL)	300995
Norman-Walker A K J sq	300995
Edkins M J	300996
Uden P F psc(J)	300996
Cleave R C *BSc(Hons)*	300998
Cavanagh J D *BEng(Hons)*	300999
Jones R T H *BA(Hons)*	300999
Bennett S *BA(Hons)*	300900
Hartley J I *B Sc (Hons)*	300900

Captains

Millsop A K G *BSc(Hons)*	110895
O'Neil Roe R H D *BSc(Hons)*	110896
Steptoe R C	110497
Bryant J E F	80897
Gidlow-Jackson M C	80897
Maynard M L	121297
Murray J O *BA(Hons)*	160698
Wells-Cole M C D *BA(Hons)*	140699
Dunlop W G *BA(Hons)*	60300

Lieutenants

Beaman M J *BA(Hons)*	160697
O'Neil Roe G C B	120897
Bryan R E G *BA(Hons)*	100898
Jellard H P *BA(Hons)*	100898

2nd Lieutenants

††Allen J M H	220997

196

Regular Category Late Entry Officers

Majors

Burrlock L C   31287
Henderson M J   *MBE*   300991
Mehrlich P R   300996

Special Regular Officers Late Entry

Captains

Cleverley R J   100497
Kelsall W J P   10498
Finnamore K J   10698

Intermediate Regular Officers

Captains

Natarajan R F   *BA(Hons)*   110895
Bryan R W   141296
Woodiwiss S R C   *BA(Hons)*   160698
Holmes N R   *BSc(Hons)*   100299
King N C Y   140699
Hill I C W   *BSc(Hons)*   90200

Gales A J   *BA(Hons)*   10400
Pettitt J C   *BA(Hons)*   130600

Lieutenants

Davies S M   *BPharm*   161297

2nd Lieutenants

Wills M C   120800

Short Service Late Entry Officers

Captains

Anning J E   170400

Short Service Officers

Captains

Green R J H   *BA(Hons)*   90200

Lieutenants

Cramer W B P   160697

Boswell C W   *BEng(Hons)*   161297
Leatherdale G T   *(A/Capt 220201)*   130498
Stafford E J   *BSc(Hons)*   100898
Ring T E   90299
Luard P J   *BSc(Hons)*   130699
Forde M H   *BSc*   90899
Scrase W G   *BEng(Hons)*   90899
Leatherdale D W   *BA(Hons)*   131299
Richards W J   190101

2nd Lieutenants

Martin D M   110699

Short Service Volunteer Officers

Lieutenants

Miller P   61098

197

THE CHESHIRE REGIMENT (22)

An Acorn leaved and slipped

Louisburg, Martinique 1762, Havannah, Meeanee, Hyderabad, Scinde, South Africa 1900-02
The Great War – **Mons**, Le Cateau, Retreat from Mons, Marne 1914, 18, Aisne 1914, 18, La Bassee 1914, Armentieres 1914, **Ypres 1914, 15, 17, 18**, Nonne Bosschen, Hill 60, Gravenstafel, St Julien, Frezenberg, Bellewaarde, Loos, **Somme 1916, 18**, Albert 1916, 18, Bazentin, Delville Wood, Pozieres, Guillemont, Flers-Courcelette, Morval, Thiepval, Le Transloy, Ancre Heights, Ancre 1916, **Arras 1917, 18**, Vimy 1917, Scarpe 1917, 18, Oppy, **Messines 1917, 18**, Pilckem, Langemarck 1917, Menin Road, Polygon Wood, Broodseinde, Poelcappelle, Passchendaele, Cambrai 1917, 18, St Quentin, **Bapaume 1918**, Rosieres, Lys, Estaires, Hazebrouck, Bailleul, Kemmel, Scherpenberg, Soissonnais-Ourcq, Hindenburg Line, Canal du Nord, Courtrai, Selle, Valenciennes, Sambre, France and Flanders 1914-18, Italy 1917-18, Struma, **Doiran 1917, 18**, Macedonia 1915-18, **Suvla**, Sari Bair, Landing at Suvla, Scimitar Hill, Gallipoli 1915, Egypt 1915, 17, **Gaza**, El Mughar, Jerusalem, Jericho, Tell' Asur, Palestine 1917, 18, Tigris 1916, **Kut al Amara 1917**, Baghdad, Mesopotamia 1916, 18.

The Second World War – Dyle, Withdrawal to Escaut, **St Omer-La Bassee**, Wormhoudt, Cassel, Dunkirk 1940, **Normandy Landing**, Mont Pincon, St Pierre La Vielle, Gheel, Nederrijn, Aam, Aller, North-West Europe 1940, 44, 45, Sidi Barrani, **Capture of Tobruk**, Gazala, Mersa Matruh, Defence of Alamein Line, Deir el Shein, **El Alamein, Mareth**, Wadi Zeuss East, Wadi Sigzaou, Akarit, Wadi Akarit East, Enfidaville, North Africa 1940-43, Landing in Sicily, Primosole Bridge, Simeto Bridgehead, **Sicily 1943**, Sangro, **Salerno**, Santa Lucia, Battipaglia, Volturno Crossing, Monte Maro, Teano, Monte Camino, Garigliano Crossing, Minturno, Damiano, Anzio, **Rome, Gothic Line**, Coriano, Gemmano Ridge, Savignano, Senio Floodbank, Rimini Line, Ceriano Ridge, Vali di Comacchio, Italy 1943-45, **Malta 1941-42.**

Regimental Marches

Quick March .Wha wadna fecht for Charlie
Slow March .The 22nd Regiment Slow March 1772
Agents . . . . .Nat West Chester Branch
Regimental Headquarters . . . . .The Castle, Chester, CH1 2DN
(Tel: Chester Mil Ext: 2926 and Civil 01244 327617)

Alliance

Canadian Armed Forces . . . . .2nd Battalion The Nova Scotia Highlanders (Cape Breton)
Colonel in Chief . . . . .HRH The Prince of Wales KG KT GCB AK QSO ADC
Colonel . . . . .Brig K Skempton *CBE* 170299

		Robinson S P U	300994	**Regular Category Late Entry**
		Ellis J R *BA MSc* dis sq(w)	300995	**Officers**
		Etherington J B	300995	
Brigadiers		Lonergan K M *MBE* sq	300995	*Majors*
Skempton K *CBE* psc	300697	Longley-Brown G J H		Jones M *MBE* sq	300995
		BSc(Econ)Hons MDA	300995	Winstanley M J *MBE MISM* 300996
Colonels		Balls J B	300997	
		Forgrave M W *QGM* psc(J)	300997	**Special Regular Officers Late Entry**
Hart M A *MBE QGM* sq	300695	Askew J M	300998	
Page C T *BA(Hons)* psc†	300699			*Majors*
		Captains		Sherlock D K	300900
Lieutenant Colonels		Watts A A *QGM*	10495	
Smith O D A *MBE* psc	300691	Strong I J *BSc(Hons)*	40795	*Captains*
Sernberg A C W N sq jsdc	300692	Cooper A P	110895	Salisbury J M	70697
Park T A *QGM* sq	300695	Jordan J P	130496	
Watters B S C *OBE* sq	300695	Henderson A J *BA(Hons)*	131296	**Intermediate Regular Officers**
Thomas G M *MBE BSc(Hons)* psc†		Gatenby G D *BA(Hons)*	141097	
	300697	Scriven P G *BEng(Hons)*	160698	*Captains*
Sharpe A R D psc	300698	Webber W B	111298	Barnbrook R ST J *BEng(Hons)*
Astle P A *MBE* psc†	300600	Mayo J R *BA(Hons)*	130600		110895
Blagbrough M D psc	300600	Mason M C *BA(Hons)*	101000	Woodward D I *BA(Hons)*	141097
Chapman N S *MBE* psc	300600			Davies C *BA(Hons)*	120298
Jennings P F A *MBE BA(Hons)* psc		*Lieutenants*		Gregory R J *MA(Hons)*	120298
	300600	Sangster D G H *(A/Capt 260400)*		Daintry J G *BSc/BA(Hons)*	90200
			150698	Redford J M *BA(Hons)*	
Majors					200700
Rule D W N *MSc* psc(IND)	300987	*2nd Lieutenants*		*Lieutenants*
Rule A W sq	300990	Meredith J A C	70899	Sernberg R A J	161297
Donnelly J P S psc *(A/Lt Col*				
220201)	300994			

Short Service Late Entry Officers

Captains

Atherton B E	10498
Collister P A	10799

Short Service Officers

Captains

Osborn A	131098
Baxter M C *BA(Hons)*	130600

Lieutenants

Goodwin A J *BA(Hons)*	120897
Press S J *BSc(Hons)*	161297
Lilley R G	130498
Somers C E (*A/Capt 260400*)	130498
Ellwood M C P *BSc(Hons)*	140698
Wilde B M *BSc(Hons)*	100898
Watts A D	120499
Guest D J	131299
Rowlands A N *BEng(Hons)*	131299
Prentice R A	80800

2nd Lieutenants

Wilson S J	100499
Byrne J D	161200

Rec Res (RARO)

Majors

Williams A P *TD CertMGMT* tacsc	140886

THE ROYAL WELCH FUSILIERS (23)

A Grenade flamed, proper; within, the crest of The Prince of Wales
In the first and fourth corners the Rising Sun. In the second corner the Red Dragon.
In the third corner the White Horse with motto, *Nec aspera terrant.* The Sphinx superscribed EGYPT.

Namur 1695, Blenheim, Ramillies, Oudenarde, Malplaquet, Dettingen, Minden, Egypt, Corunna, Martinique 1809, Albuhera, Badajoz, Salamanca, Vittoria, Pyrenees, Nivelle, Orthes, Toulouse, Peninsula, Waterloo, Alma. Inkerman, Sevastopol, Lucknow, Ashantee 1873-4, Burma 1885-87, Relief of Ladysmith, South Africa 1899-1902, Pekin 1900.

The Great War – Mons, Le Cateau, Retreat from Mons, **Marne 1914**, Aisne 1914, 18, La Bassee 1914, Messines 1914, 17, 18, Armentieres 1914, **Ypres 1914, 17, 18**, Langemarck 1914, 17, Gheluvelt, Givenchy 1914, Neuve Chapelle, Aubers, Festubert 1915, Loos, **Somme 1916, 18**, Albert 1916, 18, Bazentin, Delville Wood, Pozieres, Guillemont, Flers-Courcelette, Morval, Le Transloy, Ancre Heights, Ancre 1916, 18, Arras 1917, Scarpe 1917, Arleux, Bullecourt, Pilckem, Menin Road, Polygon Wood, Broodseinde, Poelcappelle, Passchendaele, Cambrai 1917, 18, St Quentin, Bapaume 1918, Lys, Bailleul, Kemmel, Scherpenberg, **Hindenburg Line**, Havrincourt, Epehy, St Quentin Canal, Beaurevoir, Selle, Valenciennes, Sambre, France and Flanders 1914-18, Piave, **Vittorio Veneto**, Italy 1917-18, **Doiran 1917, 18**, Macedonia 1915-18 Suvla, Sari Bair, Landing at Suvla, Scimitar Hill, **Gallipoli 1915-16**, Rumani, **Egypt 1915-17**, **Gaza**, El Mughar, Jerusalem, Jericho, Tel Asur, Megiddo, Nablus, Palestine 1917-18, Tigris 1916, Kut al Amara 1917, **Baghdad**, Mesopotamia 1916-18.

The Second World War – Dyle, Defence of Escaut, **St Omer-La Bassee**, Caen, Esquay, Falaise, Nederrijn, **Lower Maas**, Venlo Pocket, Ourthe, Rhineland, **Reichswald**, Goch, **Weeze, Rhine**, Ibbenburen, Aller, NW Europe 1940, 44-45 **Madagascar**, Middle East 1942, **Donbaik, North Arakan, Kohima**, Mandalay, Ava, Burma 1943-45.

Regimental Marches

Quick March . . . . .The British Grenadiers
Slow Marches . . . .(i) The War Song of The Men of Glamorgan
(ii) Forth to the Battle

Agents . . . . .Lloyds Bank plc Cox's & King's Branch

Regimental Headquarters . . . . .Hightown Barracks, Wrexham, Clwyd, LL13 8RD
(Tel: Wrexham Mil Ext: 8187/8188 and Civil 01978 2464521)

Alliances

Canadian Armed Forces . . . . .Royal 22e Regiment
Pakistan Army . . . . .3rd Battalion The Frontier Force Regiment
Malaysian Armed Forces . . . . .4th Battalion The Royal Malay Regiment
South African Defence Forces . . . . . .Pretoria Regiment

Colonel in Chief . . . . .THE QUEEN

Colonel . . . . .Maj Gen B P Plummer 040301

	Beaumont A J B *BSc(Hons)* aic sq(w)	300988	Lawrence I J *BSc(Hons)*	300900
	Sim R P psc	300990	Palmer M	300900
Brigadiers	Brown C T B *MIL*	300993		
Riley J P *DSO MA* psc hcsc(J) 300698	Nield D M *MBE BSc(Econ)Hons* psc(PAK)	300993	*Captains*	
	Taylor A W sq	300993	Vere-Whiting C G *BA(Hons)* *(A/Maj 120201)*	110896
	Fletcher P W	300995	Henderson A D P *LLB(Hons)*	
Lieutenant Colonels	Jones P A sq	300995		131296
Knox P J (SL) *OBE* psc 300688	Westley R J *MC* sq	300995	Spencer D D	141296
Lloyd R C sq jsdc 300689	Wheeler G H *BSc MA* psc†	300995	Llewellyn G D C	121297
Lloyd M A *MA MIMGT* psc(a)† 300690	Hume K J D *MBE BSocSc(Hons)*	300996	Hackney S R D *BSc(Hons)*	120298
Martin C P G psc(PAK) jsdc 300696	Leader M J A *BA(Hons)*	300996	Carver C M B *BSc(Hons)*	90200
Porter R J M *MBE BA(Hons)* psc† 300697	Lock N J *BA(Hons)* psc(J)	300996	**Regular Category Late Entry Officers**	
Hughes S M M *BSc(Econ)Hons* sq 300699	Slay J P *BSc(Hons)* psc(J)	300996		
Tritton I G *MBE* psc 300699	Cave I J *BA(Hons)* psc psc(J)	300997	*Majors*	
Robson P A *BSc(Hons)* psc† 300600	James D R H *MA MSc GCGI* psc(J)	300997	Davies A	300995
	Hackett R L M *MBE* sq	300698	Ravenhill N C	300997
Majors	Firth A D	300998	**Special Regular Officers Late Entry**	
Rees P C K *MBIM* sq 300984	Evans P R	300999		
Ross R J V *MBA* psc 300984	Finn A M	300999	*Majors*	
Boileau Goad J G I D *MMS* sq 300985	Laing M A	300999	Ankers A L	300900
	Freeman A J	300900		

200

Captains

Adams D	171197
Arnold G	10498
Blewitt G R	10498
Burns L P	10498

Intermediate Regular Officers

Captains

Watters D M	110895
Rawlings M E *(A/Maj 091000)*	
	80897
Davies G A R *BA(Hons)*	120298
Clarke R J *BA*	121099
Westley M E *(L/Maj 151100)*	
	121099
Clayton P J	101299
Moss R G	101299
Edwards D R *BA(Hons)*	90200
Jones N W *BA(Hons)*	130600

Lieutenants

Biggers S J *BSc(Hons) (A/Capt 040900)*	120897
Bunyard J J *BTech (A/Capt 131099)*	120398
Harris E C N *(A/Capt 131099)*	100898
Hill E C *(A/Capt 200700)*	100898

2nd Lieutenants

Farrell A T	70899
Stone G J	150400

Short Service Late Entry Officers

Captains

Irvine R R *BEM*	250496
Bauer T *BEM*	10498
Watkins W T	10499

Gough P B	100700

Short Service Officers

Captains

Coles C M *BSc(Hons)*	130600

Lieutenants

Godfrey A M *BA(Hons)*	161297
Ellis J G *BA(Hons)*	130498
Matthews J P *BEng(Hons)*	130498
Spoor T J C *BA(Hons)*	141298
Hughes D L *LLB(Hons)*	120499
Rowlands A	130699
Darch R M *BSc(Hons)*	131299

2nd Lieutenants

Harris J M	161200
Lucas J W	161200

THE ROYAL REGIMENT OF WALES (24th/41st Foot)

The Queen's Colour – **A Silver Wreath of Immortelles** borne around the colour pike
A Silver Wreath of Immortelles with the Red Dragon superimposed. The Royal Cypher. The Rose and Thistle on the same stalk within the Garter, and the Crown over. The Sphinx superscribed Egypt. A Naval Crown superscribed 12th April, 1782. *Gwell angau na Chywilydd.*

Blenheim, Ramilles, Oudenarde, Malplaquet, Belleisle, Martinique 1762, St Vincent 1797, Cape of Good Hope 1806, India, Talavera, Bourbon, Busaco, Fuentes d'Onor, Java, Salamanca, Detroit, Queenstown, Miami, Vittoria, Pyrenees, Nivelle, Niagara, Orthes, Peninsula, Waterloo, Ava, Candahar 1842, Ghuznee 1842, Cabool 1842, Chillianwallah, Goojerat, Punjaub, Alma, Inkerman, Sevastopol, South Africa 1877-8-9, Burma 1885-87, Relief of Kimberley, Paardeberg, South Africa 1899-1902.

The Great War – **Mons,** Retreat from Mons, **Marne 1914, Aisne 1914, 18, Ypres 1914, 15, 17, 18,** Langemarck 1914, 17, **Gheluvelt,** Nonne Bosschen, Givenchy 1914, Gravenstafel, St Julien, Frezenberg, Bellewaarde, Aubers, **Loos, Somme 1916, 18,** Albert 1916, 18, Bazentin, Pozieres, Flers-Courcelette, Morval, Ancre Heights, Ancre 1916, 18, Arras 1917, 18, Scarpe 1917, Messines 1917, 18, **Pilckem,** Menin Road, Polygon Wood, Broodseinde, Poelcappelle, Passchendaele, **Cambrai 1917, 18,** St Quentin, Bapaume 1918, Lys, Estaires, Hazebrouck, Bailleul, Kemmel, Bethune, Scherpenberg, Drocourt,-Queant, Hindenburg Line, Havrincourt, Epehy, St Quentin Canal, Beaurevoir, Courtrai, Selle, Valenciennes, Sambre, France and Flanders 1914-18, Struma, **Doiran 1917, 18, Macedonia 1915-18,** Helles, **Landing at Helles,** Krithia, Suvla, Sari Bair, Landing at Suvla, Scimitar Hill, **Gallipoli 1915-16,** Egypt 1915-17, **Gaza,** El Mughar, Jerusalem, Jericho, Tell' Asur, Megiddo, Nablus, Palestine 1917-18, Aden, Tigris 1916, Kut al Amara 1917, **Baghdad,** Mesopotamia 1916-18, **Tsingtao.**

The Second World War – **Norway 1940, Normandy Landing, Sully,** Odon, **Caen,** Bourguebus Ridge, Mont Pincon, Souleuvre, Le Perier Ridge, **Falaise,** Risle Crossing, Antwerp, Nederrijn, **Le Havre,** Antwerp-Turnhout Canal, Scheldt, **Lower Maas,** Venlo Pocket, Zetten, Ourthe, Rhineland, **Reichswald,** Weeze, Hochwald, Rhine, Ibbenburen, Aller, Arnhem 1945, **North-West Europe 1944-45,** Benghazi, Gazala, **North Africa 1940-42,** Sicily 1943, Coriano, **Croce,** Rimini Line, Ceriano Ridge, Argenta Gap, **Italy 1943-45, Crete, Canea,** Withdrawal to Sphakia, Middle East 1941, North Arakan, **Maya Tunnels, Pinwe, Kyaukmyaung Bridgehead,** Shweli, Myitson, Maymyo, Rangoon Road, **Sittang 1945, Burma 1944-45.**

Korea 1951-52

Regimental Marches

Quick March . . . . Men of Harlech
Slow March . . . . Scipio

Agents . . . . Holt's Branch, Royal Bank of Scotland plc, Lawrie House, Farnborough, Hants GU14 7NR

Regimental Headquarters. . . . . The Barracks, Cardiff, CF14 3YE (Tel: Civil: 029 207 81207 Mil: Cardiff Mil Ext: 8207, 8215)

Alliances

Canadian Armed Forces . . . . The Ontario Regiment RCAC
Australian Military Forces . . . . The Royal New South Wales Regiment
Pakistan Army . . . . 4th Battalion, The Baluch Regiment
South African Defence Forces . . . . 121 South African Infantry Battalion

Colonel in Chief. . . . . Maj Gen *HRH The Prince* of Wales *KG KT GCB AK QSO ADC*

Colonel . . . . Maj Gen C H Elliott *CBE.* 221099

Brigadiers

Bromhead D DE G *CBE LVO FRGS*
rcds psc hcsc(J) ph   300690

Colonels

Davies P psc†   300697
Aitken R H T psc   300698
Cholerton I D *BA(Econ)Hons* psc
psc(GE) I   300600

Lieutenant Colonels

Norrington Davies P *OBE*
LLB(Hons) psc osc(KEN)   300690
Goodall R C psc(US) psc   300692

Lloyd-Davies M (SL) sq   300694
Norrington-Davies P J psc   300695
Eagan H W R sq   300697
Wardle R N psc   300699
Powell J M N *LLB(Hons)* psc(n)†
          300600

Majors

Wilks C W *MBE BSc(Hons)* sq
          300985
Griffin M C C aic sq(w) ais 300986
Howells G *BA(Hons)* sq   300990
Beattie S J sq   300991
Kilmister J C ST J psc   300991
Davis R *MBE* osc(MAL) sq 300992
McGregor R J A *BA(Hons) MBA*
psc(GE)   300992
Snook M R *MBE BA(Hons)* psc†
          300993

Bunday N P *BA(Hons) MA* psc(J)
          300995
Napier P M L *BA(Hons)* psc† †
          300995
Barnett J C G   300996
Dunford J R *BSc(Hons) MA* 300996
Lloyd-Jones R H *BA(Hons) MPhil*
psc(J)   300996
Bromham A D C sq(w)   300997
Conway M J *BSc(Hons)*   300997
Pughe-Morgan J E D   300997
Brain E M *BSc(Hons)*   300998
Morgan-Owen J H *LLB(Hons)*
          300998
Swift J F P *MA*   300998
Wheeler D M *BSc(Hons)*   300998
Dickinson R *BA(Hons)*   300999
Cannon M K   300900
Mannings S P   300900

Captains

Butt S W D *BSc(Hons)* *(A/Maj*
050100) 110493
Watson G P F *BA(Hons)* 60894
Webb S N *BA(Econ)Hons* 10495
Welham M L *BSc(Hons)* 141295
Chudleigh C J H 70896
Jefferson P T I *BA(Hons)* 110896
Williams M 60797
Clarke A W *BA(Hons)* 131098
Crewe-Read N O *BSc(Hons)* 140699
Hill S 101299
Harris M J *BSc(Hons)* 130600

Lieutenants

Major O E R *BA(Hons)* 120297

**Regular Category Late Entry
Officers**

Majors

Hooley M sowc sq 300997
John J C *MBE* 300997
Pritchard M S A 300999

Special Regular Officers Late Entry

Majors

Wynne T J 300900

Captains

Mason A 10498
Sibbons D J 10498

Intermediate Regular Officers

Captains

Boyle S C *BSc(Econ)* 120298
Read D J *BSc* 131098
Jones H L 121099
Johnson R D *BSc(Econ)Hons* 90200
Pascoe D M *BA(Hons)* 90200
Valencia S I *BSc(Hons)* 130600

Lieutenants

Hicks G E J *(A/Capt 140498)*
130498

Short Service Late Entry Officers

Captains

Dixon P A 10499

Short Service Officers

Captains

Jones A E O *BSc(Hons)* 100299
Griffiths M D *BSc(Hons)* 140699

Lieutenants

Beynon M R G *BSc(Econ)Hons*
120297
Solosy J L 161297
Taaffe K D *BSc(Hons)* 161297
Watkins J M *BSc(Hons)* 100898
Davis M T *BSc(Hons)* 141298
Belcher I C *BSc(Hons)* 120499
Pritchard R O *BSc(Hons)* 120499
Davies G M 131299
Luke O D 131299
Gudgin R M 231299

Short Service Volunteer Officers

Lieutenants

Carter D L *BSc(Hons)* *(A/Capt
081099)* 231197

THE ROYAL GLOUCESTERSHIRE, BERKSHIRE AND WILTSHIRE REGIMENT (28, 49, 61, 62, 66 and 99)

Front
On a square of crimson a cross pattee throughout silver, charged with a
sphinx couchant upon a pedestal inscribed 'Egypt', all gold
Back
Within a laurel wreath upon a pedestal inscribed 'Egypt', a sphinx

Ramillies, Louisburg, Guadaloupe 1759, Quebec 1759, Martinique 1762, Havannah, St Lucia, Egmont-op-Zee, Copenhagen, Maida, Corunna, Douro, Talavera, Barrosa, Albuhera, Queenstown, Salamanca, Vittoria, Pyrenees, Nivelle, Nive, Orthes, Toulouse, Peninsula, Waterloo, New Zealand, Ferozshah, Sobraon, Chillianwallah, Goojerat, Punjaub, Alma, Inkerman, Sevastopol, Delhi 1857, Pekin 1860, Kandahar 1880, Afghanistan 1879-80, Egypt 1882, Tofrek, Suakin 1885, Defence of Ladysmith, Relief of Kimberley, Paardeberg, South Africa 1879, 1899-1902, Busaco.

The Great War – Mons, Retreat from Mons, Le Cateau, Marne 1914, Aisne 1914, 18, La Bassee, **Messines 1914, 17, 18,** Armentieres 1914, **Ypres 1914, 15, 17,** Langemarck 1914, 17, Gheluvelt, Nonne Bosschen, Givenchy 1914, **Neuve Chapelle,** Gravenstafel, St Julien, Frezenberg, Bellewaarde, Aubers, Festubert 1915, **Loos, Somme 1916, 18,** Albert 1916, 18, Bazentin, Delville Wood, Pozieres, Guillemont, Flers-Courcelette, Morval, Thiepval, Le Transloy, Ancre Heights, Ancre 1916, 18, **Arras 1917, 18,** Vimy 1917, Scarpe 1917, 18, Messines 1917, 18, Arleux, Pilckem, Menin Road, Polygon Wood, Broodseinde, Poelcappelle, Passchendaele, **Cambrai 1917, 18,** St Quentin, **Bapaume 1918,** Rosieres, Avre, Villers Bretonneux, **Lys,** Estaires, Hazebrouck, Bailleul, Kemmel, Bethune, Scherpenberg, Amiens, Drocourt Queant, Hindenburg Line, Havrincourt, Epehy, Canal du Nord, St Quentin Canal, Beaurevoir, **Selle,** Valenciennes, Sambre, France and Flanders 1914-18, Piave, **Vittorio Veneto,** Italy 1917, 18, Struma, **Doiran 1917, 18, Macedonia 1915-18,** Suvla, Sari Bair, Scimitar Hill, **Gallipoli 1915, 16,** Egypt 1916, Gaza, Nebi Sanwil, Jerusalem, Megiddo, Sharon, **Palestine 1917-18,** Tigris 1916, Kut al Amara 1917, **Baghdad,** Mesopotamia 1916, 18, Persia 1918.

The Second World War – Dyle, **Defence of Escaut, Defence of Arras,** St Omer-La-Bassee, Wormhoudt, **Cassel,** Ypres-Comines Canal, **Dunkirk 1940, Normandy Landing,** Villiers Bocage, Odon, Caen, **Hill 112,** Bourgebus Ridge, Maltot, **Mount Pincon,** La Variniere, **Falaise,** Risle Crossing, **Seine 1944,** Le Havre, Nederrijn, Roer, Zetten, Rhineland, Cleve, Goch, Xanten, Rhine, Bremen, **North-West Europe 1940, 44-45,** Solarino, Simeto Bridgehead, Pursuit to Messina, **Sicily 1943,** Monte Camino, Calabritto, **Garigliano Crossing,** Minturno, Damiano, **Anzio,** Corroceto, **Rome,** Advance to Tiber, Italy 1943-45, Middle East 1942, **Taukyan, Paungde,** Monywa 1942, Donbaik, **North Arakan,** Point 551, Mayu Tunnels, Ngakyedauk Pass, **Kohima,** Mao Songsang, **Pinwe,** Shweli, Shwebo, Kyaukonyaung Bridgehead, **Mandalay,** Fort Dufferin, Rangoon Road, **Myitson,** Toungoo, **Burma 1942, 44-45.**

Hill 327, **Imjin, Korea 1950-51**

Honorary Distinctions
(1st Battalion)
United States Presidential Citation

Regimental Marches
Quick March .Army of the Nile
Slow March . . . .'Scipio'

Agents . . . . .Lloyds Bank plc Cox's & King's Branch

Regimental Headquarters . . . . .Custom House, Gloucester, GL1 2HE
(Tel: 01452-522682)

Alliances
Canadian Armed Forces . . . . .The Royal Canadian Regiment
The Lincoln and Welland Regiment
The Algonquin Regiment
Australian Military Forces . . . . .11/28th Bn The Royal Western Australia Regiment
New Zealand Army . . . . .7th Bn (Wellington (City of Wellington's Own) and Hawkes Bay)
The Royal New Zealand Infantry Regiment
Pakistan Army . . . . .13th Bn The Frontier Force Regiment
South African Defence Forces . . . . . . .Cape Town Rifles (Dukes)
Kenya . . . . .3rd Battalion The Kenya Rifles

Colonel in Chief . . . . .Field Marshal *HRH The Prince* Philip *Duke of* Edinburgh
KG KT OM GBE AC GSO

Deputy Colonel in Chief . . . .*HRH The Duke of* Gloucester *KG GCVO*

Colonel . . . . .Maj Gen R D Grist *CB OBE DL* 270494

Deputy Colonel . . . . .Brig W A Mackereth *DL* 270494

Williams A P *MBE BA(Hons)* psc†
300994
Brown D A J   psc(J)   300995

Brigadiers

Daniel J D *BA(Hons)* psc(J) 300995
Davidson-Houston P E O'R-B   *CBE*
Dennis P   psc   300995
BSc(Eng) MIMGT psc†
Fontana A P K *BSc(Hons)* psc(J)
300698
300995
Gray S D *MBE* sq   300995

Colonels

Kingsberry T L   psc   300995
Durrant P J *MBE BA(Hons)* psc
Perkins C J S *BSc(Hons)* psc(J)
300692
300995
Wakelin C S *OBE* psc(CAN)
Welch N *MBE BSc(Hons)* psc†
300694
300995
Vine M S *OBE* ocds(US) psc 300696
Dutton R P   psc(J)   300996
Webster J P O *OBE* odc(US) psc(n)†
Miller S D *BA(Hons) MA* psc psc(J)
300696
300996
Purcell H M *OBE MA* odc(AUST)
Short N P   300996
jssc psc jsdc   300699
Griffin G R W *BSc(Hons)*   300998
Dutton S J   300999
Flavell P R *BSc(Hons)*   300999

Lieutenant Colonels

Maconochie C S *BSc(Hons)* 300900
Savage I M   300900
Stone D J A (SL) *FIMGT* psc 300687
Shaw M D *BSc(Hons)*   300900
Briard A (SL) aic sq(w)   300693
Lake A P B   psc odc(BE) jsdc

Captains

300693
Oxlade S J *MBE BSc(Tech)* aic sq(w)
Ross S J *BSc(Hons) (A/Maj 050800)*
300696
130495
Hony G H *MBE* psc   300697
Spandler M J *BA(Hons)*   110895
Tomlinson P C *MBE* psc   300697
Wakelin J C *BSc(Hons) (A/Maj*
Lavender C M *MBE* psc   300698
091000)   131296
Motum M J R   psc   300698
Denning D J *BA(Hons)*   160698
Harris I V K   psc†   300699
Petersen W A *BA(Hons)*   131098
Brown E D *MBE* psc   300600
McDade G A   111298
Holt R P *BA(Hons) MA* psc† 300600
Horner R G *BA(Hons)*   100299
Cook T J   101299

Majors

Franklin B R F *BSc(Hons)* sq

Lieutenants

300984
Grist C E D *BA(Hons)*   120897
Walker N J   osc(US) sq   300984
French A G L   *(A/Capt 130300)*
Bowkett S E *BA(Hons)* sq   300987
90899
Cook S G   psc   300987
Nurick M E   psc   300987

Regular Category Late Entry
Edmonds J J   sq   300989
Officers
Masters N J   psc   300989
Barlow G P *MBE* sq   300991

Majors

O'Hare T D   sq   300991
Gibson M W *MBE*   300991
Marsh J *BA(Hons)* psc† †   300993
Luckwell R J   300992
Chynoweth M   sq   300994
Turner A M   300995

Minty N W J   300996
Dineen J J *MBE*   300999

Special Regular Officers Late Entry

Captains

McLeod P W   10597
Dixon A R   10498
Stevens C S D   10498
Wood I J   10498

Intermediate Regular Officers

Captains

Biggs J R   111298
Griffiths A D *BA(Hons) MPhil*
10299
Mackenzie M R P *BA(Hons)* 140699
Penhale J P *BSc(Hons)*   121099
Dakin J T F *BSc(Hons)*   90200
Grist M R   120800

Lieutenants

Lane S   *(A/Capt 130300)*   120499
Crossley J A   80800

Short Service Late Entry Officers

Captains

Bennion S W   60798
Sumner C *MBE*   10499
Phillips B A D   20899
Stevens J A   100400

Short Service Officers

Lieutenants

Baker M R *BA(Hons)*   161297
Eden W L *BA(Hons)*   161297
Paxton P J *BA(Hons)*   161297
Deeley A W *BSc(Hons)*   130498
Kyte P D *BSc*   141298
Flexman J B J   131299
Wood A M *BA(Hons)*   131299

THE WORCESTERSHIRE AND SHERWOOD FORESTERS REGIMENT
(29th/45th FOOT) (29, 36, 45 and 95)

A Maltese Cross pommettee charged with the Garter in Gold encircling a Stag in Silver lodged on water proper thereunder a plinth inscribed FIRM in Gold the whole upon an elongated star of eights in Silver.
Upon a pedestal inscribed Firm the Lion of the Royal Crest. A Maltese Cross charged in the centre with a Stag lodged on water within a wreath of oak. A Naval Crown superscribed **1st June 1794**.

Ramillies, Belleisle, Mysore, Hindoostan, Louisburg, Rolica, Vimiera, Corunna, Talavera, Busaco, Fuentes D'Onor, Albuhera, Ciudad Rodrigo, Badajoz, Salamanca, Vittoria, Pyrenees, Nivelle, Nive, Orthes, Toulouse, Peninsula, Ava, Ferozeshah, Sobraon, South Africa 1846-7, Chillianwallah, Goojerat, Punjaub, Alma, Inkerman, Sevastopol, Central India, Abyssinia, Egypt 1882, Tirah, South Africa 1899-1902.

The Great War – **Mons**, Le Cateau, Retreat from Mons, Marne 1914, **Aisne 1914, 18**, La Bassee 1914, Armentieres 1914, **Ypres 1914, 15, 17, 18**, Langemarck 1914, 17, **Gheluvelt**, Nonne Bosschen, Neuve Chapelle, Aubers, Festubert 1915, Hooge 1915, **Loos, Somme 1916, 18**, Albert 1916, 18, Bazentin, Delville Wood, Pozieres, Ginchy, Flers-Courcelette, Morval, Thiepval, Le Transloy, Ancre Heights, Ancre 1916, Arras 1917, 18, Vimy 1917, Scarpe 1917, 18, Arleux, Messines 1917, 18, Pilcken, Langemarck 1917, Menin Road, Polygon Wood, Broodseinde, Poelcappelle, Passchendaele, **Cambrai 1917, 18**, St Quentin, Bapaume 1918, Rosieres, Villers Bretonneux, **Lys**, Estaires, Hazebrouck, Bailleul, Kemmel, Scherpenberg, Amiens, Drocourt-Queant, Hindenburg Line, Epehy, Canal du Nord, **St Quentin Canal**, Beaurevoir, Courtrai, Selle, Valenciennes, Sambre, **France and Flanders 1914-18**, Piave, Vittorio Veneto, **Italy 1917-18**, Doiran 1917-18, Macedonia 1915-18, Helles, Landing at Helles, Krithia, Suvla, Sari Bair, Landing at Suvla, Scimitar Hill, **Gallipoli 1915-16**, Egypt 1916, Tigris 1916, Kut al Amara 1917, **Baghdad**, Mesopotamia 1916-18, Baku, Persia 1918.

The Second World War – **Norway 1940**, Defence of Escaut, St Omer-La Bassee, Ypres-Comines Canal, Wormhoudt, Dunkirk 1940, Odon, Bourguebus Ridge, Maltot, **Mont Pincon**, Jurques, La Variniere, Noireau Crossing, **Seine 1944**, Nederrijn, **Geilenkirchen** Rhineland, **Goch**, Rhine, **North-West Europe 1940, 44-45**, Gogni, Barentu, **Keren**, Amba Alagi, Abyssinia 1940-41, **Gazala**, Via Balbia, **El Alamein**, Djebel Guerba, Tamera, Medjez Plain, **Tunis**, North Africa 1941-43, **Salerno**, Volturno Crossing, Monte Camino, **Anzio**, **Campoleone**, Advance to Tiber, **Gothic Line, Coriano**, Cosina Canal Crossing, Monte Ceco, Italy 1943-45, **Singapore Island**, Malaya 1942, **Kohima**, Relief of Kohima, Naga Village, Mao Songsang, Shwebo, **Mandalay**, Irrawaddy, Mt Popa, **Burma 1944-45**.

Regimental Marches

Quick March .Arrangement of 'Young May Moon' and 'Royal Windsor'
Slow March . . . .'Duchess of Kent'

Agents . . . . .Lloyds Bank plc Cox's & King's Branch

Regimental Headquarters . . . . .Norton Barracks, Worcester WR5 2PA
(Tel: Civil: 01905 354359 Mil: Worcester Mil Ext: 8726, 8727)
e-mail: rhq-wfr-@lincone.net

Outstation . . . . .Foresters House, Chetwynd Barracks, Chilwell NG9 5HA
(Tel: Civil: 0115 946 5415 Mil: 94451 85220, e-mail: rhqwfr-nottm@lincone.net)

Alliances

Canadian Armed Forces . . . . .The Grey and Simcoe Foresters
Pakistan Army . . . . .13th Battalion The Punjab Regiment
Colonel in Chief . . . .*HRH THE PRINCESS ROYAL KG KT GCVO QSO*
Colonel . . . . .Brig J P Weller *MBE* 150497

Colonels		
Heron C A C *OBE* psc(PAK)	300691
Silk G A *FIMGT* psc	300693
Hackett J R M *CBE* psc†	300694

Lieutenant Colonels		
Jackson M L *OBE* psc	300691
Smith P E W psc	300696
Jordan R J *MBE BA(Hons)* psc†	300697
Chedham F J odc(AUS) psc psc(J)	300698
Norman S W sq	300699

Majors		
Howse C R *MBE* psc	300982
Martin M W G sq	300986
Galvin K E *BSocSc(Hons)* sq sq(w)	
ais	300987
Alun-Jones P H G *MBE BA(Hons)* sq	300989
Field A W psc(PAK) *(L/Lt Col 040900)*	300990
Cotterill J H *MBE* sq	300991
Claydon M N psc(IND) sq	300993
Holden M A sq	300993
Williams S R psc	300994
Dickinson T J S	300995
Richards B L *BA(Hons)* psc(CAN) sq	300995
Pugh-Cook R M *BA(Hons)*	300996
Fitzgerald D	300997

Wardner M R psc(J)	300997
Wilford D P	300998
Preece R J G *BA(Hons)*	300999
Wadland A J A *BSc(Hons)*	300999
Brittle M A *BEng(Hons)*	300900
Dobson C H F	300900
Kimber P W *BEng(Hons)*	300900
Turner J F *BSc(Hons)*	300900

Captains		
Perks W D *LLB(Hons) AKC*	60894
Durrant R J W	130496
Richards M W *(A/Maj 021000)*	141296
Gilby P G	80897
Bryant O J H *BEng(Hons)*	100299
Russell A E *BSc(Hons)*	130600

Lieutenants

McKay A R *BSc(Hons)* — 120897
Ginn C R P *BSc(Hons)* — 161297
Wood C M *BA(Hons)* — 130498
Sandford R F *MA(Hons)* — 90299

Regular Category Late Entry Officers

Lieutenant Colonels

Elsam D J *MBE* sq — 10100

Majors

Seddon K *MBE BEM* — 300998

Special Regular Officers Late Entry

Captains

Temminck P A *BEM* — 10797

Intermediate Regular Officers

Majors

Turner J R G — 300997

Captains

Thompson N C *BSc(Hons) (A/Maj 221100)* — 141295
Glenn S H *BSc(Hons)* — 240197
Ellis J P — 70898
Crabb L D — 90499
Nowell J P *BSc(Hons)* — 140699
Thompson R J — 41000

Lieutenants

Spears A J *(A/Capt 200200)* — 130498
Wray M W *(A/Capt 050101)* — 120499

2nd Lieutenants

††Higgins A D — 100900

Short Service Late Entry Officers

Captains

Rees M C — 10698
Johnson R N — 10200

Cotterill G D — 10600

Short Service Officers

Captains

Westwood J C — 160598
Davies T E A *BSc(Hons)* — 101000
†Hughes M L *(A/Maj 011199)* — 201100
Grant N D *BSc(Hons)* — 220201

Lieutenants

Rawlinson T P *BSc(Hons)* — 161297
Catt T W R *BSc(Hons)* — 100898
Stanier J P — 141298
Canham D D *BA(Hons)* — 120499
Jerome F J E *BSc* — 120499
Hawling D A *BSc(Hons)* — 90899
Davies-Jones R L *LLB(Hons)* — 131299
Garrett A R *BA(Hons)* — 131299
Skillen J H — 131299

THE STAFFORDSHIRE REGIMENT (THE PRINCE OF WALES'S)
(38, 64, 80 and 98)

The Prince of Wales's Plume within the Stafford Knot, The Sphinx, Superscribed Egypt
The Dragon, Superscribed China

Guadaloupe 1759, Martinique 1762, Martinique 1794, St Lucia 1803, Surinam, Monte Video, Rolica, Vimiera, Corunna, Busaco, Badajoz, Salamanca, Vittoria, St Sebastian, Nive, Peninsula, Ava, Moodkee, Ferozeshaah, Sobraon, Punjaub, Pegu, Alma, Inkerman, Sevastopol, Reshire, Bushire, Knosh-Ab, Persia, Lucknow, Central India, South Africa 1878-79, Egypt 1882, Kirbekan, Nile 1884-85, Hafir, South Africa 1900-02.

The Great War - **Mons,** Retreat from Mons, **Marne 1914, Aisne 1914, 18, Armentieres 1914, Ypres 1914, 17, 18,** Langemarck 1914, 17, Gheluvelt, Nonne Bosschen, Neuve Chapelle, Aubers, Festubert 1915, Loos, Somme 1916, 18, Albert 1916, 18, Bazentin, Delville Wood, Pozieres, Guillemont, Flers-Courcellete, Morval, Thiepval, Ancre Heights, Ancre 1916, Bapaume 1917, 18, **Arras 1917, 18,** Scarpe 1917, 18, Arleux, Bullecourt Hill 70, **Messines 1917, 18,** Pilckem, Menin Road, Polygon Wood, Broodseinde, Poelcappelle, Passchendaele, **Cambrai 1917, 18,** St Quentin, Rosieres, Avre, Lys, Bailleul, Kemmel, Scherpenberg, Drocourt,-Queant, Hindenburg Line, Havrincourt, Canal du Nord, **St Quentin Canal,** Beaurevoir, Courtrai, **Selle,** Valenciennes, Sambre, France and Flanders 1914-18, Piave, **Vittorio Veneto,** Italy 1917-18, **Suvla, Sari Bair,** Landing at Suvla, Scimitar Hill, Gallipoli 1915-16, Egypt 1916, Tigris 1916, **Kut al Amara 1917,** Baghdad, Mesopotamia 1916-18, Baku, Persia 1918, **North-West Frontier, India 1915.**

Afghanistan 1919

The Second World War – **Dyle,** Defence of Escaut, **Ypres-Comines Canal, Caen,** Orne, **Noyers,** Mont Pincon, **Brieux Bridgehead, Falaise, Arnhem 1944, North-West Europe 1940, 44,** Sidi Barrani, Djebel Kesskiss, **Medjez Plain,** Gueriat et Atach Ridge, Gab Gab Gap, **North Africa 1940, 43, Landing in Sicily, Sicily 1943, Anzio,** Carroceto, **Rome,** Advance to Tiber, Gothic Line, **Marradi,** Italy 1943-45, **Chindits 1944, Burma 1943, 44.**

Gulf 1991, Wadi Al Batin

Regimental Marches

Quick March . . . . .The Staffordshire Regiment (arrangement of 'Come Lassies and Lads' and 'The Days we went a-Gipsying')
Slow March . . . .'God Bless The Prince of Wales'

Regimental Headquarters . . . . .Whittington Barracks, Lichfield, Satffs WS14 9PY
(Tel: Civil: 0121 311 3240 Mil: Lichfield Mil Ext: 3240)

Alliances

Canadian Armed Forces . . . . .4e Battalion, Royal 22e Regiment (Chateauguay)
Australian Military Forces . . . . .8/7th Battalion The Royal Victoria Regiment
Leeward Islands . . . . .The Antigua and Barbuda Defence Force
Pakistan Army . . . . .7th Battalion The Baluch Regiment
Jamaica Defence Force . . . . .The Jamaica Regiment

Colonel in Chief . . . .*HRH The Duke of York CVO ADC*

Colonel . . . . .Col T R Cottis *MBE* 011195

	Majors	
	Fennings-Mills R S psc	300980
	Lockwood J Q *MBE* psc	300988
	Joynson C J sq	300989
Brigadiers	Holt D M psc	300991
Rogers C T *OBE ADC* psc aic	Morley G W *BSc(Hons) MBA MSc*	
hcsc(J) jsdc 300698	psc† dis	300991
	Wootton R G *BA(Hons)* psc(n)	
Colonels		300993
	Foster N S sq	300994
Brown N H C psc jsdc 300694	Mattey C R D *BSc(Hons)* sq	300994
Knapper S J *CBE MC* psc 300696	Steed M sq	300994
Tanner J K *BA(Hons)* psc 300600		
	Sandiford T A *BA* psc† †	300995
	Gadd R D M	300996
Lieutenant Colonels	Horne P J *BSc(Econ)Hons MSc*	
Moss F G *MBE BSc(Hons)* MIMGT	psc(J)	300996
psc† 300693	Smallbone A T *BA(Hons)*	300996
Rider C R F *BA(Hons)* psc† 300696	Banton S J *BA(Hons)* psc(J)	300997
Hughes C G S *OBE BA* psc† *(A/Col*	Spiby R *BA(Hons)* psc(J)	300997
161000) 300697	Boath D W *BSc(Hons)*	300998
Haugh K T *MBE* psc 300698	Layton A P	300998
Rusby M R sq 300600	Hadfield A N	300999

Crowe G J CAFS	300900
Neale S B	300900
Captains	
Ross M *BSc*	10495
Niblett N M	151295
Harvey A L CAFS	60796
Rutherford D	70896
Casey S A	121297
Cripps P J S	121297
Moorhouse R S	160698
Hetherington A E	90499
Cox A D *BSc(Hons)*	90200
Hoy R A J *BA(Hons)*	80201

Regular Category Late Entry Officers

Majors

Flackett I J	300996
Huyton S	300900

208

Special Regular Officers Late Entry

Captains

Allman B R   10496
Clowes C   10498

Intermediate Regular Officers

Majors

Woodhouse G D *BA(Hons)*   300900

Captains

Bayliss G J *BA(Hons)*   100299
Richardson N S   100299
Green J E *BA(Hons)*   90200

2nd Lieutenants

Woodall T J   111299

Short Service Late Entry Officers

Captains

Styles E C   240400

Short Service Officers

Captains

James J W *BA(Hons)*   121099
Seager A P H *BA(Hons)*   121099
Jones D R *BA(Hons)*   130600
Thornton A P *BSc(Hons)*   130600

Lieutenants

Botham S E *BA(Hons)*   161297

Nicholls J M *(A/Capt 140800)*   161297
McIntyre A R *(A/Capt 180300)*   130498
Prior L D *BEd(Hons)*   140698
Burton S P *BSc(Hons)*   141298
Moore D I S   120499
Gorman G S   20899
Cook D J *BEng(Hons)*   90899
McLannahan A T G *BA(Hons)*   90899
Atherton R G *BSc(Hons)*   131299
†McCammon D W   90700

2nd Lieutenants

Bailey D J S   150400

209

THE LIGHT DIVISION

Comprising .... .The Light Infantry (2 Regular Battalions, 5 Volunteer Companies)
The Royal Green Jackets (2 Regular Battalions, 4 Volunteer Battalions)
Divisional Headquarters .... .Headquarters Infantry, Warminster Training Centre
Warminster, Wilts BA12 0DJ (Tel: 01985-2222425)
Colonel Commandant .... .Gen *Sir* John Deverell *KCB OBE* .... .010100

Divisional Lieutenant Colonel ...... .Lt Col P J Pentreath LI .... .130999

The origins of amalgamated Regiments which are now included in The Light Division are as follows:

THE LIGHT INFANTRY

On 6 October 1959
The Somerset Light Infantry (Prince Albert's) (13) and
The Duke of Cornwall's Light Infantry (32 and 46) amalgamated to form:
The Somerset and Cornwall Light Infantry

On 10 July 1968
The Somerset and Cornwall Light Infantry (13, 32 and 46)
The King's Own Yorkshire Light Infantry (51 and 105)
The King's Shropshire Light Infantry (53 and 85) and
The Durham Light Infantry (68 and 106) amalgamated to form:
The Light Infantry

THE ROYAL GREEN JACKETS

On 7 November 1958
The Oxfordshire and Buckinghamshire Light Infantry (43rd and 52nd) was redesignated:
1st Green Jackets (43rd and 52nd)

The King's Royal Rifle Corps was redesignated:
2nd Green Jackets (The King's Royal Rifle Corps)

The Rifle Brigade (Prince Consort's Own) was redesignated:
3rd Green Jackets (The Rifle Brigade)

On 1 January 1966
1st Green Jackets (43rd and 52nd)
2nd Green Jackets (The King's Own Royal Rifle Cops) and
3rd Green Jackets (The Rifle Brigade) amalgamated to form:
The Royal Green Jackets

THE LIGHT INFANTRY (13, 32, 46, 51, 53, 68, 85, 105 and 106)

A Bugle Horn, stringed, in Silver. The Sphinx superscribed Egypt. A Mural Crown superscribed Jellalabad. *Aucto Splendore Resurgo. Cede Nullis. Faithful.*

Gibraltar 1704-5, Dettingen, Minden, Nieuport, St Lucia 1796, Tournay, Dominica, **Corunna,** Rolica, Vimiera, Martinique 1809, Talavera, **Fuentes d'Onor, Salamanca, Vittoria, Pyrenees, Nivelle,** Nive, **Orthes,** Toulouse, **Peninsula, Bladensburg, Waterloo,** Ava, Aliwal, Sobraon, Ghuznee 1839, **Afghanistan 1829,** Cabool 1842, Mooltan, Goojerat, Punjaub, Alma, **Inkerman, Sevastopol,** Reshire, Bushire, Koosh-ab, **Persia, Lucknow, New Zealand, Pegu, Ali Masjid, South Africa 1878-9, Afghanistan 1878-80.** Tel-el-Kebir, Egypt 1882, Nile 1884-5, Suakin 1885, **Burma 1885-87, Modder River, Paardeberg, Relief of Ladysmith, South Africa 1899-1902.**

The Great War – **Mons, Le Cateau,** Retreat from Mons, Marne 1914, 18, **Aisne 1914, 18,** La Bassee 1914, **Messines 1914, 17, 18,** Armentieres 1914, **Ypres 1914, 15, 17, 18,** Hill 60, Gravenstafel, St Julien, Frezenberg, Bellewaarde, Hooge 1915, Loos, Mount Sorrel, **Somme 1916, 18, Albert 1916, 18,** Bazentin, Delville Wood, Pozieres, Guillemont, Flers-Courcelette, Morval, Le Transloy, Ancre Heights, Ancre 1916, 18, Bepaume 1917, 18, **Arras 1917, 18,** Vimy 1917, Scarpe 1917, 18, Arleux, Hill 70, Pilckem, Langemarck 1917, Menin Road, Polygon Wood, Broodseinde, Poelcappelle, **Passchendaele, Cambrai 1917, 18,** St Quentin, Rosieres, Avre, Lys, Estaires, Hazebrouck, Baileul, Kemmel, Bethune, Scherpenberg, Marne 1918, Soissonnais-Ourcq, Tardenois, Amiens, Drocourt Queant, Bligny, Hindenburg Line, **Havrincourt,** Epehy, Canal du Nord, St Quentin Canal, Beaurevoir, Courtrai, Selle, Valenciennes, Sambre, France and Flanders 1914-18, Piave, Vittorio Veneto, Italy 1917-18, Struma, **Doiran 1917, 18,** Macedonia 1915-18, Suvla, Landing at Suvla, Scimitar Hill, Gallipoli 1915, Rumani, Egypt 1915-17, Gaza, El Mughar, Nebi Samwil, **Jerusalem,** Jericho, Tell' Asur, Megiddo, Sharon, **Palestine 1917-18, Tigris 1916,** Sharquat, Mesopotamia 1916-18, NW Frontier India 1915, 16-17, Aden, Archangel 1918-19.

Afghanistan 1919

The Second World War – Kvam, **Norway 1940,** Dyle, Defence of Escaut, Arras counter attack, St Omer-La Bassee, **Dunkirk 1940, Normandy Landing,** Villiers Bocage, Tilly sur Seulles, Odon, **Fontenay le Pesnil,** Cheux, Defence of Rauray, Caen, **Hill 112,** Bourgebus Ridge, Cagny, Troarn, Mont Pincon, Souleuvre, Le Perier Ridge, St Pierre La Vielle, Noireau Crossing, Falaise, Seine 1944, Antwerp, Hechel, **Gheel,** Nederrijn, Le Havre, Antwerp-Turnhout Canal, Lower Maas, Opheusden, Venraij, Gellenkirchen, Venlo Pocket, Roer, Rhineland, Cleve, Goch, Hochwald, Xanten, Rhine, Ibbenburen, Lingen, Aller, Bremen, **North-West Europe 1940, 44-45,** Syria 1940, Halfaya 1941, Tobruk 1941, Relief of Tobruk, Gazala, Gabr el Fachri, Zt El Mrasses, Mersa Matruh, Point 174, **El Alamein, Mareth,** Sedjenane, Mine de Sedjenane, El Kourzia, **Argoub Sellah,** Medjez Plain, Gueriat el Atach Ridge, Si Absallah, Tunis, Djebel Bou Aoukaz 1943, North Africa 1940-43, Landing in Sicily, Solarino, **Primosole Bridge, Sicily 1943, Salerno,** Salerno Hills, Cava di Tirreni, Volturno Crossing, Monte Camino, Garigliano Crossing, Minturno. Monte Tuga, **Anzio,** Campoleone, Carroceto, **Cassino II,** Trasimene Line, Arezzo, Advance to Florence, Incontro, Gothic Line, Gemmano Ridge, Carpineta, Capture of Forli, Cosina Canal Crossing, Defence of Lamone Bridgehead, Pergola Ridge, Rimini Line, Casena, Monte Ceco, Monte Grande, Sillaro Crossing, **Italy 1943-45,** Athens, Greece 1944-45, Cos, Middle East 1942, Sittang 1942, Donbaik, **North Arakan,** Buthidaung, Ngakyedauk Pass, **Kohima,** Mandalay, **Burma 1942, 43-45.**

Kowang-San, Hill 227, **Korea 1951-53**

Regimental Marches

Quick Marches . . . .(i) Light Infantry (ii) Regimental Double Past 'The Keel Row'

Agents . . . . .Lloyds Bank plc Cox's & King's Branch

Regimental Headquarters . . . . .Peninsula Barracks, Romsey Road, Winchester, Hants, SO23 8TS (Tel: 01962 828527/29/30, Fax 5100)

Alliances

Canadian Armed Forces . . . . .The Royal Hamilton Light Infantry (Wentworth Regiment)
Le Regiment de Maisonneuve
The North Saskatchewan Regiment
The Australian Citizens Military Forces The Monash University Regiment
New Zealand Army . . . . .2nd Battalion (Canterbury and Nelson, Marlborough and West Coast) Royal New Zealand Infantry Regiment
Pakistan Army . . . . .11th Battalion The Baloch Regiment
1st Battalion The Sind Regiment
Kenya Army .1st Battalion the Kenya Rifles
Mauritius . . . . .The Mauritius Special Mobile Force
South African Defence Forces . . . . . . .Rand Light Infantry
Colonel in Chief . . . .*HM* QUEEN ELIZABETH THE QUEEN MOTHER
Deputy Colonel in Chief . . . .*HRH Princess* Alexandra *the Hon Lady* Ogilvy *GCVO*
Colonel . . . . .Gen *Sir* John Deverell *KCB OBE* 171096
Deputy Colonels . . . . .Maj Gen R V Brims *CBE* 051193
Brig C M G Elcomb *OBE* 160994
Col M A G Watts *MBE* 171096
Lt Col J K Marsham *OBE* 080995

Brigadiers

Elcomb C M G OBE BA(Hons) psc
hcsc(J)   300696

Colonels

Cousens R P OBE FIMGT psc jsdc
                          300694
Gaskell N P sq jsdc   300695
Stephenson D H R CBE psc 300695
Weeks T F L OBE psc   300697
Barry B W OBE psc† aic hcsc(J)
(A/Brig 290101)   300698
Gregson T J MBE BA(Hons) psc jsdc
                          300698
Wynne Davies D A MBA psc
psc(CAN)   300698
Rollo-Walker R M J OBE psc jsdc
                          300600

Lieutenant Colonels

Gilbert A A MBE BA(Hons) psc
                          300687
Grubb M J W BSc sq   300690
Hinde P N BSc(Hons) psc† jsdc
                          300690
Burt C (SL) BSocSc(Hons) psc(a)†
aic   300691
Lloyd-Williams R C psc†   300692
Phayre R D S BA(Hons) MIPD psc
                          300692
Sharland P R psc   300693
Amber A MBE BSc(Eng)Hons MSc
psc(a)† gw   300694
Mortimer A M W MBE psc   300695
Lerwill A T D odc(FR) osc(FR) sq
                          300696
Martin T J OBE MA psc†   300696
Pentreath P J psc   300696
Spencer J N L odc(US) psc 300696
Booth C C S nadc psc   311296
Montagu M C D BA(Hons) psc†
                          300697
De Vos J P BSc(Hons) psc† 300698
Lynch-Staunton C H C psc jsdc
                          300698
Wood D J MBE MC psc   300698
Smith R R MA psc   300699
Kellett P A BSc(Hons) MA GCGI psc
                          301299
Davies E P MBE MA psc†   300600
Evans T P psc   300600
Whitmore G LLB(Hons) psc 300600

Majors

Whistler M H L sq   300980
Jones N A DE C sq   300981
Harris R A MIMGT sq   300983
Badgery J MBE LLB sq   300984
Vincent M S R sq   300987
Blue R A sq(w) †   300988
Flecchia M D psc(CAN)   300988
Nichols D aic sq(w)   300988
Williams R G BA(Hons) psc 300988
Harris C E R sq   300989
Chambers G P psc(CAN)   300990
Sartain R P psc   300990
Tolhurst R J BSc(Hons) sq(w) ais
                          300990

Payne M J C sq   300991
Chapman J M MBE sq   300992
Mills S C D psc   300992
Topham C M E sq   300992
Hall J W MBE BA(Hons) psc†
                          300993
Waight R E C sowc sq   300993
Shircliff M J B MA psc†   300994
Goldsack M R BA(Hons) psc(IND)
                          300995
Hardy J C psc(CAN)   300995
Hudson R J BSc(Hons)   300995
Humphreys C R BA(Hons) sq
                          300995
McMurtrie T D psc(J)   300995
Radford T B MBE MA psc   300995
Scarff M T BA(Hons) psc 300995
Shields H E MBE BA(Hons)
psc(CAN)   300995
Turner E G E   300995
Cummings J R   300996
Pointing W J BA(Hons) psc(J)
                          300996
Arundell R G MA GCGI psc(J)
                          300997
Bowron J H BA(Hons) psc(J)
                          300997
Nash A S L   300997
Nicholl A R MCIM   300997
Noble S J W BSc   300997
Thornton M E BSc(Hons)   300997
Chamberlain E J R BSocSc(Hons)
psc(J)   300998
Allport A J BEng(Hons)   300999
Davies R G   300999
Head R A BA(Hons)   300999
Ilic N QGM BSc(Hons)   300900
Taylerson A A H BA(Hons) 300900
Winston-Davis M J cafs   300900

Captains

Tomkins B J H BA cafs (A/Maj
050100)   151292
Thornton N P S BA(Hons) (A/Maj
170400)   110895
Lampard B BSc(Hons) (L/Maj
011000)   111095
May N S (A/Maj 140400)   70896
de Labilliere J A D MBE BSc(Hons)
psc(J)   110896
Gorman P BSc(Hons)   131296
Faux J A   110497
Dyer B J   80897
Sheves A G   121297
Ottewell H V BA(Hons)   120298
Samsonoff A P MA(Hons)   100299
Harper T A   130599
Chisholm R A J   140699
Field A N   121099
Jackson T N R BA(Hons)   90200
Rogers H C M BSc(Hons)   90200
Turnbull M J   140400
Windsor R E BSc(Hons)   220201

Lieutenants

Evennett J D BA(Hons)   161297
Graham D N BSc(Hons)   130498

2nd Lieutenants

†Basset R W F   60998

Regular Category Late Entry Officers

Majors

Kennedy H L   300995
Jarratt D G AMIRTE   300996
Lawton C   300997
Manley T MBE   300997
Bradley G   300999
Evanson P J   300900

Captains

Howarth A BEM   130494

Special Regular Officers Late Entry

Captains

Noble R A (A/Maj 071100) 30595
Carter R H   10496
Barnes A D   270496
Bonner M   10498
Hall J (A/Maj 070100)   10498
Pickford A   10498

Intermediate Regular Officers

Captains

Livingston D G S   80897
Fox P J   11197
Hickman K C BA(Hons)   120298
Milford M E   60899
Bewick T H BEng(Hons)   121099
Lescott R A BA(Hons)   121099
Anderson A J C BA(Hons)   90200
Knowles-Jackson T J MA(Hons)
                          90200
Harris T J BA(Hons)   130600
Cook W B A MA(Hons)   80201

Lieutenants

White J M   310398
Burrows G R   131299

Short Service Late Entry Officers

Captains

Hamilton D   10498
Matthews D R MBE   10498
Gilbert G D   10499
Meggison T   10499
Wilson D MBE BEM   260499
Bell E T   70400

Short Service Officers

Captains

†Yuill R K BA(Hons)   90698
King O T   290999
Morgan G D   211099
Follett R N D BA(Hons)   90200
Casson-Crook C P BA(Hons) 130600
Penney J BSc(Hons) LIPD 130600
Vyvyan J H BA(Hons)   130600
Allman M R BA(Hons)   101000
Lynch M J D   101000
Bellamy N D MA BA(Hons)   80201

Lieutenants				2nd Lieutenants	
Clare R J *BA(Hons)*	120897	Horsford C S *BSc(Hons)*	141298	Collins J V	70499
McGuire B S *BA(Hons)*	120897	Smith R P *BSc(Hons)*	141298	Sherrington R J	70899
Shaw T E *BSc(Hons)*	131097	Spalton R J *BA(Hons)*	141298	Bowman J J	111299
Wanklyn O C *BSc(Hons)*	161297	Briggs M E *BSc(Hons)*	131299	Tame P P	150400
Cole N A *BA(Hons)*	121098	Roper O N	131299	Read B T	120800
		McGee T S	100400		

THE ROYAL GREEN JACKETS
(43rd and 52nd, King's Royal Rifle Corps, Rifle Brigade)

A Maltese Cross inscribed with selected battle honours thereon a Bugle Horn stringed and encircled with the title of the Regiment all within a wreath of Laurel ensigned with the Crown resting upon a Plinth inscribed "Peninsula" across the Tie a Naval Crown superscribed "Copenhagen 2 April, 1801" all in Silver.

Louisburg, **Quebec 1759**, Martinique 1762, Havannah, North America 1763-64, Mysore, Hindoostan, Martinique 1794, **Copenhagen**, Monte Video, Rolica, Vimiera, **Corunna**, Martinique 1809, Talavera, Busaco, Barrosa, Fuentes d'Onor, Albuhera, Ciudad Rodrigo, **Badajoz, Salamanca, Vittoria**, Pyrenees, Nivelle, Nive, Orthes, Toulouse, **Peninsula, Waterloo**, South Africa 1846-47, Mooltan, Goojerat, Punjaub, South Africa 1851-53, Alma, **Inkerman**, Sevastopol, **Delhi 1857**, Lucknow, Taku Forts, Pekin 1860, New Zealand, Ashantee 1873-74, Ali Masjid, South Africa 1879, Ahmed Khel, Kandahar 1880, **Afghanistan 1878-80**, Tel-el-Kebir, Egypt 1882-84, Burma 1885-87, Chitral, Khartoum, **Defence of Ladysmith**, Relief of Kimberley, Paardeberg, Relief of Ladysmith, South Africa 1899-1902.

The Great War – Mons, Le Cateau, Retreat from Mons, Marne 1914, Aisne 1914, 18, Armentieres 1914, **Ypres 1914, 15, 17, 18**, Langemarck 1914, 17, Gheluvelt, **Nonne Bosschen**, Givenchy 1914, Neuve Chapelle, Gravenstafel, St Julien, Frezenberg, Bellewaarde, Aubers, Festubert 1915, Hooge 1915, Loos, Mount Sorrel, **Somme 1916, 18**, Albert 1916, 18, Bazentin, Delville Wood, Pozieres, Guillemont, Flers-Courcelette, Morval, Le Transloy, Ancre Heights, Ancre 1916, 18, Bapaume 1917, 18, Arras 1917, 18, Vimy 1917, Scarpe 1917, 18, Arleux, Messines 1917, 18, Pilckem, Menin Road, Polygon Wood, Broodseinde, Poelcappelle, Passchendaele, Cambrai 1917, 18, St Quentin, Rosieres, Avre, Villers-Bretonneux, Lys, Hazebrouck, Bailleul, Kemmel, Bethune, Drocourt Queant, Hindenburg Line, Havrincourt, Epehy, Canal du Nord, St Quentin Canal, Beaurevoir, Courtrai, Selle, Valenciennes, Sambre, France and Flanders 1914-18, Piave, Vittorio Veneto, Italy 1917-1918, Doiran 1917, 18, Macedonia 1915-18, Kut al Amara 1915, Ctesiphon, Defence of Kut al Amara, Tigris 1916, Khan Baghdadi, Mesopotamia 1914-18.

Archangel 1919

The Second World War - Defence of Escaut, **Calais 1940**, Cassel, Ypres-Comines Canal, Normandy Landing, **Pegasus Bridge**, Villers Bocage, Odon, Caen, Esquay, Bourguebus Ridge, Mont Pincon, Le Perier Ridge, Falaise, Antwerp, Hechtel, Nederrijn, Lower Maas, Roer, Ourthe, Rhineland, Reichswald, Cleve, Goch, Hockwald, Rhine, Ibbenburen, Dreirwalde, Leese, Aller, North-West Europe 1940, 44-45, Egyptian Frontier 1940, Sidi Barrani, Beda Fomm, Mersa el Brega, Agedabia, Derna Aerodrome, Tobruk 1941, Sidi Rezegh 1941, Chor es Sufan, Saunnu, Gazala, Bir Hacheim, Knightsbridge, Defence of Alamein Line, Ruweisat, Fuka Airfield, Alam el Halfa, **El Alamein**, Capture of Halfaya Pass, Nofilia, Tebaga Gap, Enfidaville, Medjez el Bab, Kasserine, Thala, Fondouk, Fondouk Pass, El Kourzia, Djebel Kournine, Argoub el Megas, Tunis, Hamman Lif, North Africa 1940-43, Sangro, Salerno, Santa Lucia, Salerno Hills, Cardito, Teano, Monte Camino, Garigliano Crossing, Damiano, Anzio, Cassino II, Liri Valley, Melfa Crossing, Monte Rotondo, Capture of Perugia, Monte Malbe, Arezzo, Advance to Florence, Gothic Line, Coriano, Gemmano Ridge, Lamone Crossing, Orsara, Tossignano, Argenta Gap, Fossa Cembalina, Italy 1943-45, Veve, Greece 1941, 44, 45, Crete, Middle East 1941, Arakan Beaches, Tamandu, Burma 1943-44.

Regimental Marches

Quick Marches . . . .(i) Arrangement of 'Huntsman's Chorus' and 'Italian Song'
(ii) Regimental Double Past 'The Road to the Isles'

Agents . . . . Lloyds Bank plc Cox's & King's Branch

Regimental Headquarters . . . . .Peninsula Barracks, Romsey Road, Winchester, Hants, SO23 8TS
(Tel: 01962 828528/31)

Alliances

Canadian Armed Forces . . . . .The British Columbia Regiment (Duke of Connaught's Own)
Princess Patricia's Canadian Light Infantry
The Queen's Own Rifles of Canada
The Brockville Rifles
The Royal Winnipeg Rifles
The Royal Regina Rifle Regiment
Australian Military Forces . . . . .Western Australia University Regiment
Sydney University Regiment
Melbourne University Regiment
New Zealand Army . . . . .1st Battalion, Royal New Zealand Infantry Regiment
6th Battalion (Hauraki), Royal New Zealand Infantry Regiment
South African Defence Forces . . . . . .Durban Light Infantry
The Kaffrarian Rifles
Pakistan . . . . .2nd Battalion The Frontier Force Regiment (Guides)

Affiliations
The Royal Gurkha Rifles

Colonel in Chief . . . . .THE QUEEN

Colonels Commandant . . . .*Maj Gen A R D Pringle *CB CBE* 010199
Maj Gen A M D Palmer CBE 011000

Deputy Colonel Commandant . . . . . . .Colonel *Sir* Geoffrey Pattie pc

Brigadiers

Hayes G DE V W *CBE* rcds psc
hcsc(J)　300693
Cottam N J *OBE BA(Hons)* rcds psc
　300694
Balfour J M J *CBE* psc psc(IND)
hcsc(J) jsdc　300695
Godsal D H *MBE BA(Hons)* rcds psc
jsdc　300696
Manners-Smith M C H *CBE* rcds psc
jsdc　300697
Parker N R psc hcsc(J)　300697

Colonels

Smith M *CBE MC MSc* psc MDA
　300695
Snagge C E M psc psc(AUS)
　300695
Willing H C G psc　300695
Hearn S C *OBE* psc(PAK) jsdc
　300696
Mangnall N J *OBE* psc(n) sq 300697
Jackson J T psc　300698
Gordon J H *MBE* psc† hcsc(J)
　300699
Homer D S J *MBE* psc　300600
_____

Lieutenant Colonels

Carter J S (SL) psc　300687
Poole-Warren J A sq jsdc　300693
Martin R C J *OBE* psc(PAK) *(A/Col 180201)*　300693
Von Merveldt J-D M (SL) psc300693
Athill J A psc jsdc　300695
Carrow R J psc jsdc　300695
Beattie C E I *MA CGIA* psc† 300696
Carter N P *OBE* psc psc(J) *(A/Col 061100)*　300696
Smith M B D *MBE* sq jsdc 300696
Plastow J I S *MBE* psc　300697
Steel R A *MAPM* psc　300697
Brown D W psc(PAK)　300698
Cunliffe J R psc　300698
Tobey D M *MA* psc　300698
Butler E A *MBE BA(Hons) MA* psc†
psc(J)　300699
Schute J C C psc　300699
Winser R P osc(MAL) sq　300600
Worsley A E H *MBE* psc　300600

Majors

Day D C sq　300984
Kitchin M A D sq　300985
Mieville C J sq　300985
Matters R P sq　300986
Schofield P J F *MBE* odc(BE) sq I
　300986
Winsloe M R sq　300991
Foucar A C sowc sq　300992
Bedford S E R sq　300994
Emck T H *MBE BA(Hons)* psc
　300994
Mangham M D W *BA(CombHons)*
psc(W)　300994
Adams M J *BA(Oxon)Hons*
MA(Cantab&Oxon)001 M A (CIT)
psc†　300995
Balls P J A　300995

Doran M J *BA(Hons) MA* psc(J) †
　300995
Maciejewski J C W *BA(Hons)*
MA(Hons) psc(J)　300996
Plummer S P *BA(Hons)* psc(J)
　300996
Sanders P N Y M psc(J)　300996
Corden-Lloyd N C　300997
Thomson R J *MA(Hons)* psc(J)
　300997
Jones H R W　300998
Ovey R J D *BSc(Eng)Hons* 300998
Sulocki C A　300998
Sykes F C *BA(Hons)*　300998
Copinger-Symes T R *BA(Hons)*
　300999
Kitson N J *BA(Hons)*　300999
Wright W S C　300999
Ashmead-Bartlett A S　300900
Bull S H　300900

Captains

Shaw R H S *(A/Maj 011200)* 10495
Dunphie C K *BSc(Hons) (A/Maj 190800)*　141295
Roberts B L G *BA(Hons) (A/Maj 120301)*　110896
Keyte S V R *BA(Hons) (A/Maj 021000)*　131296
Collins C S *LLB(Hons)*　70897
Yeats G R E　70897
Kitson J F *BA(Hons)*　120298
Richardson J A *BSc(Hons)* 121099
Goodwin-Hudson C P *BA(Hons)*
　130600
Turner R J R *BSc(Hons)*　101000
Webster R J *BA(Hons)*　080201

Lieutenants

Hoskins R J *BSc(Hons)*　141298
Higgs J S *BA(Hons)*　90899
Davies G N　221200

2nd Lieutenants

††Wells W J D　50999

Regular Category Late Entry Officers

Lieutenant Colonels

Uyl A　21100

Majors

Sawyer W M　300995
Duncan D J　300996
Smith T L *MBE*　300996
Wright R L　300998

Captains

Jones P M　40195

Special Regular Officers Late Entry

Captains

Poyner G G　10496
McEvoy J J V *BEM*　10497
Watson K A　10497
Harding P H G　10498
Needham J H A *BEM*　10498

Intermediate Regular Officers

Captains

Foster-Brown M E *BA(Hons)* 110896
Mason S D ph　141296
Baring A R　110497
Sanford G J *BSc(Hons)*　120298
Moodie I R J *(A/Maj 050201)*
　80398
Hill J R　140699
Streatfeild R G *BA(Hons)*　90200
Scrase-Dickins W R S *BA(Hons)*
　41000
De La Rue T E ph　210200
Steel H C *BSc(Hons)*　130600

Lieutenants

Grand T H *LLB(Hons)*　120897
Hastings I D *(A/Capt 010500)*
　191297

2nd Lieutenants

††Shuttleworth B A　100900
††Streatfeild R C　100900

Short Service Late Entry Officers

Captains

Edwards G W *MBE*　20899
Gray R V　70400
Robson M R　70400

Short Service Officers

Captains

Runciman A M　10196
Kemp W J S *BA(Hons)* ph 120298
Brooksby G　10498
Wilson M C P *BA(Hons)*　140699
Sale G W A *BSc(Hons)*　120400
Wingfield E M *BAMOD*
　130600
Chapman B H *BA(Hons)*
　101000
Egan W P *BA(Hons)*　101000
Teale N A *BA(CombHons)*　101000
Monk S P *BA(Hons)*　80201

Lieutenants

Burton D A M *BA(Hons) (A/Capt 290800)*　120897
Child S E *BSc(Hons)*　120897
Prideaux W J *BSc(Hons) (A/Capt 270700)*　120897
Stringer R M *BA(Hons)*　120897
Fisher C H *BA(HonsCantab)* 161297
Gayner J R H *BA(Hons)*　161297
Pope J C A *BA*　130498
Verstringhe J D *BSc(Hons)* 140698
Kingsbury E W G *BA(Hons)* 100898
Peters E G L *BSocSc(Hons)* 100898
Barber T B　141298
Husband A J *BA(Hons)*　141298
Morris A R *BA(Hons)*　141298
Posgate I T *BSc(Hons)*　90299
Libby W H *MA(Hons)*　130699
Ridland A　130699
Horrocks A B *BA(Hons)*　90899
Torrance H J R *BSc(Hons)*　90899
Strong A W　61099

Fulton J A G	*BA(Hons)*	131299		*2nd Lieutenants*		Braithwaite J R O	150400
Hill C D F		100400	Brine R O		310100	Corry E C	120800
			Hodson A S		20400	Wood R F T	161200

THE ROYAL IRISH REGIMENT
(27TH (INNISKILLING), 83RD, 87TH AND
THE ULSTER DEFENCE REGIMENT)

An Irish Harp and Crown surrounded by a wreath of shamrock with the regimental title inscribed

Martinique 1762, Havannah, St Lucia 1778, 1796, India, Cape of Good Hope 1806, Maida, Monte Video, Talavera, Bourbon, Busaco, Barrosa, Fuentes d'Onor, Java, Tarifa, Ciudad Rodrigo, Badajoz, Salamanca, Vittoria, Pyrenees, Nivelle, Niagara, Orthes, Toulouse, Peninsula, Waterloo, Ava, South Africa 1835, 1846-7, Sevastopol, Central India, Tel-el-Kebir, Egypt 1882, 1884, Relief of Ladysmith, South Africa 1899-1902.

The Great War – **Mons, Le Cateau,** Retreat from Mons, **Marne 1914,** Aisne 1914, La Bassee 1914, **Messines 1914, 17, 18,** Armentieres 1914, **Ypres 1914, 15, 17, 18,** Nonne Bosschen, **Neuve Chapelle, Loos,** Frezenberg, Aubers, Festubert 1915, Gravenstafel, St Julien, Bellewaarde, **Somme 1916, 18, Albert 1916,** Bazentin, Pozieres, Guillemont, Ginchy, Le Transloy, Ancre, Ancre Heights, **Arras 1917,** Scarpe 1917, Pilckem, Langemarck 1917, Polygon Wood, Broodseinde, Poelcappelle, **Cambrai 1917, 18, St Quentin,** Rosieres, **Hindenburg Line,** Lys, Bailleul, Beaurevoir, Kemmel, Courtrai, Selle, Sambre, **France and Flanders 1914-18,** Kosturino, Struma, **Macedonia 1915-17,** Helles, Landing at Helles, Krithia, **Suvla,** Sari Bair, Landing at Suvla, Scimitar Hill, **Gallipoli 1915-16,** Egypt 1916, **Gaza, Jerusalem,** Tell' Asur, Megiddo, Nablus, **Palestine 1917-18.**

The Second World War - **Dyle,** Withdrawal to Escaut, Defence of Arras, **St Omer-La Bassee,** Ypres-Comines Canal, **Dunkirk 1940, Normandy Landing,** Cambes, **Caen,** Troarn, Venlo Pocket, **Rhine, Bremen,** North-West Europe 1940, 44-45, Two Tree Hill, **Bou Arada,** Stuka Farm, Oued Zarga, Djebel Bel Mahdi, Djebel Ang, **Djebel Tanngoucha, North Africa 1942-43,** Landing in Sicily, Solarino, Simeto Bridgehead, Adrano, **Centuripe,** Salso Crossing, Simento Crossing, Malleto, Pursuit to Messina, **Sicily 1943,** Termoli, Trigno, San Salvo, **Sangro,** Fossacesia, **Gariglino Crossing,** Minturno, **Anzio, Cassino II,** Massa Tambourini, Liri Valley, Rome, Advance to Tiber, Trasimene Line, Monte Spaduro, Monte Grande, **Argenta Gap,** San Nicolo Canal, **Italy 1943-45,** Leros, Middle East 1942, **Malta 1940, Yenangyaung 1942,** Donbaik, **Burma 1942-43.**

Seoul, Imjin, Korea 1950-51

Regimental Marches

Quick March . . . . .Regimental March of the Royal Irish Regiment 'Killaloe'
Slow March . . . .'Eileen Alannah'

Regimental Headquarters . . . . .St Patrick's Barracks, Ballymena, Co Antrim, BT43 7BH
(Tel: 028 25661379)

Alliances

Canadian Armed Forces . . . . .The Princess Louise Fusiliers
2nd Battalion The Irish Regiment of Canada (Sudbury)
The Irish Fusiliers of Canada (Vancouver Regiment)(ceased)
Australian Military Forces . . . . .Adelaide University Regiment
New Zealand Army . . . . .2nd Battalion (Canterbury, Nelson, Marlborough and West Coast)
Royal New Zealand Infantry Regiment
Pakistan Army . . . . .1st Battalion The Punjab Regiment
9th Battalion (Wilde's) The Frontier Force Regiment
South African Defence Force . . . . .South African Irish Regiment
Gibraltar .The Royal Gibraltar Regiment

Colonel in Chief . . . . .HRH *The Duke of* York *CVO ADC*

Colonel . . . . .Gen *Sir* Roger Wheeler *GCB CBE* 010796

Deputy Colonels . . . . .Maj Gen P C C Trousdell *CB* 010796
Brig D Strudley *CBE* 010797
Brig R D O'Lone 200998

Regimental Colonel . . . . .Col J S Douglas *OBE* 010799

		Deverell J D *MPhil* psc	300698	*Lieutenant Colonels*	
		Douglas J S *OBE MSc* psc(IND) jsdc	300698	Jackson A J R *OBE MCGI* psc† jsdc	300689
Brigadiers		Andrew R F C *OBE* psc jsdc	300699	Moody J M W *OBE* sq	300689
		Brooks J C W psc	300699	Thom C E *OBE* psc jsdc	300690
Keenan D H *OBE* psc osc(ZIM) sq jsdc	300600	Harber W R *OBE BA(Hons)* psc	300699	Glover E sq	300691
		Potter A M F *OBE* sq jsdc	300699	Hislop G F *OBE* psc	300692
		Liles I R *OBE* psc	300600	Hodgson K *OBE* psc jsdc	300692
Colonels				Sloan C P C *MBE LLB(Hons)* psc†	300692
Baxter P ST J L *BA* psc†	300696	————		Davidson B R N *MBE* sq	300694
Rowe R G *BA(Hons)* sq	300697			Camp T J *MM* psc	190994

Clements M J   psc(AUS)   300695
Rochelle J M   *MC* odc(US) psc(CAN) osc(KU)   300695
Baverstock N A C   *MBE MA* psc†
(A/Col 151200)   300696
Loudon A J   *MBE BA MA* psc† psc(J)   300696
McCann K G   *OBE BSc(Hons)* sq
jsdc   300696
Reid A L   *OBE BA(Hons)* psc†   300696
Drury F D F   *MBE BSc(Hons)* psc   300697
King P J   *OBE BA(Hons)* psc
psc(CAN)   jsdc   300697
Rollins JW   *MBE BSocSc(Hons) MBA*
psc sq(w)   300697
Urquhart M N S   *OBE* psc   300697
Fordham S A   *OBE* sq jsdc   311297
Bruce R D   psc† jsdc   300698
Buckley W H   *BA(Hons)* psc   300698
Burrell N G   *MA* psc† psc(J)   300698
O'Hanlon M P J   *BSc(Hons)* psc†   300698
Callow L J D   *MBE BEM* sq   300699
Collins T T C   *BSocSc MA* psc†   300699
Stafford I W H   psc   300699
Bettesworth G P   sq jsdc   311299

Majors

Hutchison C L R   sq   300980
Maccarthy-Morrogh J T D   sq   300980
Barry J F G   *MIMGT* sq sq(w)   300981
Linford J   *MIMGT MIPR* sq *(A/Lt Col 011100)*   300982
Meeke B A   sq   300987
Devlin M D C   sq   300989
Harvey P J   *MBE* psc   300989
Jones N H   psc AIS   300989
Jones A D   sq   300990
Maxwell W   *BSc MDA MIMGT MDA* sq(w) †   300990
Russell R G   sq   300990
Spender G F A   psc   300990
Morrissey J C   *AIMGT* tacsc sq   010391
Douglas J C   sq   300992
Kelly M J   sq   300992
Babington D J   *BA(Hons)* sq(w) †   300993
Hart A M   300993
McCord A C J   *MBE MA* psc†   300993
Robinson R A   *BA(Hons) MA* psc†   300993
Barrett R J   *BEng(Hons)*   300994
McFrederick M J   *MA MA(Hons)* psc(J) †   300994
Burke S M   *BA(Hons) MDA*   300995
Cattermull S   *BSc(Hons) MA* psc(J)   300995
Cullen A K   300995
Hartigan M P   *MA* psc   300995
Lai T J   *MA* psc(J)   300995

McGovern M A J   *MA(Hons) MDA* psc(J)   300995
Chalmers D M   300997
Freely E B M   psc(J)   300997
Gillanders R J R   *BA(Hons) GCIM* psc(J)   300997
Boyd R J   300998
Briggs M D   300998
Murdoch M B   300998
Murphy W M   300998
Marks C R   300999
McGrory S M   *BA(Hons)*   300999
Morphew R E R   300999
Crossen R J A   *BA(Hons)*   300900
Guy W P R   *BA(Hons)*   300900
Mason P E M   *BSc(Hons)*   300900
Ruddock M W   *BSc(Econ)Hons*   300900
Walker P A J   *BA(Hons) BTP*   300900

Captains

Toomey B J   *BSc(Hons) (A/Maj 040900)*   060894
Thomson R G J   *BSc(Hons) (A/Maj 041200)*   010495
Vosper J A L   *BSc(Hons) (A/Maj 300500)*   130495
Weir C R J   *BA(Hons)*   110895
Hart R M   *BSc(Hons)*   130796
Shirley S J   *BSc(Hons)*   110896
Taylor N J   *BEng(Hons)*   131296
O'Hara C S   *BA(Hons)*   120298
Given L W G   *BSSc*   100299
Lowry A C   *BA(Hons)*   121099

Lieutenants

Humphries E R   *BSc(Hons)*   130498
Hall B R H   120899

Regular Category Late Entry Officers

Majors

Collins P A   300997
McKeown R W   300997
Turtle T J   *BEM*   300998

Captains

Bailie K B   G *(A/Maj 040799)*   010995

Special Regular Officers Late Entry

Captains

Garner M   220396
Benson H   *(A/Maj 270899)*   010697
McClean J A   010498
Topping K   170898

Intermediate Regular Officers

Majors

Roberts S F   *MBE UD*   310787

Captains

Johnston T A   *BSc(For)*   010495
Hyland G M S   110497
Beck M J   *BSc(Hons)*   160698
Pickett A P   111298
Laverty R J   *BA(Hons)*   100299
Rosenfeld S W   *BA(Hons)*   100299
Rogan T R J   090499
Lundy S M P   *BA(Hons)*   140699
Kane R J   130300
Humphreys J A   *BA(Hons)*   130600
Shannon D G   *BSc(Hons)*   130600
Ahmed N   *BSc(Hons) MSc*   101000
Cleland R D F   *BJUR LLB*   111000

Lieutenants

Simms H A C   161297
Kenny D B   130498
Middleton D G   120499
Holden S C   070700

Short Service Late Entry Officers

Captains

McFarland M C V   010498
Orwin D W   010498
Creggan A J   130999
Fox K J   *BEM*   060400

Short Service Officers

Captains

Bland J R C   140400
Sweeney D J   *BSc(Hons)*   300400

Lieutenants

Crow V R T   *BSc(Hons)*   160697
Rea E J W   *(A/Capt 210600)*   160697
Atkinson S P   *BEng*   020198
Harbison A S   *BSc(Hons)*   140698
Orwin D R   *BSc(Hons)*   100898
Harty P O S   *BSc(Hons)*   141298
McCleery D K   *BEng(Hons)*   090299
Stewart P J   *BA(Hons)*   120499
Duggan M P M   130699
Heaven M D   *BA(Hons)*   130699
Potter M L F   *BA(Hons)*   090899
McIndoe G J   *BSocSc(Hons)*   131299

2nd Lieutenants

Hogg P W   100499
McDonald S S   161200

Short Service Volunteer Officers

Captains

Marks S J J   *BSc(Econ)Hons*   010100

THE PARACHUTE REGIMENT

Upon a spread of wings, an open parachute; above the Royal Crest

"Utrinque Paratus"

The Second World War – **Bruneval, Normandy Landing,** Pegasus Bridge, Merville Battery, **Breville,** Dives Crossing, La Touques Crossing, **Arnhem 1944,** Ourthe, **Rhine, Southern France,** North-West Europe 1942, 44-45, Soudia, **Oudna,** Djebel Azzag 1943, Djebel Alliliga, El Hadjeba, **Tamera,** Djebel Dahra, Kef el Debna, North Africa 1942-43, **Primosole Bridge,** Sicily 1943, Taranto, Orsogna, Italy 1943-44, **Athens,** Greece 1944-45.

Goose Green, Mount Longdon, Wireless Ridge, **Falkland Islands 1982**

Regimental Marches

Quick March . . . . .Ride of The Valkyries
Slow March . . . . .Pomp and Circumstance No 4
Agents . . . . .Holt's Branch, Royal Bank of Scotland plc, Lawrie House, Farnborough,
Hants GU14 7NR
Regimental Headquarters . . . . .Browning Barracks, Aldershot, Hants GU11 2BU (Tel: 01252 349217/642)
Move in 2002 Flagstaff House, Colchester CO2 7SW (Tel: 01206 78 2102)

Alliance

Australian Military Forces . . . . .8th/9th Battalion, The Royal Australian Regiment
Canadian Armed Forces . . . . .The Canadian Airborne Regiment (Disbanded)

Colonel in Chief . . . .*HRH The Prince of Wales KG KT GCB AK QSO ADC*

Colonel Commandant . . . . .Gen *Sir* Mike Jackson *KCB CBE DSO*

Regimental Colonel . . . . .Lt Col S J Barry 100100

	Gallagher J C *BSc(Hons)* psc(a)†	Martin J R sq 300984
	300691	Baillon R J F sq jsdc *(A/Lt Col*
	Rolfe-Smith B P S (SL) psc 300691	*050301)* 300988
Brigadiers	Cobley P R *MBE BA BEd* sq 300692	Kennedy P psc 300989
Freer A R *OBE* rcds psc hcsc(J)	Gandell M P psc *(A/Col 110900)*	Weighell G R sq 300989
311297	300692	De Tscharner Vischer N J sq 300991
	Davies G G *MBE* sq 300693	Orpen-Smellie G R sq *(A/Lt Col*
Colonels	Barry S J psc 300694	*080101)* 300991
Hicks C F *OBE* psc jsdc 300694	Butler P R *MBE* sq 300695	Barrett J M *MBE* psc 300992
Dennison P E *OBE* sq 300695	Farrar P R *BSc* psc† 300695	Fox M A *BA(Hons)* sq 300992
Fletcher H M *CBE LLB(Hons)* psc	Parkinson D C *OBE* psc jsdc 300695	Laurence W J sq 300992
psc(J) jsdc 300695	Chapman C *BA(Hons)* psc psc(J)	Ramirez M R R *MBE BA(Hons)* sq
Crosland J H *CBE MC* sq 300696	300696	300992
Snook A W G *OBE MIMGT MIPD*	Finch C J *BA(Hons) M A (Oxon)*	Wallis G sq *(L/Lt Col 151099)*
psc 300696	*PGCE* psc†	300696	300992
Kershaw R J *BA(Hons)* psc(GE) I	Fletcher H M *LLB(Hons)* psc 300696	Cooper D A *MSc* psc(IND) 300993
jsdc 300697	Kennett A C P *MBE BA(Hons)* psc	Boyns C R 300994
Malkin A V psc(GE) I 300698	*(A/Col 010800)* 300696	Charlton A *MA* psc† 300994
Benest D G *OBE BA(Hons) CGIA*	Smith I W *MBE* sq 300696	Lowe M P *MBE BA(Hons)* psc†
psc† 300699	Hollins P D T psc jsdc 300697	*(A/Lt Col 220201)* 300994
Howard-Gash R H *BSc(Hons)* psc	Davies N R *MBE MC* psc 300698	Waddington C C *MBE* psc† 300994
300699	Hutton N A *BSc MCGI* psc† 300698	Warner D M *BA(Hons)* psc(PAK)
Gibson P M *DSO MBE* psc(AUS)	Bashall J I *BA(Hons) MA* psc†	300994
300600	300699	Baldwin B L psc(J) 300995
Ibbotson J R *MBE BA(Hons)*	Campbell W M *MA* psc(AUS)	Chiswell J R psc 300995
psc(CAN) jsdc 300600	300699	Christie M P psc(J) 300995
Page J D *OBE MA* psc 300600	Handford J D sq 300699	Drakeley L A P *BEd(Hons)* psc(J)
Shaw J D *MA* psc† hcsc(J) 300600	Leigh D M sq 300699	adp 300995
	Lorimer J G *MBE MA* psc 300699	Jackson A T D *BA(Hons)* psc† †
	Mason A D *OBE* sq jsdc 300699	300995
	Baird J N *BSc(Hons) MCGI* psc†	Stratta A M *BSc(Hons)* 300995
Lieutenant Colonels	300600	Thomson R J psc(J) 300995
Gullan P H *OBE MC MIL*	Grant M P *LLB DipLP GCGI*	Turpie P *BEng(Hons) MSc* psc†
odc(AUS) 300686	odc(AUS) psc† † 300600	300995
Martin B K (SL) *OBE BSocSc(Hons)*	Wilford J G *MBE MA* psc 300600	Kemp C P *BA(Hons)* 300996
psc osc(ZIM) 300687		O'Sullivan J S S psc(J) 300996
Argue M H (SL) *MBE MC* sq I	*Majors*	Ryalls P J *BA(Hons)* osc(FR) I*
300689	Houghton M G psc *(A/Lt Col*	300996
Poraj-Wilczynski J J P sq 300690	*011000)* 300983	Williams R J E *BSc(Econ)Hons MDA*
		psc(J) 300996

219

Edgeley M D S *BSc(Econ)Hons*
                                     300997
Hill G P psc(J)   300997
Lavender G W *BA(Hons)* psc(J)
                                     300997
Livingstone G R *BSc(Hons)* 300997
McLeod-Jones M I   300997
Nott M   300997
Wills M R *BEng(Hons) MSc*   300997
Halsall D R *BSc(Hons)*   300998
Harrison A S D *BA(Hons)*   300998
Rogers A M C   300998
Scott R A   300998
Stephenson J R G   300998
Wright A M *BSc(Econ)Hons*   300998
Titcombe C M   300999
Williams H S   300999
Boyd J   300900
Clark A V   300900
Halse T H   300900
Jackson A B *BA(Hons)*   300900
Robson J S   300900
Smith A M *BSc(Hons)*   300900
Sweet A J   300900
Winkle D P   300900

Captains

Clegg C J P *(L/Maj 010698)*
                              131292
Smith F G N *BA(Hons)*   10495
Cradden L P B *BSc(Hons)*   91295
Timms G M *BA(Hons)*   141295
Fuery E J J *BA(Hons)*   60296
Wright G *MA(Hons)*   60296
Jowett A B   130496
Coates J A *BA(Hons) MA*   131296
Pike W J M   110497
Gray M J D F   160697
Radbourne B A *BA(Hons)*   141097
Champion N P F *BSc(Hons)*   120298
Sandry E D   131098
Loden J M H *MA BA(Hons)*   100299

Lieutenants

Sinclair J M   100298
Humm C J *(A/Capt 181099)*
                              100898
Pearson M R E *BA(Hons)*   90899
Thomson R F   90899

2nd Lieutenants

†Cartwright E G R   60998

Regular Category Late Entry Officers

Lieutenant Colonels

Guest G *MBE*   10199
Muir M I R MC   231099
Flavell A *MBE*   120600

Majors

Seekings K V *MBE*   300991
Coutts G sq   300993
Hill J *MBE QGM•*   300993
Lambert D N *MBE*   300993
Sargent K J   300995
Brammer J E *QGM BEM*   300996
Cook G P   300996
Heycock D J   300996

Morgan E W *MM*   300996
Toland F   300997
Edwards R T   300998
McGill W G G *MC*   300998
Robson D F   300998
Collins D J   300999
Maguire S F *DCM*   300999
Young D J *MBE*   300999
Cracknell J E   300900
Gow A D   300900

Captains

Aitken T D *(A/Maj 121296)*
                              100593

Special Regular Officers Late Entry

Majors

Smith W R   300998
Cleaver P *MBE QGM BEM*   300999

Captains

McCulloch W S *(A/Maj 090899)*
                              150396
Ashcroft G K *(A/Maj 280599)*
                              10496
Camp J E   10496
Rodgers P D   10496
Middleton E M *BEM*   170896
Brown A *MBE MM QGM BEM*
                              310397
Hayward S J *MBE*   180597
Coogan A F   10498
Daly M P D *PC*   10498
Davey S *BEM*   10498
Hanlon M D   10498
Hayde R H   10498
Higgs J M *MBE BEM•*.   10498
Lodge P J   10498

Intermediate Regular Officers

Captains

Allum J M   151295
Kewell J A *BEng*   230996
Donnellan R J   201296
Kivell G E *BA(Hons)*   230697
Flynn P A   80797
Noble R J   121297
McManus K J C   201297
Davies J A *BA(Hons)*   120298
Dawson A G   120298
Parry M J   120298
Shervington M W *BA(Hons)*   20498
Blair P A *BA(Hons)*   160698
Tovell M *BA(Hons) MA*   160698
Napier S J   170199
Copperwaite N J *BA(Hons)*   100299
Embleton-Forrest J R   140699
McDonald J S *BA(Hons)*   140699
Lewis R D   60899
Britton S J *BSc(Hons)*   90200
Jackson M E   140400
Richardson C A *BSc(Hons)*   101000

Lieutenants

Jarvis D O W *BSc(Econ)Hons*
  (A/Capt 140999)   90796
Mann D J *BEng(Hons)*   100898

Blakeley D M *(A/Capt 190700)*
                              90899
Kingsbury O J *(L/Capt 011199)*
                              131299
Matthews D J   131299

Short Service Late Entry Officers

Captains

Hall P C   230496
Bowen F D   10497
Lightowler K   30497
Taylor R A   10797
Wright K B   10498
Abols D *DCM*   30898
Russell S A   10499
Hannah K W *MBE BEM*   20499
Ward D K I *BEM*   50499
Noble T K   190499
McNaughton P A   10599
Parry R E   260599
Cameron K   40400
Bailey I P *MM*   60400
Britton D A *QGM*   60400
Dixon B   60400
Goreing A J   60400
Stanbridge D M *QGM*   60400
Simpson M J   160101

Short Service Officers

Captains

Knox R J I *BA(Hons)*   131098
Redding A R *BSc(Hons)*   131098
Richards M A *BA(Hons)*   100299
Murray-Jones G V *BSc(Hons)*
                              140699
Dale N J *BA(Hons)*   130600
Thornett J A *BSc(Hons)*   130600
Worthington D P *BA(Hons)*   130600
Todd R *BSc*   120700
Tancrel J L   280900
Chester D E G *BA(Hons)*   101000
Davison G *BA(Hons)*   101000
Hobbs M J R *BA(Hons)*   101000
McNelis M J *BA(Hons)*   101000
Miller D G K *BA(Hons)*   101000
Wareing A M   101000

Lieutenants

Cansdale M T *BA(Hons) (A/Capt
  111000)*   120297
Gillett E S *MEng(Hons)*   120297
McCurry R R *BScEng(Civil)* 120297
Laing A C *MA(Hons)*   160697
Rostron J A *BSc(Hons)*   120897
Gill M   101297
Keri-Nagy C F *BSc(Hons)*   161297
Morgan S P *BA(Hons)*   161297
Bosley A R *MA(Hons)*   100298
May A R *BSc(Hons)*   130498
Ellicock M J H *BA(Hons)*   100898
Wild R A *LLB(Hons)*   100898
Ainsworth S J   141298
Fisher J R *BEng(Hons)*   141298
Hargreaves H G *BA(Hons)*   141298
Mackay I   141298
Paxton E W   120499
Prior C J *BSc(Hons)*   120499
Sharp L C *BA(Hons)*   120499
Whiting J D C *BA(Hons)*   120499

Burke M A *BA(Hons)*	130699	Thomson H G B	70800	Crouch N J	161200
King M P *BA(Hons) MA*	130699	Hook N A	80800	Smith R J	161200
Taylor M A *BSc(IIons)*	130699	Lincoln-Hope G M	80800		
McGrath S R *BSc*	90899	Wright D C	121200		
Roberts L M *BSc(Hons)*	90899	†Murphy G J	80101		
Butcher J E N *BA(Hons)*	131299				
Pott T B L	131299			**Short Service Volunteer Officers**	
Savage J M	131299	*2nd Lieutenants*			
Hill M C	100400	Pounds J S	100499		
Truett A J E *(A/Capt 220101)*		Swann M A	100599	*Lieutenants*	
	100400	Muhammed U A T	70899	Knighton L H	11200

THE BRIGADE OF GURKHAS

Two Kukris pointing upwards the blades crossed in saltire their cutting edges outwards

Comprising .The Royal Gurkha Rifles (2 Regular Battalions)
The Queen's Gurkha Engineers
Queen's Gurkha Signals
The Queen's Own Gurkha Logistic Regiment

Brigade Headquarters . . . . .Headquarters The Brigade of Gurkhas
Airfield Camp, Netheravon, Wilts SP4 9SF

Colonel Commandant . . . . .Gen *Sir* Sam Cowan *KCB CBE* 010694

Colonel . . . . .Col W F Shuttlewood *OBE* 301000

Chief of Staff . . . . .Maj M L R Forman 160600

Brigade March

Quick March .Yo Nepali

Alliances

Canadian Armed Forces . . . . .The Queen's Own Rifles of Canada

Brunei Armed Forces . . . . .The Royal Brunei Land Forces

Australian Military Forces . . . . .The Royal Australian Regiment

New Zealand Army . . . . .2nd/1st Battalion, The Royal New Zealand Infantry Regiment

The origins of amalgamated Regiments now included in the Brigade of Gurkhas are as follows:

THE ROYAL GURKHA RIFLES

On 1 July 1994

The 2nd King Edward VII's Own Gurkha Rifles (The Sirmoor Rifles)

The 6th Queen Elizabeth's Own Gurkha Rifles

The 7th Duke of Edinburgh's Own Gurkha Rifles and

The 10th Princess Mary's Own Gurkha Rifles amalgamated to form:

The Royal Gurkha Rifles

THE ROYAL GURKHA RIFLES

Two Kukris pointing upwards, the blades crossed left over right, cutting edges outwards,
Ensigned with a crown, all in silver.
Authorised to carry the Queen's Truncheon granted for distinguished Service at Delhi in 1857.

Amboor, Carnatic, Mysore, Assaye, Ava, Bhurtpore, Aliwal, Sobraon, Delhi 1857, Kabul 1879, Kandahar 1880, Afghanistan 1878-80, Tirah, Punjab Frontier, Burma 1885-87.

The Great War - **La Bassee 1914, Festubert 1914, 15, Givenchy 1914, Neuve Chapelle, Aubers, Loos,** France and Flanders 1914-15, **Helles, Krithia, Suvla, Sari Bair, Gallipoli 1915, Suez Canal, Megiddo, Egypt 1915-16, Sharon, Palestine 1918,** Shaiba, **Kut al Amara 1915, 17, Ctesiphon, Defence of Kut al Amara, Tigris 1916, Baghdad, Khan Baghdadi, Sharqat, Mesopotamia 1915-18, Persia 1918, North West Frontier India 1915,** Baluchistan 1918.

Afghanistan 1919

The Second World War - Iraq 1941, Deir es Zor, Syria 1941, **Tobruk 1942, El Alamein,** Mareth, **Akarit,** Djebel el Meida, Enfidaville, **Tunis,** North Africa 1942-43, **Cassino I,** Monastery Hill, Pian di Maggio, Campriano, **Poggio Del Grillo, Gothic Line, Tavoleto, Coriano,** Poggio San Giovanni, Montebello-Scorticata Ridge, **Santarcangelo,** Monte Reggiano, **Monte Chicco,** Lamone Crossing, Senio Floodbank, **Bologna,** Sillaro Crossing, **Medicina,** Giaina Crossing, **Italy 1944-45,** Greece 1944-45, North Malaya, **Jitra,** Central Malaya, Kampar, **Slim River,** Johore, Singapore Island, Malaya 1941-42, **Sittang 1942, 1945,** Pegu 1942, 1945, **Kyaukse 1942, 1945,** Monywa 1942, Shwegyin, **North Arakan, Imphal, Tuitum,** Tamu Road, Shenam Pass, Litan, **Bishenpur, Tengnoupal,** Shwebo, **Mandalay, Myinmu Bridgehead, Fort Dufferin,** Maymo, **Meiktila,** Capture of Meiktila, Defence of Meiktila, **The Irrawaddy, Kyaukmyaung Bridgehead Magwe, Rangoon Road,** Pyabwe, Toungoo, Point 1433, Arakan Beaches, Myebon, **Tamandu, Chindits 1943, 1945, Burma 1942-45.**

Falkland Islands 1982

Regimental Marches

Quick March .The Black Bear
Double March . . . . .The Keel Row
Slow March (Band) . . . . .God Bless The Prince of Wales
Slow March (Pipes) . . . . .The Garb of Old Gaul

Affiliated Regiments
The King's Royal Hussars
The Royal Scots (The Royal Regiment)
The Royal Green Jackets

Agents . . . . .Holts Branch, Royal Bank of Scotland plc, Lawrie House, Farnborough, Hants, GU14 7NR

Colonel in Chief . . . . .HRH The Prince of Wales *KG KT GCB AK QSO ADC*

Colonel . . . . .Brig P T C Pearson psc hcsc

Regimental Secretary . . . . .Lt Col (Retd) W J Dawson *OBE*

Brigadiers	Hughes G A C psc	300698	Archer S A PC sq(w) †	300992
	Palmer J C psc	300600	Forman M L R sq	300993
Pearson P T C *CBE* psc hcsc(J)	Rowe N D J psc	300600	O'Leary T D P sq	300993
311297			Oates Q E sq	300993
Willis D R D'A *CBE MA* psc 300699	*Majors*		Beven R G J *BA(Hons)* sq	300994
	Gay P H *MIMGT* sq	300679	Bullock P C psc	300994
Colonels	Davidson C J L sq	300980	Rigden I A *MA* psc	300994
	Davies G L sq	300980	Thomas I N A *BA(Hons) MA* psc†	300994
McNeil A psc†	300691	Mossop R N C psc *(L/Lt Col*		Warren C F psc	300994
Hayes D G *MBE* sq jsdc	300698	*240194)*	300980	Forbes A W A	300995
Shuttlewood W F *OBE* odc(US) psc	Coleman R H sq	300983	Lawrence J C *MBE MSc FRGS* dis †	
300600	Tekbahadur Gurung *MBE* sq	300985	*(A/Lt Col 050201)*	300995
	Roe M T psc	300986	Nias S R psc(J)	300995
	Wylie Carrick N D sq	300986	Robinson J G psc(J)	300995
Lieutenant Colonels	Gouldstone M P H *MBE* sq *(A/Lt Col*	Stevens N J H sq	300995
O'Donnell T J (SL) *MBE BA* odc(US)	*030301)*	300987	Warrington T C ST J *BA(Hons)* psc†	300995
sq	300686	Manikumar Rai S *MBE* aic sq(w)		Bourne A J P *BA(Hons) MA* psc(J)
Purves J J *MBE FRGS* psc	300695		300987	300996
Bijaykumar Rawat psc	311295	Clesham B P *MBE* ndc nadc odc(IT)	Jones A G	300996
Theobald M W L psc(GE)	300696	sq	300988	O'Keeffe G M *BSc(Hons) MA* psc(J)
Crane S D *OBE MA* psc†	300697	Glanville G R J *MBE* sq	300988	300996
Holley L A *MBE*	300697	Dewing S J M psc	300989	Logan I ST C *BSc(Hons)* psc(J)
Lillingston-Price M M *OBE* psc	Griffith A P M psc *(A/Lt Col*		300997
300697	*060900)*	300991	Wombell C D	300997
	Redding J P *GCGI* psc †	300991		

Elliot J A MA(Hons)   300998
Darby C B   300999
Hannah P W BA(HonsCantab)   300999
Lawrence F M BA(Hons)   300999
Blackford M S   300900
Gilderson S J P   300900
O'Donnell D G F BA(Hons)   300900
Robinson D J BA(Hons)   300900
Strickland G M BA(Hons)   300900

Captains

Estyn-Jones D BA(Hons) (A/Maj
310599)   151095
Birch J N B BA(Soc)Hons   141295
Fowkes L E BEng(Hons)   10796
Hill A P   70896
Naylor Q W M BA(Hons)   110896
Daines R J ph   141296
Marcandonatos S C BEng(Hons)
141097
Rea F J LLB   160698
Douglas R A L   140699
Timmis C E   121099
Branch D H   90200
Beresford-Jones P G BA(Hons)
80600
Davies J P   101000
Murray J C BLE(Hons)   080201

2nd Lieutenants

††Picton C R   220997
††Janvrin E D C   50999

Intermediate Regular Officers

Captains

Jackman T C M   70896
Reedman M H   (A/Maj 280800)
131296
Pitchfork P R G BA(Hons) (A/Maj
010900)   170197
Marafono W H BA(Hons) MSc
131098
Alexander-Cooper A G BA(Hons)
100299
Hoy D P S BSc(Hons) (A/Maj
110700)   100299
Hinxman T L B BA(Hons)   90200
Ross C R BSc(Hons)   130600
Dennis C F BA(Hons)   080201

Lieutenants

Kefford W R   (A/Capt 131299)
100898

Short Service Late Entry Officers

Captains

Upadhya S   (A/Maj 161000)
10792
Dewan S   10400
Gurung S   10400

Short Service Officers

Captains

O'Malley C G S BA(Hons)   160698
Martin T B   111298

Briggs C D R BA(Hons)   310300
Ganpatsingh R E BSc(Hons)   130600
Miller G N   101000
Pike T W BEng(Hons)   101000

Lieutenants

Boryer C R BA(Hons) (A/Capt
250900)   120897
Hakes R T BA(Hons)   120897
Kinsella-Bevan D B BA(Hons)
161297
Crowe C N A BA(Hons)   140698
Garside S J BA(Hons)   140698
Follett J C R BA(Hons)   100898
Hyman D A BSc(Hons)   100898
Jones J W A BSc(Hons)   100898
Lyle I C BSc(Hons)   100898
Sale A B J   141298
James M J BSc(Hons)   130699
Meredith J C BA(Hons)   130699
Aucott N J BA(Hons)   90899
Lea N S F BA(Hons)   131299
Pettigrew J S   121200

2nd Lieutenants

Chandler S W M   10599
Gifford B P   181099
Pack D T   111299
Barker T D P   150400
Roberts A M   161200

**Short Service Commission
(Gurkha)**

Captains

Suryaprasad Upadhya   010499
Sankar Gurung   010400
Sudan Dewan *BEM*   010400

**The Gurkha Commissioned
Officers**

Queen's Gurkha Officers

Majors

Lalitchandra Dewan   150698
Tikendradal Dewan   190798
Indrakumar Limbu   161199
Dharambahadur Gurung *MVO*
200300
Hitman Gurung   230600
Somamtshering Sherpa   080900
Bhimbahadur Gurung *MVO*   011200

Captains

Jagmohan Rai   280794
Gangabahadur Gurung   280795
Lalitbahadur Gurung   011095
Laxmiparsad Limbu   171095
Chandrabahadur Gurung   130296
Gaubahadur Gurung   010796
Kamalprasad Gurung   010796
Laxmibhakta Bantawa   171196
Hitman Gurung   010798
Narkaji Gurung   010798
Rajendra Gauchan   060798
Lokbahadur Gurung   020898
Tejbahadur Gurung   180898

Harkaraj Rai   180898
Dhanbahadur Rai   180898
Nirmal Rai   271098
Bishnukumar Pun   091198
Harkaraj Rai   061298
Bhaktabahadur Limbu   090299
Dilkumar Rai   090299
Raju Gurung   210299
Hikmatbahadur Gurung   010799
Imankumar Gurung   010799
Hemantkumar Rai   010799
Hemchandra Rai *BEM*   010799
Devraj Gurung   160799
Shivakumar Limbu *MBE*   200799
Khusiman Gurung   180899
Panchabir Rai   020899
Ashokkumar Rai   110100
Gobindababu Rai   110100
Guptaman Gurung   200300
Krishnaparsad Gurung   010400
Shamsher Gurung   050600
Padambahadur Limbu   110700
Tikaram Limbu   110700
Hembahadur Thapa   110700
Rajendra Sherchan *MBE*   310700
Dilbahadur Gurung   010401
Jayaprasad Gurung   010401
Rambahadur Pun   010401

Lieutenants

Nabinkumar Siwa   090196
Lokbahadur Pun   200397
Bombahadur Limbu   260298
Muktijang Gurung   060398
Kishorkumar Gurung   220498
Purnabahadur Gurung   010798
Madankumar Gurung   010798
Rane Gurung   090798
Rajan Mall   190798
Bhaktabahadur Thapa   020898
Bishnuparsad Gurung   180898
Krishnakumar Thapa   180898
Bhuwaniparsad Limbu   010998
Sahabir Rai   271098
Umeshkumar Pun   271098
Yadapkumar Gurung   151198
Khusiman Gurung   231198
Purnaprasad Limbu   270199
Malin Pradhan   090299
Indrabahadur Gurung   210299
Manbahadur Rai   300399
Kaji Sherpa   300399
Sovitbahadur Hamal Thakuri   010799
Durgabahadur Ramjali Pun   010799
Dhanbahadur Kunwar   010799
Khimbahadur Thapa   010799
Hitman Gurung   010799
Chandrabahadur Limbu   200799
Yubaraj Tamang   070999
Kishorekumar Gurung   070999
Lalbahadur Gurung   181099
Yambahadur Khatri *MBE*   151199
Krishnkumar Rai   110100
Siriparsad Limbu   260100
Surendra Gurung   200300
Amarsing Thapa   010400
Pumabahadur Gurung   050600
Balram Ghale   110700
Santosh Ghale   110700
Bijaykumar Limbu   110700

224

Gyanbahadur Limbu	110700	Thamanbahadur Gurung	310700		
Dilkumar Rai	110700	Ashok Sen	310700	Bijayant Sherchan	031100
Ganeshkumar Rai	110700	Yambahadur Rana	280800	Angphula Sherpa	220201
Dammarbahadur Shahi	140700	Samundra Gurung	190900	Padambahadur Gurung	010401

THE QUEEN'S GURKHA ENGINEERS

Two kukris points upwards the blades crossed in saltire, their cutting edge outwards, surmounted by the Royal Engineers' grenade, over the handles a scroll with the motto "Ubique". The whole is surrounded by a wreath of laurel surmounted by a Queen's crown issuant thereon from the wreath a scroll; The Queen's Gurkha Engineers'.

Regimental Marches

Pipes

Quick March . . . . .Far O'er the Sea

Military Band

Quick March . . . . .Wings

Affiliated Corps

The Corps of Royal Engineers

Affiliated Colonel-in-Chief . . . .*Her Majesty* THE QUEEN

Colonel . . . . .Lt Gen A D Pigott *CBE* 090300

Short Service Commission (Gurkha)		Queen's Gurkha Officers			
				Dalbahadur Limbu	010699
				Dhanbahadur Chand	010401
				Dudhprasad Gurung	010401
Majors		*Majors*			
Mahendraprasad Gurung	300900	Damar Ghale	280599		
		Captains		*Lieutenants*	
Captains		Chitrabahadur Gurung	010798	Benuprasad Limbu	010799
Hombahadur Limbu	010198	Dilparsad Limbu	010798	Bhismaraj Gurung	050799

226

QUEEN'S GURKHA SIGNALS

The front of the figure of Mercury, holding a caduceus in the left hand, on a globe, all in silver, supported in his dexter hand. The Crown in gold, two kukris in saltire the blades upwards and inwards also in silver, thereunder a scroll inscribed *"Certa Cito"* and below nine laurel leaves.

Regimental March
Quick March . . . . .Scotland The Brave

Affiliated Corps
Royal Corps of Signals

Affiliated Colonel-in-Chief . . . .*HRH* THE PRINCESS ROYAL *KG KT GCVO QSO*
Colonel . . . . .Brig S M A Lee *OBE* 010295

		Rajendraman Gurung	151099	Yamkumar Gurung	010400
Queen's Gurkha Officers		Yogesh Thapa	010400		
		Krishnabahadur Gurung	010400		
Majors				**Short Service Commission**	
Navindrabikram Gurung	200300	*Lieutenants*		**(Gurkha)**	
Captains		Dhanbahadur Gurung	010798		
		Mahendrakumar Limbu	151099	*Majors*	
Santa Pun	050997	Yamhahadur Rana	121199	Krishna Gurung *BEM*	020493
Hitman Gurung	070299	Nirmalkumar Bhattachan	250200		

THE QUEEN'S OWN GURKHA LOGISTIC REGIMENT

An eight-pointed star in silver, thereon a Scroll inscribed *"Queen's Own Gurkha Transport Regiment"*. Issuant therefrom a wreath of laurel all in Gold, over all two kukris in saltire, the blades Silver, the hilts Gold, ensigned with the Royal Cypher in Gold.

Regimental March

Quick March . . . . .On Parade

Affiliated Corps
Royal Logistic Corps

Affiliated Colonel-in-Chief . . . .*HRH* THE PRINCESS ROYAL *KG KT GCVO QSO*

Colonel . . . . .Maj Gen P C C Trousdell 271093

Queen's Gurkha Officers		Krishnabahadur Gurung	010797	Sovitbahadur Hamal Thakuri	010799
		Rudrabahadur Sahi	010798	Mekhbahadur Gurung	260799
Majors				Khimprasad Gauchan	221199
Chitraj Limbu *MVO*	060300	*Lieutenants*		Shobhaman Golay	010400
Captains		Gyanbahadur Limbu	010797	Tirtharaj Gurung	310700
Bhalaman Rai	281095	Dudman Gurung	010798		

SPECIAL AIR SERVICE REGIMENT

A winged representation of King Arthur's Sword Excalibur striking downwards
woven on a shield with the motto "Who Dares Wins"

The Second World War – **North-West Europe 1944-45, Tobruk 1941, Benghazi Raid, Torbruk 1941, North Africa 1940-
43, Landing in Sicily,** Sicily 1943, Termoli, Commacci, Italy 1943-45, Greece 1944-45, Adriatic, Middle East 1943-44
1943-44

Falkland Islands 1982, Gulf 1991, Western Iraq

Regimental March

Quick March . . . . .March du Regiment Parachutist Belge
Slow March . . . . .Lillie Marlene

Alliances

Australian Military Forces . . . . .The Special Air Service Regiment
New Zealand Army . . . . .1st New Zealand Special Air Service Group

ARMY AIR CORPS

A laurel wreath surmounted by The Crown within the wreath, an eagle

The Guidon
In the first corner the badge of the Glider Pilot Regiment. In the second and third corners the AAC monogram and in the fourth corner the badge of the Royal Artillery.

Falkland Islands 1982

Gulf 1991

Wadi al Batin

Regimental Marches

Quick March . . . . .Recce Flight
Slow March . . . . .The Thievish Magpie

Agents . . . . .Royal Bank of Scotland plc, Holt's Farnborough Branch,
Laurie House, Victoria Road, Farnborough, Hants GU14 2HJ

Corps Depot . . . . .School of Army Aviation, Middle Wallop, Stockbridge, Hants SO20 8DY
(Tel: 01980-674272)
(nearest railway station Andover)

Regimental Headquarters AAC . . . . . . .HQ Director Army Aviation, Middle Wallop, Stockbridge, Hants SO20 8DY
(Tel: 01980-674426)

Alliance

Australian Military Forces . . . . .Australian Army Aviation

Colonel in Chief . . . . .HRH The Prince of Wales KG KT GCB AK QSO ADC 060292

Colonel Commandant . . . . .Gen *Sir* Michael Walker *GCB CMG CBE ADC Gen* 200594

Brigadiers

McQueen P D P psc(AUS) ph
                                300694
Coward G R *VC OBE* psc† hcsc(J)
ph   300600
Folkes R P D *OBE ADC BA(Hons)*
psc ph   300600

Colonels

McMahon W A psc† ph pl 300693
Blount C sq ph(cfs) ph(i) ph 300695
Goodsir J *CBE* sq ph 300697
Thursby N D D sq ph 300697
Goble T J L *MA* psc† ph 300699
Greenhalgh J G *DFC* psc ph 300600
Husband D *OBE BSc(Hons)* psc† ph
                                 300600

_____

Lieutenant Colonels

Hall N S C (SL) *MBE* sq ph 300686
Schofield M psc ph 300689
Parker N P sq ph 300690
Westcott A *CGIA* psc† ph 300690
Joyce D K psc ph 300691
Simkins A J N sq ph 300691
Stirk W J Q sq ph(i) ph sq(w)
                                 300691
Wilton C J A nadc sq ph 300691
Lawes R J (SL) sq ph 300692
Gibson A M psc ph 300693
Bourne J A sq ph 300694
Rowland-Jones S D *MBA* sq ph
                                 300694

Walch C W sq ph 300694
McDonnell J M P psc(AUS) ph
                                 300695
Parish J B *BA(Hons)* psc† I* ph
                                 300695
Roberts P C *MBE* psc ph *(A/Col*
050101)   300695
Andrews R M *BSc(Hons) MRAeS*
MInstD MIMGT psc† ph 300696
Caplin N J *BSc(Hons) CGIA* psc† ph
                               300696
Edwards P A W *MBE* sq ph 300696
Manning C W sq ph 300696
Moss N J W *BSc(Hons)* psc† ph
                               300696
Bourne A P sq ph 300697
Eustace R J sq ph 300697
Oatts A R B psc† ph 300697
Rutter J W sq I* I ph 300697
Sinclair-Kemp B psc ph 300697
Stewart C J P sq ph 300697
Thomson I R psc† psc(J) ph 300697
Collett C *MA(Hons) GCGI* psc† psc
ph sq(w)   300698
Mackie I D sq ph 300698
Marshall S W *GCGI* psc† sq ph
                               300698
Northam H C *MBE* sq ph(cfs) ph
                               300698
Sivewright W J sq jsdc ph sq(w)
                               300698
Turner D P psc† psc(a)† ph 300698
Wright P J ph sq(w) tp 300698
Baulf C H G *MBE* sq ph 300699
Chafer K I psc ph 300699
Hogan C D sq ph 300699
Piper P G sq ph 300699

Sharpe A P *BSc(Hons) MSc ARCS*
psc† ph sq(w) tp 300699
Short D S *BA(Hons)* psc ph 300699
Welch S N *BSc* sq ph 300699
Burton I R *BSc(Hons) IEng MRAeS*
ph(i) ph sq(w) tp 300600
Butler B R E sq ph 300600
Cubbin M A *MA* psc† ph 300600
Eadie P A psc(n)† psc(n) ph 300600
Hyslop C S sq ph 300600
Mellows W A N sq ph 300600
Venn D F *BA(Hons) MSc* dis ph †
                               300600

Majors

Scott-Hopkins R M sq ph 300980
Southgate R L *AFM* sq ph 300982
Hall G W *BSc(Hons)* sq ph 290384
Webb A K *MSc AMRAeS* MESE ph
sq(w) tp 300985
Byrne I B sq ph sq(w) ais 300986
Adams P G *AFC BSc(Hons)* psc
ph(cfs) ph(i) ph 300987
Tracy R H sq ph(i) ph 300987
Davidson I R D sq ph 300988
Sheeley G J *AFC BA(Hons) MIL* sq
ph 300988
Tanner S R S sq ph 300988
Fagg D A sq ph 300989
Betteridge M J sq ph 300990
Floyd H A ph(cfs*) ph(cfs) ph(i) ph
                               300990
Sharp T A sq ph 300990
Crosby R I gw ph sq(w) 300991
Gibson N D *BSc MSc* dis ph sq(w)
                               300991

McNulty P J   ph sq(w) tp   300991
Barbone A W   *DipTPM PGDA MSc*
ph sq(w) t   300992
Coburn M A   *BSc(Hons)* sq ph sq(w)
†   300992
Ford G J   *MSc* gw ph sq(w)   300992
Hindley R J W   *BSc MSc* gw ph sq(w)
                                  300992
Hopkins N ST J   sowc sq ph   300992
Spink G E   *MSc* gw ph sq(w)   300992
Terrett E P G   ph(cfs) ph(i) ph sq(w)
                                  300992
Wellesley A E   ph sq(w) † *(A/Lt Col*
120201)   300992
Wiley A G C   *MSc* gw ph sq(w)
                                  300992
Greenhalgh M R   odc(GE) psc ph
                                  300993
Haig A J R   sq ph   300993
Hazou J N   pl(cfs) ph pl   300993
Mitchell R J   *BEng(Hons) MSc* gw ph
sq(w) †   300993
Bullen P J S   sq ph   300994
Le Gresley E M   psc(J) ph(i) ph
                                  300994
Leakey R A   *BA(Hons) PGCE* ph
sq(w) †   300994
Nicholas D A G   *BA(Hons)* cafs psc†
ph(i) ph   300994
Watts N J I   psc ph(cfs) ph   300994
Whiteside M C   *BSc(Hons) FRICS*
psc† ph   300994
Barnard S   *MA* psc(J) ph   300995
Baxter M R   *BEng(Hons)* ph   300995
Birkett A A R   *BSc(Hons) MSc* psc(J)
ph   300995
Claydon C J   *MA* psc(J) ph   300995
Dalton N J   *BSc(Hons) MSc* psc(J) dis
ph   300995
Felton R F P   *MBE BSc(Hons)* psc†
psc ph   300995
Geal A   sq ph   300995
Goodman A J   ph pi   300995
Gossage A A   psc(J) ph   300995
Griffiths T Y   ph   300995
Himbury S J E   *BSc(Hons) MDA*
MIMGT sq ph   300995
Keith A R K   ph   300995
Meyer D H   *AFC BSc(Hons)* ph(cfs)
ph(i) ph   300995
Tucker A V   *BSc(Hons)* psc† ph
                                  300995
Webber J   ph pl sq(w)   300995
Budd F G   *BA(Hons) MSc* psc(J) gw
ph   300996
Falconer G P   *BSc* psc(J) ph   300996
Green R M   *BSc(Hons) MDA MA*
psc(J) MDA ph   300996
Houlton A V   ph   300996
Iceton A   *AFC* ph tp   300996
Illingworth J T E   *BA(Hons) MSc*
psc(J) ph   300996
Orr J C M   *BSc(Hons)* ph sq(w) tp
                                  300996
Osborne D G S   *BSc(Hons)* ph
                                  300996
Thompson N F   ph sq(w)   300996
Barnes M J   *MCGI* ASQ ph   300997
Bryant J D   ph   300997
Dick G H   ph   300997
Hibbert R J   sq ph   300997
Lambert A N   ph   300997

Leach S C   ph tp   300997
Marlow I D   *MSc MSc* sq gw ph
                                  300997
Mills A M   *BSc(Hons) BSc(Hons)*
MSc dis ph sq(w)   300997
Owen G L   *MA(Hons)* ph   300997
Scarratt W A   ph   300997
Sexton N D   *BA(Hons) MA* psc(J) ph
                                  300997
Smith M J V   ph   300997
Turner S   ph   300997
Anderson J F M   ph   300998
Cash A T G   *BA(Hons)* ph   300998
Cook P M   ph   300998
Davies C   *BEng(Hons)* ph   300998
Holmes D   ph   300998
McClure S   ph   300998
McGinty M S   ph   300998
Palmer A H   *BEng(Hons) MDA* ph
                                  300998
Shaw B   *BSc(Hons)* ph   300998
Banks N A   *BSc(Hons)* ph   300999
Butler C L S   *BA(Hons)* ph   300999
Clements I S   *BSc(Hons)* ph   300999
Facer J M   ph   300999
Logan P D O   *BSc(Hons)* ph   300999
Moores C A   ph   300999
Power A J   ph   300999
Suddards P D   *BA(Econ)Hons* ph
                                  300999
Tennant P P   *MA(Hons)* ph   300999
Tilley G A   ph   300999
ØDennison T E S   *BSc(Hons)* ph
                                  300900
Greenacre J W   ph   300900
Miller J   *BSc(Hons) ARCS* ph   300900
Smith I D   *BSc(Hons)* ph   300900
Wharmby N C   ph(cfs) ph tp
                                  300900

Captains

Lamb A W   ph   150291
De Labilliere S D D   ph   110895
Olney R A   *BSc(Hons)* ph   110895
Price N D B   ph   151295
Cook J P   *BEng(Hons)* ph   120496
ØPennell F S   ph   130496
Thornton D J   ph   80796
Trower D K P   *BSc(Hons)* ph *(A/Maj*
140201)   131296
James M S   ph   110497
Butterworth E J   *BSc(Hons)* ph
                                  70897
Lytle C M S   ph   70897
Howard-Higgins C M G   ph   80897
Martin S J   ph   80897
Peake T N   ph(i) ph   80897
Amlot D C J   *MBE* ph   121297
Jarvill R G   ph   121297
Senior J S   *BSc(Hons)* ph   121297
Hayhurst P M   *BSc(Hons)* ph   70898
Maloney R E   *LLB(Hons)* ph   70898
Anderson W I E   ph   111298
Feenan P G   *BA(Hons)* ph   111298
Keating M R   ph   111298
Whitehead B R   ph   90499
Zvegintzov S D J   ph   90499
Lodge S J   ph(i) ph   120599
Threapleton R   *BSc(Hons)* ph   60899
Wilkins D M   *BA(Hons)* ph   60899
Youngs R E A   *BSc(Hons)* ph   60899
Ackrill M J D   ph   101299

Bourne S P A   *BA(Hons)* ph   101299
Dawson N S   101299
Tedman P T   ph   290700
Hargreave T M M   120800

Lieutenants

Matheson J I D   *BA(Hons)*   160697
Bird A R   *BA(Hons)* ph   161297
Scott C W D   ph   100898
Ball R D H   141298
Etherton S W D   90299
Hart S E   90299
Parnell J L   *BA(Hons)*   90899

2nd Lieutenants

††Barr J T M   220997
Lee J L   220997
†English N G   60998
†Higgins A J N   60998

**Regular Category Late Entry
Officers**

Lieutenant Colonels

Ryan J N   ph(cfs) ph(i) ph   270799
Joicey R A   051299

Majors

Anderson E   *MBE AFC* sq ph(cfs*)
ph   300992
Hoal W J   *BSc(Hons)* sq ph   300992
Ions C J   *MBE BA(Hons)*   300992
Besseling R P   *BEM FISM*   300993
Davis J   *BEM* ph(cfs) ph   300993
Dunscombe C J   ph(cfs) ph(i) ph
                                 300993
Richie P J   *MRAeS* ph(i) ph tp
                                 300993
Ward J H   *MBE* sq   300993
O'Brien W C   *DFM&bar.* ph(cfs)
ph(i) ph   11093
Lawton J S   *AFC* ph(cfs) ph(i) ph
                                 300994
Meech L K   300994
Rennie D   300994
Roberts D F E   ph(cfs) ph   300994
Douglass P K   ph(cfs) ph(i) ph
                                 300995
Gardiner H J   300995
Martin P J   ph(cfs) ph(i) ph   300995
Barton P   sq   300996
Gray A T   ph(i) ph   300996
Herlihy W G   *MBE*   300996
Walsh I G   *BEM* ph(cfs) ph(i) ph
                                 300997
White W J   300998
Chick C G   *MBE*   300900

Technical Aviation Instructors

Bailey K V   *AFC* ph(cfs) ph *Maj*
                                 011084

Special Regular Officers Late Entry

Majors

Blyth J R   300995
Barratt P   ph(i) ph   180797

Hall I P   ph(cfs) ph(i) ph   300997
Pidgeon S J   ph   300997
Pring A J   AMIEIE ph(cfs) ph(i) ph
300998
Green S P   ph(cfs) ph   300999
Manning M P   ph(cfs) ph   300999
Western M   ph(cfs) ph   300600
Rumgay L   300900
Torpy M W   AFM ph(cfs) ph   300900
Wright J D   ph pl   300900

Captains

Nicholson D   (A/Maj 270300)
101195
Bennion S   200496
Ince B L   260996
Blair R S   ph(i) ph   30197
Lambert R   ph(cfs) ph(i) ph (A/Maj
280599)   40497
Elsey S R   130697
Bishop R G   200897
Rowell J F   110997
Whitehouse N P   91097
Whittle A   MBE ph(cfs) ph   120298
Cavanagh A R   10498
Cutting R I   10498
Daly C M   ph(cfs) ph   10498
Galston M P   ph(cfs) ph(i) ph   10498
Graham S P   ph   10498
Humphrey K J   10498
Pengilly S C   ph(i) ph   10498
Sterenberg A F   10498
Todd I W   10498
Tregaskes T C   BEM   10498
Wood S P   10498
Gell D A   ph   250598
Bennett P E   131098

Intermediate Regular Officers

Majors

Willis D J   ph(i) ph pl   300997
McBride T D   gw ph(i) ph   300999
Godfrey A D   ph(i) ph   300900

Captains

Thwaites J M   ph   30390
Burnand M S   BEng ph   141295
Donovan J M   BSc(Hons) ph   120496
King J P   BEng(Hons) ph   110896
Willman A H   ph   110497
Corrigan D   BEng(Hons)   240497
Inman A P   ph(i) ph   80897
Wheeler P R D   80897
Taylor J E   MA(Hons) ph   90897
Button P D   BSc(Hons) ph   141097
Bell G E   MEng(Hons)   291097
Thompson D L   BSc(Hons) ph
121297
Gordon A O   ph   260398
James D A   ph(i) ph   90498
Whelan M G   BSc(Hons)   90498
Whitehead G P   ph(cfs) ph(i) ph
90498
Rundle G M   BSc(Hons) ph   210199
Whipp C K   ph   90499

Lieutenants

McKenzie J F   ph (A/Capt 180499)
130498

2nd Lieutenants

††Harwood C C   100900
††Sugden R F   100900

Short Service Late Entry Officers

Majors

King P J   ph(cfs) ph(i) ph   300995
Johnson T   300997
Bennett R G   300998
Dempsie J W   BEM   300998
Davies R S   MBE ph   300999

Captains

Pike E D D   ph(cfs) ph(i) ph   100292
Turner R   ph   70396
Barraclough S M   100797
Best G J   ph   10498
Clarke S J G   ph pl   10498
Judd P S   ph(cfs) ph   10498
Marshall K A   ph(i) ph   10498
McGee H   10498
Richards A B   10498
Wilson C P   ph   10498
Durrant C G   ph   60498
Pocock G C   110598
Vaughan A P   ph(cfs) ph(i) ph
310898
Martin P D   20998
Hesslewood K B   280998
Thompson R   11098
Smith G M   ph(cfs) ph(i) ph   301198
Molloy R C   MBE   11298
Martin M H   ph   31298
Anderson K   ph   271298
Lea C M   ph(cfs) ph(i) ph   10199
Barnes M G   ph pl   60199
McPhee W A   ph(cfs) ph(i) ph 60199
Cranch P A   AFC ph(cfs) ph(i) ph
10299
McKeown N C   MBE ph(cfs) ph(i) ph
120499
Manzur A A W   ph(i) ph   130999
Monk D J   ph(cfs) ph(i) ph   130999
Armstrong E K   200999
Bayley P   ph(i) ph   41099
Catchpole D J   41099
Weetman J   41099
Harding T R F   ph(i) ph   261099
Moyes A L   ph(i) ph   151299
Smart R W   ph(cfs) ph(i) ph   140100
Redwood D A   310100
Ramage R L   130300
Burnett R F   ph(cfs) ph(i) ph   30400
Dundas R   30400
Hearn C C   30400
Kerr J   30400
Sargent D G   30400
Straw P   30400
Taylor T   30400
Wright J P   30400
Hoyle A S   260900
Peters M L   201100
Hickson G L   111200

Short Service Officers

Captains

Sheriff P M   BA(Hons) ph   121297
Finlay M J D   BSc(Hons) ph   20498

Minards R F   ph   90498
Wilkes N C   BSc(Hons) ph   90498
Johnston I   BSc(Hons) ph   120698
Knight N J   BA(Hons) ph   120698
McEwen C G   BSc(Hons) ph   120698
Stein R G J   BA(Hons) ph   120698
Frankel T H   BEng(Hons) ph   70898
Mawer R J   BEng(Hons) ph   100998
Campbell P B   BEng(Hons) ph
91098
Robb M D   BSc(Hons) ph   70299
Morgan E J A   BA(Hons) ph   120299
Brown M J   BEng(Hons) ph   90499
Cameron-Davies M G   ph   90499
Greenwood M T   BSc(Econ)Hons ph
60899
Tench N F   BSc(Hons) ph   141099
Peters I J S   BSc(Hons) ph   101299
Rogers A T   BSc(Hons) ph   160100
Hill S R G   BSc(Hons) ph   100200
Lees J C H   BSc(Hons) ph   120200
Neville M J   MA(Hons) ph   120200
Passmore N J   BA(Oxon)Hons ph
120200
Phayre R K K   BEng(Hons) ph
120200
Punchard D B   BSc(Hons) ph   120200
†Williams A P   10300
†Blackman D E C   200300
Blee A M   BSc(Hons) ph   140400
Williams D E   BA(Hons) ph   80600
Dunlop R A   ph   160600
Eriksen D H   BA(Hons) ph   160600
Geering T J   BA(Hons) ph   120800
Gilks A M   BEng(Hons) ph   120800
Law H C E   BA(Hons) ph   41000
Stobo A P   BSc(Hons) ph   111000
Songhurst-Thonet P V   BSc(Hons) ph
181100
Waugh J A T   BA(Hons) ph   181100
Milne A P   BA(Hons) MA ph   161200
ØNicholson L A H   BMus(Hons) ph
161200
Cuthill R T   BSc ph   161297

Lieutenants

Stirling A C   BSc(Hons) ph   161297
ØDingsdale H M   BA(Hons)   100298
Moore T R   100298
Murrell J R   MEng(Hons) ph   100298
Roberts M D   BA(Hons)   100298
Van Beever J G   BA(Hons) ph
100298
Wilcock M P   BEng(Hons) ph
130498
O'Leary G J   BSc(Hons)   140698
Dean P J   BEng(Hons) ph   100898
ØFrater R S   BSc(Hons) PGCE ph
100898
Ponde A T   BSc(Hons)   100898
Pritchard J G   BSc(Hons) ph   100898
Pillans R K   BEng(Hons)   21298
ØHughes E M   BA(Hons)   131298
ØCliff A E   BSc(Hons)   90299
Clark S G G   BSc   120499
Hare A C R   BSc(Hons)   120499
Loxton D R   BSc(Hons)   120499
ØMonk M K E   BSc(Hons)   130699
Cunningham R D   90899
Eeles W T H   BA(Hons)   90899
Foran M D   BEng(Hons)   90899
Hillman C P G A   BSc(Hons)   90899

McKenzie J R K *BA(Hons)*	90899	
Pittaway T W J *BSc(Hons)*	90899	
Robinson S D *BA(Econ)Hons*	90899	
Foreman E *BEng(Hons)*	250999	
Ward M B ph	11099	
Ashley R N	11199	
Guy D J *BSc(Hons)*	131299	
Lewis P H *BA(Hons)*	131299	

Murray J C ph	131299
Nicoll A M V *BSc(Hons)*	131299
Pickering C S C ph	131299
ØRamsay C M	131299
Rodaway S J	131299
Lilley N J ph	100300
Bushell J M W ph	100400
Mack A W D ph	80800

Brietsche S P	281100
Anderson J B ph	121200

2nd Lieutenants

Aplin M T ph	100499
Morgan E J ph	70899
Pannett J G A	70899
Harris A W	161200

ROYAL ARMY CHAPLAINS' DEPARTMENT

Upon a wreath of laurel and oak a Maltese Cross. In the centre a quatrefoil voided with a circle inscribed with the motto *"In this Sign Conquer"*. The whole ensigned with The Crown.

For Jewish Chaplains

Upon a wreath of laurel and oak a Star of David. In the centre of the Star, a circle containing a quatrefoil voided. The whole ensigned with The Crown.

Regimental Marches

Quick March . . . . .Trumpet Voluntary
Slow March . . . . .Trumpet Voluntary

Agents . . . . .Holts Branch, Royal Bank of Scotland plc, Lawrie House, Farnborough, Hants

Alliances

The Canadian Armed Forces . . . . . . .Chaplains' Branch
Australian Military Forces . . . . .The Royal Australian Army Chaplains' Department
New Zealand Army . . . . .Royal New Zealand Chaplains' Department

Patron . . . . .THE QUEEN

Chaplains are appointed by the Parliamentary Under-Secretary of State for the Armed Forces, on the nomination of the following accredited representatives of the various denominations, and in their religious ministrations to the troops are under the oversight of these representatives respectively:

Church of England . . . . .Archbishop of Canterbury's Episcopal Representative,
    Little Bailie, Sturminster Marshall, Wimborne Minster, Dorset BH21 4AD

Jewish . . . . .The Secretary, The Jewish Committee for H M Forces, *Woburn House,*
    25 Enford Street, London, W1H 2DD

Methodist Church . . . . .The Secretary of the Methodist Royal Navy, Army and Royal Air Force
    Board, *76a Countess Road, Amesbury, Wiltshire, SP4 7AT*

Presbyterian Churches:

  Church of Scotland . . . . .The Convener, Committee on Chaplains to H M Forces,
    Department of Divinity with Religious Studies, University of Aberdeen,
    Aberdeen, AB24 3UB

  Free Church of Scotland . . . . .The Representative on the Interdenominational Advisory Committee,
    Offices of the Free Church of Scotland,
    Edinburgh, EH1 2LS

  Presbyterian Church in Ireland . . . .The Convenyer, Forces Committee,
    Church House, Fisherwidk Place, Belfast, BT1 6DW

  Presbyterian Church of Wales . . . . .The Representative on the Interdenominational Advisory Committee
    53 Richmond Road, Cardiff, CF2 3UP

Roman Catholic Church . . . . .Roman Catholic Bishop of the Forces (RC)
    Bishops Oak, 26 The Crescent, Farnborough Park,
    Farnborough, Hants GU14 7AS

United Navy, Army and Air Force Board comprising:

  Baptist
  United Reformed Church . . . . .The Secretary of the United Navy, Army and Air Force Board,
    The Holt, 109 Willingdon Park Drive, Estbourne, East Sussex BN22 0DF

Note: Chaplains of the Church of Scotland, and the Presbyterian Church in Ireland are distinguished by the letters (C of S), Chaplains of the Free Church of Scotland and Presbyterian Church of Wales by the letter (P), Roman Catholic Chaplains by the letters (RC), Methodist Chaplains by the letter (M), United Board Chaplains by the letters (UB) and Jewish Chaplains by the letter (J).

Chaplains with no distinguishing letter belong to the Church of England

Chaplain-General ranking as Major General
The Ven J Blackburn QHC 120500

Deputy Chaplain-General ranking as Brigadier
The Rev D E Wilkes OBE QHC 050500

Principal Roman Catholic Chaplain (Army) ranking as Colonel
The Rt Rev Mgr K Vasey OBE VG QHC 170597

Chaplains to the Forces (1st Class)
ranking as Colonels

Howson P J Rev *QHC MA BSc*	100495
Bryan L H Rev	130797
Whitton J P Rev *BD MA*	10399
Cable P J Rev *AKC*	300399
Heaver D C Rev *BTh*	101299
Walters D M T Rev *BA DipTh*	170100

_____

Chaplains to the Forces (2nd Class)
ranking as Lieutenant Colonels

Price A H Rev *MBE DipTh*	10791
Hadfield G F Rev *BSc(Hons) DipTh* *(A/1st Class 221200)*	210192
Cook J C D Rev *MA*	90295
Nicholson E C Rev	70495
Dailly J R Rev	20896
Elliott B Rev *BA(Hons)*	181196
Pillar K J Rev	161296
Rowland P C Rev	170697
Mitchell R M Rev *DipTh*	171197
Sussex G B Rev	181197
Rutherford P M Rev *MA MTh*	31297
Bretel K M Rev	10298
Parselle S P Rev *LTh*	200898
Alker J S Rev *MBE*	151298
Cumberlidge A W Rev *CertTh ACIB*	250199
Knights Johnson N A Rev *BA(Hons) MTh*	260299
Hall R J Rev *MBE*	10399
Kelly D H Rev	10799
Robbins S Rev *BD AKC*	291099
Majcher P L Rev *BD*	10401
Savage K G Rev	10401

Chaplains to the Forces (3rd Class)
ranking as Majors

Loveday J M Rev *AKC*	160790
Prince K V Rev	30990
Forbes Turner T J Rev *(L/2nd Class 200697)*	40291
Tee J T Rev	141292
Paris A B Rev *(L/2nd Class 141099)*	80294
Bell K D Rev *MA CTH*	90195
Stevenson M R N Rev *MA DipTh*	90195
Ashton W G Rev *BA(Hons) BA(Theol)*	30495
Gough J R B Rev *BA(Hons) MTh*	30495
Martin A M Rev *BA BD*	30795
Atherley K P Rev	40995
McCartney R C Rev *FRCM AMIRTE*	40995
Ritson J D Rev	40995
Whiting S Rev *BA*	91095
Coulter D G Rev *BA(Hons) BD PhD (L/2nd Class 120100)*	220396
Woodhouse J Rev *BA(Hons)*	80596
Thomas A H Rev *BD DPS*	210696

Griffith S E Rev *BTh DipTh CTH*	20796
Broddle C S T Rev	110996
Jones M V Rev *DipTh*	110996
Caddell M P Rev	270397
Hillary L T J Rev	81297
Eagles P A Rev *BA(Hons) BA(Oxon) AKC CTH*	270198
Prentice D K Rev *BSc BD CertEd*	110598
Vickers P Rev *LTh*	210998
Irwin P A Rev *BA(Hons) BD MA*	91098
Walker S M M Rev *BA(Hons)*	191098
Aitchison J W Rev *BD*	10299
Barber F P A Rev	10399
Kingston D V F Rev *BD DipTh*	220399
Crossey N N Rev *BA(Hons) MA(Hons) DipTh*	140699
Evans I A Rev *BD DipCOUNS*	140699
Langston C M Rev *BCombStuds*	20600
Cook N L Rev *BA(Hons)*	10900
Merceron D J Rev *BA(Hons)*	101000
Pluck R R Rev *BTh*	101000
Priest R M Rev *BA DipHE*	101000
Totten A J Rev *BA(Hons) BTh*	101000

Chaplains to the Forces (4th Class)
ranking as Captains

Butler T Rev *DipTh*	120691
Wright P S Rev	20994
Cole T A R Rev *BD MA(Hons)*	120695
Morton M P Rev *BA(Hons) MA CTH*	120695
Bosher P R Rev *CTH*	190296
Lloyd A P Rev *CertTh BA(Hons) DipEURHum*	190296
Maxted N A Rev	190296

Intermediate Regular Officers

Chaplains to the Forces (3rd Class)
ranking as Majors

Joyce K R Rev *MBE TD BSc(Hons) GOE*	180397
Hayter R W Rev *AIB*	50997
Coslett A A Rev *CTH*	130798

Short Service Officers

Chaplains to the Forces (3rd Class)
ranking as Majors

Hills P L Rev *BEd DipTh LTCL ACP*	10988
Williams R E Rev *BD PGCE DipTh*	50994
Green R L Rev *BA(Hons)*	90195
Pollard J A H Rev *BTh*	80596
Hemmings R A Rev *BD MThEOL DPS*	
McKnight T R Rev *BEd MA DipTh*	40297
Aston J L Rev *BA DipEd*	260897

Walton B Rev	91097
Macleod R N Rev *BA(Hons) BD PGCE*	60498
Franklin S A Rev *BD*	181099
Roemmelle M P Rev *BA MA(Theol)*	310100
Roskelly J H E Rev	210200
Millson B D Rev	80600
Pearson B D Rev	101000
Macdonald C Rev *BA*	200201

Chaplains to the Forces (4th Class)
ranking as Captains

Mentzel K D Rev	80993
Allison N E Rev	150694
Gosnell N Rev *BA(Theol) MA*	150694
Downes R J Rev	250994
McCulloch A J R Rev *BD MA(Hons)*	120695
Llewellyn N A Rev	10995
Hernandez D F Rev	310196
Skinner I T Rev *BA*	100696
Parker M D Rev *BA(Hons)*	10996
Ball J Rev *BA BA(Hons)*	141096
Cooper A J Rev *BA(Hons) CTH*	141096
Lister W B Rev *BA(Hons) BA(Hons)*	141096
Macleod C A Rev *MA(Hons)*	141096
McDowell N G Rev *BA(Hons)*	141096
Okeeffe M A Rev *BA(Theol)*	141096
White R J Rev *DipTh*	141096
Fava M P D Rev *BA(Hons)*	270197
Maynard C A Rev *BA(Hons)*	160697
McCormack P J Rev *BD*	160697
Moss C D J Rev	160697
Place T R Rev *CTH*	160697
McCafferty W A Rev *BA*	280997
Barry K G Rev *BAMOD*	131097
Cumming D J Rev *MPhil*	131097
Davies D W Rev *DipTh*	131097
Despard M F Rev	131097
Christian M R Rev	260198
Duff A J Rev	260198
Gandiya L F Rev	150698
Mackenzie S L Rev *BD*	150698
Mitchell C A Rev *BA CTH*	150698
Olliff R Rev *CTH*	150698
Steele A C Rev *BPhil(Ed) BA(Hons)*	111098
Aldred P J Rev	181098
Moesel J S Rev *BTh*	181098
Woollaston B Rev	181098
Evans N A P Rev *BA(Hons)*	240199
Butler C S Rev *BA(Hons) CTH*	150299
Connolly D Rev *BD*	150299
Rowlands M H Rev	140699
Wanliss H Rev	140699
Barrett D J Rev	41099
Farrell N D Rev *BA*	41099
Patterson P W Rev *BA(Hons)*	41099
Thatcher S B Rev	41099
West E R G Rev *BA(Hons)*	41099
Campbell D R J P Rev *RMN*	310100
Cobain A R Rev *MSc BA(Hons)*	310100
Abeledo B J A Rev *BA*	80500
Durant W J N Rev *BA(Hons)*	80500

Groocock C J Rev *DipTh*	80500		Jarvis R C M Rev *MA(Hons) MPH*
Crosbie A M Rev	110900	Duncan J C D Rev *BD MPhil*	*CTH* 290101
Mills P J Rev	110900	290101	Stewart M P M Rev 290101

THE ROYAL LOGISTIC CORPS

A gilt eight pointed-pointed star forming the background, upon which, in gilt, is a laurel wreath. Also in gilt, 2 crossed axes lie above the laurel wreath. Onto the axes is superimposed the Garter, in Oxford blue, bearing the Garter motto, in gilt, within which is centrally placed a shield bearing the arms of the Board of Ordnance. The shield sits on a field of scarlet enamel. A gilt Monarchal crown displaces the uppermost point of the Royal Star. Beneath the Garter is a scroll bearing the motto "WE SUSTAIN".

Regimental March

Quick March . . . . .On Parade

Agents . . . . .Holt's Branch, Royal Bank of Scotland plc, Lawrie House, Farnborough, Hants GU14 7NR

Regimental Headquarters . . . . .Dettingen House, Princess Royal Barracks Deepcut, CAMBERLEY, Surrey GU16 6RW *(Tel:* 01252-340880*)*

Alliances

Australian Military Forces . . . . .The Royal Australian Corps of Transport
The Royal Australian Army Ordnance Corps
The Royal Australian Catering Corps
New Zealand Army . . . . .The Royal New Zealand Logistic Regiment
Indian Army . . . . .Army Service Corps of India
Army Ordnance Corps of India
Pakistan Army . . . . .Army Service Corps of Pakistan
Army Ordnance Corps of Pakistan
Sri Lanka Army . . . . .The Sri Lanka Army Service Corps
The Sri Lanka Army Ordnance Corps
Malaysian Armed Forces . . . . .The Malaysian Service Corps
The Malaysian Ordnance Corps
South African Defence Forces . . . . . . .Personnel Service Corps of the South African National Defence Force
Canadian Forces . . . . .The Canadian Forces Logistics Branch

Affiliated Regiment
The Queen's Own Gurkha Logistic Regiment

Colonel in Chief . . . . .HRH THE PRINCESS ROYAL *KG KT GCVO QSO*

Deputy Colonels in Chief . . . . .HRH *The Duke of* GLOUCESTER *KG GCVO*
Hon Maj Gen *HRH The Duchess of* KENT *GCVO*

Regimental Colonel . . . . .Col K M Tutt OBE ADC 191199

Representative Colonel Commandant . .Maj Gen G A Ewer *CB CBE* ret pay 010499
Colonels Commandant . . . . Maj Gen A W Lyons *CBE* ret pay 050400
Maj Gen D F E Botting *CB CBE* ret pay .050493
*Maj Gen D L Burden *CB CBE* ret pay 010196
Maj Gen P A Chambers *MBE* ret pay 050400
Maj Gen M S White *CB CBE DL* ret pay .050498
Brig A Fisher 050498
Maj Gen J D MacDonald *CB CBE DL* ret pay 050493

Honorary Colonel Commandant . . . . .Lord Levene *of Portsoken KBE* 050493

Honorary Colonel Commandant . . . . .Col W Cockburn *CBE TD* 010196

Brigadiers

Flanagan P A *MA* psc† osc(ZIM) 300691
Dalby-Welsh T *ADC* psc 300693
Brown T MCG *OBE CGIA* psc† PC 300694
Evans P A D *OBE* psc† hcsc(J) jsdc 300694
Foxton P D *CBE FInstPet* rcds psc o pi 300694
Kerley M *CBE QGM* rcds psc† ato hcsc(J) 300695
Ratazzi R E *CBE* rcds psc 300695
Jeffrey D R *MDA MInstD MCIT MILOG CGIA* psc† hcsc(J) MDA 300696

Kerr J S *CBE* psc(PAK) S hcsc(J) s 300696
Rook R *OBE* psc† ato jsdc o 300696
Roycroft M J *MSc CEng MInstD MBCS MILOG* psc† dis o 300696
Elderton C R *OBE* psc† ato o 300698
Steirn C M *CBE* psc 300698
Wood M D *MBE MA* psc aic hcsc(J) 300698
Cash B J *MIMGT FFA* sq PC 300699
Hewitt C A *MBE CGIA* psc† o pi 300699
Maggs P J T *CBE* psc† 300699
Rees I D O *BSc(Hons)* psc im jsdc 300699

Cowlam S P *MBE MPhil CGIA* psc† hcsc(J) 300696
Wharmby M J *OBE* psc ato jsdc o 300600

Colonels

Macfarlane D S psc psc(AUS) 300690
Den-Mckay C A *OBE* sq aic 300692
Lawson R J *MIMATM* ocds(SP) aic sq(w) 300693
Rossiter P R *BA(Hons) BSc(Hons) MBA FRGS FIMGT AIL FHCIMA MRIPHH* sq I 300693
Barnes J R *BSc(Eng)Hons* psc† 300694
Chaganis P *OBE* psc(a)† psc 300694

Fielden J D *LVO MBE* sq jsdc 300694
Tutt K M *OBE BA(Hons)* psc 300694
Bugler R W *MA* psc 300695
Harrison R I *OBE* sq 300695
Verge P D sq 300695
Aitken E B C psc 300696
Barr S J *BSc(Eng)Hons* psc† aic 300696
Bowles J M *MBE* sq t 300696
Dowdle M *MCIT MIMGT MILOG* psc 300696
Mobley B G sq im 300696
Nowosielski-Slepowron W E *BSc(Hons)* psc† aic (*L/Brig 060999*) 300696
Smith A R M psc 300696
White T M *MBE* psc ato 300696
Davies G G psc 300697
Fox G B L psc† 300697
Gillott G *BSc(Hons)* psc† 300697
Maynard P C *OBE MSc MIMGT MIExpE* sq ato im sq(w) 300697
Medley R G sq im o pi 300697
O'Hare J H *OBE BSc(Hons)* psc(n)† ato 300697
Owen S F *OBE* sq o 300697
Abbott I W *OBE MDA TEng(CEI) AMIMI* rcds psc† MDA 300698
Barton A B psc† jsdc 300698
Gosling P psc jsdc 300698
Kane J M *OBE CGIA* psc† 300698
Lewington M H psc† o pi 300698
Little J J *OBE* psc† 300698
Macfarlane I C *BA(Hons)* psc† 300698
Morrison R J *OBE* sq jsdc 300698
Torrington W S *MHCIMA* sq 300698
Wallace J R *OBE BA(Hons)* psc hcsc(J) 300698
Bacon R J *MBA MCIT MILOG* psc t 300699
Beattie R *MSc* psc psc(a) 300699
Cummings P B G sq 300699
Hazlewood G A psc ato jsdc 300699
Hood A M psc 300699
Hooper R J psc 300699
Kent D J sq PC 300699
Morley A J *MSc* ato gw o sq(w) 300699
Morrison J G *BCom MSc MIExpE CGIA* ato MDA MDA o (*A/Brig 131200*) 300699
Murray C J psc psc(J) 300699
Robertson D S *BSc(Hons) MDA MHCIMA* sq MDA 300699
Smith S P *MBE BA(Hons)* psc ato im o 300699
Toms M R *MBE* psc 300699
Wilcox M E psc† ato o sq(w) 300699
Hall S C *BSc MSc* psc† im jsdc 311299
Addy S N *MSc* sq im o pi 300600
Askew J G *OBE* psc† 300600
Bradley D C sq 300600
Callan P G M *BSc(Hons)* psc(GE) jsdc o 300600
Campbell I S psc ph 300600
Josling N B *BSc(Hons) MILOG* psc aic 300600

Kerr D J *BSc* sq ato † 300600
Lloyd N P *OBE* psc† o pi 300600
McGarr G *OBE MMS* psc 300600
ØRollo S J psc o 300600
Stanton W E *MSc CEng MBCS MILOG* df psc† aic o 300600

_____

Lieutenant Colonels

Burr L S *OBE* psc S 300687
Cairns D P C sq 300687
Geddie G K (SL) *OBE* sq im 300687
Morrison A G (SL) *MBE* sq jsdc 300687
Stone A T J (SL) sq o s 300687
Fisher A J C *MBE* psc† osc(ZIM) jsdc 300688
Ballinger B W *BSc(Eng)Hons* psc 300689
Ginn R G (SL) psc(CAN) pi 300689
Lilley G D (SL) sq 300689
Rapple T B (SL) *BSc(Hons)* psc(n)† ato im 300689
Rust M J sq 300689
Allen J F J *MBE* sq sq(w) 300690
Bradley C R sq im o 300690
Chambers C R *BSc(Econ)Hons MCIT* sq t 300690
Davison M J *MBE GM* ato im sq(w) 300690
Draper C F R psc 300690
Ells D R (SL) *OBE* sq im 300690
Firth P psc jsdc 300690
Harper P W *MSc* sq 300690
Morgan J W sq im jsdc 300690
Moules K A *BSc(Hons)* psc o 300690
Neill J R (SL) *LLB(Hons)* sq 300690
Poole P M *MBE* sq 300690
Bridges A *MSc* im jsdc o sq(w) 300691
Forrest J A sq t 300691
Hillyer C G *TEng(CEI) FSERT* sq PC 300691
Ingram M D *OBE* psc ato 300691
Jackman C H (SL) ato im sq(w) 300691
Keen M R (SL) sq 300691
Plowright N R psc (*A/Col 271100*) 300691
Quinn Hall D R aic jsdc sq(w) 300691
Reehal P S sq 300691
Robertson P A psc 300691
Simpson A E R (SL) *MSc* dis ato sq(w) 300691
Blaber P W G sq 300692
Blatherwick M *MBE GM MSc MIMGT* ato im o sq(w) odc(IT) 300692
Campbell R G C *MCIT* sq 300692
Carman R T *DMS* sq im 300692
Clough J H *OBE BSc(Eng)* sq 300692
Crowe S J *MBE MSc* sq ato im o 300692
Dickinson P M *MBA* sq lc 300692
Morrison N D sq 300692
Newman-Carter J S (SL) t 300692
Woods P R *MSc* sq 300692
Alexander M C S sq 300693

Doherty D B *MSc* ato im sq(w) 300693
Frere J S B *MBE BA(Hons)* psc jsdc 300693
Ham F A (SL) sq o 300693
Inman J P *BSc* psc† im 300693
Longland J psc 300693
Sutherland A W sq jsdc 300693
Tonkins W C *BEM MSc* sq im 300693
Weeks H E E sq ato 300693
Anderson K B sq (*A/Col 180101*) 300694
Budd P V *OBE BSc(Hons) MIMGT FHCIMA MRSH* sq 300694
Fairbrother B N *BSc(Hons)* lc sq(w) 300694
Hawkey C *MCIT* sq t 300694
Hughes H A *BA(Hons) FRGS MIMGT AFA* sq PC 300694
Littlewood D sq 300694
Marvin E W *MIMGT* sq jsdc 300694
Miller J C *BA(Hons) FHCIMA* sq lc 300694
O'Leary C J *MILOG FInstPet* sq im o pi 300694
Parsons J D o sq(w) ais 300694
Ritchie J D M *MSc MIMGT MILOG* aic im o sq(w) 300694
Southworth R J sq o pi 300694
Withers W G sq lc 300694
Alexander I C *OBE* sq jsdc 300695
Baker R M sq 300695
Caldwell D R *MSc* sq ato im 300695
Hemingway C J *BSc(Hons)* sq(w) 300695
Knowles J E *MCIT* sq t 300695
Lanham M R *MBE* psc 300695
Lloyd-Jukes E *BA(Hons)* psc(IND) 300695
Macarthur I W psc RLY 300695
Robinson R F *MBE BSc* psc(GE) 300695
Rowley R K *MSc* psc(IND) 300695
Varley M J psc(AUS) psc(J) 300695
Bennett P S *BSc(Hons)* psc† 300696
Brook P C *BSc(Eng)Hons* psc† psc(n) 300696
Fleet S J *MBE* psc 300696
Forster T P M *OBE* psc S s 300696
Humpherson N P *BA(Hons)* psc† 300696
Norton D J sq 300696
Preston K N sq 300696
Raby P D *MBE BSc(Hons) MILOG* psc† jsdc 300696
Shouesmith D J *BEd* psc† (*A/Col 180900*) 300696
Start N T *OBE MCIT* psc t 300696
Wilberforce J F G *BA BSc(Hons)* psc pi sq(w) 300696
Bragg S D sq jsdc 311296
Arkinstall J *BEM* sq 300697
Baker P J A psc psc(J) 300697
Bristow A D psc S 300697
Castell R G A psc 300697
Collins D J *MIExpE CGIA* psc† ato 300697
Copeland I M psc psc(J) 300697
Couch T psc pi 300697
Cowling A P *OBE* psc 300697

Crossman P C *BA(Hons) MDA* MDA
o pi sq(w) 300697
Edwards R K sq ato 300697
Govan S psc 300697
Groves B N *OBE* sq fs s 300697
Harris P *QGM FISM MILOG*
MIExpE ato o sq(w) † 300697
Kirkbride P L *PGDA* sq jsdc t
300697
Laden R ST L *MSc* sq jsdc 300697
Libbey R W psc(AUS) 300697
Lilley M R *MBE* sq 300697
Lowe J G O *MBE* sq jsdc 300697
Martin D J R *MBE BSc(Hons) MSc*
MILOG psc† MDA 300697
McKeegan R D *MSc* sq S im s
300697
ØMcMahon H E *MBE BEd(Hons)*
psc 300697
O'Sullivan G A *MBE QGM MSc* sq
ato im 300697
Parrott A J *MA MCIT MILOG* psc
300697
Patrick R J *MSc* ato im o sq(w)
300697
Ruff D B sq jsdc 300697
Russell M H F psc 300697
Speight A M sq 300697
Stamps P F psc† S 300697
Wickham M C *MBE QGM* ato o
sq(w) 300697
Wymbs E J sq 300697
Carlisle W M *BA(Hons)* psc† 300698
Clacher A D C *MBE BSc(Hons)*
sq(w) 300698
Cooper S R psc† ato 300698
Dixon-Warren R A psc OSC(KU)
300698
Downes J A S *MA* psc† 300698
Frankland D P *MBE* psc 300698
Harris C D M sq 300698
Hickson M G psc(n) 300698
Langford C D *MSc* im 300698
Lewis J W psc t 300698
Maginniss C H *BA(Hons)* psc RLY
300698
Maxwell R J C *MBE* psc ato 300698
McMahon M J psc 300698
McPherson I A *OBE BEM* sq 300698
Medcalf M F odc(IT) sq ato 300698
O'Grady P A *LLB(Hons)* sq 300698
Oliver M R *MILOG MIExpE* ato
sq(w) 300698
Peacock R *MSc* psc† psc(J) dis
300698
Phillips A W *MBE* sq 300698
Prince C R psc(IND) 300698
Scully C F sq 300698
Shilston M L *MIExpE* psc(n) ato o
sq(w) 300698
Smellie N A *MBE MSc* sq ato im
300698
Taylor A S sq 300698
Warwick P sq 300698
Robinson R *MBE* sq 311298
Barsby N I *AMRSH* psc 300699
Beavis R G *MBE BEd* sq 300699
Bevan J D *MBE* psc psc(J) pi
300699
Bouch M C psc ato 300699
Boyd A T *MBE* sq ato o 300699
Brown P J psc 300699

Clews M J psc 300699
Cook D E *OBE* psc 300699
ØDixon C A *BSc(Hons) MA* psc† pi
300699
Dolamore M I *MBE BSc(Hons)* ato
sq(w) 300699
Dunn M L psc 300699
Faulkner M E sq PC 300699
Green A M ato sq(w) 300699
Grinstead J S *MBE BHum MSc* psc s
300699
Herring R J sq ato 300699
Kneale G D *MBE BSc(Eng) MSc* mvt
sq 300699
Law A R *BSc(Eng)Hons MSc* psc†
ato gw o 300699
McCall P J *BA LHCIMA* psc 300699
Nash J P *BEd* psc 300699
Newell D *MSc* ato im o sq(w)
300699
Poffley M W *BA(Hons) MA* psc†
300699
Rowe A G psc 300699
Smith P M psc(a) † 300699
Smith J C D *BA* psc† ato 300699
Thorpe P J *BSc FLS* sq 300699
Wand N J sq PC 300699
Wensley C J *BA(Hons)* psc† 300699
Alberry P E *MSc* jssc sq 300600
Bates P J psc 300600
Blong C *MA GCGI* psc† pi 300600
Brant I S *BSc(Eng)Hons MSc* psc ato
o † 300600
Cameron R B *MSc* dis sq(w) 300600
Cassidy I S J sq 300600
Challis N P *MSc* sq im pi 300600
Cox P G *OBE BSc(Hons) PGCE* sq
300600
Davis M J sq ato o 300600
Fraser W G *MBE PGDA* sq t 300600
Gilroy R J *BA(Hons) MSc MILOG*
sq(w) AIS 300600
Gosney P J *BSc(Hons)* psc† im pi
300600
Griggs C J sq 300600
Jones P A *MBE* psc(AUS) 300600
McGuigan P J *BA(Econ) BSc DMS*
sq im 300600
Mead W *BSc* psc pi 300600
Oxborough R J *BSc(Hons) MBA*
CertEd GCGI psc† s 300600
Pearce G R *MBE AMRSH* psc
300600
Pettet G F psc 300600
Redwood P A sq s 300600
Roberts S R psc 300600
Ryder D *BEM* sq 300600
Simon A H *BA(Hons) MA(Hons)* psc
300600
Small R S sq PC 300600
Underhill M C H *MBE MILOG* sq
300600
Whittaker K N *MBE BSc(Hons)*
GCGI psc† im 300600
Winchcombe P P psc† ato 300600

Majors

Gunson J N *MBE GM* ato sq(w)
311278
Couzens A P sq owc t 300980
Dalley M J *FInstAM MCInstPS*
MIPD sq S o s 300980

Gout J J R *MBE* sq 300980
Greenwood T B *BSc* sq S s 300980
Harness B *AMRSH* owc s sq(w)
300980
Marshall I *BA MSc MIMGT MILOG*
MIExpE ato im sq(w) 300980
Rees D T sq 300980
Laird J S o 250182
Dexter I R J *BSc(Econ)Hons* psc o
300982
Graham C J M sq o pi 300982
Ferguson D F B sq 300983
Hannaway G E M *MBA* im o pi
sq(w) 300983
McNally N J *MSc MCIT MILOG*
MInstPet sq im o pi 300983
Dyer E J G 300984
Graham S *MIMGT MILOG* sq t
300984
Ormerod I S *BA(Hons) DipTD MCIT*
MILOG sq 300984
Parle M E ato o sq(w) 300984
Richards F T sq(w) adp 300984
Simonds R G psc pi 300984
Burnett M J sq ato 300985
Harris P C sq o pi sq(w) 300985
Kay R *BA* sq 300985
Murphy M G sq S o 300985
Palmer P sq 300985
Pearson W E sq ato o 300985
Tayler T *BA* sq(w) AIS 300985
Denning T M 300986
Hanlon P R sq ato o *(A/Lt Col*
011000) 300986
Jackson K A sq S s 300986
John S E *BA(Hons) MBA MDA* sq
MDA o s 300986
Martin R H D sowc sq S 300986
Mosedale I R sq 300986
Mould P L . sq 300986
Parrott D E P *BSc(Hons) MSc MIQA*
MIMGT MILOG MIExpE MCGI
psc(n)† ato gw im 300986
Phillips F S *MSc* im 300986
Pope N S *BA* sq 300986
Selley R J psc† 300986
Ward R S D sq pi 300986
Bower L A sq 300986
Brehaut N F G sq *(A/Lt Col 170201)*
300987
Brown H M *BA(Hons) MCIT* sq t
300987
Byrne D R sq 300987
Canning N P *PGDA* sq t 300987
Duncan P A osc(P) sq 300987
Eagle M R G *BSc MDA MIExpE*
MRPharmS ato sq(w) 300987
Emmett C N P sq o pi sq(w) 300987
McCulloch J A *DipTPM PGDA* sq t
300987
Osborne P G sq pi (A/Lt Col
220301) 300987
Rees M S sq 300987
Singer A J *MSc* ato im sq(w) *(A/Lt*
Col 50301) 300987
Slade S H *MSc MSc GRADIPD* S im
o sq(w) 300987
Tilt S C sq lcc t 300987
Wiggell J F *MBE MSc* ato im sq(w)
300987
Bray A J sq 300988
Cole W O sq 300988

Dunlop C S   sq lc   300988
Edwards M B   *BA(Hons)* sq   300988
Fenwick M A   sq pi   300988
Ford M J   *BA(MIL)* sq   300988
Grieveson M W   *MBE QGM BCom
MSc* ato im o sq(w)   300988
Harding A N   *DipTPM* sq t   300988
James M R P   *MIPR* sq owc   300988
King S J   *PGDA* S o s t   300988
Knoll P R   300988
Mapstone M R J   sq sq(w) ais
300988
Morris J K   *MSc* psc im t   300988
Murley G W   sq   300988
Oldham R W J   *MBE* sq ato o sq(w)
300988
Rainey W D   *BA(Hons) MBA
GRADIPD* sq *(A/Lt Col 021299)*
300988
Wilson P   *BSc(Hons)* sq im o   300988
ØArcher R   *MHCIMA*   300989
Beagle P R   psc s   300989
Beardsell M L   *MSc* sq *(A/Lt Col
260201)*   300989
Bedborough L R   sq ph   300989
Campbell N G   sq   300989
Carins J E   *MSc* ato gw sq(w) 300989
Collinson G T   *MBE PGDA* sq t
300989
Dawson L I M   *DipTPM PGDA
AMBCS* owc sq(w) t AIS *(A/Lt Col
060900)*   300989
Goodall J A   *BSc(Hons) MILOG* psc†
300989
Heaton S   sq   300989
Jenkins S G   *MSc MSc* dis sq(w)
300989
Le Sueur M R   *MSc* sq o   300989
Pearce S M W   sq   300989
Perks F R   *BA MSc MILOG* mvt aic
sq(w)   300989
Simpson M C   sq   300989
Starling J A   *BSc(Eng)Hons MSc·
CEng MIEE* psc† gsd   300989
Taylor J P   *DipTPM PGDA* sq(w) t
ais   300989
Thorn J P   *MIL* sq   300989
Wilde P A   *MSc MIPD* sq   300989
Williams J M   *MSc* sq im sq(w)
300989
Argyle G W   sq   *(A/Lt Col 310301)*
300989
Bagnall-Oakeley M A   *BA(Hons)
MPhil* psc† o   300990
Barkes C J   *MSc* dis sq(w) *(A/Lt Col
260900)*   300990
Bazire M H   *MBE MBA* psc†   300990
Crossen E H   *BSc* psc   300990
Dyer P C   *MSc* psc† ato gw   300990
Flack C   sq *(A/Lt Col 311000)*
300990
Gregori L S J   *MSc* psc† dis *(A/Lt Col
171198)*   300990
Harvey C J   *MBE* psc   300990
Hibbert J C   sq   300990
Hotson N G M   *BA* sq(w)   300990
Howard R N   *BSc* psc† *(A/Lt Col
160301)*   300990
Kerce J A   *BA(Hons)* sq PC   300990
Kershaw G B   *BSc MDA MIMGT
MDA* sq(w) †   300990
Kirkham S J F   *DipTPM* sq t   300990

Mouat T N   *MBE* psc ato   300990
Parsons S A   *BEd* sq   300990
Taplin A P   psc   300990
Ball J D   psc(AUS)   300991
Blake S L   sq s *(A/Lt Col 150101)*
300991
Coveney R M   sq s sq(w) *(A/Lt Col
130301)*   300991
Croxford D J   *PGDA* sq owc t
300991
Devonshire R M   *BSocSc(Hons) MSc
MSc MILOG* dis sq   300991
Elwell R S   sq   300991
England M R   sq(w) AIS *(A/Lt Col
060900)*   300991
Harbinson T J   psc   300991
Heil B   *MSc* sq   300991
Hollas D I   *MBE* psc *(A/Lt Col
160201)*   300991
Hutton W L   o pi sq(w) ais   300991
Jobbings T N   ato o sq(w)   300991
Jones R S   sq   300991
Lawson M M   *PGDA* sq t   300991
Le-Var R W   sq s   300991
Martin F A S   *PGDA* sq t   300991
McIntosh J K   sq   300991
Mollison K   *GM MA(Hons) MIExpE
MCGI* psc† ato *(A/Lt Col 030999)*
300991
Morgan C G   *BSc(Econ)Hons*
psc(CAN) sq pi   300991
Morris C C   *BEM* sq   300991
Pope M C   ato sq(w)   300991
Ruddock I D   *BA(Hons)* osc(SP) sq
ato   300991
Simpson P W H   *MBE* ato EOE sq(w)
300991
Smith A J P   sq s   300991
Sturges I J   *BSc* sq pi   300991
Walker C I   *BSc* sq pi sq(w) ais
300991
Warden P A   *BSc(Eng)Hons* sq(w)
300991
Appleton M R   *MBA* sq(w)
300992
Attard R A   sq *(A/Lt Col 150201)*
300992
Bennett V   sq   300992
Blackwood B W   sq ato o   300992
Breeze R D   sq   300992
Brownbridge J E   *BA(Hons) PGDip*
300992
Code C R   *MSc GRADIPD* dis sq(w)
300992
Dade R   o sq(w)   300992
Greathead R F   sq pi   300992
Green C M   psc   300992
Hayward L M   sowc sq   300992
Hook M H J   ato sq(w)   300992
Jeffries P A   *PGDA* PC sq(w) *(A/Lt
Col 060900)*   300992
Jones R C   300992
Judge R E G   sq   300992
Lee C N D   sq ato   300992
Macintyre B H   sq PC   300992
Mathie R A   psc   300992
McGowan K N F   sq   300992
Morgan N D   sq   300992
Ockleston D R   *MCGI* psc ato 300992
Parker A G   psc   300992
Redding J M   *BSc(Eng) MA MSc
GRADIPD* sq(w) †   300992

Reeve D W   psc sq   300992
Russell C N M   sq   300992
Scurfield R W S   *BSc(Hons)* sq(w)
ais   300992
Searles T E D   *GradIPD* sq   300992
Simpson J P   *MSc* pi sq(w) †   300992
Sinclair P J   sq   300992
Vickers M D   psc   300992
Wiggins D A   sq   300992
Wilson P A   *BSc* lcc owc sq(w) ais
300992
Woodman T G W   *MBE* sq   300992
Wyse W P P   *DipTPM BSc* sq t
300992
Allen J R   *MSc* dis ato sq(w)   300993
Ash J P   psc   300993
Bamford S D   *BSc(Hons) PGDA
MBA MILOG* sq(w) t   300993
Barton N I M   *BA(Hons)* sq   300993
Belgum C   *MSc* sq   300993
Cave R A   *BSc(Econ)Hons* psc†
300993
Courtier M S   *BSc(Hons) PGDA*
sq(w) t   300993
English S N   *BA(Hons)* psc†   300993
Gascoigne R J   *BSc(Hons) PGDA* sq
300993
Gibson A M   *BA(Hons)* psc† ato
300993
ØHaigh C   *BA(Hons) PGDA* sq t
300993
ØHarrill C E S   *BSc MA MRSH* psc†
S s   300993
Harris M E   *BSc(Econ)Hons PGCE*
ato sq(w)   300993
Jay R E   sq   300993
Johnston A K B   sq   300993
Jones A R   *BSc* ato sq(w)   300993
King P M   *BSc PGDA* sq t   300993
Macnish C J   psc *(A/Lt Col 180101)*
300993
Marshall S A   *BSc* ato sq(w)   300993
McKend I G   *BA(Hons) AITI* psc(GE)
I *(A/Lt Col 311000)*   300993
Mee J B   *BSc(Hons) MSc* dis sq(w)
300993
Nixon A C   *BSc(Hons)* pi sq(w)
300993
Paramore A   s sq(w)   300993
Pepper M E   *BSc(Hons)* sq(w)
300993
Powell D S   *BSc(Econ)Hons MSc* sq s
300993
Pratchek N D S   *BA PGCE MSc
GRADIPD* sq   300993
ØProsser C A   *BA(Hons)* psc† s
300993
Randall P C   sq   300993
Rendall J S   sq   300993
Robinson L M   *BSc(Hons) MRIN* sq
300993
Rowe M H   *PGDA* sq(w) t   300993
Shepherd N R   *BSc(Hons)* sq   300993
Shilton A R   *DipTPM BA(Hons)
PGDA* sq(w) t   300993
Towndrow D W   *MSc* ato gw sq(w)
300993
Tysoe A R   sq   300993
Watkin S J   psc(n) sq *(A/Lt Col
040101)*   300993
Watkins L H   psc *(A/Lt Col 010301)*
300993

Gibson R A 300997
Giggins J W ato 300997
Gordon I A *MBE* 300997
Haywood M L 300997
Holt M H *BSc(Hons)* 300997
Hughes G K M *BA(Hons)* 300997
Jordan S K ato 300997
Jouques N A 300997
Kerkeling-Sheerin R J *BSc(Hons)* ato 300997
Lane P J I 300997
Lawrence G J ato 300997
Leadbeater A R *BA(Hons)* ato 300997
Lewis P J psc(J) 300997
Llewellyn N psc(J) 300997
Loftus R J *BEng* pi 300997
Manson R I 300997
McVey A G J *BSc(Hons)* ato 300997
Nicholl R G 300997
Rawlinson M G s 300997
Stewart S A PC 300997
Sunderland D R H 300997
ØTargett B F 300997
Thompson R D 300997
Urquhart R K 300997
Vaughan G E *BEng(Hons)* pi 300997
Whattoff C R J 300997
Wheelton S P psc(J) 300997
Whitelegg D *BSc(Hons)* 300997
Williams I D 300997
Wright G G 300997
Allen D *BA(Hons)* 300998
Amison D P *BSc(Hons) PGCE* 300998
Barnsley J *BSc* pi 300998
Bex A G *BSc(Hons)* ato 300998
Busby W R *MSc MILOG* 300998
Convery J C ato 300998
Cooper M O *BSc MSc* pi 300998
Corrigan E A 300998
Cranmer J H 300998
Cunningham G B *BA* 300998
Dunne R 300998
Edwards P J pi 300998
Ellis S W *GCGI* ato 300998
Garside A T *BA(Hons)* 300998
Gittins R E 300998
Gosling D C *DSR(R)* 300998
Harrison J W *BSc(Hons) MSc* dis 300998
Henderson A F *BSc(Hons)* 300998
Heron S D 300998
Hollingworth M J *MA* 300998
ØKing F M *BSc(Hons)* 300998
Langridge S R *BSc(Hons)* 300998
Maber-Jones A S *MILOG MIExpE* ato 300998
Malcolm B G ato 300998
Mitchell J B A 300998
Mosedale K A *BA(Hons)* ato 300998
ØPeak D P PC 300998
Pennell R M *BSc(Hons)* 300998
Rose C J S *BSc(Hons)* 300998
ØSavage A A *BSc(Hons)* 300998
Scattergood I D ato EOE 300998
Skipper I 300998
Smith P G 300998
Smith T D 300998
Stokes A P *BEng(Hons)* 300998
Stone P 300998

Symon J B s 300998
Taylor S C 300998
Taylor A J ato 300998
Tully S W ph 300998
Weir R A M *BA(Hons)* 300998
White S P R *BA* 300998
Williams P N 300998
Woodford D R 300998
Yarnold P G 300998
Albon D A *BA(Hons)* 300999
Bastin J D ato 300999
Bell T D pi 300999
Benbow R M 300999
Blackburn J W *BEng(Hons)* ato 300999
Brown J M 300999
ØCampbell M A *BSc(Hons)* PC 300999
Connelly J C 300999
Couper A A 300999
Davies R G ato 300999
Davis C J s 300999
ØDe Gale J S *BA(Hons)* 300999
Devine B J 300999
Duddy D G 300999
Elms D L 300999
Evanson-Goddard M A *BA(Hons)* 300999
Fleming S C D *PGDA* t 300999
Galloway J W 300999
ØGiles L M *BSc* 300999
Harris A J *MRSH* 300999
Head K A ato 300999
Henson C J *QGM* ato 300999
Heywood S G *BSc* 300999
Hobbs M A B *BSc* ato 300999
Hoff A P *MSc* 300999
Holder P D *AIS* 300999
Hopkinson A S J *BA* 300999
Hubbard R P 300999
Keppel-Compton R T 300999
Kerr-Ruston S P *BEng(Hons)* ato 300999
ØKimber A E *BSc(Hons)* 300999
Lodwig N S 300999
Marston T J E 300999
McMahon S C pi 300999
Moore M P *BSc(Hons)* pi 300999
Muir T W 300999
Mutch G A ato 300999
Nelson D M *BSc(Hons)* 300999
ØNevin A V 300999
Park D E 300999
Paterson J R C pi 300999
Potter M J 300999
Pugh G J 300999
ØReid F M U *BSc(Hons)* 300999
ØRobb J T ato 300999
Rodham P 300999
Rudd M N ato 300999
ØSchofield R A *BSc(Hons)* 300999
Songhurst N D *PGDA* 300999
ØSummersgill S A *MA* ato 300999
Thomson G M 300999
Thorman W *BSc(Hons)* 300999
Thurgood A M ato 300999
Tinning S J 300999
Vickerman P M 300999
Whiley M J *BSc(Hons)* 300999
Wilson J M 300999
Allison N C 300900
Atkins J W *BA(Hons)* 300900

Baker K H *MIExpE GCGI* ato 300900
Barnes H C 300900
Blackmore T R *BSc(Hons)* cafs 300900
ØBrunton T J *BSc(Hons)* 300900
Burgess T A W ato 300900
Campbell M R J 300900
Carey D M 300900
Corrie D N 300900
Cotton P D ato 300900
Davey G W *BSc(Hons)* 300900
Edwards P W pi 300900
ØFellowes T 300900
Fenn J D 300900
Fletcher S D 300900
Francis C J 300900
Houston P B *BA* 300900
Hutchings S T 300900
Jurd N D 300900
Kerner J R 300900
Kitching S A *BSc(Hons)* 300900
Lammiman S A *BSc(Hons)* 300900
Lillywhite A C 300900
Lobb G R ato PC 300900
Lumsden M W 300900
Matthews C C 300900
McNeil R J 300900
ØNelson E M ato 300900
Nodder F D *BSc(Hons)* 300900
Parry A J 300900
Patrick A W 300900
Pemberton-Pigott T J D 300900
Poole D ato 300900
Prescott N K ato 300900
Roberts D 300900
Smith R C 300900
ØSmyth B J *BSc(Hons)* 300900
Sorrell A P *BSc(Hons)* 300900
Steel K 300900
ØStephens E J *BA(Hons)* 300900
Stringer J E C 300900
Taylor N J 300900
Taylor M J L 300900
Thomson P A 300900
ØTilley A A 300900
Timmis J R H pi 300900
Tipler R J W 300900
Violet C M PC 300900
ØWebb F S *BA(Hons) DipM* 300900

Captains

Hughes P 300488
Gallagher P J P 100891
ØGlasgow C A *(A/Maj 231000)* 120492
Beckett D J ato 121293
ØFarleigh D A *BSc* 101294
ØPhipps H L *BSc(Hons)* 101294
Belza D J PC 010495
Bowler C M cafs 010495
ØErrington J 010495
Illingworth P M ato 010495
Luedicke D G *BA(Hons)* 010495
Maddison A *BA(Hons)* pi 010495
Nanovo V T *BA(Hons)* pi 010495
Slater T M *BEng(Hons)* ato 010495
Torrington N S R *BSc(Hons)* 010495
Weir R D *BSc GCGI* cafs 010495
McRae A D *BA(Hons)* ato 120495
Moore P A *BEng(Hons)* 130495

Austin M R ato	110895
Blenkinsop N R BA(Hons) PC	110895
ØBryce M M BSc(Hons)	110895
Clouston D S BEng(Hons)	110895
Moffat A D BA(Hons)	110895
Moverley G M ato	110895
Mowle J E BSc(Hons)	110895
ØRobins K	110895
Smith P T BA(Hons)	110895
Sunderland J D V BA(Hons) PC	110895
ØSwain C V BSc(Hons)	021195
Pugh C C BSc(Hons)	241195
ØMcRae S C V BSc(Hons) pi	011295
ØWakelin N J BEng(Hons) pi	131295
ØEnraght-Moony E BSc(Hons)	141295
ØMcNeil K A BSc(Hons)	141295
Roberts C A BSc(Hons) pi	141295
Stocks M D BSc(Hons)	141295
Dempsey M J C ato	151295
Ewart-Brookes G	151295
Griffiths A	151295
Hirst S A ato	151295
Lemasurier M A BEng(Hons)	151295
Lilley J K ato	151295
Kay T J	040296
Bacon R J W BA(Hons) DMS pi (L/Maj 100700)	220296
McClellan P R	210396
ØLuck A C BSc(Hons)	120496
Beck E W T	130496
Calvert P V E	130496
Elsegood C ato	130496
Frankland K L ato	130496
ØJenkins G A MBE	130496
Stanton A J	130496
Clegg C J BA(Hons)	170696
Marshall D BA(Hons)	090796
Baker R A GM ato	070896
Donnachie J P	070896
Hing M J	070896
McGraw R J pi	070896
Moore P E BSc(Hons) ato	070896
Powell G J ato	070896
Smith J B BSc(Hons)	070896
ØWellington L A	070896
Blake A M BSc(Hons) ato	110896
Dietz M P R BA(HonsCantab)	110896
ØGrimes R BA(Hons) PGCE	110896
ØLeighton R E BA(Hons)	110896
Reyland D A BSc(Hons) ato	110896
ØCurnow A L BA(Hons) PC	241096
Macintyre A C H MA(Hons)	241096
Ashman D A BSc(Hons) ato	131296
McCormack T S BSc(Hons) ato	131296
Skinsley P M BSc(Hons)	131296
Summons J S BA(Hons) ato	131296
ØTurnbull S J BA(Hons)	131296
Caldicott M E G BSc(Hons) ato	141296
Clark M L BSc(Hons)	141296
Forrest R J E	141296
Goymer M	141296
Hanford S	141296
Mason D M	141296

Weetman S G	141296
Harris G P R ato	010497
Tickner M	040497
Collins M A (A/Maj 151100)	110497
Downie I G	110497
Johnstone D M ato	110497
Lewis A G BSc(Hons) ato	110497
Priest J S R ato	110497
Rychlik-Hadley J M BSc(Hons)	110497
Wagstaff R PC	300697
ØBeaney S E BScEng(MECH)	070897
ØPerrett E J BSc(Hons)	070897
Cox C C pi	080897
ØDelap S B	080897
Dodgson K P pi	080897
Essex M A	080897
Maxwell D M	080897
Shakespeare A J S	080897
Smith W J M BSc(Hons) ato	080897
Williams A C ph	080897
Kara B S	200897
Evanson-Goddard A C BA(Hons)	130997
Barnett M S PC	051097
Williams J N BSc(Hons) ato	131097
ØDermody K F BSc(Hons)	141097
Barron R BSc(Hons)	121297
Bowers I R O pi	121297
Claridge M K pi	121297
Finch M J BSc	121297
Jenkins D E ato	121297
Mellor S L	121297
Mulholland D V	121297
Pile D H BEng(Hons) cafs	121297
Richards R M J	121297
Walker C D	121297
Askew R A C BA(Hons) PC	120298
ØBoyne H J BSc(Hons)	120298
ØCarter H S BA(Hons)	120298
ØDreelan T A ph	120298
Preston M A BSc(Hons) pi	120298
Rea D M ato	230298
Driver-Williams C T G ato	180398
Donoghue C	090498
Holman N F	090498
Luedicke M E ato	090498
Macleod C C BSc(Hons)	160698
ØMcDonald V	160698
Nurse I G BSc(Hons)	160698
John C W	090798
De Lukacs Lessner De Szeged C J P PC	070898
Haigh K BSc(Hons)	070898
Parker A J BSc(Hons)	070898
Sollitt P A	070898
Taylor M G	070898
Booton A W	131098
Church S A BA(Hons)	131098
ØLewis C M BA(Hons) PGCE	131098
ØSmith J A B BA(Hons) OLPM	131098
ØStephens A K BA(Hons)	131098
ØStileman E J BSc(Hons)	131098
Rhodes A J	111298
Scott Z D C BA(Hons) ato	111298
Asbee J R G BSc(Hons)	100299
ØGeorge R L BSc(Hons)	100299
ØRawdon-Smith K H	100299

ØRoberts L M BEd(Hons)	100299
Stevenson S J BA(Hons)	100299
ØWilkinson G H MA	100299
Beauman K M MILT PC	090499
ØBenbow E C S	090499
Docherty D W	090499
Norris A M A ato	090499
Pembroke K D ato pi OLPM	300499
ØLovell H J BSc(Hons)	140699
ØLowth G C BA(Hons)	140699
Poole I	090799
Brady R L	060899
Gittins T J	060899
ØReilly A E BA(Hons)	060899
Jermy S P ato	101299
ØLedger J S	101299
Marcus A S ato	101299
Pope E L ato	101299
Spicer A B	101299
Stanford N J BSc(Hons)	101299
Stockdale A ato	101299
Bunkle O G BA(Hons)	090200
Herbert P A BSc(Hons)	090200
ØSkennerton D T BA(Hons)	090200
Fisher S J ato	140400
Webberley G L	150400
ØReece J L BSc(Hons)	130600
ØWentworth V A S BA(Hons)	130600
Comer M J	120800
ØMartin T J H	120800
Moss R J	120800
ØBowler M C BA(Hons)	101000
Rhodes J E R BSc(Hons)	101000
ØPegler N K ato	161200
Racey D	161200
ØReid V C BSc(Hons)	80201

Lieutenants

ØThompson H L MEng(Hons)	270296
Bell A J	160697
ØHeppinstall K A BSc(Hons)	160697
Teasdale M W BA(Hons) (A/Capt 141100)	131097
Davidson W A	131297
ØMcClellan S A (A/Capt 131299)	161297
Thompson C (A/Capt 270300)	161297
ØBaxter J C MA(Hons)	100298
Clark S J BA(Hons)	130498
Foote M A BA(Hons)	130498
ØHadadine L A BA(Hons)	130498
Kay B J	130498
Macartney A T (A/Capt 020900)	130498
ØMorgan J M BA	130498
Pugh G G BA(Hons)	130498
Read D (A/Capt 030400)	130498
Skinner D E	130498
Wood T J BA	130498
ØClarke K M BEng(Hons)	100898
ØGourlay F	100898
Lawson A J (A/Capt 030400)	100898
Middleditch M J F ato (A/Capt 100400)	100898
ØAllison V D	131198
ØMoseley J C BSc(Hons)	141298

Wyatt A G	141298
Bratcher S D *MEng(Hons)*	090299
Hankins L P *BEng(Hons)*	120499
Hopes D L *BSc(Hons)*	090899
Keel G A *BEng*	090899
Trebilcock M N J	090899
ØVenn J M *BSc(Hons)*	090899
ØWillcocks R D *BSc(Hons)*	090899
Williams S A *BEng(Hons)*	090899
Hanson C I	101299
Dunning B A J	131299
Edwards J	131299
Genko M R	131299
Hall D R	131299
ØJones T L	131299
Stables W	131299
ØDisney R L	171299
Cooke S G	121200

2nd Lieutenants

Dick E J A	141296
††Evans D J	220997
ØBeckett S H C	220997
ØBarron M V	311097
ØDuffus J L	311097
ØJennings H M	060998
ØO'Brien C	060998
Ashton M A	100499
Geary A J C	070899
ØClarke K L	050999
ØCurling R K	050999
ØLeather K J	050999
ØScott N C	050999
Moy J S J	111299
ØStaples C R	110900
ØWatson A M *BSc(Hons)*	110900

Regular Category Late Entry Officers

Lieutenant Colonels

Hobson J F *BEM* sq(w)	021296
Myers S *MBE MA BA(Hons)*	
	010198
Stocks R D *MBE MInstTA MILOG*	
	120298
Graham S	270598
Winkle D J A	040998
Walton R M	010199
Byrne T C *MBE*	010599
Russett D M	070599
Cochrane D C *MIPD*	300599
Ryan C D *MBE*	281099
Irvine W D	010100
Long P J	310100
Chapman M J ato	090600
Kitchen J *BEM*	040900

Majors

Fuller K R	300988
Atkinson C N *MSc MIPD* sq I *(A/Lt Col 311000)*	
	071088
Hymers B	300989
Goff R	300990
Larke N G	300990
Lund J R	300990
Coull P	300991
Griffiths R A	300991
Jones M C *MBE*	300991
Miller K A	300991
White C R *MBE*	300991

Williams P M *MBE*	300991
Bragger B W	300992
Coulter J *MBE*	300992
McGivern J P	300992
Mitchell P *MBE QGM* ato	300992
Ross J E	300992
Nicholson K *MBE BEM*	270293
Cleeton D C *BEM*	300993
Corthine M S *BEM*	300993
Davies R *MBE BEM*	300993
Flowers T J T	300993
Gray S	300993
Moran M *MBE BEM* sq	300993
Morris C	300993
Spence J	300993
Stableford P W	300993
Stapley R D	300993
Sutterby P	300993
Atherton J L *MBE*	300994
Corbey R G	300994
Cornet A B	300994
Hammett P T *BSc(Hons) MBA MHCIMA*	
	300994
Sockett C J *BEM*	300994
Stripe M G ato	300994
Tones D V	300994
Arkley S	300995
Beatty P G	300995
Blomquist A P	300995
Cochrane A S	300995
Ferguson G R *QGM&bar.* ato	
	300995
Hancock P	300995
Montgomery D J	300995
Neve M F *MBE*	300995
Osbourn C P	300995
Phillips C	300995
Taylor B J *QGM* ato	300995
Tillotson B D	300995
Wenlock F	300995
Baker P M J	300996
Bentley J	300996
Bustard R	300996
Capeling J W *CEng MIRTE MIET*	
	300996
Cockburn R R ato sq(w)	300996
Davidson A O	300996
Dempsey N *BEM*	300996
Earey J L A *MBE QGM* ato sq(w)	
	300996
Foley P	300996
Green D *MBE*	300996
Hale D M *MBE*	300996
Jones D E sq(w) ais	300996
Law A C	300996
Masters D *MBE*	300996
McCarten P D *MBE*	300996
McCourt G R	300996
Osborne C	300996
Shields P J *MBE QGM AMInstTA MISM*	
	300996
Smith D J D	300996
Thorogood A D ato	300996
Woods A J *DipEH*	300996
Woodward S J *MIMGT MISM*	
	300996
Beauchamp P J	300997
Binks M K	300997
Blyth W F *BEM MInstTA MILT AIIRSM*	
	300997
Gilbertson M PC	300997
Gordon G	300997

Graham M G sq	300997
Green J	300997
Jory M J	300997
Kendall J W *MBE*	300997
Leadbeater C G	300997
Lemerle A R	300997
Lynch P R	300997
Maidment D C	300997
McCluskey J R	300997
Mehigan C P	300997
Pratt R M	300997
Stephens C R	300997
Thomson W T E	300997
Tomlinson K sq	300997
ØWaddington D PC	300997
Cambridge S PC	300998
Cook D T	300998
Crowshaw R S	300998
Dunstan K	300998
Fielder C	300998
Foster S J	300998
Hannant D G	300998
Haverty M T	300998
Hawkins A *QGM* ato	300998
Middleton D E	300998
Moore R G	300998
Ormiston T	300998
Prior T	300998
Rimmer J	300998
Walker C A	300998
Bendall M A *MILOG*	300999
Cutler H J *BEM MICFM MIMGT MISM*	
	300999
Jackson W R	300999
Lovell J F	300999
Neary J S	300999
Tock B J	300999
Townsend A K *BEM*	300999
Widdows P B *AMILOG*	300999
Green M J *BA BA(Hons) MSc MInstAM MMS MDA*	
	300900
Riley K J	300900

Captains

Downes L A	021094
Walker R K B *MBE* PC	110396

Special Regular Officers Late Entry

Majors

Barton G *DipRSM*	240596
Coast J A	300997
Balding J R T *GM* ato	090498
Read L J *MISM*	300998
Binks D *MBE*	300999
Cook J A	300999
Fletcher A F E	300999
Gore J M	300999
Haslam N *BA(Hons)* PC	300999
Saddington A P ato	300999
Ziverts G	300999
Bayston R B *MBE*	300900
Brown T E *MBE*	300900
Buckley A	300900
Chubb G K ato	300900
Hurry P M *GM* ato	300900
Maclachlan I J	300900
McLane G S *MBE*	300900
Petty G D *BEM*	300900
Walden M *MBE MISM MILOG*	
	300900

Young G	300900

Captains

Fryer A	171293
Phillpotts R G	140194
Christopher C D	200594
Carruthers L	300994
Boole S G	030495
Lonnen S T *MBE MISM MILOG*	
MBIFM	260495
Robertson G D *BEM*	280595
Hart T	250695
Bruce I J	190795
ØDunn M A T	230795
Townell S M	050196
Aggett C R *MBE*	130296
Wilson M J	180496
Sutherland D W	100696
Willingham S *MBE MCIT MILOG*	
	080796
Cass R W	120896
Stickings K A	080996
Murray A PC *(A/Maj 260101)*	
	301196
Guilfoyle C G *(A/Maj 041200)*	
	060197
Main A J A	020297
David C M	060297
Comrie T W	100297
Robinson S A	030497
Couling B T *(A/Maj 120600)*	
	180497
Eades C N	180497
Everill M W D	180497
Illidge A C	180497
Latham-Boal N P ais *(A/Maj*	
210899)	180497
Wood P J	180497
Cross K A *BSc* ato *(A/Maj 210800)*	
	240497
Obrien S *MBE QGM* ato	030797
Tomkins C E *BEM*	041297
Bush C N	010498
Leach J D	010498
Lomas C H *MBE BEM*	010498
McLelland R J *QGM*	010498
Russell A	010498
Short B R	010498
Daley L J N	241299

Intermediate Regular Officers

Majors

Alcock R M	151286
Prewer E R sq lcc PC	300987
Duff G M	300995
ØHosking S R s	300995
Ba-Tin M P sq	300996
St Matthew-Daniel A O *LHCIMA*	
	300996
Eaves M D	300997
Searle A L W PC	300997
Yates A	300997
Collins R A PC	300998
Boxhall C E S	300999
Clark A C	300999
King P R	300999
Lusher S G	300999
March K L PC	300999
Porter A B PC	300999
Costley A ato	300900

Hannam S P	300900
ØLuedicke A C *BA(Hons)*	300900
Poulson A	300900

Captains

Smith D A ato	081290
Stewart M D PC	310194
Hawthorne M J	090394
ØCollier-Mcgirr G A *BA(Hons)*	
	060894
White R D *GCGI*	010995
Stevens D A	151295
Wilkinson A J *MA(Hons) (A/Maj*	
180101)	040796
Clarke J R	141296
Hay L J	141296
Hall T A	080897
Dermody J G *BSc*	141097
Hesketh M J *BSc(Hons)*	141097
Wallace-Dutton J C	141197
Davies J J ph	121297
Masters A R	121297
Leach M R	190198
ØParr R L *BA(Hons)*	120298
Wilkinson M I N *BSc(Hons)*	260398
ØFairbairn A J E *LLB(Hons)* PC	
	310398
Lambert M W A PC	090498
Scannell M A *BSc(Hons)* pi	090498
ØBower A L *BA(Hons)* PC	120698
Blair-Tidewell J T *BA(Hons)*	160698
ØDarby C J B *BSc(Hons)*	070898
Gould T R *BSc(Hons)*	070898
Birkby A M *BEng(Hons)*	131098
Sorungbe K A O O *BSc(Hons)*	
	131098
ØProbert N J	281198
ØThom R C *BA(Hons)*	111298
Tonkins W R J	111298
ØWhiteley V J *BA(Hons)* ato	111298
Hood M A *BA(Hons)*	100299
Watkins S J R *BSc(Hons)*	100299
ØElvidge L M	090499
Owen J D	090499
Rickard L M	090499
Bracey J E *BSc(Hons)*	140699
ØAinsworth E L *BA(Hons)*	060899
Bowyer P K *BSc(Hons) BTech* ato	
	121099
ØLittle S C *BA(Hons)*	121099
ØPollitt T H *BSc(Hons)*	121099
Moxon C D	161199
Flint N G A V	101299
Browne R J	171299
Springall N E	110100
†Calkin C D	240100
Beaumont P M K *LLB(Hons)*	
	090200
ØFroggatt E C *BA(Hons)*	090200
Davie A R *BSc(Hons)*	130600
Organ P A	100700
†Foreman S P	110700
Egan R J	120800
Howard B K ato	120800
ØHanlon C L M *BSc(Hons)*	101000
ØMcHale M L *BA(Hons)*	101000
Rogerson P C *BSc(Hons)*	101000
Cameron H C	241000
Falinski S J	161200
Grimwood N J *BEng(Hons)*	080201

Lieutenants

Brazier D *(A/Capt 011099)* 030497	
ØWinton H *BEng*	120897
ØAllen E F *BA(Hons)*	131097
ØGodber S *BEd(Hons)*	131097
Miller D T *BA(Hons)*	130498
Rattenbury C J *(A/Capt 151199)*	
	130498
Barton-Hope S C *(A/Capt 140800)*	
	100898
Gill J R W *BSc(Hons)*	100898
Leeper J F B *(A/Capt 060400)*	
	100898
Leng R A *BEng(Hons)*	100898
Reehal P S	100898
Venn T D *BSc(Hons) (L/Capt*	
180700)	100898
Phillips J E *(A/Capt 280200)*	
	191298
Hawkins T M D	120499
Loudon A R	220699
Cufley N W	041199
Jenkinson S F	100300
Anderson N D	080800
ØRolfe G L	080800
Punter A C	121200

2nd Lieutenants

Aspin M D	100499
ØBoden L S	070899
Palmer B	111299
Duggan A L	150400
Howard R M	150400
Rathbone J W F	120800
Vintner A R	120800
††Sugdon G R	100900
Ivison K M D	161200

Short Service Late Entry Officers

Majors

Atkins S D	300999
Hardman L V	300999
Mackenzie S J	300999
Anderson N	300900
Barnett B R	300900

Captains

Church K B *(A/Maj 080299)*	
	160993
Gardiner T W	190795
Wall D J PC	260795
Belshaw K J	210196
Roberts S J *BEM*	030297
Oliver J *(A/Maj 070200)*	170297
Biles S L	100497
Batty M K	111297
ØParkin D *BEM*	050298
Bland M	190298
Bailey M C	260298
Anderson H S	010498
Brown R	010498
Elmer M T	010498
Fraser T D	010498
Griffiths S P	010498
Grimsley J P *QGM*	010498
Johnson G A	010498
Jones R *MHCIMA*	010498
King D A	010498
King P J *MBE*	010498
Lambert A P *MBE*	010498

McBride J C *MBE* 010498
Milnes P 010498
Orr G 010498
Parker I 010498
Parr C 010498
Pascoe J E 010498
Pennie G B 010498
Phillips V R 010498
Pibworth A J 010498
Player R B 010498
Robinson G 010498
Robinson M D 010498
Routledge C J 010498
Schofield K D 010498
Senior A R   PC 010498
Smith R 010498
Stratton D M 010498
Treadwell A S *BEM* 010498
Vaissiere I P 010498
Vernam P D   *(A/Maj 020400)*
010498
Wells P R 010498
Wellstead T P   *(L/Maj 010400)*
010498
Knox P J 200498
Scannell P *BA(Hons) MA* 200498
Fox D G 050598
ØMiller C 110598
Woodley C R 110598
Fisher A K 080698
Fyvie S G   *(A/Maj 301000)* 150698
Thomas R I 150698
Paterson R 250698
Cooper M I 290698
Biggs M 270798
Emerton C D 170898
Smith P D 170898
Hawker G L 140998
Davidson I R 091298
ØHickson S *BEM* 040199
Irving F 110199
Parsons G 010299
McFarlane M J 010399
Brooks G C 010499
Buechel S M 010499
Lear K W 010499
Mullock D C 010499
Staples A F 010499
Stocks G W 010499
Thomas G 010499
Jessermino M J 190499
Starbuck C W 190499
Majeed M I 040599
Hunt M B 030699
McCreanor A P *BEM* 250699
Baker R 050799
Goundry T 050799
Shields J F 050799
Thornley M H S 090799
Cheetham N E 190799
Kerr J 190799
Badder P W 020899
Golding P J 060999
Henry M C 060999
Sisi C A 060999
Snape P D 041099
Symon J W 181099
Percival B I 050100
Ogden P R *MBE* 140200
Rimmington R K 210200
Blues K H S 030400
Harris M R 030400

James R H 030400
Kelly J A 030400
Lupton C N 030400
O'Hagan T 030400
Robjohns S C 030400
York J E 070400
Fleming J A 100400
Roskelly J K 100400
Gould D J 170400
Orourke K 280400
Boardman I A 020500
Nichol M H J 020500
Sanderson N R 020500
Cartwright P 080500
Loader N T 010600
Evans C M 120600
Faulkner J E 260600
Fraser C W W 030700
Shepherd R R 180700
Smith K M 210700
Joinson C 290800
Allsop P J 110900
Long S C 180900
Smith A W 021000
Ring T J 091000
Young G P 091000
Scott W N 271100

Short Service Officers

Captains

ØAtkinson K L *BSc(Hons)* 120496
ØCooke G *BSc(Hons)* 110896
ØFacer P S *BSc(Hons)* ph 141097
Asquith D A P *BSc(Hons)* ato 121297
Chohan M J *BA(Hons)* PC 120698
Dymond N R M   PC 160698
Russell G A *BA(Hons)* ph 160698
ØHutton E *BSc(Hons)* 131098
Whitbread L F *BA(Hons)* 131098
Godderidge D *BSc(Hons)* pi 111298
Darmanin R 141298
Broad A J 210199
Tomes P R 210199
Pelan A J *BA(Hons)* ato pi OLPM
100299
ØCoulston J L 140699
Hurst I G 140699
ØBland V J *BSc(Hons)* 060899
Clark M P *BA(Hons)* 060899
Davies S P   ph 060899
Gascoyne A J *BSc(Hons)* 060899
Hearn F A *BA(Hons)* 060899
ØLyle S A *BSc(Hons) MPhil*
060899
Williams M T *BSc(Hons)* 071099
ØHalley T F C 121099
ØSercombe V A *BSc(Hons)* 121099
Brady N P *BA(Hons)* 131099
Tasker R R *BSc(Hons)* 021299
Ferguson S J *BSc(Hons)* 101299
Morgan D H *BEng* 101299
ØWest N *BSc* pi 101299
Na Nakhorn J *BA(Hons)* 090200
Martin M W *BA(Hons)* 120400
Bowen C N 140400
McCoy R 140400
Revell J P 140400
Marr J R D *BA(Hons)* 200400
ØCouper E K *BA(Hons)* 130600
Haynes A J *BA(Hons)* 130600
Smith N A *BA(Hons)* 130600

ØBrown C J M *BA(Hons)* 101000
ØCobley C L *BSc(Hons)* 101000
Cooper G A *BA(Hons)* 101000
Dutson J N *BA(Hons)* 101000
Fullerton K G *BSc* 101000
Hall J C *BSc(Hons)* 101000
Hart R M *BA(Hons)* 101000
ØLearney S *BA(Hons)* 101000
ØMadams A M *BA(Hons)* 101000
ØMcCormick E J *BSc(Hons) DipHE*
101000
ØShipley J L *BA(Hons)* 101000
ØSwinburne E J *BA(Hons)* 101000
Cornell S A *BA(Hons)* 080201
Lennard A *MEng(Hons)* 080201
ØTownley R E *BA(Hons)* 080201

Lieutenants

Brown J L *BA(Hons)* 051296
McCrann J S D *BEng(Hons)*
   (A/Capt 111200) 120297
Stuart M K *BA(Hons)   (A/Capt
301100)* 120297
ØCargill S D *BA(Hons)   (A/Capt
260201)* 160697
ØCowan C *BSc(Hons)   (A/Capt
050900)* 160697
Haywood G A *BA(Hons)* 160697
Hendry L P *BSc(Hons)* 160697
Smith T L *BEng(Hons)* 160697
Luckett S P *BEng* 120897
Moreton M J *BA(Hons)* 120897
Steel W O J *BSc(Hons)   (A/Capt
010600)* 120897
ØWarwick P Z *BA(Hons)   (A/Capt
011000)* 120897
Black A D *MA(Hons)   (A/Capt
50201)* 131097
Stuart C P *MEng   (A/Capt 090101)*
131097
Smalley C N 221097
Chapman I G *BA(Hons)* 161297
Clarke R A H *BSc(Hons)* 161297
ØHayes R L *BSocSc(Hons)* 161297
ØHilton M J *BSc(Hons)* 161297
Hoban J *BA(Hons)* 161297
Mathias A H *BSc(Hons)* 100298
Howe S R C *BA(Hons)* 100298
ØHunter K J *BA(Hons)* 100298
ØLewis A R *BSc(Hons)* 100298
ØSanford A J E *LLB(Hons)* 100298
Shepherd J A J *BEng(Hons) MEng*
100298
Randall C J 220298
Stevens R J   *(A/Capt 060400)*
060498
Hampton-Stone C   *(A/Capt 290800)*
130498
Warren D P *BSc(Hons)* 130498
West J C *BSc(Hons)* 130498
Wilson M P *BSc* 130498
Rouse R A 170598
Crossland T J *BSc(Hons) MA*
Symonds T J *BA(Hons)* 140698
Strafford V M *FIMH* 020798
Eggett N 180798
Beaumont K D N 100898
Brassington J D *BSc(Hons)* 100898
Dines S J *BSc(Hons)* 100898
Jackson S D *BSc(Hons)* 100898
Mears L C *BSc(Hons)* 100898

ØSimmons E K *BSc(Hons)*	100898
Stainthorpe P E *BA(Hons)*	100898
Wheddon J H *BA*	100898
ØWoodward J M *BA(Hons)*	100898
ØCust J E *BA(Hons)*	121098
Hamilton A S *BEng(Hons)*	121098
Young D A	031198
Le Grande S C	131198
Krykunivsky N V	141198
Tribble N W	161198
Alexander C A	261198
Amey R S	141298
ØBanks K *(A/Capt 271100)*	141298
ØCrabbe H M *BSc(Hons)*	141298
ØEmmerson R A *BSc(Hons)*	141298
Fincham M J G *BA(Hons)*	141298
ØHull S C *BA(Hons)*	141298
ØLee A V *BSc(Hons)*	141298
Marshall J H *BSc(Hons)*	141298
Prendiville A J *BSc*	141298
ØCook S J	100399
ØConway S L *BA*	120499
Cutter M G B *BSocSc(Hons)*	120499
Fawsitt J C *BA(Hons)*	120499
Fitzgerald-Finch L C *BSc*	120499
Gatward J R *BSc(Hons)*	120499
Rees S S *(A/Capt 11200)*	120499
ØSimms H E G *BA(Hons)*	120499
ØCooper N *MA(Hons) MSc*	130699
ØLamont K A *MA(Hons)*	130699
Allen R J	270699
Cope P N	020899
Bennett E N J	090899
ØBoulton S A *BA(Hons)*	090899

Futter R J *BSc(Hons)*	090899
Marsden S H *(A/Capt 140800)*	090899
ØPettitt A H N *BSc*	090899
Steer C A *BSc(Hons)*	090899
Townsend S N *BSc(Hons)*	090899
Weatherston P D *BSc(Hons)*	090899
Ritchie P J *(A/Capt 080101)*	191099
ØEdwards A D	111199
Kemp S N	121199
Crew N	011299
ØBunn A J S	131299
ØEmmott H M *BA(Hons)*	131299
Enever M *BA(Hons)*	131299
Nott D S *LLB(Hons)*	131299
Parker M *BEng(Hons)*	131299
ØSparks H E *BA(Hons)*	131299
ØVan Der Merwe C T	131299
West A F *BA(Hons)*	131299
ØWincott G M *BA(Hons)*	131299
Yates C N *BSc(Hons)*	131299
Field S J D *(A/Capt 140800)*	100400
Clarke R S	050600
Fisher D J	050600
Allen P A *BSc*	070700
Flett D J J	070700
Lewis E C C	070700
ØParry N J	080800
ØBowes-Crick K L	111100
Aumonier B	121200
Chisholm G J P	121200
Heap A D	121200
Sparkes A J	121200

2nd Lieutenants

Austen T A	020299
Joynes N G	100499
ØMiles S J	100499
ØRedwood C A	100499
Clark A R	070899
Hallett R G	070899
ØQuick S	061299
Paull J	120200
Colbourne M J	150400
Evoy C G	120800
Falinski N M	120800
Preece B L	120800
Windsor M G	120800
Nicolson C	161200

Short Service Volunteer Officers

Majors

Norman J R *TD•*	010495

Captains

ØMulhern S *BA*	020897
ØMaddison G *BSc(Hons)*	010498
Battersby D M *BSc(Hons)*	010399

Rec Res (RARO)

Majors

Merritt J B sq	170180

ROYAL ARMY MEDICAL CORPS

The Rod of Aesculapius the Serpent in Silver within a wreath of Laurel all gold thereunder a scroll inscribed 'IN ARDUIS FIDELIS' in silver the whole ensigned with the Crown in gold

Regimental Marches

Quick March . . . . Here's a Health unto His Majesty
Slow March . . . . .Her Bright Smile Haunts Me Still
Agents . . . . Holts Branch, Royal Bank of Scotland plc, Lawrie House, Farnborough, Hants
Corps Headquarters. . . . . former Army Staff College, London Road, Camberley GU15 4NP
(Tel: 01276 63344*)*

Alliances

The Canadian Armed Forces . . . . Medical Branch
Australian Military Forces . . . . .The Royal Australian Army Medical Corps
New Zealand Army . . . . .Royal New Zealand Army Medical Corps
Pakistan Army . . . . .Army Medical Corps
Sri Lanka Army . . . . .The Sri Lankan Army Medical Corps
Zambia Army . . . . .Zambia Army Medical Service
South African Defence Forces . . . . . . .South African Medical Service

Colonel in Chief. . . . . *HM* QUEEN ELIZABETH THE QUEEN MOTHER

Colonels Commandant. . . . . Brig T B N Oldrey ret pay 141297
Brig M J Ratcliffe ret pay 010199
* Brig K MacG Stephens ret pay 191199
Brig G E Ratcliffe ret pay 010101

Brigadiers

Garnett R A F *OBE PhD MB ChB*
BSc DPhysMed CPSM FRCPED
140792
Brown J R *QHP MA MSc MB BCh*
DCH FFOM 190894
Conroy M D *QHP MB BCh BAO*
DCH DObstRCOG FRCGP
080295
Lynch P *MD ChB FRCP*
DObstRCOG 010496
Winfield C R *CBE BM BCh*
MRCP(UK) DCH FRCP 010496
Houghton I T *MLA LLM MD BChir*
FRCA LMSSA FHKCA FHKAM
130996
Hopkins G O *MB BS MRCP(UK)*
MRCS DPhysMed FRCPED 280597
Lillywhite L P *MBE MSc MB BCh*
MFOM psc 150399
Smith D W *QHP MB ChB*
DObstRCOG MRCGP FRCGP
210599
Creamer I S *MC MSc MRCS LRCP*
FIMGT DFFP MHSM MFPHM psc
311299
Macmillan A H M *QHP MBChB*
FFPHM psc 240100

Colonels

Tinsley M J *MB ChB BSc MRCGP*
DObstRCOG jsdc 270790
ØCurran A *MB ChB MRCGP DCH*
DObstRCOG 121190
Richardson J C *MSc MB BChir*
MRCS LRCP DRCOG MRCGP
FRCPI 041091
Ismaili N A *MB ChB FRCS* 300592

Anderson R M L *MB ChB*
MRCPsych 110594
Box C J *MSc MB BS DRCOG*
DAvMed MFOM AFOM 150596
Lyon Dean C W *MB ChB MRCGP*
FRCGP 040896
Batty C G *MBE MSc MB ChB*
FRCSEd FRCS(Glasg) MFOM
AFOM FPCERT 070896
Roberts P *MBE QHS MS MB FRCS*
010397
Symon T *MB ChB* 190597
Thornton R *MD MSc ChB DIH*
DAvMed MRAeS MFOM ph 280797
Millar K N A *MB ChB psc* 030897
Shepherd A F I *MB ChB BAO*
FRCSEd 110598
Cogbill K L *MB ChB DRCOG*
020798
Braithwaite M G *OBE MB ChB DIH*
DRCOG DAvMed MFOM ph
070798
Mellor S G *MB BS FRCS* 090898
Jones R M *MSc MBBS DObstRCOG*
FRCPath MRCPath MRCP RCPED
020998
ØDuggan E J *MB ChB BSc FRCS*
051298
Finnegan T P *MSc MBBS MFOM psc*
311298
ØWells J M *OBE MSc MB ChB*
DRCOG MRCGP 010899
Lawrenson G W *MSc MB ChB*
DRCOG DFFP MRCGP 040899
Miller S A ST J *MSc MB BChir*
MRCGP DRCOG FFPHM 060899
Staunton M A *MB BS MRCS LRCP*
FRGS MRCGP 090999
Fabricius P J *MBBS FRCP* 010200
Skipworth J F *MBChB FRSH DFFP*
030200

Hannon C *MB BCh MRCGP*
DRCOG 030700
Ineson N *MBBS FRCP* 310700
Graham J T *MSc MB ChB BAO*
MFCM MFPHM 010800
Von Bertele M J *OBE MB BCh*
DAvMed DIH MFOM rcds jsdc ph
010800
Galbraith K A *MA BM BCh BA*
FRCS 090800
Griffiths M F P *MB ChB BSc*
FRCSEd DO 161200
World M J *MD BS FRCP MRCS*
070101
Van Lare J P *MB ChB DPM* 060201
Sahi S P *MBBS MRCP* 100201

Lieutenant Colonels

Lansley P H *MB ChB MRCGP*
DRCOG MFFP 100888
Pani C K *MBBS DA* 270988
Saggar S N *MBBS FRCA DA*
030589
Kempster S J *MB ChB* 010290
Ghosh D *MB BS* 250490
ØBergman B P *MBChB DPH*
MIMGT FRSH DFFP MFPHM
140790
Whiteoak R *MBBChir FRCP*
080891
Price B A *MD MS MBBS FRCS*
LRCP MRCS 170991
Bolton J P G *MSc MB ChB MRCGP*
DRCOG 011091
Kabuubi J B L *MB BS MRCP MRCS*
FRCP 081091
Gamble D S C *MB BCh MRCPsych*
301091

*Representative Colonel Commandant for 2001

Burgess J E *MB BS MRCGP MRCS LRCP DRCOG (A/Col 230998)* 011191
ØPiper M E *LMSSA MRCPSYCH* jsdc 031291
Sreenivasa Rao P M *MD MBBS MRCOG DipVen* 010292
Bhatt B M *MD MBBS MRCP(UK) FRCP* 160292
Hosni A A *MB BCh FRCSEd* 160292
Moorthy B *MBBS FRCP MRCP(UK) MD(PAED)* 160292
Abdul-Aziz L A S *FRCPI FRCP* 120492
Bosanquet H G *MB ChB MRCPSYCH* 230592
Forber R K J *MB BChir MMedSci FRCS AFOM FRCS(Eng) (A/Col 010499)* 050892
Ansah-Boateng Y *MB ChB MRCPath* 270493
Hawley A *OBE MB ChB DMCC* psc hcsc(J) *(A/Col 190299)* 010893
Hoad N A *MB BChir FRCP MRCP* 070893
Little J F M *MB BS* 120893
Dieppe C *MB BS MRCGP DRCOG* 220893
Allen J C *MB ChB FRCS(Glasg)* 240893
Miles D M *MB ChB DFFP MRCGP* 310893
Thomson A D *MB ChB DFFP MRCGP* 210294
Strowbridge N F *MB BS DA* 020494
Stewart M P M *MBChB FRCS GLAS(OR* 150494
Sloss J M *MSc MB BS FRCSEd MRCPath* 100694
Bonnici W *MRCS LRCP DCH MRCGP* 240694
Saleh M S *MBBCh DA* 070994
Brooks T J G *MSc BChir LMSSA MRCPath* 091094
Jackson C J *MB BS MRCS LRCP* 140295
ØBoxer C M *MBBS BSc MRCP* 190295
Parker C J R *OBE MB BS DTM&H AFOM* psc 240295
Stone J M *FFARCSIrel* 040595
Jagdish S 110595
Cooper N K *MB BCh FRCSEd DLO DDHM MFOM AFOM* 080695
Langford D P *MBBS MRCGP* 200695
Burge T S *MB ChB FRCS* 140695
Leach A J *DiplMCRCSEd MB ChB DRCOG DFFP FRCGP* 010895
Gillespie P N *MB ChB BAO DCROG MRCGP* 080895
Simpson R G *MB ChB DRCOG MRCGP FRCGP* 210895
Bisset R J *MBChB MRCGP DRCOG* 010995
Jeevaratnam E A J *MBBS DA* 030995
Palmer I P *MB ChB MRCPSYCH* 300995
Vassallo D J *MRCS LRCP FRCSED* 061295
Menzies A R 010296

Ward P J *MRCS LRCP DA* 010296
Keeling J D *MB BS DRCOG MRCGP FPCERT* 010896
Timothy H R *MB BS FRSH MRCGP FPCERT* 060896
Hands C A H *MRCS LRCP* 130896
Kerr A D *MB BCh MRCGP* 240896
Gill R M F *MB MMedSci BS MFOM MRCGP* 100996
Rowan J F *OBE MBBCh MRCGP DRCOG* 230996
Cordell R F *DiplMCRCSEd MBBS BSc DCH MRCGP DRCOG* 010697
ØFolkes S E F *MSc MB BS MFOM AFOM* 010897
McCurdie I M *MB BS MRCGP MRCP(UK) DRCOG* 010897
Morgan-Jones D J *MBE MB BS MRCGP* 010897
Williams A N *MB BChir MMedSci DTM&H MFOM AFOM* 010897
Williamson R H B *MSc MBChB MFOM MRCGP* psc(J) 010897
Adams M S *MBBS BSc* ph 030997
Pollak T E *MBChB* 011197
McMenemy P *MBChB MRCGP DRCOG* 010298
Collins D M S *MBBS FPCERT* 020298
Tuck J J H *MBBS* 170498
Mills A S *BCh BAO DFFP MRCGP DRCOG* 250598
Diack G A M *MB ChB DRCOG* 040798
Baker D *MMedSci MFOM MRCGP* 010898
Hodgetts T J *DiplMCRCSEd MBBS FRCP MRCP* 010898
Johnson P A *MB BS DAvMed DIH AFOM DRCOG* ph 010898
Jones T J *MB BCh BSc* 010898
ØMacleod J J *MB ChB BSc MRCGP* 150898
Cain P A *MBBCh* sq ph 070998
Roberts M J *BM BCh DA(UK) FRCA* 010299
Terrell A G *MSc MBChB* psc(J) 050299
Bricknell M C M *DM MMedSci MFOM FPDip DFFP DMCC MRCGP DRCOG* 010899
Clasper J C *DiplMCRCSEd MB ChB FRCSED* 010899
ØHorrocks C L 010899
Kay J L *MBChB MRCGP DRCOG* 010899
Malyon A D 010899
Parker P J *MB BCh BAO FRCSED* 010899
Wheatley G 010899
ØYoung J J *MBBS DCH MRCGP* 010899
Owen J P *MB MMedSci ChB MFOM AFOM* 180899
ØCarter J T *MBBS MRCGP* 260999
Ross D A *MBBS* 030200
Firth M *MBBS FRCR* 120200
Oommen J *MD MBBS DA FFARCSIrel* 070300
Bhabutta R K *MBChB* 010800
Bowen J R C 010800

Etherington J *MRCP* 010800
Gemmell I M M *MBChB FRGS MFOM AFOM FPCERT* 010800
Hobbs C M *MBBChir FRCSED* 010800
Sadler P J *FRCA* 010800
Timothy J R *MB BS BSc MRCGP* 010800
Bailey D J W *MBBS FRCR* 060800
Sharma S K *MBBS DFFP MRCGP DRCOG* 080800
Croft A M J *MSc MB BS MIL DMCC MFPHM FFPHM I* 160201

Majors

ØHodgson B H *MB ChB MRCGP DRCOG (A/Lt Col 010494)* 310788
Kane G G *MBChB BMedSci FRCSED* 010892
Williams D 020892
Harrigan M J *MBBS MMedSci AFOM* ph 050992
ØCarnegie-Brown P M 010893
Hendrickse A D *BM DA FRCA* 010893
Kent A W *MBChB FRCS(TRAND* 010893
Sharma D *MSc MBChB BA FRCS ACLS FRCPS(GLAS)* 180194
Bennett N J *MBBS FRCS(Eng)* 010294
Curry I P *MBBS* ph 010894
Edwards D P *DiplMCRCSEd MBChB FRCSED* 010894
England M H *MBBS AFOM MRCGP* 010894
Jacks A S *MBBS BSc* 010894
Nicol A M *MB ChB MRCGP DRCOG* 010894
Price-Thomas S P *MBChB DRCOG DFFP MRCGP* 010894
Rooms M A *BM* ph 010894
Rossiter N D *FRCSED* 010894
Scott C W D *MBChB MRCGP DRCOG* 010894
Gale R G *BMBCH FPDip MRCGP DRCOG REMT* 030894
Smith N P 300994
Weir M J S *MBChB MRCGP* 010295
Banfield G K *MBChB DLO FRCSED* 010895
Beardmore C E *MBBS MRCGP* 010895
Cantelo R A R *MBBCh* 010895
Connor P *MBChB* 010895
Jeffery S L *MBChB ScFRCPS(GLAS) FRCSED* 010895
Mistlin A *MBBS* 010895
Pambakian S *BSc DA(UK) FRCA* 010895
ØRoughton S A *MBBS DFFP MRCGP* 010895
Wilson D R *MBChB MRCP(UK)* 030995
McBroom R J 300995
Slade M A 300995
Hill P F 010296
Richards P R *MBChB* 190696
Bowley D M G *MBBS FRCS(Eng)* 010896

Bushby A J R *MB BChir* ph 010896
ØChittenden H B *MBBS FRCSEd*
010896
Dalrymple P A *DFFP MRCGP*
DRCOG D C C H 010896
Duncan R J *MBBS* 010896
Ellis G A *MBBS* 010896
McMurtry I A *MBBCh FRCS(Eng)*
010896
Smith H R *MBBS MRCP* 010896
Standley D M *FRCS(Eng)* 010896
Tarn M *BM* 010896
Willman A S *MB BS* 010896
Woods D R *MBChB DRCOG*
010896
Russell R J 050896
ØMorgan E R 300996
Toney M A 300996
Bingham M T *MBBCh MRCGP*
DRCOG 021096
Pooley D L J *BEM* 010597
Beaton K C *MBBS BMedSci (A/Lt*
Col 260500) 030697
Gibb I E *MBChB FRCSED* 010897
Henning J D R *MBBCh ACLS*
010897
Parkhouse D A F H *MBBS* 010897
Swan T F 010897
Babbage S F 300997
Woodhouse J I J A *MBBS DFFP*
MRCGP 010298
McAllister P D *MBBS* 010898
ØWoolrich L H 040898
Griffiths A D *MBChB BMedSci*
FRCA 230898
Lewin J H *MBChB* 230898
ØPalmer J V *MBBS* 240898
Townend C J *RRC RGN* 300998
Barker C T *MBBS MRCPSYCH*
010299
Baidwan J S *MBBS* 140800
Bell M S 300900
Firth R C 300900
Heatlie R J 300900

Captains

ØWalters P L 070896
Byles D A 090200

Lieutenants

Wilson D A J 240897
ØKottritsch S J 141298
†Mills B D R 110700

Administrative Officers

Colonels

Best M C sq 300697
Newell R J *RMN* psc jsdc 300697
Howe S C *RGN* sq jsdc 300699
Foster T R sq 130999
Morris D J sq 311299
French M T sq 150100
Pitcher T S *RGN* sq jsdc 300600

Lieutenant Colonels

Baker P B *BA FIBMS* sq 010791
Baines C 300695
Dickinson C J *MSc* sq 300696
Read I G *BEM* sq 300696

Tredget F S sq 300696
Dubaree A *FISM* sq 300697
Eadon B F J *MBE BSc MRPharmS*
sq MDA 300697
Godkin M P sq aic 300697
Johnston S J sq 300697
Moodie R H *MCIEH* sq 300697
Pearson J E sq 300697
Brown D P *BEM* sq 311297
Hubbard P J sq 311297
Barnes P W sq 300698
Mannering P G sq 300699
Pemberton M V *DCR(R)* sq 300699
Solly K sq 300699
Tibbit K J sq 300699
ØWellington V A sq 300699
Holt K *BEM* 311299
McIntosh J H psc 311299
Griffin K M sq 300600
Phillips B 300600

Majors

ØAshpitel A H 060388
Millwater C A sq 300991
Ravenscroft A J 300992
Williams E D 300993
Sippe R A J *MCSP* sq 300994
Graham B sq 300995
John P F *DipEH* 300995
Lawrence S R 300995
McBride H G M 300995
Murray J W 300995
Nadin M N *SRMLT FIBMS* 300995
Rees A J sq 300995
Saunders D E 300995
Campbell S W ph 300996
Harrison P sq 300996
Douglas R *BEM* 300997
Jefferson P G 300997
Jose A M 300997
Murray R 300997
Spooner A T 300997
Stewart D *MBE* 300997
While-Paddon R N 300997
ØWills R A *MSc* 300997
Barfi W K 300998
Boreham A C 300998
Hair J C 300998
Lawrence R C 300998
Rowland T L *MPhil B Sc (Hons)*
300999
ØBell F J 300900

Captains

Bell A R *(A/Maj 220201)* 200494
Watters C R 010495
Edwards M J 090498
De Rouffignac P *BSc(Hons)* 100299

Regular Category Late Entry Officers

Majors

Lindley M J 300994
Crowe I R J *MIHE FRSH MCIEH*
MIOSH 300995
Myers G L 300995
Cromar D A 300996
Johnston J R 300996
Pentony P L V 300996
Knight D P 300997

Welsh D A C 300997

Administrative Officers

Captains

Allard G R *Lt Col 010600* 031187
Bruce J J *Maj 300995* 010192

Special Regular Officers Late Entry

Majors

Baker R A F *MBE FIBMS* 300997
Bernthal P A *FIBMS* 300997
Layton K 300997
Minden D F *MBE MCSP EN(G)*
300997
Roberts K I *DipEH* 300997
Beamer J *DCR(R)* 300998
Collie D 300998
Irving G 300998
Jeng M *MBE DipRG&RT MCSP*
DipTRG 300998
Jubb M J *MCSP* 300998
Laher R A I 300998
Lee K T *MCSP FETC* 300998
Paterson S N *MCSP* 300998
Steadman P F P 300998
Thomas G D *MCSP* 300998
Greener J W D *MCSP* 300999
Kettle J N *DipEH* 300999
Tervit T *QGM* 300999
Anderson S 300900
Buxton A T 300900
Twell A F 300900

Captains

Nixon S J *CMS EN(G) CertEd (FE*
091295
Charleson J *(A/Maj 050499)*
260297
Leach G S 250997
Daniels P H 010298
Bell G B L *(A/Maj 230899)* 010498
Charnick A 010498
Godfrey G J 010498
Holmes M J 010498
Knott S J *(A/Maj 151299)* 010498
Moran M *(A/Maj 161000)* 010498
Partington N D *MBE* 010498
Pickering N J *MIPD* 010498
Riley W A 010498
Ryan M A *(A/Maj 091000)* 010498
Simpson I 010498
Jones D A *BEM* 210798

Administrative Officers
Majors

Reid R 300900

Intermediate Regular Officers

Lieutenant Colonels

Titley J V *MB BS* 260494
Barraclough C J *MB ChB* 010295
Goshai H *MBE MB ChB* 010299
Howe G B *MBBS MRCPSYCH*
160899
Owers R C *MA MBBS MRCGP*
DRCOG 010201

Majors

ØDunn R M	010894
ØHolden L G (A/Lt Col 120600)	
	010894
Miller J H MBChB MRCP	010894
Campbell A D K MBChB DFFP MRCGP	030895
King L J MRCP FRCR	030895
ØMitchell N J MBChB	060296
Cawston P G MBBS DRCOG	
	210497
Mulkern E M	010897
ØOrr L E MBChB MRSC FRCS(Eng)	
	010897
Rosell P A E MBBS B Sc (Hons)	
	010897
Tong J L MB ChB	010897
Palmer J M	030299
McErlain M J MBChB MRCS	
	010899
McCluskey A J	300999
Gupta S MBBS FRCA	270200
ØDuncan S J MCSP	300900
Emerton S M RGN	300900
Flint C	300900
Langley J S	300900
Pealin D K RGN	300900
Powell S J	300900
Searight S R C	300900
ØSidebottom S L	300900
Stewart G MILOG MRPharmS	
	300900
ØWilliams E F MRPharmS	300900
ØWright L J	011100

Captains

Jeffery R G F BSc(Hons) (A/Maj 201099)	060894
ØJennings E R M	180295
Southwood T J	091095
Steele T P (A/Maj 280699)	060296
Humphries M I	200596
Cameron E A DipM	120298
ØBaker S L	160698
Tracey S R	140699
ØHanks T A	090200
†Johnston A M MBChB	250800
†Woghiren O R E	250800

Administrative Officers

Majors

Turner I W MIMGT MInstAM DMS sq	300985
Barrett A J	300985
ØSlay D S	300999
ØEdmonds K E	300900

Lieutenants

ØRussell P M	120897
Taylor M I	150199

Short Service Late Entry Officers

Captains

Healy M J MCSP	250997
Campbell B (A/Maj 140800)	
	010298
ØCain A L	010498

Gardener J N MBE	010498
Hulme D J	010498
Massocchi S A	010498
Neaves A D SRP	010498
O'Riordan K D	010498
Ralph D J MRSH MCIEH MIOA	
	010498
Stewart J M (A/Maj 231000)	
	010498
Travis A M	010498
Young R S (A/Maj 071100)	010498
Doliczny R M	280898
Hunter I P L DipEH	060300
McKean W M	030400
Woolger S P	030400
Maccallum A S	030700
Summers R H	070800
Moore G W	290800

Administrative Officers

Majors

ØFrater A D	300996
Hartley N F CertMGMT	300997

Captains

Davies S J J	010498
Elliott M P R (A/Maj 180900)	
	010498
Kirkpatrick I R	010498
Magee M	010498
Rump G	010498
Smith S A	010498
Walker G	010498
Wilson D L	010498
Batcock J A	010798
Best J P (A/Maj 100101)	010798
Wynn D A	010798
Jackson A J S	010499
Knight R	010499
Mackland J	010499
Sexton B E	010499
Thresher N J	010499
Murdy R	130300
Coy M	030400
Germaine M A	030400
Hall S A	030400
Woolsey T S	030400

Technical Officers

Majors

Fletcher J M DipEH	300997
May A	300997
Greenslade D J MISM ASPS	300998
Shannon C K MCSP FETC	300998

Captains

Wright P A	161098
Fitchett G A	110900

Short Service Officers

Lieutenant Colonels

Walsh G R MBChB FRCA FFARCSIrel	
	160297
Jefferies N J	260898

Majors

Finch P J C MBBS MRCPSYCH	
	290791
Robertson D G MBBCh MRCGP FPCERT DCH	290992
Daoud R A MBBCh FRCPS(GLAS) FRCS(Eng)	250994
Hood M P	011294
Khan M MBBCh BAO MRSH	
	060895
McLean A D MBChB BSc FRCSED	100895
Iyer R	180895
Greaves I	210896
Anwar R M MSc MBBS LRCP LRCS LRCPS MASEE FRCPS(GLAS)	
	010397
ØCubison T C S	010897
Ralph J K MBChB	010897
Vautier G MB MRCP	231197
Capanni P D MBChB	010298
ØAckroyd C R	010898
ØCole A B J	010898
Colman G	010898
Fraser N B MBBS	010898
ØHayes S C	010898
Hunter S MBChB BSc FRCSED	010898
Prakash D ChM MChOrth MBBS FRCSGLAS(OR FRCSED	020898
Russell M Q DRCOG	100898
Cox J K	110699
Garner J P MBChB	010899
Heppell P S J MBChB	010899
Hinsley D E	010899
Houston D J K MBChB	010899
Lowes T MBBS	010899
ØMutimer J E	010899
Ramalingam T MBBS	010899
ØWhite L A MBBS DRCOG	010899
Anderson K D MBChB	020899
Baker A K MBChB	080899
Fulton G W O MBBS	010200
Adams S A MBChB	020200
Glover N M	010800
ØIngram K J MBChB	010800
McNicholas J J K	010800
Aldington D J	020800
Boos C J MBBS	020800
Crichton D G MBChB	020800
Dhillon S BMBCH FRGS	020800
Harban F M J MBBS	020800
Papworth J E J MBChB	020800
Porter C J	020800
Stubbs M C MBChB	020800
Mountain A J C MBChB	030800
Singer D M F MBChB FRCSGLAS(OR	070800
Shah Z H MBChB	080800
Byrne J J MBChB	070900

Captains

ØHeywood J W BA(Hons) BSc(Hons) MSc MCSP SRP	310893
ØMacgregor-Skinner A M	270295
Hepburn I D	010795
Burgess K R MBBS DFFP DRCOG DCH	020895
Austin G R MBBS	070296
Carlton J P MBBS	090296
Zaffar S H	080396

Alleway P *MBBS*	300496	
Woolley T	010696	
ØLove-Jones S J *MBBS B Sc (Hons)*		
	010896	
ØMcLaren R M *BMBCH*	010896	
ØTaylor L M	010896	
ØWight K C	010896	
Woods J A *MBBS*	010896	
Hayman J J *BM*	050896	
Bourne S C *MBBS*	070896	
ØBrookes C M	070896	
ØBrutus E C *MBBS*	070896	
Carter P A *MBChB*	070896	
Clare G A *MBBS*	070896	
Fraser N H *MBBS*	070896	
ØGallaher J M *MBChB*	070896	
ØGarstang J J *DCH*	070896	
ØGlover R E *DRCOG*	070896	
Harris N M	070896	
Ingram M *MBChB*	070896	
ØMcLennan J V	070896	
Phillip R D	070896	
Roulston P *RGN*	070896	
Taylor J M B	070896	
ØWoodhouse T	070896	
Cash I D *BM BSc*	080896	
Bloodworth S B *MBChB*	190896	
Lewis J *MBBS BMedSci*	080996	
Tynan M P *MCSP*	210996	
ØWilkinson T J	061096	
Hennessy E P *MBChB*	231296	
Farquharson P A *MCSP*	010397	
ØFidell K J	010397	
Gallagher V E	010397	
Thomas G O R	170397	
Babicki J W	060897	
Ball J E	060897	
Butler M	060897	
Clokey G J	060897	
Davies M S *B Sc (Hons) RNMH*		
	060897	
Delves G H	060897	
ØEverest A J *B Sc (Hons)*	060897	
ØGreasley L A *QGM*	060897	
Hill J J	060897	
ØJohnstone A A	060897	
Khan K N	060897	
ØMaccoll L J	060897	
Malcolm P C	060897	
ØMoore C A	060897	
Nordmann G R *MBChB*	060897	
Potter S J O *ABPI*	060897	
ØRichter A G	060897	
Theakston S D	060897	
ØWalton-Knight N A	060897	
ØCallaghan L C	070897	
Nicholson-Roberts T C	150897	
Finn A P	300897	
ØGolding M F	140997	
Horne S T	151297	
Forrest A K	301297	
East A J	040298	
Liddington R A *MRPharmS*	040298	
Masud S P	040298	
Enness W M J	090298	
Gadeke C M L	090298	
ØFleming J L	010398	
ØShaw R B	010398	
White C R	220698	
Gaal P J	250698	
ØBaptie J A	050898	

ØBayley S E	050898	
Bill A S	050898	
Bird J H	050898	
Carter J R	050898	
ØClaydon L E	050898	
Davies M L	050898	
Geoghegan J	050898	
Green M B	050898	
Isles M G	050898	
†Lawson E M	050898	
Lewis P J	050898	
Rowlands T K	050898	
Slater J C	050898	
Taylor S C	050898	
Toms M E *MBChB*	050898	
Tredget A D	050898	
Bennett M A V	130898	
Philpott M A *MCSP SRP*	250998	
Hepburn M J	061098	
Maytham G D	141298	
Le Feuvre A J	030299	
ØLees D M *MRPharmS*	030299	
ØMurray G *BA BS*	030299	
Appanah D *B Sc (Hons)*	190299	
Crew T A	230299	
ØShepherd J M P *MCSP SRP*		
	010399	
ØLeary R J	140699	
Gurney I	030899	
ØAtun A R	040899	
ØCaddy A J	040899	
Diacon M J	040899	
Eardley W G P	040899	
Fordham G T	040899	
Keilloh D A	040899	
ØKenwright K A	040899	
Lawton G S	040899	
Lord S R	040899	
Opie N J	040899	
ØSchmidt A C	040899	
Smith M R	040899	
ØStephenson V J	040899	
Taylor D M	040899	
Seddon J P	060899	
Fellingham W H	170899	
ØFowler S *MCSP*	010999	
Saunders M S	030999	
ØHolmes R J	210999	
ØRoffey S C	210999	
ØKilby V M	211099	
ØSmith J A	061199	
West A F *B Sc (Hons)*	040100	
Anakwe R E B	020800	
ØCrawford A L	020800	
Luke D P	020800	
†Mackay Brown A L	020800	
ØMilne A C	020800	
Perry J	020800	
†Simms M G N	020800	
West A T H	020800	
ØJones V H	240800	
†Ezekwe C K C	250800	
†Forbes A T	250800	
†McNee P A J *MRCP*	250800	
†Reavley P D A *MBChB*	250800	
ØTurnbull S A *RGN*	250900	
ØGrafton E E	101000	
ØHarvey J S	101000	
Romanovitch A P G *BA(Hons)*		
	101000	
ØVarney C R	101000	

Lieutenants

ØKimbell J S	010895
ØSutton L *LLB(Hons)*	160697
ØTacon H B *BSc(Hons)*	100298
Kieboom M H C	130498
ØGraham P J K	140798
ØSimmons P S	060898
Williams S J	100898
ØChandler J H G	221098
Connolly M J	221098
Oakes M N	141298
Hallsworth S N	010299
ØThornalley M J	090299
ØMead N K	190399
ØBrewis E A	130699
†Bartels O J M	150699
†Aslam S A	300699
ØBedwell B M	300699
†Briard R J	300699
†Graves A B	300699
†Leclerc S P *RGN*	070799
†Townend M A	070799
ØHutley E J	120799
ØPeck V J	120799
†Walker N M	120799
†Wright C R	130799
ØBenn H E M	150799
†Dodd O M	150799
†Griffiths D E	150799
ØGriffiths S A	150799
ØHamilton V J	150799
†Hunt P A F	150799
†Martin N A J	150799
ØCameron-Ross L	160799
†Reid D F	210799
Sandle P J	131299
West C M	131299
†Ramasamy A	231299
†Hodgson C L	250100
†Taylor C J	270100
†Roberts L J	280600
†Brookes M J *BMedSci*	300600
†Jeffery N P	300600
†Rollo J A S	040700
†Edgar S G	100700
†Folman M E	110700
†Tarmey N T	110700
ØRoss D H	120700
ØHart A V	140700
ØAylward G L	240700
†Evans B J	240700
ØBaker L E M	221200

2nd Lieutenants

†Nowell J L	010892
†Carey D B	020796
††Babicki A A	010896
ØHarrison M C	310797
†Ardley C N *PGCE*	010897
†Booth T C	010897
ØDarbyshire A H	010897
†Guthrie H C	010897
ØHairsine H J	010897
††Haldane A G	010897
††Hardman R D	010897
††Harrisson S E	010897
ØHerd M K	010897
††Hill N E	010897
††Hooper T J	010897
ØNicholson K R	010897
†Rao A	010897

††Siddiqui Y U	010897	††Reed R C	010899	Winfield D B	090897
††Tyrrell M D	010897	††Round J A	010899	Mahan J K	050898
ØWalsh S M S	010897	††Sanders G J	010899	ØMcKinnon K A	050898
††Weller D M	010897	††Singleton J A G	010899	Moor P S	050898
ØWells H J	010897	††Thavapalasundaram S	010899	Moore A J	050898
††Williamson K P	010897	ØWatts S K	010899	ØScotton J E	050898
ØWoods K L	010897	ØWelsh A H	010899	Speers A G	050898
ØPatil M L	251197	††Wilde G D	010899	Stutt M A	050898
††Pope C D	251197	††Wilkinson D J P	010899	Williams A	050898
†Thorpe R J	251197	††Williams J R	010899	Myers A F	040899
††Wheatley R J	251197	†Allan R J B	140999		
††Anderson D B	010898	††Gilmore A J	181199		

Lieutenants

††Bailey K G H	010898	††Thomas H W I	181199	ØBapty S E M	010800
††Barker T	010898	†Carroll P C	090200	ØPark C L *MBBS*	010800
††Clack J D	010898	††Chambers D	180400	ØPrice N J *MBBS*	010800
††Cox A T	010898	†Fernando M C D *MPhil*	180400		
††Dickinson A J	010898	††Hume D C	180400		

Administrative Officers

Captains

ØFenwick K J	010898	††White J S	180400	Stone D C	160698
††Fetherston C R	010898	††Wyldbore M	180400	ØJaques V A	120599
††Foster M A	010898	ØEyre-Brook A J	050700	Benn A L	140699
††Grant J	010898	††Harold A J	050700		

Lieutenants

††Granville-Chapman J	010898	††Rodger M P	050700	Searson D J *(A/Capt 131100)*	
ØHolbrook S N	010898	ØTurney L A	050700		120897
††Johnson S A	010898	††Booker R J	010800	ØBrass C J	161297
††Knott J J W	010898	††Booker T E F	010800	ØCallow P S	100898
††Macleod B M G	010898	ØClark T L	010800	Jenkins R T V *BA(Hons)*	130699
††Martin S F	010898	ØCooper C T	010800	ØMasling C H	130699
†Richards C G *BA(Hons) FRSA*		ØEngland R J	010800	ØHall-Thompson B R	090899
	010898	††Fletcher T E	010800	ØSmith L M	090899
ØRollins S E A	010898	ØGoldsmith C R	010800		
ØTinley H J	010898	ØHart S J	010800		

Technical Officers

2nd Lieutenants

††Walker N R	010898	ØHodgkinson J	010800	ØReece A J	140999
ØCross E A S	181198	ØHolmes C E	010800		
††Nwume H O	181198	ØMacleod N J	010800		

Non-Medical Officers

Captains

ØObi N E	181198	††Poole R B	010800	ØWhite R M	250994
††Vickers S G	181198	††Stuart A J	010800		
†Aitken S A	270499	††Wall W D	010800		
††Macdonald D J M	270499	††Wood T A	010800		

Short Service Volunteer Officers

Majors

††Walker J	280499	ØBennetts S H	010900	Stewart H J *MBBCh BAO DRCOG*	
††White P L	280499	ØBrookes E R	140900	*DRCOG*	231193
††Calder A A	060799	ØMorris C L	140900		

Captains

†Parker D A	060799	††Park C K	140900	ØScarff S H	130297
ØRoyston C L	070799	††Stansfield T J	140900		
††Ballard M S	010899	††D'Vaz A P	161100		
ØBennett R L	010899	††Lewis S E	161100		
††Bramall J C	010899	††McKeon N P	161100		
ØBrown K V	010899	ØWiseman N J	161100		
††Darbyshire M	010899				
ØDart R F	010899				

Pharmacists

Captains

ØEely-Sedding C E A	010899		
††Evans P A	010899	ØBaker H *BPharm MRPharmS*	
††Hale P J	010899		180295
ØHemming A V J	010899	Patrick K	060897
††Johnstone T J	010899	Stevens M T	060897
ØLithgow Smith K M	010899	Ward N J	060897
††Pynn H J	010899		

CORPS OF ROYAL ELECTRICAL AND MECHANICAL ENGINEERS

Upon a lightning flash, a horse forcene gorged with a coronet of four fleurs-de-lys, a chain reflexed over its back and standing on a globe. Above, a crown upon a scroll bearing the letters "REME"

Arte et Marte

Regimental Marches

Quick March . . . . .Lillibulero and Aupres de ma Blonde
Slow March . . . . .Duchess of Kent
Agents . . . . .Holt's Farnborough Branch, Royal Bank of Scotland plc, Lawrie House, Victoria Road, Farnborough, Hants, GU14 7NR
Corps Headquarters . . . . .Regimental Headquarters REME, (Box H075) HQ DEME(A), Hazebrouck Barracks Arborfield, Berkshire RG2 9NJ (Tel: Arborfield Cross (0118) 976 3480*)*

Alliances

Canadian Armed Forces . . . . .Electrical and Mechanical Engineers
South African Defence Forces . . . . . . .Technical Services Corps
Australian Military Forces . . . . .The Corps of Royal Australian Electrical and Mechanical Engineers
Indian Army . . . . .Corps of Electrical and Mechanical Engineers
Pakistan Army . . . . .Corps of Electrical and Mechanical Engineers
Sri Lanka Army . . . . .The Sri Lanka Electrical and Mechanical Engineers
Malaysian Armed Forces . . . . .The Royal Malaysian Electrical and Mechanical Engineers

Colonel in Chief . . . . .Field Marshal *HRH The Prince* Philip *Duke of* Edinburgh *KG KT OM GBE AC QSO*

Colonels Commandant . . . . .Maj Gen A J Sharman 010496
Maj Gen D J M Jenkins *CB CBE* 011197
Maj Gen P V R Besgrove *CBE* 140299
*Maj Gen L D Curran 010300
Maj Gen D L Judd 010101

Brigadiers

Wildman M L *BSc(Eng)Hons (EUR ING) CEng FIEE FIMGT* rcds psc hcsc(J) *(A/Maj Gen 251099)* 300690
Ball A D *CBE MA CEng FIEE* psc† aic me   300693
Huntley M *BSc* psc† hcsc(J) me   300695
Chuter J W *OBE BSc(Eng)Hons MSc CEng FIMechE* psc† ee gw   300696
Middleton S G *ADC BSc(Eng) CEng MIMechE* psc† ae   300696
Campbell J C *BSc(Eng)Hons CEng MIMechE* rcds psc† me   300698
Croucher R J *MA CEng FIMechE* psc† me   300698
Tyler T N *MA* psc† ae   300698
Coleman R N *BSc(Hons) CEng MIEE* psc† me   300699
Cort P C *BSc(Eng)Hons (EURING) CEng FRSA MIEE* psc† jsdc me   300699
Matthews S C *BSc(Eng) (EURING) CEng FIMechE* psc† me   300699
Rickard R I B *BSc(Eng) CEng FIMechE FIMGT* psc† me   300699
Sharpe P R *BSc(Eng)Hons MSc CEng MIEE MIMGT* psc†   300600

Colonels

Capper M J *BSc(Eng)Hons CEng FIMechE* psc† jsdc me   300690
Paskell C W *BA(Hons) MDA FIMGT* psc† jsdc me   300692

Ashley W A *BSc(Eng)Hons FIEE* psc†   300693
Peregrine R B *BSc(Eng)Hons CEng MIMechE CDipAF* psc† me 300693
Ross N D *BA(Hons) CEng MRAeS* sq ae sq(w)   300693
Owen R G *BTech(Hons) CEng MIMechE MIPD* me sq(w) 300694
Knudsen N P *BSc(Eng) CEng MIMechE FRAeS* psc† ae   300695
Blair-Pilling I C D *OBE BSc(Eng)Hons MSc CEng MIMechE* sq jsdc me sq(w) dis   300696
Ferguson K E *BEng(Hons) CEng MIMechE* psc† me *(A/Brig 190301)*   300696
Goldsack A H *BSc(Eng)* sq jsdc me sq(w)   300696
King A A *BSc(Eng)* psc ee   300696

Wright D M H *BSc(Hons) MSc MPhil CEng FIEE* psc† ee gw   300696
McNinch H H *MBE BSc(Eng)Hons CEng MRAeS* psc† ae   300697
Morris A D *BSc(Eng)Hons MBA CEng MIMechE* psc† me   300697
Tetlow S J *MBE MSc CEng MIMechE* psc† dis hcsc(J) *(A/Brig 081200)*   300697
Williams N T S *MBE MA CEng MIEE* psc†   300697
Burnett B A J *MA CEng MIEE* psc† ee sq(w)   300698
Dale I C *BSc(Eng)Hons MSc CEng MIEE* psc† dis   300698

McCarthy P T *BSc(Eng) CEng FIMechE* psc(n)† me   300698
McPherson A M *BSc(Eng)Hons MSc CEng MIMechE MRAeS AE* psc† ae gw   300698
Paine A P *MA CEng MIEE* psc† ee sq(w)   300698
Philp A R *BSc(Eng) CEng MIMechE MRAeS* psc ae sq(w)   300698
Andrews S M *MBE MA CEng MIEE AMRAeS* psc† ae jsdc   300699
Bulmer M R *BSc(Eng)* psc† 300699
Cameron S J S *BSc(Eng) CEng MIMechE MRAeS* sq ae   300699
Hulmes R J *BSc(Eng)Hons LLB(Hons) (EURING) CEng MIEE MIMGT* sq ee sq(w)   300699
Kemp H A *OBE BSc(Eng) MDA CEng MIMechE* psc†   300699
Martin R A *BSc(Eng) CEng FIMechE* sq(w) †   300699
Ward C *BSc(Eng) CEng FIEE* psc(a)† ee   300699
Anthistle A *BSc(Eng) CEng MIEE* psc†   300600
Gray P A *MA CEng MIMechE* me sq(w) †   300600
Hughes G *BSc(Eng)Hons CEng MIMechE* psc† ae   300600
Jarvis S A M *MA CEng MIEE* sq ee sq(w)   300600
Oldnall M W D *MA MSc CEng MBCS* psc† dis ee sq(w)   300600
Thorpe D A R *BSc(Eng)Hons CEng FIMechE* psc(a)† me sq(w) 300600

*Representative Colonel Commandant for 2001

254

Lieutenant Colonels

Postgate K G (SL) *BSc MSc MIMGT mvt sq(w)* 300686
Lamb K I F *BSc(Eng)Hons CEng MIMechE sq me sq(w)* 300687
Booth A A B *BSc(Hons) CEng FIEE sq ae sq(w)* 300688
Hall A D (SL) *BSc CEng MIMechE sq(w)* 300688
Mount R A (SL) *CEng MRAeS MIMGT ae sq(w)* 300688
Andrews D W (SL) *BSc(Eng) MSc CEng MRAeS odc(US) psc† ae gw* 300689
Garland P M (SL) *BSc(Hons) BSc(Eng) CEng MIMechE sq* 300689
Haverson J *BSc(Eng)Hons CEng MIMechE me sq(w) †* 300689
East G R (SL) *BSc(Eng)Hons (EUR ING) CEng FIMechE me sq(w)* 300690
Graham W H *BSc(Hons) CEng MIMechE I* me sq(w)* 300690
Nixon T E (SL) *MIEE TEng* 300690
Pickford A J *BSc(Eng)Hons CEng MIMechE me sq(w)* 300690
Yeoman M P L *BSc(Eng)Hons CEng MIMechE ae sq(w)* 300690
Jagger R L *CEng MIMechE MRAeS ae sq(w)* 300691
Loweth J R *BSc(Eng) MSc CEng MIMechE mvt me sq(w)* 300691
Maddison D (SL) *BSc(Eng) CEng MIEE MIMGT psc† ee* 300691
Watson A M (SL) *MSc CEng MIMechE MBCS dis me sq(w)* 300691
Carruthers S J *BSc(Eng) CEng MIMechE sq ae* 300692
Johnson D A *BSc(Hons) AMIEE sq(w)* 300692
Nutt B *OBE BSc(Eng)Hons CEng MIEE ee sq(w)* 300692
Perks T W *BSc CEng FIMechE AMIEE AMRAeS MIMGT ae sq(w)* 300692
Ravn J T *BSc(Eng) CEng MIMechE sq me* 300692
Bethell J J *BSc(Eng) MDA CEng MIMechE me sq(w)* 300693
Bowman M F *BSc(Eng)Hons CEng MIMechE AMRAeS ae jsdc sq(w) (A/Col 021000)* 300693
Cameron H R *BSc(Eng) MDA MSc CEng MRAeS ae MDA sq(w)* 300693
Collins I G R *BSc(Eng) MSc CEng me sq(w) adp* 300693
Craig J A *BSc(Eng) IEng MIMechE MIMechIE psc† me* 300693
Drayton N R *BScTech psc† psc(n)* 300693
Phipps A *BSc(Eng) MSc AMIEE ee gw sq(w)* 300693
Thomson A F *CEng MIMechE psc ae* 300693
Cooke D J *BSc(Eng) CEng MIMechE AMRAeS ae sq(w) (A/Col 240700)* 300694

Graham I P *BSc(Eng) CEng FIMechE me sq(w) †* 300694
Marwaha T S *BEng(Hons) MSc CEng MIEE gw sq(w)* 300694
Milne T D *BSc(Eng)Hons CEng MIMechE psc† me* 300694
Robertshaw P S *MBE BSc(Eng) CEng MIEE psc(n)† me* 300694
Egan D H *MSc CEng MIEE psc†* 300695
Hamilton B W *MSc CEng MIMechE MIMGT ae gw sq(w)* 300695
Moore N *MBE BSc(Hons) psc†* 300695
Rotchell L R *BSc(Eng)Hons ae sq(w)* 300695
Welsh A K *BSc(Eng) CEng MIMechE ae jsdc sq(w)* 300695
Dixon M F *MA MSc CEng MIMechE psc† gw me* 311295
Brown G S *BSc(Eng) CEng MIEE psc†* 300696
Frostick M C *OBE BSc(Eng)Hons psc†* 300696
Jones B A *BSc(Eng) CEng MIMechE sq sq(w)* 300696
Mathew T C *BSc(Eng)Hons CEng MIMechE psc ae* 300696
May N C *MA CEng MIMechE MIEE sq(w) †* 300696
McCall B W *BSc(Hons) CEng MAPM MIEE psc† (A/Col 011100)* 300696
Saville J R C *BSc(Eng)Hons CEng MIMechE psc†* 300696
Sowray S T *BSc(Eng)Hons MSc CEng MIMechE psc† ae* 300696
Topp A E *MBE BSc(Eng) MSc (EUR ING) CEng MIMechE mvt sq(w)* 300696
Usher L J *BSc(Eng) CEng MIMechE CDipAF MIMGT me sq(w)* 300696
Crawford J P *BSc(Eng) MSc CEng MRAeS ae ph sq(w)* 300697
Duncan A D *BSc(Hons) MSc CEng MIEE psc†* 300697
Laidler R J *BSc(Hons) CEng MIEE sq(w)* 300697
Longmore P *BSc(Eng)Hons MSc CEng MIEE psc† gw* 300697
Mulroy J *BSc(Eng)Hons sq jsdc* 300697
Rodger D J *BSc(Eng)Hons MRAeS ae sq(w)* 300697
Ross I W *BSc(Eng) CEng MIMechE sq me sq(w)* 300697
Rouse J F *MA MSc PhD CEng MIEE MIL psc† gw (A/Col 020301)* 300697
Simpson I S *BSc CEng MIMechE psc† (A/Col 150900)* 300697
Sparks N R S *BSc(Hons) MSc GRADIMechE mvt me sq(w)* 300697
Tudor M J *BSc(Eng) CEng MIEE sq sq(w)* 300697
Curry P C *BSc(Hons) CEng MIEE MILOG sq(w) †* 300698
Edwards J M *BSc(Eng) CEng MIEE sq(w)* 300698

Gould N *BSc(Eng)Hons CEng MIMechE MIRTE MIMGT sq(w) †* 300698
Jaques P W *BEng(Hons) MSc CEng* 300698
Mills T *BSc(Eng)Hons MSc CEng MRAeS psc† ae gw* 300698
Nowak A M P *BSc ae sq(w)* 300698
Ransom M *BSc(Eng)Hons MSc CEng MIEE ae sq(w) †* 300698
Abbott J P J F *MSc CEng MIMechE psc†* 300699
Boswell M J *BSc(Eng) MSc CEng MIMechE psc† psc(J)* 300699
Brown A R *BSc(Eng) MSc psc†* 300699
Bywater J J *BSc(Eng)Hons MSc CEng MRAeS ae gw sq(w)* 300699
Drapper C J *BSc(Eng) CEng MIMechE ee me sq(w)* 300699
Eke D M *BSc(Hons) MSc CEng MRAeS ae sq(w)* 300699
Feldmanis E C *BSc(Eng) MSc CEng MIMechE I sq(w)* 300699
Hughes M A *MSc sq(w) †* 300699
Miller P H K *MBE BSc(Hons) sq sq(w)* 300699
Steadman V R *MA MIMechE sq(w) †* 300699
Tugby M *BSc(Eng) CEng MIEE psc† ae* 300699
Williams S M *BA BSc(Eng) CEng MIMechE MIMGT I sq(w)* 300699
Wright G S *BSc(Eng)Hons MSc (EURING) CEng MIEE psc† gw* 300699
Armstrong M A *MSc CEng MIMechE psc† ae* 300600
Barclay W J R *BSc(Eng)Hons MSc CEng MIEE ee sq(w)* 300600
Crook R *BSc(Eng)Hons MSc CEng MIMechE psc†* 300600
Davies J G *BScEng(Elec) MSc CEng MIEE MIMGT gw sq(w)* 300600
Ensor J A *BSc(Hons) MBA MSc CEng MIMechE psc†* 300600
Henderson J M R *MSc CEng MIMechE psc†* 300600
McAvoy D A *BA BA(Hons) MDA MSc CEng AMIEE MDA sq(w)* 300600
Mitchell P G *MSc CEng MRAeS psc† ae* 300600
Oakes M C *BSc(Eng)Hons MSc FRGS AMIMechE MIPD psc(n)† †* 300600
Shewry P A *BSc(Eng)Hons MSc CEng MIMechE MIMGT MILOG psc†* 300600
Shimmings M R *MSc CEng MIMechE psc† dis* 300600
Williamson S *MSc CEng MIMechE psc†* 300600
Wyatt R G P *MSc CEng MIMechE psc†* 300600

Majors

Snodgrass J D *BSc(Eng)Hons (EUR ING) CEng MIMechE me sq(w)* 300980
Lawrence I G *MA me sq(w) AIS* 300981

Oswald C J R *CEng MIMechE* sq me 300982

Thompson S R *BSc(Eng) MSc MSc CEng MIMechE MIEE* gsd sq(w) 300982

Marlow E D *BSc CEng MIEE MIMGT* ee sq(w) 300984

Pearse M J *BSc(Eng) CEng MIMechE* me 300984

Marsden P J *MA* sq(w) 300986

Bartlett D M *BSc(Eng)* ae sq(w) 300988

Colling S J *BSc(Eng) CEng MIEE* sq(w) 300988

Horsfield P J *MSc CEng MIEE* ee sq(w) *(A/Lt Col 131100)* 300988

Moore G P *BSc(Eng) CEng MIMechE* psc† 300988

Callun M P *BSc(Eng)Hons* ae sq(w) 300989

Stanley I M *MSc CEng MIMechE* mvt aic sq(w) 300989

Curry N R *BSc(Eng) CEng MIMechE MIEE* sq(w) † 300990

Gilbert J P *BSc(Eng) CEng MIMechE* ae sq(w) 300990

Laborda M A *BSc(Hons) MSc* dis sq(w) 300990

Lister B J *BSc(Eng) CEng MIMechE* sq(w) 300990

Walker A C C *BSc(Eng) MSc CEng MIMechE* sq(w) † 300990

Young K T *BSc(Eng)* sowc sq ae 300990

Barker M *BSc(Eng) MSc MSc* mvt sq(w) 300991

Holliday S H *MSc* gsd sq(w) 300991

Marshall A C *MSc CEng MIEE ACMA* dis sq(w) 300991

McClean B C W *BSc(Hons) MSc CEng MIMechE* psc† 300991

Metcalfe C W *MSc* mvt sq(w) 300991

ØProwse G M *MBE BSc CEng MIMechE PGCE* psc 300991

Birrell A M *BSc(Eng)Hons MSc CEng MIMechE* dis sq(w) *(A/Lt Col 041200)* 300992

Duncan I W *BSc(Hons) CEng MIMechE* sq(w) 300992

Kelly W R *BSc CEng MIMechE* sq(w) 300992

Smale D S *BSc(Eng)Hons MSc CEng MRAeS* ae gw sq(w) 300992

Weatherall S P *BSc(Hons) MSc* psc† 300992

Cowan W D *BSc(Eng)Hons MSc CEng MIMechE* sq(w) 300993

Groves C P *BSc(Eng)* sq(w) 300993

Hill J A *BEng MSc (EURING) MIEE* gw sq(w) 300993

Hull D E *BSc(Eng)Hons MSc CEng MIMechE ACGI* sq(w) 300993

Kinsey G J *BEng(Hons) CEng MIEE* sq(w) 300993

Moorhouse D J *BSc MSc CEng MIMechE* mvt sq(w) 300993

Parsons I M *BSc(Hons) MSc CEng MIMechE* psc† sq(w) 300993

Preston A D *BSc(Eng)Hons MSc CEng MIEE* sq(w) *(A/Lt Col 150301)* 300993

Wormington J C *MSc AMIEE* psc† 300993

Allen A A *MBE BEng MSc DipMGMT AMIMechE* ae gw sq(w) 300994

Ansell D N T *BSc(Eng) MSc CEng MIMechE* mvt sq(w) 300994

Chambers M *BSc(Hons) MSc CEng MIMechE* sq(w) 300994

Farrell W J *BSc(Hons) MSc CEng MRAeS MIMATM* ae gsd sq(w) 300994

Gagen D *MBE BSc(Hons) MSc CEng MIMechE* sq(w) 300994

Halladay N *BEng(Hons) MSc CEng MIEE* sq(w) *(A/Lt Col 111100)* 300994

Judd J C *MSc CEng MIMechE* psc† *(A/Lt Col 111200)* 300994

Power J *MBE BEng(Hons) MSc CEng MRAeS* psc† ae *(A/Lt Col 040101)* 300994

Steele N *MSc MSc CEng MIMechE* psc† dis † 300994

Taylor S J *MSc AMIEE* gw sq(w) 300994

Teare A D *BSc(Eng) MSc CEng MIMechE* psc† 300994

Todd R C *BSc(Hons)* 300994

White J N *BSc(Hons) MSc CEng MIMechE* mvt sq(w) 300994

Wilson P A *BSc(Hons) MSc* gsd sq(w) 300994

Adkins I C *BSc(Hons) MA MBA MSc* psc(J) 300995

Armstrong P J *BSc(Hons) MSc CEng MIEE* psc† 300995

ØBacon H C *BSc(Hons)* ae sq(w) 300995

Belgum G R *MSc MISM* sq(w) † 300995

Bennett R N H *BSc(Hons) CEng MIEE* psc† 300995

Betteridge A J *MBE MSc CEng MIMechE* psc† psc(a)† 300995

Brittain J R *BEng(Hons) MSc* psc† ae *(A/Lt Col 311000)* 300995

Brown P I *BSc(Eng)Hons MSc CEng MIMechE* psc sq 300995

Case R H *BEng(Hons) MSc AMIEE* psc(J) gw 300995

Champion D L *BTech(Hons) MSc CEng MIMechE* dis sq(w) 300995

Clarkson M A *BSc(Eng)Hons MSc CEng MIMechE ACGI* psc(J) 300995

Clyde J I *BSc(Hons) MSc FRGS* mvt sq(w) 300995

Court M L *BEng(Hons) MSc MIMechIE* psc(J) 300995

Downes A S *BEng(Hons) MSc CEng MIMechE* psc† ae 300995

Easton D W *BEng(Hons) CEng MIEE* sq(w) 300995

Fitzgibbon D J *BEng(Hons) MSc* psc(J) ae 300995

Fram R C *BEng(Hons) MSc CEng MIMechE* psc(J) 300995

Gaunt M J *BEng(Hons) MSc CEng GRADIMechE MRAeS AE* psc(J) ae 300995

Golding S P *BEng(Hons) MSc MIEE* dis sq(w) 300995

Golding D H *BEng(Hons) MSc CEng MIMechE* sq(w) 300995

Holborn B R *BEng MDA* sq 300995

Irving W G *BSc(Hons) MSc CEng MIMechE* psc(a)† osc(US) 300995

Joels B D *BEng(Hons) MSc* psc(J) 300995

McLay E *BEng(Hons) MSc* psc(J) sq 300995

Miller P *BEng(Hons) MSc* psc† ae gw 300995

Milner C S *BSc(Hons) MSc AMIMechE* sq(w) 300995

Mitchell G I *MBE BEng(Hons) MSc AMIEE* psc† ae 300995

Munday M N *BEng(Hons) MSc AMIMechE* psc(J) 300995

Murdoch C J *BEng(Hons) MSc* psc(J) sq 300995

Nitsch R M B *MBE BSc(Hons) MSc* psc(J) 300995

Purnell M J *BEng(Hons) MSc* psc(J) dis 300995

Ringrose M C *BEng(Hons) MSc CEng* ae 300995

Robinson A T *BSc(Eng)Hons MA ACGI MSc CEng MIEE* psc(J) 300995

Rogers I C *BEng CEng MRAeS* ae sq(w) 300995

Sherman J A *BEng(Hons) MSc* psc(J) ae 300995

Smith G C *CEng MIEE* ae sq(w) 300995

Thomson A D M *BSc(Hons) MA MSc CEng MIEE MILOG* psc(J) 300995

Thorpe R P *MSc CEng MIMechE* psc sq(w) † 300995

Went A C *MSc* psc† ae 300995

Williams R D *BSc(Hons) CEng MIMechE* psc(J) ae 300995

Winthrop I S *BSc(Hons) MSc CEng MIMechE MIMGT* ae 300995

Young R J *BSc(Hons) MSc* psc(J) 300995

Ahl A C *BSc(Hons) MDS* psc(AUS) 300996

Aspray R J *MSc CEng MIMechE* psc(J) ae 300996

Bryant A J *BSc(Eng)Hons MSc* mvt sq(w) 300996

Cosgrove R P *BEng(Hons) MSc AMIMechE* psc(J) sq 300996

Eggett T J *BEng(Hons) MSc MSc* dis ae 300996

Ellis J A *BA(Hons) MA CEng MIEE* 300996

Evans C M *BEng(Hons) MSc* ae 300996

Eyre R H *BSc MSc* gw 300996

Fitton M J *BSc(Hons) MSc* ae 300996

Frendo S P M *BEng(Hons) MSc* gw sq(w) 300996

Frostick P C *BEng(Hons) MSc* gw 300996

Gibson I P *BEng(Hons)* 300996

Gyorffy T A *BEng(Hons) MSc* 300996

256

Howard A C S *BSc(Hons) MSc* ae
sq(w)   300996
Mackay E A C R *BA(Hons) MSc*
psc(J) sq ae   300996
McNeil I N *BSc(Hons) MSc CEng*
MIEE sq(w)   300996
Pendlington M A *BEng(Hons) MSc*
psc(J)   300996
Robson H J *BEng(Hons) MSc* psc(J)
                                   300996
Sayer T M *BEng(Ilons) MSc* psc(J)
                                   300996
Smith S A *BEng(Hons)*   300996
Snape M G *BEng(Hons) MSc* psc(J)
ae   300996
Stradins P J *BEng MDA* sq *MDA*
                                   300996
Thursz J C M *BEng(Hons) MSc*
CEng MIMechE psc(J)   300996
Welsh R P *BEng MSc CEng*
MIMechE sq   300996
Wilson M C *MA* sq(w) ais   300996
Bedding D P *BEng CEng MIMechE*
                                   300997
Bryson D *BEng(Hons) MSc CEng*
MIEE psc(J)   300997
Bullard M J A *BSc*   300997
Clarke K J *BEng BEng(Hons) MSc*
                                   300997
Coxon N J *BEng(Hons) MSc CEng*
MIEE gw sq(w)   300997
Critchley R D *BEng(Hons)*   300997
Davies P G *BSc(Hons) AMIEE*
                                   300997
ØEbling M J C *BEng(Hons) MSc*
CEng MIMechE   300997
Ferguson C R *BEng(Hons) MSc*
AMIEE dis ae sq(w)   300997
Fitzpatrick D P *BSc(Hons)*   300997

Harrison J R *BEng(Hons)* ae sq(w)
                                   300997
Jones M B *BEng(Hons)* ae   300997
Lloyd-Baker D H *BEng MSc* dis
                                   300997
May N M *BEng(Hons)*   300997
McEwen P J *BEng(Hons)*   300997
Paris H V I *BSc(Hons) MSc*   300997
Perrett R C *MBE BEng(Hons) MSc*
AMIEE dis   300997
Railton I *BEng(Hons)* ae   300997
Robson C *BEng(Hons)*   300997
Rogers M T *BSc(Eng) MSc* ae gw
sq(w)   300997
Soar J R *BEng(Hons) MSc CEng*
MIMechE sq   300997
Stiff D *BSc(Hons) CEng MIMechE*
sq   300997
Bell C W *BSc(Hons) CEng MIEE*
                                   300998
Cooper R J *BSc(Hons)*   300998
Crichard G *BEng(Hons) CEng* ae
                                   300998
Croager P M *BA(Hons) BSc(Hons)*
                                   300998
Cunningham A *BEng* ae   300998
Dale A J *BEng(Hons)*   300998
Edmondson D W *BEng(Hons) CEng*
MIEE   300998
Fletcher P L *DMS*   300998
Foster J P *BEng BEng(Hons)* ae
                                   300998

Haddow R J *BEng(Hons) CEng*
MIEE   300998
Heal E R B *BEng BEng(Hons) CEng*
MIMechE   300998
Kaley A S *MEng(Hons) CEng*
MIMechE   300998
King S J *BEng(Hons)*   300998
Leach M J *BSc(Hons) MSc* ae gw
                                   300998
McClean C T *BA(Hons) MA* 300998
Mitchell C S *BEng*   300998
Norman D L   300998
Warner S J B *BEng(Hons) CEng*
MRAeS ae   300998
Beard A H *BEng(Hons) MIEE*
                                   300999
Beck P J *BEng(Hons)*   300999
Burke B T *BEng(Hons)* ae   300999
Clarke J R *BEng(Hons)*   300999
Copestake T W *BEng(Hons) CEng*
MIMechE   300999
Jack I H *BSc(Hons)*   300999
Joy M H W *BEng(Hons) CEng*
MIMechE   300999
Lang S M *BEng(Hons) MIMechE*
                                   300999
ØMcAvoy N J *BSc(Hons)* ae 300999
McCurrach J L *MA AMIEE*   300999
Mitchell A P *MEng MA*   300999
Netting A G *BEng(Hons)*   300999
Nevin S G *BEng BEng(Hons)*
                                   300999
Pettifor P J *BEng BEng(Hons) MSc*
                                   300999
Scott D G *BEng(Hons)* ae   300999
Sumpter T D *BEng(Hons)*   300999
Szalay S P J *BSc(Hons)*   300999
Teskey A J *BEng(Hons)*   300999
Thorpe D M *BEng(Hons)*   300999
White P J *BSc(Hons)* ae   300999
Wilson D *BEng(Hons)*   300999
Wise P A *BEng(Hons)*   300999
Woodcock M P W   300999
Atkinson A S *BEng(Hons)* ae
                                   300900
Bastone D C *BSc(Hons)*   300900
Collins B E *BEng(Hons)*   300900
Dear A M *BEng(Hons)* ae   300900
Eastman D J *BEng(Hons) CEng*
AMIEE GRADRAeS ae   300900
Forster A N *BEng(Hons)* ae   300900
Fraser-Hitchen A *MIMechIE* 300900
Griffiths A W A *BEng(Hons) CEng*
MIEE   300900
Hall T A *BEng(Hons)* ae   300900
Houldsworth A P *BSc(Hons) CEng*
MIMechE   300900
Kohler G M *BEng(Hons) AMIMechE*
                                   300900
Lewis A *BEng(Hons)*   300900
Marie P S *BSc* ae   300900
McEvoy D J *BEng(Hons)*   300900
Pattison N K *BSc(Eng)Hons* 300900
Pestridge D C L *BEng(Hons)* 300900
Potts D H *BEng(Hons) CEng MRAeS*
ae   300900
Rorison A   300900
Stace N K *BEng(Hons)*   300900
Stuart A J W *BEng(Hons)*   300900
Syme A B *BEng(Hons) FRGS*
GRADRAeS ae   300900
Taylor R N *BTech* ae   300900

Theakston N S T *BEng(Hons)*
                                   300900
Waddington S T *BEng(Hons) CEng*
MIMechE   300900
Ward A H *BEng(Hons)*   300900
Yates N   300900

Captains

Brock B I *BEng(Hons)*   050991
Wetherall S S *BEng(Hons)*   090892
Garbutt R M *BEng* ae *(A/Maj*
030700)   110493
Bridges S R *BEng (A/Maj 221199)*
                                   121293
Saunders L R *BSc(Hons) CEng*
MIEE MIMGT (A/Maj 170700)
                                   060894
Brewer I C *BEng*   010495
Butler J F *BEng(Hons) (A/Maj*
040900)   010495
Campbell C J *BEng(Hons)* ae ph
                                   010495
Earner S C *BEng CEng MRAeS* ae
(A/Maj 100400)   010495
Fitzsimons B P *BEng(Hons)* ae
(A/Maj 110900)   010495
Garbett R N *BEng(Hons) AMIEE* ae
                                   010495
Johnstone A W   010495
McCarthy L D L *BSc(Hons)*   010495
Richards D A *BEng(Hons) (A/Maj*
040900)   010495
Shaw D I   010495
Thomas D M *BEng(Hons)*   010495
Vickers S D *BEng(Hons)*   010495
Learmonth M A   160695
Hall D E *BEng(Hons)*   070895
Burden W D H *BEng(Hons)*
MIMechE   110895
Gordon Sawyers H J *BEng(Hons)*
AMIEE   110895
Rodwell L S *BSc(Hons)*   110895
Thorne A R *BEng(Hons)*   110895
Crook D H *BEng(Hons)* ae   130995
Knurbin M M *BEng(Hons)* ae
                                   170995
Hallett P J *BEng(Hons)*   280995
Somerville P D *BEng(Hons)* 161095
Barnard A C *BEng(Hons) AMIEE*
                                   161195
McGeoch M *BEng(Hons) CEng*
MIEE ae   231195
Smyth M S *BEng(Hons) AMIMechE*
ACGI   141295
Broster C N ae   151295
Casey S J B   151295
Chivers M A *BEng(Hons)* ph 151295
Holford S W *BSc(Hons)*   151295
Phillips I J *BEng(Hons)*   151295
Robinson D P *BEng(Hons)* ph
                                   151295
Tabrah A *BSc(Hons) AMIEE* ph
                                   151295
Weller N B   290196
Lewis P M J   260296
Watt J F   110396
Moore N E *BEng(Hons)* ae   130496
Treharne J S *BEng(Hons) AMIEE*
                                   100696
Atkins A P *BSc(Hons)*   070896
Bainger A J *BEng(Hons)*   070896
Smeaton N V *BSc(Hons)*   070896

Sweeting C *BEng(Hons)* ae 070896
Turnbull R S *BEng(Hons)*
AMIMechE ae 070896
Heardman J *BEng(Hons)* 110896
Thorpe N B *BEng(Hons)* 110896
Powell M W 221196
Edwards M J *BEng(Hons)* 131296
Lawrence K J *BEng(Hons) AMIEE*
ph 131296
Duncan N J M *BEng(Hons)* ae
141296
Jeavons M D *BEng(Hons)* ae 141296
Price H M *BEng(Hons)* ae 141296
Kelly-Smith D L *BEng(Hons)* ae
060297
Catton M D *BEng(Hons)* ae 110497
Horsefield B *BEng(Hons)* 110497
Morgan C S *BEng(Hons)* 110497
Bovill C *BSc(Hons)* ae 240497
Smith A M *BSc(Hons)* 010697
Owsnett N 210697
Batty D C *BEng(Hons)* 070897
Johnson P A *BEng(Hons) AMIMechE*
ae 070897
Cope M D *BEng(Hons)* 080897
Crossfield S B *BEng(Hons)* 080897
Gibb R M *BEng(Hons)* ae 080897
Hughes P B *BEng(Hons) CEng*
MRAeS ae 080897
Loader P G *BEng(Hons)* 080897
Payne M C *BEng(Hons)* psc 080897
Reeves D *BEng(Hons)* ae 080897
Wade M D *BEng(Hons)* ae 080897
Genin C H R *BEng(Hons)* 121297
Gillies T J *BEng(Hons)* ae 121297
Hogben M J *BEng(Hons)* 121297
Karim M A *BEng(Hons)* 121297
O'Brien D K W *BEng(Hons)* ae
121297
Platt C J *BEng(Hons)* ae 121297
Prosser P D *BEng(Hons)* 121297
Spurr G P *BEng(Hons)* 121297
Woodward C W N *BEng(Hons)* ae
121297
ØFindlay W E *BEng(Hons)* 090198
Torbet J D *BEng(Hons)* 310198
McArthur P J *BEng(Hons)* 120298
Wall G M *BEng(Hons)* 120298
McGready A H *BEng(Hons)*
AMIMechE ae 260398
Lawrence M S *BScEng(MECH)* ae
090498
Watters E G *BScEng(MECH)*
090498
Hopp R M 140498
Sampson J J *BEng(Hons)* 040798
Baxter R J *BSc(Hons) BTech* ae
070898
James K M 070898
King C *BEng(Hons)* 070898
Williams I *BEng(Hons)* 070898
Shilling M W *BEng(Hons)* 091098
ØPhillips C P *BA* 131098
ØHart R *BEng(Hons) MSc* 231198
Cobbett A P 011298
Gill P J 111298
Kolczak R *BEng(Hons)* ae 111298
Small M C *BEng(Hons)* ae 111298
Trengove I R 210199
ØHairsine A C *MPhil BA* 100299
Lewin M R *BEng(Hons)* 100299
Rae N R *BEng(Hons)* 100299
Calvert N S *BEng(Hons)* ae 090499

Holmes T M *BEng(Hons)* 030699
Penfold S D *BEng(Hons)* 140699
Shenton R K *BEng(Hons)* Dis
140699
Roberts D A *BEng(Hons)* ae 060899
Owen P G *BEng(Hons)* 121099
Ballard P R *BEng(Hons)* 090200
ØBradley-Walker S L *BSc(Hons)*
090200
Hayward J P *BEng(Hons)* 090200
Norton A R A *MEng* 090200
Reeve C F *BEng(Hons)* 090200
Trembath J S *BEng(Hons)* 090200
Hirst T D *BA(Hons)* 140400
ØFarthing N E *BEng(Hons)* 130600
ØJohnston A *BSc(Hons)* 130600
Nasse S E *BEng(Hons)* 130600
Ireland C S *BEng(Hons)* 120700
Johnson J *BA(Hons)* ae 120800
Macinnes B C *BEng(Hons)* 120800
Wallace J 171000
Coghlan P R *BEng(Hons) AMIEE*
080201
Cook T M *BEng(Hons)* 080201
Howard I D *BEng(Hons)* 080201
Shannon A E N *MEng(Hons)* 080201

Lieutenants
ØBruce E J *MEng* 160697
Arnold M R *BEng(Hons)* 161297
Holdstock C M *BSc(Hons) AMIEE*
161297
Jones A L S *BEng(Hons) GRADRAeS*
161297
Willis S G *BEng(Hons)* (A/Capt
110900) 161297
†Bernal E B M W *MEng BA* 100298
ØFaithfull-Davies E J *MEng(Hons)*
100298
Palmer C H *BA(Hons) MEng*
CDipAF 100298
ØPickering L H *BEng* 100298
Owens P S *MEng(Hons)* 140698
Briggs A 100898
Doyle N D *BEng(Hons)* 100898
Evans C P *BEng(Hons)* 100898
Halksworth B D *BEng(Hons)* 100898
Jones B P *BEng(Hons)* 100898
Robertson A M *BEng(Hons)* 100898
Smith S G *BEng(Hons)* 100898
Steptoe D B 180998
Lord D C *MEng BA* 090299
Clayton A A *MEng(Hons)* 130699
ØAmos G H *BEng(Hons)* 090899
Hawker D T *BEng(Hons)* 090899
ØHawkes R V *BEng(Hons)* 090899
Langham S J R *BEng(Hons)* 090899
Reid M F *BEng(Hons)* 090899
Wilcox M A *BEng(Hons)* 090899
ØRoberts S L *BEng(Hons)* 131299
Jones C C 100400
Adams A D 080800
Haslam D R 080800

2nd Lieutenants
††Taylor B R G 220997
ØHollins J M 060998
†Kidd M J F 060998
††Saha S N 060998
Tolhurst P J 070899
Oldridge T D 111299

Trangmar A F 111299

Regular Category Late Entry Officers

Lieutenant Colonels
Heffernan P K M *FIMS* sq 010198
Dimmock R G *IEng MIRTE*
MIMechIE 300699
Cullen A W 010999
Hinds P A *BA MSc* sq(w) 250999
Knee T C sq 300600
Smy B S *MBE MISM MASMC*
010101

Majors
Coward S C *BEM* 010488
Roach P F sq(w) 010488
Nicholls B J sq(w) 300989
Taylor W G *MIMGT MILOG*
010190
Clutson D P sq(w) 300990
Davison M 300990
French M C *TEng(CEI) MIMGTechE*
sq(w) 300990
Golder S V *IEng MIIEE* sq(w)
300990
Leslie K J *BSc(Hons) BSc(Hons)*
MDA sq(w) *(A/Lt Col 010200)*
300990
Clarke D *IEng MIRTE MIMGT LCGI*
300991
Hawkes P S J *IEng FIEIE* sq(w)
(A/Lt Col 091000) 300991
Plumb J *BA MSc CEng IEng MRAeS*
sq(w) 300991
Gardner J K *BA* 300992
Henderson W G *MBE IEng AMRAeS*
sq(w) 300992
O'Keefe P C *IEng MIMI AMIRTE*
(A/Lt Col 011100) 300992
Soper L J 300992
Vaughan D F *IEng MIRTE MIMGT*
MIMGTechE 300992
Chant M D *IEng* sq(w) 300993
Gibson P D *MIMGT MISM* 300993
Horne J H 300993
Parsons J R *BEM* 300993
Pollard R D 300993
Brookes P W *IEng FIIEE* sq(w)
300994
Brown M J *IEng MIMGT MIEIE F I*
E I E sq(w) 300994
Cook A R *TEng(CEI)* 300994
Crichton J I *IEng MIRTE* 300994
Deane J C B *MISM* 300994
Haslam R W *MISM TEng* sq(w)
(A/Lt Col 200201) 300994
Logue W J *IEng MIMI MIRTE*
300994
Miles K A *IEng MIMechE AIRTE*
300994
Nesmith W sq(w) 300994
Painter D E *IEng MIRTE* sq(w)
300994
Ravenscroft R A *IEng AMRAeS*
sq(w) 300994
Stipling T W sq 300994
Andrews T A 300995
Barney M J *IEng MISM MIMechIE*
300995

Bartlett L *IEng FIEIE* sq(w) 300995
Cripps M D *IEng MIMechE* 300995
Fenwick J *BEM* sq(w) 300995
Jenkins M A *MBE MA MSc IEng MIMGT MIPD F I E I E* sq(w) 300995
Johnson A *IEng MIRTE* 300995
Savage M *MBE IEng MIRTE MISM* 300995
Whitington M S *MIMGT FISM MILOG* 300995
Burgess D F *IEng MIMechIE* 300996
Campbell A U *MBE IEng F I E I E* 300996
Collins A W *BEM* 300996
D'Sylva C R J *IEng MISM MIEIE* 300996
Hall P *BA BA(Hons) MSc* 300996
Luff R K *BSc(Hons) MSc CEng MBCS MIMGT MIAP* sq(w) 300996
McMahon P 300996
Nulty P B *IEng MIIEE FISM MIET* sq(w) 300996
Reynolds M B *IEng MIMechE* 300996
Tuck-Brown R P 300996
Burns P C *IEng* 300997
Chadwick J E T *IEng MIMechE MISM* 300997
Coady T S *IEng FIMechE MIIEE MIMGT* sq(w) 300997
Graham M F *MSc IEng MIIEE* gw 300997
Hall P A *MBE IEng AMRAeS* 300997
Hardy N P *IEng AMRAeS* 300997
Hills G B 300997
McCreesh D *MISM* 300997
Seeckts M *IEng FIIE(Elec) MIPD* 300997
Smith B T 300997
Turner N 300997
Williams N J G 300997
Burnett D A 300998
Fitzgerald D A 300998
Hood M W 300998
Muir E G *MISM MILOG* 300998
Sands M T *BA BSc(Hons)* sq(w) 300998
Ward I D *IEng MIMI MIRTE* E 300998
Douthwaite S P *IEng AMIRTE* 300999
Dutson D P A 300999
Licence I P *MBE IEng* 300999
Mason S R *MBE* 300999
McMenemy J B *IEng FIIEE* 300999
Milmer P J *BEM* 300999
Willder K J 300999
Sked K 300900

Captains

Rooth F G *(A/Maj 140998)* 011095

Electrical and Mechanical Assistant Engineers

Tyler B T *OBE IEng FIMechE FIRTE MIMGT MIET* sq(w) *Maj 300988* 140485

George B W *MBE IEng MISM MIET* sq(w) *Lt Col 160698* 171286
Smith M D sq(w) *Lt Col 300697* 050587
McQuilton K C *BSc(Hons)* sq *Lt Col 170400* 130787
Poffley M A *MBE IEng FIEIE* sq(w) *Maj 300989* 010987
Piper T L *MIRTE TEng Maj 260489* 131287
Heelis M C *MBE IEng MIRTE* sq(w) *Lt Col 010799* 010488
Oliver M W *IEng AMRAeS Maj 300990* 010488
Wadsworth M D *Maj 300990* 010488

Special Regular Late Entry Officers

Majors

Spence D 300998
Hopley A J *IEng MIRTE* 300999
Layton M R *DMS MSc IEng MIMGT MIEIE* 300999
Branagan A *BSc(Hons) MIEIE* 300900
Cooper I S *IEng AMRAeS* 300900
Dean M P *BSc IEng FIEIE* 300900
Derbyshire M F *IEng FIEIE* 300900
Rankin A D J 300900
Smith S J *IEng AMRAeS* 300900

Captains

Muirhead J *IEng MIIEE MIMGT MISM FIE (A/Maj 220299)* 060194
Buffin M F *(A/Maj 210800)* 281195
Jackson C J *IEng MIET (A/Maj 080500)* 030196
Mulholland D J *(A/Maj 310899)* 040296
Alp J A *IEng MISM MIEIE (A/Maj 301000)* 010496
Fuery G J *BEM (A/Maj 310100)* 080496
Graham N M *(A/Maj 310100)* 080496
Love R J *IEng MIMGT DMS FIEIE (A/Maj 250699)* 080496
Turner M S *(A/Maj 220399)* 080496
Jones R G *IEng MIMechIE (A/Maj 040900)* 160297
Gadd T P H *(A/Maj 140998)* 190497
Lagadu S P *BSc(Hons) MIMechE* 190497
Lovett P H M *BA IEng FSERT FIIE* 190497
McClung J *IEng MISM MIMechIE* 190497
McNally O P *(L/Maj 301099)* 190497
Peters R M *BSc (A/Maj 010500)* 190497
Rapley A N *(A/Maj 310100)* 190497
Scholefield C E S *IEng FIMechIE MIMechIE* 190497
Short M J *IEng MIMechE (A/Maj 061299)* 190497

Stoddart J A *(A/Maj 240299)* 190497
Taylor N I *IEng MIRTE* 190497
Parsonson S R *(A/Maj 040900)* 051297
Harris S J *IEng AMRAeS* 040198
Cole G J *(A/Maj 280700)* 120198
Smith P W 290398
Burnie J W *(A/Maj 190600)* 010498
Corroyer I M 010498
Griffiths J W G *MBE IEng MIMechIE* 010498
Jenkins P C *(A/Maj 271100)* 010498
Pain P J *(A/Maj 100101)* 010498
Tizard M J *IEng FIIE(MECH) (A/Maj 040100)* 010498

Intermediate Regular Officers

Majors

Parsons A *BEng(Hons)* ae 300997
Sharples N J P *BEng(Hons)* 300900

Captains

ØDulson S L *BEng(Hons)* 101294
Low I M *BEng(Hons) (A/Maj 070101)* 110895
Tessem-Cotton E *BEng(Hons) AMIEE MCIBSE* 091195
Twiss G A *BEng* 031295
Butler R *BSc* 110896
Hulme A M *BEng(Hons)* 141097
Hamilton S P *B Sc (Hons)* 020198
Howard-Harwood M I *BEng(Hons)* 120298
Clarke I *BEng(Hons)* 160698
ØGill L C *BEng(Hons)* 160698
Ware M J *BEng(Hons)* 160698
Bailey S D *BEng* 131098
ØJames L C *BSc(Hons) MSc* 131098
Kerton M S *BEng(Hons)* ae 131098
Stratton-Brown T J *BEng(Hons)* 131098
Taylor P R *BEng(Hons)* ae 100299
Barham E M H *BEng(Hons)* 140699
Mills A J *MA BA(Hons)* 140699
Worrell D I C *BEng(Hons) AMIEE* 140699
Evans A I *BEng(Hons)* 121099
Ash T E *MEng(Hons)* 090200
Binnie D P *BSc(Hons)* 090200
Rogers A J *BEng* 090200
Bremner A *BSc* 130600
Stuart A P D *BEng(Hons)* 130600
East G *BEng AMIEE* 101000
ØHollis S J *BEng(Hons)* 101000
Howarth A J *BSc(Hons)* ae 101000
Allen P J *BEng(Hons)* 080201
Brayshay D D *BEng(Hons)* 080201
Kinkaid P *BEng(Hons)* 080201
Warren G A J *BEng(Hons)* 080201

Lieutenants

Boud C S *BEng(Hons)* 131097
Curran Q S *MEng* 131097
Ackroyd C A *BSc (L/Capt 180900)* 161297
Dove-Dixon J G A *BEng(Hons)* 161297

Smith D J *BEng(Hons) AMIMechE*
    130498
White J A *BEng(Hons)* 100898
Dixon L *BEng(Hons)* 080800
Horn M B 121200

2nd Lieutenants

Coy L B 100499
ØHall S E 100499
Evans G C 150400
ØPurves S H 100900
††Symons M J 100900

Short Service Late Entry Officers

Captains

Hunter G L *(A/Maj 100599)*
    011294
Shore D D *IEng MIMechIE (A/Maj 010499)* 190295
Lince D G *MISM (A/Maj 291199)*
    140296
Omand D W *MISM (A/Maj 260499)*
    080496
Butterworth G *BA MIQA IEng MIPD FIEIE* 190497
Rabbidge P P 190497
Smith J S *(A/Maj 140700)* 190497
Uttley J 190497
White C L *IEng MIMechE* 190497
Thompson K W *BSc BSc(Hons) CEng IEng MRAeS (A/Maj 260500)*
    011297
Stubbington D J *MIRTE (A/Maj 280699)* 211297
Nichol D *AIIRSM* 050198
Booth R *(A/Maj 130899)* 100198
Bates C *BEng(Hons) CEng MRAeS NEBOSH* 120198
Birley B T *BEM IEng FIIE(MECH) MIRTE MIIRSM* 120198
Fountaine I H F *MIIEE (A/Maj 120201)* 120198
Gooderson P T *BSc IEng MIEIE AMIQA F I E I E (A/Maj 240700)*
    120198
Paine R B *BSc IEng AMRAeS (A/Maj 110900)* 020298
Bate A 010398
Alexander G 010498
Bowden M A *IEng MIIEE* 010498
Brazier M R 010498
Burton A 010498
Cannon S B 010498
Cheek J C S 010498
Comerford I M *IEng MIMechE*
    010498
Cowen S D 010498
Dalzell M *MIIEE MISM* 010498
Dennis M H *(A/Maj 070700)* 010498
Drage L R *MIMechIE* 010498
Evans S J 010498
Fishwick M A *MBE MISM MIOSH*
    010498
Flower B T J 010498
Gallacher I C M 010498
Gee B J 010498
George W H *MIEE* 010498
Gill J D *IEng MIMGT MIMechIE CPC (A/Maj 131100)* 010498
Hardman D M 010498

Hewson G A 010498
Hodgson D A *BSc* 010498
Holden G 010498
Laverton M V M 010498
McCracken A *(A/Maj 080101)*
    010498
McDougall W D 010498
McMillan P *(A/Maj 021000)*
    010498
Oliver C B 010498
Parkinson A J *BSc* 010498
Reynolds J K 010498
Selby T 010498
Sherwood N A 010498
Stephenson P E 010498
Welsh W E *IEng MISM* 010498
White D W *IEng MIEIE* 010498
White K D 010498
Woolnough P 010498
Wren D P *IEng FIIE(Elec)* 010498
Wright G R G 010498
Young A 010498
Burgess M L 030498
Devlin C 060498
Smillie C P *IEng MIIEE* 060498
Coomber R R 240498
Eggett G J 240498
Gordon M R 240498
Dowling C J *MSc* 080199
Hill B L N *IEng* 080199
Hodgson T 080199
Howells S I 080199
Imrie B H 080199
Manning J P 080199
Penfold B H *BEM* 080199
Print S A 290199
Grant C J 120299
Jolley K J *BSc* 120299
Park R 120299
Smith B D 120299
Sparrow D M 120299
Bush D *BSc* 190299
Hothersall M 190299
Jackson N D 190299
Kenyon R A 190299
Harrower R A 260299
Hillman C G 260299
Kitchener B C J 260299
Neary A S 260299
Tweedy G R 260299
Jones P D *DipEURHum* 050399
Evers W A 190399
Rosie L R 190399
Carling C M 090499
Wells R W *BEM IEng* 160499
Alderson S 230499
Lowry J A 230499
Stewart G S *BEM* 230499
Wilson T E *BA BSc(Hons) MA*
    230499
Woollam R A 230499
Coey G H 050100
Oatham G 050100
Moles R T 070100
Bennett M B 100100
Richardson R J 100100
Baker M S *BEM* 170100
Lloyd R A 170100
Morton S P 170100
Ritchie A C 170100
Griffiths M R *QGM* 010200
Noble K 110200

Denton P D 210200
Christie D 280200
Morrison R B 280200
Fisher P E *MBE* 010300
Piearce M P *BSc* 010300
Goldsworthy D M 060300
Murdoch B 120300
Aspinall D M 270300
Bradbury J G 270300
Green D J K 270300
Nugent K 270300
Copley-Smith S P 260400
Bradley K W 010500
Grout S W 010500
Henderson R J 010500

Short Service Officers

Captains

Elmes A *BEng(Hons)* 120298
Smith G R G *BEng(Hons) ph*
    131098
Myers S A *BEng(Hons) ae* 140699
Millar J M 121099
Snell A J *BEng(Hons)* 130600
Hill S M D *BEng(Hons)* 080201

Lieutenants

Dickson D G *BEng(Hons)* 131097
Robinson P E *BEng(Hons)* 131097
Brown M *MEng(Hons)* 100298
Hartman L J *BEng(Hons)* 140698
Rook T W *BEng(Hons)* 140698
Young M I *BSc(Hons)* 140698
ØBrooks J L *BEng(Hons)* 100898
Williams R I *BEng(Hons)* 100898
Lynch D 090998
Stevenson M D *BA(Hons)* 121098
ØBlackmun N C *BEng(Hons)*
    141298
Hampshire A J *BEng(Hons)* 141298
ØMcFadyen R *BEng(Hons)* 141298
ØSalter A H *BEng(Hons)* 141298
Sullivan F K *BEng(Hons)* 141298
Anders-Brown D S 150199
James R C J *BEng(Hons)* 090299
Miles K J *BEng(Hons)* 090299
Paris D *MEng(Hons)* 090299
Eves M P *BEng(Hons)* 120499
Jones S D *BEng(Hons)* 120499
Walker I E *BA(Hons)* 120499
Chambers S P *BEng(Hons)* 130699
Ford A D *BEng(Hons)* 130699
ØTarr E A *MEng(Hons)* 130699
Dymow N 060899
Cummings P A *BEng(Hons)* 131299
Dougall G C *BEng(Hons)* 131299
Elliott A R *BEng(Hons)* 131299
Howat J W *BEng(Hons)* 131299
Reynolds S J *BEng(Hons)* 131299
Thomas R J *BEng(Hons)* 131299
Wilson-Maccormack S C *BEng(Hons)* 131299
Flett J J 180400
Hart J N 150500
Foster L G 150800
ØEllis L K 161200

2nd Lieutenants

ØBrown C P T 100499

ADJUTANT GENERAL'S CORPS

A laurel wreath surmounted by a crown; within the wreath the Royal Crest. Beneath a scroll inscribed
ANIMO ET FIDE in silver.

Regimental March

Quick March . . . . .Pride of Lions
Slow March . . . . .Greensleeves

Agents . . . . .Holt's Branch, Royal Bank of Scotland plc.

Regimental Headquarters . . . . .Worthy Down, Winchester, Hants SO21 2RG (Tel: Civ:01962 887630 Mil Ext 2630*)*

Colonel in Chief . . . . .THE QUEEN

Deputy Colonels in Chief . . . .*HRH The Duchess of* Gloucester *GCVO*
Hon Maj Gen *HRH The Duchess of* Kent *GCVO*

Colonel Commandant . . . . .Gen *Sir* Mike Jackson *KCB CBE DSO* 231098

Assistant Colonel Commandant . . . . . .Maj Gen A P N Currie 010599

The antecedent Corps included in the Adjutant General's Corps are as follows:

STAFF AND PERSONNEL SUPPORT BRANCH

On 6 April 1992
Royal Army Pay Corps
Women's Royal Army Corps (less those transferred to other Arms and Services)
and the Staff Clerks of the Royal Army Ordnance Corps
were amalgamated to form
Staff and Personnel Support Branch

On 1 April 1993
Regimental Clerks from all Arms and Services of the Army joined the Branch

PROVOST BRANCH

On 6 April 1992
Corps of Royal Military Police and
Military Provost Staff Corps became:
Provost Branch

On 4 March 1997
The Military Provost Guard Service joined the Branch

EDUCATIONAL AND TRAINING SERVICES BRANCH

On 6 April 1992
Royal Army Educational Corps became:
Educational and Training Services Branch

ARMY LEGAL SERVICES BRANCH

On 6 April 1992
Army Legal Corps became:
Army Legal Services Branch

STAFF AND PERSONNEL SUPPORT BRANCH

A laurel wreath surmounted by a crown, within the wreath The Royal Crest. Beneath a scroll inscribed ANIMO ET FIDE in silver.

Antecedent Corps March

Quick March . . . . .Imperial Echoes

Branch Headquarters . . . . .Worthy Down, Winchester, Hants SO21 2RG
(Tel: Civ: 01962 887228 Mil: Ext 2228)

Alliances

South African Defence Forces . . . . . . .Finance Service Corps

Deputy Colonels Commandant . . . . . . .Brig G K Ramsey *CBE* ret pay 231098

Director . . . . .Brig V Batchelor *OBE* 080600

Brigadiers

Duncan M H *MBCS MIDPM* sq(w)
adp   300697
Leighton R *BSc(Hons) FCMA* sq
                                   300698
ØBatchelor V *OBE* sq   300600

Colonels

ØDowson J *BSc MInstD MIMGT
MIPD* rcds psc *(A/Brig 120201)*
                                   300696
Lane S A *ACIB* sq jsdc pfc 300697
Oakley C T G(a) sq(w) adp 300697
ØTrehern A *BA PGCE* sq jsdc
                                   300698
Walker M J *MBCS* sq(w) adp 300698
Wolsey J N *OBE* psc jsdc 300698
ØDavies D F *OBE* psc jsdc 300699
ØMcCord I M *BA(Hons)* psc jsdc
                                   300699
Dransfield N sq pfc   300600
Farrington W H sq   300600
ØKitchener C J *OBE* sq(w) ais
                                   300600
ØLauder M F *MBE BSc(Hons)*
psc(n) jsdc   300600
———
Lieutenant Colonels

Peerless D J *MSc* dis pfc sq(w)
                                   311289
Barrett P J *OBE AMBCS* pfc sq(w)
adp   300690
Weaving B E *FCMA* sq pfc 300691
Keating P G J pfc sq(w) adp 300692
ØWestlake S J sq   300692
Fairclough A R sq   300695
Kearns J N M *BA(Hons) MSc* dis
sq(w)   300695
Ryder D J *MA MSc* psc† dis ee
                                   300695
Willis P L D sq pfc   300695
Brown A *MIMGT FCIPD* sq 300696
Marriner S J *MBE* psc† psc *(A/Col
061100)*   300696
ØRansom J L *MBE* sq pfc   300696
Rouse R L G pfc sq(w) ais 300696
Wee T G *ACIS* sq pfc   300696
Cameron E C pfc sq(w) ais 300697
Gleed S M *BA* sq(w)   300697

Lamb P A *MSc ACIS* MDA pfc sq(w)
                                   300697
McCulloch D B *RGN RCNT* sq(w)
ais   300697
Raikes G E W T *MBE BA FCMA
ACIS* sq pfc *(A/Col 091000)*
                                   300697
Stovell R J *BSc(Eng)Hons MSc ACIS
ACIB* dis sq(w)   300398
ØDathan J A *ACIS* sq pfc 300698
Gallagher M J sq   300698
Morgan R H *BA(Hons)* psc 300698
Stafford K sq   300698
Thompson P C sq   300698
Walker W R sq   300698
Gibson D A *BA(Hons) ACMA ACIB*
sq   300699
Lemon M J A S J *FCIS* sq pfc
                                   300699
ØMoffat N P *BA(Hons) MA* psc†
Sernberg J R J *LLB(Hons) MSc* dis
sq(w)   300699
Smith K *MInstAM FETC MIAM* sq
                                   300699
Stevenson A C psc   300699
Taylor J C *ACMA* sq   300699
Walker A J sq   300699
Ward A J sq sq(w)   300699
Watters J W sq   300699
ØThomson I *BSc(Hons) MA
MRPharmS MCGI* psc(a)†   311299
Birkhead C J sq   300600
Jones G W sq   300600
Jukes D T F sq(w)   300600
ØMurdoch N A psc   300600
Smith S A sq   300600
ØKershaw D sq   300900

Majors

Moralee S C adp   151280
ØLe Gassick W A *MBE* sq 300982
Brown N *ACIS* sq(w) adp   191282
Rutherford D M   310783
Cubbon D M sq   300984
Case D R   300985
Horsman G P *ACIS* pfc sq(w) 300985
Roberts M D sq(w) ais   300985
Lebeter J *ACIS* sq   300988
ØMcGregor L W I sq pfc   300988
Bright J *MBE AINSTAM LRPS*
                                   300989

Dobbs G L A   300989
Farrington A sq(w)   300989
Smith-Jones G C sq   300989
ØYoung J M sq pfc   300989
Broad D C *BA(Hons) MSc* psc† dis
                                   300990
ØFord C E *BSc(Hons) DipEd* dis
sq(w)   300990
Frazer I S W *AINSTAM*   300990
Pool M G sq pfc   300990
Row N A ph   300990
Collins R M *BA(Hons) MA MBA* psc
                                   300991
ØCunningham E E psc   300991
Hazell P M sq pfc   300991
Nobbs C G *AIBMS* odc(BE) sq
                                   300991
Connor F J *BSc(Hons)* sq(w) ais
                                   300992
Coole N sq sq(w)   300992
Coulter B sq(w)   300992
Pearce M F *MBCS* sq(w) ais 300992
Ronaldson D A A sq   300992
Baines J J *ACMA* sq   300993
ØCallaghan M S *BA(Hons)* sq
                                   300993
Davie W F sq   300993
Dawson E J *ACMA* sowc sq 300993
ØJoyce L K *BA(Hons)* sq G(ss)
                                   300993
Kaye S A sq G(ss)   300993
King S D T sq   300993
ØMartin K J *BA(Hons)* sq 300993
May S J G(ss)   300993
Russell N A sq   300993
Smith B L *M A (Oxon) MSc* psc† †
                                   300993
Spencer B D   300993
Ward R T *ACMA* sq *(A/Lt Col
311000)*   300993
ØWilliams B I *MA(Hons)* sq *(L/Lt
Col 040900)*   300993
ØWood D E sq(w)   300993
ØFrost F E sq   300994
Meldon P *FISM* sq   300994
ØMunday V K *BSc(Hons)*   300994
Savage T R sq *(A/Lt Col 161000)*
                                   300994
ØWalters Davies B *BA(Hons) MDA*
psc   300994
Adey P A   300995
ØBarbone C E L   300995

Beaumont C J	300995
Benwell N R	300995
Burns P R *MA* psc(J)	300995
ØCadec S J *BEd* sq	300995
ØCallow L E	300995
ØCastle F E *BA(Hons)*	300995
ØDeasy S sq	300995
ØForster-Knight A K *BA(Hons)*	300995
ØGlover L C *BA(Hons)*	300995
Goodman R T *MBE* sq	300995
ØGriffiths R C *BSc SRD*	300995
ØGrundy F J *MA GCGI* psc†	300995
ØLang V	300995
ØMyers J E	300995
O'Hara D G	300995
Pearson G M sq	300995
Pomroy M A sq(w)	300995
ØRobertson V C *BSc* psc(J)	300995
Rose A J G(ss)	300995
ØSmith J M *BEd* psc†	300995
ØThomas J C	300995
ØToal K M *MA(Hons)* psc(J)	300995
Watt D S *BSc(Hons)* im sq(w)	300995
Adam S R psc(J)	300996
ØBroomfield K M	300996
ØCastle-Smith S J *LLB(Hons)* psc(J)	300996
ØCollier-Jackson T K *BA(Hons)* sq	300996
ØCorcoran L J sq(w) ais	300996
ØDaly K L	300996
ØFisher S B	300996
Heward R M psc(J)	300996
ØLavender L M *MBE CMS* sq	300996
Pope A M *BSc(Hons) MSc* dis sq(w)	300996
Thorp D A	300996
ØWalker T *FIAB*	300996
Walsh M W	300996
Bowen P F *ACMA*	300997
ØErskine-Tulloch S *BSc(Hons)*	300997
Hellings N J G *BSc(Hons)*	300997
Leslie S A	300997
ØNorris L R *BSc(Hons) PGCE*	300997
ØOwen A M *ACMA* sq	300997
Thomson I D *ACMA* sq	300997
Turner P R	300997
ØWoollard M L	300997
ØWorsley T C *BA(Hons)* psc(CAN)	300997
ØSinclair R E	290398
Barrington D G *MAAT* sq(w) ais	300998
Dean A M G(ss) sq(w) ais	300998
Jaggard-Hawkins I M	300998
ØJames Park E A *BA(Hons)*	300998
Jewell C D sq(w)	300998
King B P	300998
ØMunro A E *BSc(Hons)*	300998
Patterson L *BA(Hons)*	300998
ØPrice-Jones T L	300998
ØSmith J *BA(Hons) ACMA*	300998
Staines S P J	300998
ØWilford L D	300998
ØFitzpatrick L J H *BEng(Hons)*	300999

ØGillies K L	300999
ØGowland S L *BSc(Hons) FRGS ACIS*	300999
ØHassell A C *BA(Hons)*	300999
ØHull C L *LLB(Hons) MSc* dis	300999
Larner A	300999
Medley J C ais	300999
ØMiller N M *BSc(Econ)Hons*	300999
ØPoole J C *BA(Hons)*	300999
Robson T	300999
Sykes M P *BSc(Hons) MSc* dis	300999
Thompson J H	300999
Woodhill N G *BSc(Hons) MSc* dis	300999
Burton-Doe M M T *ACMA*	300900
Gorski S W *DipSUR*	300900
ØMcKinney-Bennett E A	300900
ØSelby A J *BSc(Hons)*	300900
Spencer P G	300900
White A G *BSc(Hons)*	300900
Wright I J *BEng(Hons)* ae	300900

Captains

Hollas M R	80595
Stirling-Stainsby I J ph	80995
Jeffrey J P	121095
Smart I J J	290396
ØJones L B *BA(Hons)*	30496
ØNicholas P J *BSc(Hons)*	120496
Parkes S K *(A/Maj 290800)*	230596
ØMoore P J *BSc(Hons)*	110896
ØGould K S *BSCComb(Hons)*	180896
ØPenhallurick H L *BSc(Hons)*	200896
Pinchen G M *BSc(Hons)*	131296
ØFerguson S A	110497
ØHughes K	80897
ØCunningham A	40698
Rutherford D J	40698
Large I G *BSc*	70898
Young D	131098
ØMacphee J J	111298
Bye W P F *BSc(Hons)*	100299
ØWilkinson R P *BSc(Hons)*	100299
Breen A P	90499
Cann M R	90499
Ledger D W	90499
Lockwood N H *BSc(Hons)*	90499
ØKennedy Y *BSc(Hons)*	140699
ØDennis H L	60899
Doig A J	140400
Lawson M S *LLB(Hons) Dip L P*	20900
Watkinson J M	101000
Price P K *LLB(Hons)*	80201

Lieutenants

ØStrongman C E	240694
ØHowitson E L *BEng(Hons)*	100898
ØTye C *BSc(Hons)*	100898
ØBooth C E *BA*	90899
Griffiths A D	90600

2nd Lieutenants

ØAlexander S	60998
ØWilliams A E	150400

Regular Category Late Entry Officers

Lieutenant Colonels

O'Keefe D W	140398
Bond R J E sq	51298
Morse R J	201000

Majors

McCall R *MBE*	300986
Akbar R A *BA MInstAM CertEd*	10189
Fryer I *BEM* sq	300990
Bogunovic M	300993
Bontoft C *PGDip MBCS AINSTAM* ais	300993
Kelly T J	300993
Baddeley M W	90394
Davies C	300994
Thompson K W	300994
Cleeve S F I	300995
Booth S	300996
Cotton M J R *MBE* sq	300996
Dougan W J	300996
Unsworth J T	300996
Curtis G N *BEM*	300997
Gillespie R M adp	300997
Hollis S A	300997
Wells R W	300997
Bingham R *BEM*	300998
Breach I A *AINSTAM MISM FIAB*	300998
Pinkney L *BSc ACMA AINSTAM*	300998
Stroud W K *BEM MISM*	300998
Harradine J C D *BEM*	300999
Taylor M C	300999

Special Regular Officers Late Entry

Majors

Thorpe K C	300996
ØDavies B	300998
Donoghue S J	300998
Durrant R W	300998
Amos G M *BEM*	300999
ØCassam A	300999
Charge G B	300999
Cotton A	300999
Crow G D	300999
Johnson I A	300999
Burton S T	300900
Cerson A J *MISM*	300900
Greenwood B W *MISM*	300900
Rolfe C F	300900
Skidmore S R *FISB FIAB*	300900
ØTwigg L E	300900

Captains

Lannon P F	130994
Obrien A S	11295
Tilley J	20196
Day A C	240496
Lamb J A	240496
Weetman P D	240496
Stainburn K M P	70297
Cowan R N O	260297
Foster I I	260297
Last G *(A/Maj 131299)*	260297
Moore W D *(A/Maj 100700)*	260297

Bartlett P W R 10498
Collard P *BEM* 10498
Dewberry J *MBE* 10498
Gorton D R *MBE* 10498
Hayes A J 10498
Joy M 10498
Morris C D 10498
Robertson S 10498
Wallace R B 10498
Wright G S 120999

Intermediate Regular Officers

Majors

ØTickner A J 300996
Marsh S 300997
Pyle S D *BA(Hons)* 300998
Brooks G *ACIB* 300999
Horn B 300999
ØJones L I *FIAB* 300999
Jones M 300999
ØBushell G M *BA(Hons)* 10300
Hartley C P 300900

Captains

Shephard S J 80894
Bartlett A J *(A/Maj 140800)* 40295
ØMendonca S A 10495
Graham H J 190396
ØThorne D L *BA(Hons)* 120496
Ford M J *BA(Hons)* 100696
ØHayes C *BPharm MRPharmS* 110896
ØSadler R I W *BA(Hons)* 200896
Barrett R C 300996
Badger J *BA(Hons)* 131296
Brown A P 50797
ØVaughan-Arbuckle C D 80897
ØDoig J R *BA(Hons) DipTP* 120298
Shanahan N A *BSc(Hons)* 120298
ØBeer L M *BA(Hons)* 140699
Knell P J *BSc(Hons)* 140699
Brown K G 170799
Wilkins Q M 60899
ØDavison L E *BSc(Hons)* 121099
ØShanahan P A *BSc(Hons)* ph 121099
ØMurphy C M 101299
Allison D A *BA(Hons) DipM* 90200
ØO'Callaghan C T *BSc(Hons)* 90200
ØFletcher J *BA(Hons)* 101000
ØWhiting V J *BA(Hons)* 101000

Lieutenants

ØSmith L C *(A/Capt 030700)* 150298
ØFord S M 131198
ØBiggs M A 200599

2nd Lieutenants

††Calderhead W G 291099

Short Service Late Entry Officers

Majors

Courtice R A 300996
ØKay K B 300997
McKay B 300997
Orfanelli R T A 300997

Plaistow C H A *AINSTAM MISM* 300998
Crawford A 300999
ØPlatt A M 300999
Whitley C F A 300999
Green J P 300900
Walker P M 300900

Captains

ØJennings J 130994
Rose S 210495
Kimmins A W 180895
Weston P C 180895
Beazley J 240496
Godden V T 240496
Millings P P 240496
ØMorgan Monk L R *(A/Maj 130999)* 240496
Woodward P Q *MBE* 240496
Headford P A *BEM* 260297
Bargrove M J *MISM* 230697
Addison P J *BEM* 10498
Blyth S 10498
Briggs G J 10498
Corker P 10498
ØCritchell J 10498
Evans P 10498
Getty J P 10498
Jackson C 10498
ØJeffery E 10498
Leaver P C 10498
Lowe A J *BEM* 10498
McCluskey D 10498
Patrick J A 10498
Pendlebery I 10498
Potterton S D 10498
Robson S G *(A/Maj 040100)* 10498
Strachan J C J *MBE CertEd* 10498
Watts M J 10498
Blakeway C 240498
Malone D N 240498
Martin B *LRSC* 240498
Stow B A 240498
Wilson R C 240498
Bennington R A 210898
Cowley T P 210898
Cox S L Y 210898
Hart C J P 210898
ØJohnston L A 210898
Maguire T J 210898
Marshall D J 210898
Miller S R 210898
Reid P A 210898
Barker G S 230499
Brindle I G 230499
Dunford A A 230499
Hotchkiss A J 230499
Lindsay-Smith M R 230499
ØMacdonald J A 230499
Mayfield S R 230499
Straw D G 230499
Firth C A *MBE* 200899
Lindsay J B 200899
Manners D R 200899
Marsden T L 200899
Brookes L H 40100
Grant C D 40100
Grover C 40100
Leahy J M 40100
Meredith A G 40100
ØButterworth D 280400
Cox M R 280400

Day M S 280400
Gahan P A *MIMGT* 280400
Garnett D P 280400
Sanders R E 280400
Waite D R 280400
Walesby J W 280400
Wilkes J A 280400
ØAshman A D 250800
Ashman P 250800
Casey M 250800
Davey K N 250800
Martin J E 250800
Renihan D M 250800
Ward P J 250800
Whiteside A J 250800
Duncan I B 50101
Eagle P R 50101
Lade S J 50101
McInally J E D 50101
Simmons A J 50101

Short Service Officers

Majors

Leigh P S *TD ACIB* 140497

Captains

ØHart I L *BA (A/Maj 190201)* 110895
ØThompson H T *BA(Hons)* 30496
ØLarmour V C *BA(Hons)* 120496
ØStammers H J *BA(Hons)* 110896
Jenkins M A 50797
ØKay A R *BA(Hons)* ph 131097
ØCrew A J *BSc(Hons)* 141097
Mayer C A M 10298
Little J W *BSc(Hons)* 100299
McMenamin J J *BA* 140699
ØShaw J J ph 170699
Oconnell A J *BSc* 121099
Hawkins W D 101299
ØBroadhead S R *BSc(Hons)* 90200
ØCox A E *BAcc* 90200
ØPatterson K R *BA(Hons)* 90200
ØCrowther S *BTech* 180300
ØBatchelor L M *BA(Hons)* 101000
ØCampbell J J 101000
ØClark S L A *BA(Hons)* 101000
ØLloyd R H *BA(CombHons)* 101000
ØLovett M L *BA(Hons)* 101000
Banks H *BSc(Hons)* 80201

Lieutenants

Concannon J G P *BSc(Hons)* *(A/Capt 221100)* 160697
Fallon J V *BA(Hons)* 160697
ØWyer K A *MA(Hons)* 160697
ØDay J N *BA(Hons) (A/Capt 210800)* 120897
ØParsons H J *BSc(Hons)* 161297
ØTarlton A J 161297
ØThomson H J *BA(Hons)* 161297
Woolley P N 161297
ØDevereux K J L *BA(Hons)* 100298
ØHunter E K L *BA(Hons)* 100298
Ratnaike M P *BA(Hons)* 130498
Farren M A *BA(Hons)* 100898
ØMcAuley L 160199
Omara J M *MA(Hons)* 90299
ØSly Z *BA(Hons)* 120499
ØLyford A L M 130699

ØMills A E M *BSc(Hons)*   90899
ØBlair L C *BA(Hons)*   131299
ØDunlop S C *BSc(Hons)*   131299
ØHamilton-Green E   *(A/Capt 130700)*   131299
Murray J J *BA(Hons)*   131299
Smyth C *BSc*   131299
Vardy S M   *(A/Capt 020101)* 131299
Dexter S E   100400

2nd Lieutenants

Read D G   150399

Short Service Volunteer Officers

Majors

ØBradshaw E A *LLB MA MA(Ed) WS DipRSA*   30387

ØWalton R E *BA*   180795

Captains

ØMcVey G S *BSc(Hons)*   120393
ØNicholson L V   10100

PROVOST BRANCH
AGC (RMP)

RMP: Within a laurel wreath, the Royal Cypher with Crown above. Beneath, a scroll inscribed "Royal Military Police"
MPS: The Royal Cypher ensigned with the Crown thereunder a scroll inscribed MILITARY PROVOST STAFF CORPS all gold.
MPGS: The Royal Cypher ensigned with the Crown and thereunder a scroll inscribed MILITARY PROVOST GUARD SERVICE in gold, the whole surmounting crossed Government keys in silver

Antecedent Corps Marches

Quick Marches . . . . .The Watchtower (RMP)
The New Colonial (MPS)
Steadfast and True (MPGS)

Branch Headquarters . . . . .Trenchard Lines, Upavon, Pewsey, Wilts SN9 6BE
(Tel: Civ: 01980-615656 Mil: Ext 5656)

Alliances

Canadian Armed Forces . . . . .Canadian Forces Security Branch
Australian Military Forces . . . . .The Royal Australian Corps of Military Police
New Zealand Army . . . . .Royal New Zealand Military Police
Pakistan Army . . . . .Corps of Military Police (Pakistan)
Sri Lanka Army . . . . .The Sri Lanka Corps of Military Police
Malaysian Armed Forces . . . . .Malaysian Military Police

Deputy Colonel Commandant . . . . .Maj Gen F R Dannatt *CBE MC* 010499

Director . . . . .Brig M Nugent 151099

Brigadiers		Forster-Knight E O *LLB(Hons) MA GCGI* psc†	300600	Wilson S S 300995
		McIvor P A C A *MIMGT* sq	300600	Roberts M 300996
Nugent M *BA* psc†	300600			Vale G *BSc(Hons) MBA* sq 300996
		Majors		King J V 300997
				Moore J S 300997
Colonels		Thompson G A C sq	300980	Williamson M A 300997
		Barton I R *MIPD* sq	300981	ØHerbert A C *BA(Hons)* 300998
Figg A J *OBE* sq	300699	Backler J A A sq	300982	Seal A I 300998
Findlay C A *MBE BA DipEd CGIA* psc†	300699	Farrelly P E *BSc/BA(Hons)* sq	300982	Wassell L S 300998
Wood W *BArch(Hons) MBA* psc†	300699	Hayes S G sq	300984	ØBuck V W 300999
Cuthbert-Brown M *MBA* psc jsdc	300600	Edwards G R *LLB(Hons)* sq(w) ais	300988	ØPurnell S N 300999
Giles D C N *LLB(Hons)* psc	300600	London J E S sq *(A/Lt Col 011099)*	300988	ØWaring J R *BA(Hons)* 300999
———		Oughton R A B *BA(Hons)*	300988	Warren I S 300999
		Ridout N J *MIL* sq	300988	Fielder S M 300900
		Russell S J sq	300989	
Lieutenant Colonels		Faithfull L sq ais	300990	*Captains*
		Davie R J *BSc(Hons) MIPD DMS* sq	300991	Shepherd H R *(A/Maj 061100)* 10495
Nelson J A J *MIMGT* sq	300688	Green J T sq	300993	Charvat J P I A G *BA(Hons)* 141295
Bacon K T *OBE*	300692	House P C *BA(Hons)* sq	300993	Young T J *BSc(Hons) ARCS* 141295
Lanham J W sq	300692	Moore R M *MBA* sq	300993	Boniface P D *BEng(Hons)* 131296
Powell G L	300692	Petrie J C *MBE* sq	300993	ØWaterworth C A *LLB* 131296
Baber J H *MBE* sq	300693	Shanks A E C	300993	Titchener M F 110497
Boyd S F *LLB(Hons)* psc† jsdc *(A/Col 280201)*	300693	Malin K *BSc(Hons)* sq *(L/Lt Col 011000)*	300994	Wellington P F 151298
Bergin D J A *OBE* odc(US) sq aic	300695	Evanson G W	80495	ØRoylance E K *BSc(Hons)* 100299
Barnard N M B sq	300698	ØBrown S J	300995	Meredith S 90499
Lawson D A L psc	300698	Cairns P S M A *BA(Hons)* odc(BE)	300995	Banks A M *FRGS* 60899
Prosser I E sq jsdc	300698	Dorset S	300995	Grogan A J 60899
Palmer R W *BSc* sq	300699	Jordan A P	300995	Sawyer A M J 60899
Stenning I A R *MBE* sq	300699	Macgill J S	300995	
Warren R W *MBE* psc	300699	Parry-Jones D B *BSc(Hons)*	300995	*Lieutenants*
Watton T P *OBE MIPI MIMGT* sq	300699	West R C A *BA(Hons)*	300995	Miller K S *(A/Capt 010299)* 161297
Baillie P F *BA(Hons)* psc† †	300600	ØWest F T *BA(Hons) MA GCGI* sq(w)	300995	ØRobinson J M 100898
				2nd Lieutenants
				ØRingrose L A 110900

Regular Category Late Entry Officers

Lieutenant Colonels

Lindop F M MBE	10199

Majors

Silk R W MBE sq	300991
Miller C R	300992
Attridge P R	300993
Blake K J BEM	300993
Taylor G sq	300993
Ambrose I C MBE	300994
Axup R R MBE sq	300994
Bottomley M C BEM	300994
Wooldridge E J	300995
McCrorie W	300996
Millar S D	300996
McNally M K ais	300998
Rowley D N	80299
Murray A W MBE	300999
Grainger M A B Sc (Hons)	300900

Captains

Bell-Walker K (A/Maj 080299)	10694

Special Regular Officers Late Entry

Majors

McDonald G M	300900
Pickering D E	300900

Captains

Pollard G H	210296
Watson J W	210296
Greetham R J	280296
Higgs S J	60597
Downie M R	10498
Faulkner A	10498
ØRoberts K	10498
Shaw W	10498
Lark M	70498

Intermediate Regular Officers

Majors

ØForsythe B L	300900
Gartland D M	300900
Neal D S BA(Hons)	300900

Captains

ØBatty F M MA (A/Maj 290600)	101294
Nealon A D BSc(Hons)	110895
ØMayhead S E	110497
ØParkes N M BA(Hons)	141097
Parke F S	70598
Watt W I M FIIE(Elec)	91098
ØHudson S C BSc(Hons)	140699
ØHarris K D	90200
ØHeighington C BSc(Hons)	101000
ØLayton-Shaw G L BA(Hons)	101000

Lieutenants

Packer P M	260398
ØNugent G BA(Hons) (A/Capt 091000)	130498
Ather C A	290998
ØBulley L K	291199
Scott K W	131299

Short Service Late Entry Officers

Majors

Lynes J R	300997

Captains

Hunt P G	270896
Denison R J	300397
Ansell S J	10498
Dobson O J BEM	10498
Jones P T R	10498
Jones A G	70498
Roberts H A	70498
Smith D A	70498
Tilley L A	70498
ØHolliday M B	10399
Hagues P H	70499
Lightowler J M	70499
Rowland T J	70499
Beresford S L	50400
Bird M R	50400
Milburn P T J	50400
ØMiller K L	50400
Janes P A	41200

Short Service Officers

Captains

ØWells B BSc(Hons)	280196

Tomlinson E J BA(Hons)	110896
Inman J M	141097
Osborne M C BA	160698
Patton M R F	250499
Baysting D L BSc(Hons) MSc	140699
ØFreshwater J S	101299
ØGoring K E	80700
Dray D J	110700
Hendy S A BSc(Hons)	101000
ØMcNeill V E	211000

Lieutenants

Hipkins J R D	140991
ØSmith S L BA(Hons)	120897
ØLindsay E A BSc(Hons)	161297
Anderson J M	140598
ØCorani S J	100898
ØMurphy L K BSc(Hons)	100898
Quantrell A C (A/Capt 101098)	100898
ØBowen L A	141298
ØNeal L A BA(Hons)	120499
Hutchison D J BSc(Hons)	130699
ØJohnson E L BMus(Hons)	130699
Rusdale-Jones M I H	260699
Hall M C BSc(Hons)	90899
Alecock J R	241199
Greaves B T BA(Hons)	131299
Hibbert J M BSc(Hons)	131299
ØMunro K BA(Hons)	131299
Walters G M PGCE BA(Hons)	131299
Hornsby L B	280900

2nd Lieutenants

ØGreenfield C	100499
Young J P	131299

Rec Res (RARO)

Captains

Barry T R F T	250783

PROVOST BRANCH
AGC (MPS)

Regular Category Late Entry Officers

Licence A D *MBE*   300997

Short Service Late Entry Officers

Majors

Burton P M   300995

Captains

Baker P L   10498

Corcoran R G *MBE*	10498
Hull A J	150199
Wilson N B	70499

268

EDUCATIONAL & TRAINING SERVICES BRANCH

A Laurel wreath surmounted by a crown, within the wreath The Royal Crest.
Beneath a scroll inscribed ANIMO ET FIDE in silver

Antecedent Corps March

Quick March . . . . .Guadeamus Igitur and The Good Comrade

Branch Headquarters . . . . .Trenchard Lines, Upavon, Pewsey, Wilts SN9 6BE
(Tel: Civ: 01980-615703 Mil Ext: 8703*)*

Alliances

Australian Military Forces . . . . .The Royal Australian Army Educational Corps
New Zealand Army . . . . .The Royal New Zealand Army Education Corps

Deputy Colonels Commandant . . . . . . .Maj Gen F R Viggers *MBE* 110500

Director . . . . .Brig P S Purves *CBE* 300699

Brigadiers

ØPurves P S *CBE MA MLitt* psc
300699
Filler M S J *BEd* psc   300600

Colonels

Winfield K O *MA* psc I* jsdc 300694
Simmonds G M *OBE MA MIMGT
FCIPD CGIA* psc†   300695
Aitken D *MSc* dis sq(w)   300697
Brister A W E *BA(Hons)* psc 300699

Lieutenant Colonels

Jenkins J H *BSc(Hons) MSc MIMGT
FCIPD* sq   300687
ØSmith E A *BEd MA MSc(Econ)
PhD*   300687
Maley T *BA(Hons) MSc(Econ)* sq
300688
Atkins B M *BSc(Hons) MA* sq
300690
Martindill C J *MA MEd MSc FCIPD*
sq   300690
Moore T C R *OBE BA(Hons)
MSc(Econ) FRGS MCIPD FCOLLP*
sq *(A/Col 010101)*   300690
ØCalliss A C *BSc(Hons) MEd*
300691
Ciaglinski R Z A *BA MEd* sq *(A/Col
140201)*   300691
Wither J K *MA MSc(Econ) CertEd* sq
300691
Clifton S J P *BSc(Hons) MSc PGCE*
psc† dis   300692
Green S I *BA(Hons) MLitt MIPR* sq
(L/Col 310300)   300692
Lawson K G *OBE PGCE MSc* sq
300692
Pittendreigh D W *MA MSc PGCE
FCIPD*   300692
Wright M J *MSc FCIPD* sq   300692
ØHall V H *BA(Hons) MSc PGCE* dis
sq(w)   300693
Morrison R K *MEd*   300694
Powell T B D'E *MA MBA DipTCH
FRSA MInstD* sq cl I   300694

Caswell C J *BA(Hons) MSc PGCE
FCIPD* psc jsdc   300695
Douglas R W *BEd* psc   300695
Munro A A C *BA(Hons) MA(Hons)
MEd MCIPD* sq(w)   300695
Burgess S C *MEd MSc* dis sq(w)
300696
ØMartin V J *BA(Hons)* I* jsdc
300697
Cartwright D T *MBE BSSc MEd
DipBA* sq   300698
O'Connell S H *BEd(Hons)
MEd(EdTech) CertEd* sq jsdc
300698
Tarrant P M *BEd(Hons) MEd* sq
300698
Davis C *BSc(Hons) MSc ARCS
CPhysMInstP CPhys* dis sq(w)
300699
Draper G *BSc(Hons) MEd(DIST)* sq
300699
Hopwood D *BEd(Hons) MA MSc* sq
MDA   300699
Russell P M *MEd MIMGT MCIPD*
sq   300699
Wilson D G *BA MEd* sq   300699
Buxton A *BEd(Hons) MEd(EdTech)*
sq   300600
ØMoncur G F *MBE MSc PGCE*
sq(w)   300600
Rabbitt A J *MA ALCM MIL PGCE* sq
I* I   300600
Thomson A J *BSc(Hons)*   300600

Majors

Sales J B *BA* I   290779
Holloway D *BA*   110881
Thomas A G *BA*   30981
Harvey W J *MA MSc(Econ)* 120983
Hannan J P *MA MEd MIMGT*
270484
Hopkins I N *BSc(Hons) DipHE*
40385
Willcox-Jones P W *BEd(Hons) MEd
CertEd*   50785
Lewis-Cooper C *BSc(Hons) MEd
MCIPD* sq   130286
Keenan A W *MSc DipEd* dis sq(w)
40386
Cardy A J *BA(Hons) PGCE MEd* I
60986

Standish M P *MEd* sq   290986
Wakefield M I *BA(Econ)Hons MLitt*
11087
Burn D F *BEd(Hons) MA MIL* I
31087
Dickins M A *BA(Hons) MEd MCIPD*
31087
McBirnie D *BA(Hons)* I   31087
Howells R T *BA(Hons) MSc(Econ)
FCIPD MCIPD* sq   300988
Hunter C J *MEd MLitt*   300988
Leach G W *MEd MCIPD*   300988
Wilkinson I *BA(Hons) MIL PGCE*
300988
Woods A B *BEd(Hons) MEd(EdTech)*
sq   300988
Walker E P *BA(Hons) MA(Ed)
MSc(Econ) PGCE MCIPD* sq
300789
Beer J M *BA(Hons) MA PhD* df sq
300989
Douglas C *BA(Hons) MEd* sq(w)
300989
Hanlan C G *BSc(Hons) MEd* sq(w)
300989
Harris S J *BSc(Eng)Hons MSc* dis
sq(w)   300989
Hazledine D W *MEd* sq   300989
ØJones B E C A *BA(Hons) MA
PGCE*   300989
Shepherd D A *BA(Hons)* dis sq(w)
300989
Thomson B G *MA* sq(w)   300989
Whitfield A D T *MBE BEd(Hons)*
300989
Wright E J *BSc(Hons) MEd PGCE* sq
300989
Carolin R *BA(Hons) MEd PGCE* sq
300990
Gibson G C *BA(Hons) MA* sq
300990
ØLambert S J *BSc(Hons) MEd* sq
300990
ØLangford D E *BEd(Hons)
MSc(Econ) ASTA*   300990
Bailey M S *BA(Hons) MEd PGCE* sq
300991
Butterfield A W *BSc(Hons) MEd
PGCE* sq *(A/Lt Col 111200)* 300991
Ellison S *BSc(Hons) MA PGCE* sq
sq(w)   300991
Lambert P J *MSc* sq   300991

Mack A R *BA(Hons) MA MPhil PGCE* sq 300991
Olley G W J *BEd(Hons) MA* sq G(ss) 300991
Tognarelli W G *BSc(Hons) MA* 300991
ØWildman H *BA MSc(Econ) ALA* sq 300991
Wilson N J *BEd(Hons) DipHE FRGS* sq 300991
ØCran C *BSc(Hons) MEd* 300992
Hopkins K W *MSc* sq sq(w) 300992
Jenkins D *BSc(Hons) MSc PGCE MEd* sq 300992
Jolleys R H *BA(Hons) MA(Econ) FRGS PGCE* sq 300992
Maher N *BA(Hons) MEd MPhil PGCE* sq 300992
Moore E L *BA(Hons) MEd PGCE MCIPD* sq 300992
Pendlenton R M *BA(Hons) MA PGCE* sq 300992
Smith D K M *MA(Hons) MIL* 300992
Twentyman N G *BEd(Hons) MEd MIMGT MCIPD* sq 300992
Waller I M G *BEd MA MIITT MIMGT* sq 300992
ØBruce F *MA(Hons)* 300993
ØMaclean L M *BA MEd DipExMTG* 300993
Morris G S *BSc(Hons) MEd PGCE* sq 300993
ØEllis S *BEd(Hons)* 300994
Gibb D M *BSc PGCE* 300994
King A N *BA(Hons) PGCE* 300994
Lewis N R *BSc(Hons)* 300994
Mahoney M W *BA(Hons)* 300994
Russell H A S *BSc(Hons) PGCE MEd MCIPD* sq(w) 300994
ØBrown E H *BSc* psc(J) 300995
ØConvery C S *BA(Hons) MA(Ed) PGCE* sq 300995
ØDickinson M F *BA(Hons) MA PGCE* sq 300995
Duxbury R I *BSc(Hons) MEd PGCE* 300995
ØFinney E E *BSc(Hons)* 300995
ØFinney L F *BSc(Hons) MSc* dis sq(w) 300995
Rothwell A *MSc PGCE* psc(J) dis † 300995
ØSwinyard L F M *BSc(Hons) MA PGCE* 300995
ØThomson J M *BEd(Hons) MA* 300995
ØWeir K A *BA(Hons) PGCE* 300995
Woods G M *BA(Hons) CRE MA PGCE* 300995
ØYoung S A *BA(Hons) MA* sq 300995
ØCrighton J I *BA(Hons) MA* 300996
ØDavidson J M *BEd* 300996
Dawson T J *BA(Hons)* sq 300996
Deans A J *BSc(Hons) PGCE* 300996
ØGammon J A *BA(Hons)* 300996
Gardner C D A *BSc(Hons)* 300996
ØJohnstone C *MA MEd MSc PGCE* psc(J) 300996
Jones N A *BSc(Hons) MSc(Econ)* 300996

Lightfoot C M R *BA(Hons) PGCE* 300996
ØPullman S *BSc(Hons) Ed(EdTech) PGCE FCIPD* sq 300996
Simpson H A *MBE MA MA(Ed)* sq 300996
ØVingoe E D F *BSc(Hons)* 300996
ØAhern S L *BEd(Hons)* 300997
ØFoxley C E *BSc(Hons) PGCE* 300997
Frost A J *BA(Hons) PGCE* 300997
ØHall I E *BA(Hons) PGCE* 300997
ØKnell K E *BSc(Hons) PGCE MBA MBA FETC* 300997
Thompson R F *BA(Hons) PGCE* 300997
ØChristopher C H *BSc(Hons) PGCE* 300998
ØClaridge M *BEd(Hons) DipHE* 300998
ØElmes D A *BA(Hons) PGCE* 300998
ØHolmes S J *BEd(Hons)* 300998
ØJones M C M *BSc(Hons) PGCE* sq ais 300998
Plant D J *BA(Hons)* 300998
Whitehead J R *BA(Hons) PGCE* 300998
ØAllen W A S *BEd(Hons)* 300999
ØBuchanan J A *MA(Hons)* 300999
Cottrell P J *BA(Hons) PGCE* 300999
Crome D J *BEd(Hons)* 300999
ØGartland S *BA(Hons)* 300999
ØIson S J *BSc(Hons)* 300999
Lodge D R *BA(Hons) MA(Hons)* 300999
ØMurrison S E *BSc(Hons) PGCE MSc MSc* 300999
Reed P W *BA(Hons) PGCE* 300999
Farthing T *BSc(Hons) PGCE* 300900
Hammond R F E *BA(Hons) M A (Oxon) PGCE* 300900
ØMurray S *BA(Hons) MPhil* 300900
ØNorthover B A *BA(Hons)* 300900
Whyte D P *BA(Hons)* 300900
ØWood L E *BEd(Hons)* 300900

Captains

Child K A B *BEd(Hons)* 110493
ØHunter J F *BA(Hons)* 60894
ØPalmer K L *BA(Hons) PGCE* 91294
ØHayward H A *BA(Hons)* 10495
ØHulm S J *BA(Hons)* 10495
ØTosi C *BSc(Hons)* 10495
Atkinson M J *BEd(Hons)* 110595
ØBowman E L *BEd(Hons)* 110895
Rameshni N *BSc(Hons)* 110895
Firth P M *BEd(Hons) CMS* 141295
Green P P *BA(Hons)* 120496
Pogson R K J *BSc(Hons)* 120496
ØRigby E N *BSc(Hons)* 120496
Ellis T B *BA(Hons)* 110896
ØHarrison R J *BA PGCE* 110896
Trowbridge E J *BA(Hons)* 110896
Reynolds P *BA(Hons) PGCE* 120298
ØAddison A C *BA(Hons)* 160698
Booth N A *BA(Hons) PGCE* 160698

Hayman M E *BA(Hons)* 160698
ØPease J M *BSc(Hons) PGCE* 160698
Sharp M P G *BSc(Hons) PGCE* 160698
ØSheldon J *BA(Hons)* 131098
Charles A *BSc(Hons)* 100299
ØLivy S A *BSc(Hons) MA* 100299
Ward A J *BSc(Hons) PGCE* 100299
ØBell J L *BA(Hons)* 140699
ØCovell E L *BA(Hons)* 140699
ØGibbs K M *BSc(Hons) PGCE* 140699
ØMarsh L J *BA(Hons)* 140699

Lieutenants

Reeve D *BSc(Econ)Hons PGCE* 161296
ØSteel S A *BA(Hons)* 120297
ØSliney C C *BA(Hons)* 120800

Regular Category Late Entry Officers

Majors

Bornstein D *BA CertEd* 300989
Pickles K M *BA(Hons) MIL I* 300989
Yarrien P A *MEd MINSTAMDip* 10193
Leigh M J *MA* 300995
Kirk A W 300996
Ball M J P *BSc(Hons) MA PGCE* sq 300997
Dowsett J *BA(Hons) MA MEd MCIPD* 300997
Gorczyca A J *BA(Hons) MSc PGCE* 300997
Mann J L *BA FIEIE* 300998

Special Regular Officers Late Entry

Majors

Craggs G *MA CertEd (FE* 300998
Macdonald A R *PGCE* 300999

Captains

Morgan H J *FIL* 50793
Newman P 10896
Reeds A H *CertEd (FE* 10896
Cheshire S J *BSc (A/Maj 021000)* 300697
Malpass C J *CertEd* 300697
Bamforth K *PGCE MIL* 10498
Cape C S E *PGCE* 10498
Cockram M C 10498
Edwards C S *CertEd* 10498
Johnson I P *BA(Hons) MA* 10498
Micallef-Green S A 10498
Ridley M A *PGCE GCGI LCGI* 10498
ØCzernik K J L 80498

Intermediate Regular Officers

Majors

ØGlover S J L *BA(Hons)* 300992
Bishop A *BA DipHE* 300999

Reid A J A *BSc(Hons) BEd PGCE*
300999
Elliott B J *BA(Hons)* 300900
ØJohnson K L *BA(QTS)(Hons)*
300900
Stanley A R *BA(Hons) DipTEFL*
300900

Captains

ØSelley B J *BSc(Econ)Hons PGCE*
101292
ØBailey T S 10194
ØReid R M 140594
Polhill S M *BA(Hons) PGCE* 60894
ØRumsey M A *BA(Hons) PGCE*
131295
Browne A K *BSc(Hons) PhD* 300496
Mallett S J *BSc(Hons)* 120298
Barltrop S W *BA(Hons) MSc* 160698
Harding J K A *BA PGCE* 100299
ØHolloway K J *BA* 100299
ØRowlands M A *BSc(Hons) PGCE*
100299
ØTorbet K M *BA(Hons) PGCE*
100299
Cable G *BA(Hons) MIL* 60699
Foster J D *BEd(Hons)* 140699
Francis P B *BA(Hons)* 140699
ØKelley K G *BSc(Hons)* 140699
Taylor G J *BSc(Hons)* 140699
ØSkidmore L E *BEd(Hons)* 121099
ØMcQuade K L *MA(Hons)* 90200
ØGeorge P M *BSc(Hons)* 130600
ØSherlock C K *BA* 130600
ØTaylor A D 101000

Lieutenants

ØHamlin J *BMus(Hons)* 140496

Short Service Late Entry Officers

Majors

Whiting R J *BEd* 300996
Bartlett K J *MSc IEng FIIE(Elec)*
CertEd (FE 300998

John M P *CertEd (FE* 300999

Captains

Harrison-Brown S D 300697
Bergman S T *BSc(Hons)* 10498
Laws T W 10498
Betts R C *BSc PGCE* 80498
Sutcliffe S 80498
Hewett I S *PGCE* 210898
Barclay H 230499
Martin P T *BSc(Hons) PGCE* 230499
Scott N M *MM PGCE* 230499
Shanahan A C 230499
Alger R C 280400
Cruse T 280400
Saunderson G T 280400
Stobart A J 280400
Evans R N *CertEd* 250800
ØMundy L E 250800
ØSanderson V 250800
Powell N 50101

Short Service Officers

Captains

ØWalshaw A J *BA(Hons)* 110896
Simpson J *BEng(Hons) BA* 171097
Hair P S *BA(Hons)* 120298
Murdoch J M *BSocSc(Hons) MA*
160698
Charman J R *BA(Hons)* 131098
Nicol J D *BA(Hons)* 291198
ØMatson T J *BA(Hons)* 90200
ØAlmonds C T *BSc(Hons)* 10500
Blower T J *MSc BA(Hons)* 130600
ØHuins A L *BA(Hons)* 130600
Tallack J M *MA BA(Hons)* 130600
ØBaxter K I *LLB(Hons)* 101000
Caruana S R *BSc(Hons) PGCE*
101000
ØGatheridge T *BA(Hons)* 101000
ØHemmings V E *BEd(Hons)* 101000
Martin G A *BSc(Hons) PGCE PC*
(A/Maj 260600) 101000
ØWhitehead A D *BA(Hons) PGCE*
101000
ØYardley K L *BSc(Hons)* 101000

ØBriggs A R *BA(Hons)* 80201

Lieutenants

Jennings J C *BSc(Hons) PGCE*
280496
ØWilden K M *BSc(Hons) PGCE*
161296
Hutchison I M *BEd(Hons)* 120297
ØTattersall P J A *BSc(Hons)* *(L/Capt 260600)* 120297
Manning N R *BSc(Hons)* 20397
Henning A P *BA(Hons)* 160697
ØDix S E *BSc(Hons)* 100897
ØFigg C E *BA(Hons)* 100897
ØWilmshurst J R *BA(Hons)* *(L/Capt 140400)* 120897
Tosh W M *BA(Hons)* 161297
Murphy D D *BA(Hons)* 100298
Rankin E L *MA(Hons)* 100298
ØRedman R J 130498
Midgley C J *BSc(Hons)* 140698
ØMagowan M E *BA(Hons)* 90898
Collyer S J *BSc(Hons)* 100898
Dexter R G A *BCombStuds* 100898
ØJennings S J *BSc(Hons)* 100898
ØSunderland S C *BA(Hons)* 100898
Taylor J D *BSc (A/Capt 011200)*
100898
Winfield J I B *BSc(Hons)* 100898
Sterling M 121098
Terblanche C 21298
Chamberlain D F *BA(Hons)* 131298
ØGraham F *BSc(Hons) DipEd*
131298
ØWard V R *BA(Hons)* 131298
Smith B R *BCom(Hons)* 10299
Denning G F *BA BA(Hons)* 90299
ØDiamond R *BSc(Hons)* 90299
Janvier C E *BA(Hons)* 90299
ØPrudhoe K H *MA(Hons)* 90299
Galle N 120499
ØMiller N A *LLB(Hons)* 120499
Ketterer M T *BA(Hons)* 130699
ØHodder E *BA(Hons) PGCE* 90899
Milton J I C *MA(Hons)* 70899
Burt A D *BA(Hons)* 131299
ØTaylor C D *MA BA(Hons)* 150400

ARMY LEGAL SERVICES BRANCH

The Figure of Justice superimposed upon the Globe surmounted by The Royal Crest. Behind the Globe Crossed Swords with blades uppermost on a black ground within a circle inscribed "Justitia in Armis" On a Scroll below "Army Legal Corps"

Antecedent Corps March

Quick March . . . . .Scales of Justice

Branch Headquarters . . . . .Directorate of Army Legal Services, Trenchard Lines, Upavon, Pewsey, Wilts SN9 6BE (Tel: Civ: 01980 615989 Mil: Ext 5989)

Alliances

Canadian Armed Forces . . . . .Canadian Forces Legal Branch
Australian Military Forces . . . . .The Australian Army Legal Corps

Deputy Colonel Commandant . . . . .Maj Gen *His Honour Judge* D H D Selwood ret pay 010196

Director . . . . .Maj Gen G Risius *CB* 010497

Brigadiers

Bryant P J *OBE LLB(Hons)* 300698

Colonels

Garraway C H B *MA* 300695
Austin R P M 300696
Howell D M *OBE LLB(Hons)*
(A/Brig 300499) 300698
Paphiti A S *LLB* (A/Brig 090201) 300698
Vowles S G *BA(Hons)* 300699
———

Lieutenant Colonels

Adams G A R *LLB(Hons)* 200192
Jones N J H *LLB(Hons)* 310192
McEvoy P D *OBE LLB(Hons)*
(A/Col 010698) 70292
Greasley C *BA(Hons)* (A/Col 120499) 211193
ØSullivan R *LLB(Hons)* 300894
Conway M D *LLB(Hons)* 21094
Morrison A M *LLB(Hons) WS* 300395
Lloyd R A *BA(Hons)* 140495
Bullough C G J *BSc(Econ)Hons* 210795
Bowman J C *LLB* 300995
Reddin D G *MBE LLB(Hons)* 70296
ØMiskelly C 140197
Stythe J N *LLB(Hons)* (A/Col 170101) 81097
Pierce R J *LLB(Hons)* 11098
ØEyton-Jones J A *LLB(Hons)* 240499
ØMcGarr L M *LLB(Hons)* 110699
Yates D N *MBE LLB(Hons)* 130400
Armstrong C A *LLB(Hons) CPLS BL* 30500

Majors

Moore A G *LLB(Hons)* (A/Lt Col 100397) 11094
Mercer N J *BD LLM* (A/Lt Col 010499) 300995
Jones N F *LLB(Hons) LLM* (A/Lt Col 250598) 111295

Batty R J *BA(Hons)* (A/Lt Col 300799) 260296
Clapham N W J *LLB(Hons)* (A/Lt Col 170599) 260296
ØRidge S K *BA(Hons)* (A/Lt Col 290399) 260296
Lythgoe S G S *LLB* (A/Lt Col 060300) 120496
Stewart D M *BA(Econ) LLB* (A/Lt Col 250400) 191197
Moreland N F *LLB(Hons)* (A/Lt Col 021000) 250998
McClelland J *MBE LLB(Hons)* (A/Lt Col 150500) 140199
Whitwham C *LLB* (A/Lt Col 150500) 180299
Coombes G D *BA(Hons)* 50399
ØPeters E K *LLB(Hons)* (A/Lt Col 080101) 110699
Dakers M B *DPLS LLB(Hons)* 130899
Barnett C M J *LLB(Hons)* 11099
Johnston J A E *LLB(Hons)* 280100
ØBowen J L *LLB(Hons)* 300600
ØMcNeil L *LLB(Hons)* 151000
Glover E F *LLB(Hons)* 10201
McDonnell S *BA(Hons)* 10201

Captains

Eble K J *(A/Maj 010600)* 300696
Wakefield D C *BA(Hons)* (A/Maj 300899) 290996
Taylor A *BSc(Hons)* (A/Maj 020500) 60997
Fryatt A G *BA(Hons)* 10398
Simpson N J *BA* (A/Maj 190600) 10398
Wheatley A E R *DipLP BA(Hons)* (A/Maj 010500) 10398

Special Regular Officers Late Entry

Captains

ØBowman H E *BSc(Econ)Hons* 130200

Short Service Officers

Majors

Hardy J B 50399
Pegg J G *LLB(Hons)* 60200
Culver M J *LLB(Hons)* 290900
ØBraddick-Hughes C E 10201

Captains

Frend D P *BA(Hons)* (A/Maj 220399) 10297
ØJones V A *LLB(Hons)* (A/Maj 200999) 60997
Sadler D J W *BA(Hons)* 60997
Woodman J J *BSc(Hons)* 280997
ØMcAvock S G *LLB(Hons)* (A/Maj 240100) 291097
ØCook E S *LLB(Hons)* 50198
Allen R A *LLB(Hons)* (A/Maj 011000) 120998
Clifton R 120998
Cole M P J *BA(Hons)* 120998
ØDavies P J *BA(Hons)* 120998
Davies G R 120998
Davies G E *BSc(Econ)Hons* (A/Maj 030101) 120998
Gray B A *DipLP BA(Hons)* (A/Maj 080900) 120998
Harold F D 120998
Heppenstall N G G *BA(Hons)* (A/Maj 070800) 120998
Hockley P I *LLB(Hons)* (A/Maj 160301) 120998
ØLewis S J 120998
Buckham A P *LLB(Hons)* 270299
Christie D G *LLB(Hons)* 280299
Dreelan I C J *LLB(Hons)* 280299
Siddique B *LLB(Hons)* 280299
ØCresswell K *LLB(Hons)* 120999
Robbins P J *BA(Hons) MA* 120999
Wade M R *LLB(Hons)* 120999
Banga B S 130200
Bartlett A T *BSc(Hons)* 130200
Blatchford C R *BSc(Hons)* 130200
ØBrown A C 130200
†Cowx C J *BA(Hons)* 130200
ØDavies P M *LLB(Hons)* 130200
†Finlayson A G W *LLB(Hons)* 130200

Gray R *LLM BA(Hons)*   130200
ØHornsby N C *LLB(Hons) DipLP*
                            130200
Read R J *LLB(Hons) DipLP* 130200
†Phillips D W   200300

ØAmbrose W A R *LLB(Hons)*
                            170900
ØCharlton K E *LLB(Hons)*   170900
ØDunn C F *BA(Hons)*   170900
ØGould C A *LLB(Hons)*   170900

†Hamlet C T P *LLB(Hons) PGDip*
                            170900
†Hamnett R T *LLB(Hons) MA*
                            170900
†Heron C P *BA(Hons)*   170900

ROYAL ARMY VETERINARY CORPS

The Figure of Chiron in Silver within a wreath of Laurel thereunder a Scroll inscribed ROYAL ARMY VETERINARY CORPS the whole ensigned with the Crown all gold

Regimental Marches

Quick March . . . . .Regimental March of The Royal Army Veterinary Corps (Arrangement of "Drink Puppy Drink" and "A-Hunting We Will Go")

Slow March . . . ."Golden Spurs"

Agents . . . . .Holts Branch, Royal Bank of Scotland plc, Lawrie House, Farnborough, Hants

Corps Headquarters . . . . .Ministry of Defence (Army Veterinary & Remount Services), Gallwey Road, Aldershot, Hants GU11 2DQ
Aldershot Military 3532

Alliance

Pakistan Army . . . . .Pakistan Remounts, Veterinary and Farm Corps

Colonel Commandant . . . . .Maj Gen R D S Gordon *CBE* 300401

Hon Colonel Commandant . . . . .Brig P G H Jepson *BVSc MSc MRCVS* ret pay .290997

	Clift D T	230797	Lyne R T 10498
Brigadiers			Thornton R S *MBE* 10498
Roache A H *QHVS BVSc MRCVS*	**Regular Category Late Entry Officers**		Pope R C 161098
31097	*Lieutenant Colonels*		
Colonels	Hobson P C *MBE BEM*	240100	**Short Service Officers**
Warde A S *BVetMed MVSc MRCVS*			
300697	**Special Regular Officers Late Entry**		*Majors*
———			Reilly J D *BVSc MRCVS* 11295
Lieutenant Colonels	*Captains*		ØBowerman M R *BVetMed MRCVS* 10800
Macdonald D A *BVM&S MSc*	Sheriff M *(A/Maj 020398)*	120697	ØHolmes J F *VetMB MRCVS* 10800
MRCVS (A/Col 031299)			Morrison M C E *BVetMed MRCVS* 10800
140296	**Intermediate Regular Officers**		
Ogilvie-Graham T S *MBE BVM&S MRCVS CBiolFIBiol* 230697	*Majors*		*Captains*
White D S *BVMS MRCVS* 11298	ØCottrell T S	10101	ØHughes P V *BVSc MRCVS* 11096
Majors			Moran I E *BA* 10897
Marks P R *(A/Lt Col 010900)*	**Short Service Late Entry Officers**		Robinson M R *BVSc MRCVS* 140998
10794	*Captains*		Denham H D C *BVMS* 10999
Smith N C *BVetMed MRCVS* 10894			ØTunley B V 10999
Carruthers H R G *BVMS MRCVS* 240995	Ham C	10498	ØGledhill K L 10900
			†Taylor J A 10900

SMALL ARMS SCHOOL CORPS

A Vickers Machine Gun, thereon a pair of crossed rifles with bayonets fixed, a crown within the angle formed by the rifles above the machine gun; the whole within a laurel wreath; on the wreath scrolls inscribed on the left side "small" on the bottom "arms" and on the right side "school"

Regimental March

Quick March . . . . .March of the Bowmen

Agents . . . . .Lloyds Bank plc

Corps Headquarters . . . . .Headquarters Infantry,
Warminster Training Centre, Warminster, Wilts BA12 0DJ
(Tel: 01985-222397 (Mil Ext: 2397))

Colonel Commandant . . . . .Lt Gen C N G Delves *CBE DSO* 010401

Commandant . . . . .Col M S Vine *OBE*

Chief Instructor . . . . .Lt Col G J Lacey *MBE*

		Conway J P sq(w) *Maj 300994*		Hastie R G *(A/Maj 310700)*	10498
			150488	McCarthy S	10498
Regular Category Late Entry		Hall P A *Maj 300997*	10192	McDougall J J *(A/Maj 180399)*	
Officers		Tomlin R L *Maj 300998*	10192		10498
				Whitchurch J L	10498
Majors				Evenden G	220598
Benson N	300998			Dinley S J *MBE*	111298
Evans G A	300998	**Special Regular Officers Late Entry**			
Taylor F L	300998				
Hood C R	300999				
Paterson W jsdc	300900	*Majors*			
		Dickson C S	300999	**Short Service Late Entry Officers**	
Advisers Infantry Weapons					
		Captains		*Captains*	
Captains		Bexon A R dis *(A/Maj 030100)*		Adams C S	60498
			230296	Riddell A A	50399
Lacey G J *MBE Lt Col 180199*		Aitken A G	250396	Atkinson A	90499
	10686	McClelland A E *MBE (A/Maj*		Bissett R J	160799
Miller A *Maj 300993*	151286	*290500)*	160996	Gallagher K J	11099
Thompson P *MBE Maj 200395*		Sharp J W	110797	Skinner G	280200
	200387	Crowther H N	10498	Sandison K A R	10600

ROYAL ARMY DENTAL CORPS

Within a Laurel wreath a dragon's head and sword; beneath a scroll bearing the motto "Ex dentibus ensis"
The whole surmounted by a crown

Regimental March

Quick March . . . ."Green Facings"

Agents . . . . .Holts Branch, Royal Bank of Scotland plc, Lawrie House,
Farnborough, Hants, GU14 7NR

Corps Headquarters . . . . .RADC RHQ. The Former Staff College, London Road, Camberley, Surrey
GU15 4NP (Tel: 01276-412753 Fax: Not yet known)

Alliances

Australian Military Forces . . . . .The Royal Australian Army Dental Corps
New Zealand Army . . . . .The Royal New Zealand Dental Corps

Colonel in Chief . . . . .Her Royal Highness The Duchess of Gloucester GCVO 170600

Colonels Commandant . . . .*Col B A Hopkin MSc BChD ret pay 010198
Brig R A Smart ret pay 010197

Hon Colonel Commandant . . . . .Prof A Harrison TD 020796

Brigadiers

Poole S J *MSc MGDSRCSEng*
MGDSRCS(Edin) LDS 80101

Colonels

Montgomery J I *MSc BDS*
DRDRCS(Ed) 300388
Jeffrey R S *BDS* 140389
Phillip R M H *MSc BDS FDSRCPS*
GLAS DOrth LDSRCS 80192
Townsend M R *QHDS MSc BDS*
MGDSRCSEng 70793
Bradley J R *MSc BDS FRSH*
MFGDP(UK) LDSRCS 80893
Atkins C A *BDS MGDSRCS(Edin)*
DDPH 270494
Hardy J H *MSc BDS MGDSRCSEng*
MGDSRCS(Edin) DipFOD 60195
Holloway F E *MSc BDS LDSRCS*
110196
Watson F *MSc BDS*
MGDSRCS(Edin) 260796
James C M *BDS MGDSRCSEng*
DGDPRCS(Eng 50897
Lomax S P *MSc BDS*
MGDSRCS(Edin) 101297
Pretsell I A *BDS MGDSRCSEng*
311297
Woodward-Court P *BDS*
MGDSRCSEng 90798
ØCunningham H J *MSc BDS*
LDSRCS 311298
Gaw D A *MSc BDS MGDSRCSEng*
MGDSRCSEd 10799
Harper J R C *BDS* 161299
Haigh B *BDS MGDSRCSEd* 120900
Anderson J Q *LDS FRSH*
DGDPRCS(Eng 111000
Cox S R M *MSc BDS MGDSRCSEng*
LDSRCS 280101

――――

Lieutenant Colonels

Jones E G *BDS* 271280

Forsey K C *BDS* 240482
Mathews R *MSc BDS MGDSRCSEng*
201195
Goulbourn A J *BDS* 40982
George A G *BDS* 90183
I'Anson R C *BDS* 200783
Fairclough J *BDS MGDSRCSEd* 141183
Fairclough J *BDS MGDSRCSEd*
150988
Young N M *BDS MGDSRCSEng*
230192
Isherwood S J *BDS* 30792
McCormick R J *BDS*
MGDSRCS(Edin) FDSRCSEng
20892
Beare W A V *MSc BDS FDSRCSEng*
DRDRCS(Ed) 170992
Diggins M H *MSc BDS*
MGDSRCSEd 151292
Seal M T *MB ChB BDS FDSRCSEng*
190892
Clark R N W *FDS FRCSED* 10293
Kasasian M A G *BDS FRSH*
MFGDP(UK) LDSRCS
DGDPRCS(Eng 10694
McGarry P T *BDS FDSRCSEng*
200395
Bryant D G *BDS FDSRCSEng*
10795
Partridge S *BDS CertMGMT*
DGDP(UK) 241195
Williams M D *BDS FDSRCPS*
131295
ØBerresford J C *BDS* 130198
Lane I B F *MBE BDS DGDP(UK)*
psc(J) 250699
Dixon R *BDS psc(J)* 311299
Boulcott M N *BDS DGDP(UK)*
170600
Preece J M R *BDS* 311200
Wilkinson A J *BDS* 270294
Roberts G V *BDS* 290595
ØBrooks I *BDS MGDSRCSEd*
140795
Carmichael E B *MBE BDS* psc
140795
Black W C *BDS MGDSRCSEd*
150995

Snoad R J *MSc BDS MGDSRCSEd*
201195
Colquhoun R K *BDS MGDSRCSEng*
131295
Hebburn-Heath S P *BDS* 80796
ØMcComb S A F *BDS*
MGDSRCSEng DGDP(UK) 191196
Gillespie I H S *BDS FDSRCSEng*
230497
Mulford A *BDS* psc 170797
ØBamber E A *BDS* 161297
Jones G W *BDS* 140298
ØParrott L A *BDS* 170898
Creasey S J *BDS MIAM* 20899
Heath G C *BChD MGDSRCSEng*
MFGDP(UK) 181299
McDonald A M *LDSRCS* 120100
Hamilton I K *BDS* 30101

Majors

Johnston D P *BDS* 290693
ØWallace J *BDS* 190993
ØFrankland S L *BDS* 131293
ØHurley S J *BDS* 131293
Mackenzie N *BDS FDSRCPS*
190694
Case A C *BChD LDSRCS* 30893
ØLockwood N E *BDS* 80195
ØSealy-Thompson L A *BDS* 70795
ØMcMeekin N S *BDS* 150795
ØRichardson K M *BDS DGDP(UK)*
150195
ØHeselton S *BDS* 120795
Mercer I J *BDS LDSRCS* 50896
Davies T J *BDS* 131296
Thomas A K *BDS* 20697
Combes J G *BDS* 311299
McColl E M *BDS* 280698
Deans J A B *BDS* 140600

Captains

Ansell M J 10896

*Representative Colonel Commandant for 2001

Regular Category Late Entry
Officers

Majors

Morris D sq	300996
Collinson C J	300998

Non-Dental Officers

Sweeney G M   *Lt Col 110900*
240490

Special Regular Officers Late Entry

Captains

Stephens R *DMS (A/Maj 010900)*
10197
Sharp J   10498

Intermediate Regular Officers

Lieutenant Colonels

Davies J A *BDS*	140291
Hodgeon G *BDS*	300199
ØKennedy J E *BDS*	240600

Majors

Welsby C *BDS DGDP(UK) LDSRCS*	
	220993
Young P R *LDSRCS*	300195
ØWalters M C *BDS*	40198

Captains

Valler L M   10996

Short Service Late Entry Officers

Captains

ØRamsey C M	10197
Sutton G	181099

Short Service Officers

Majors

ØJones K A *BDS MFGDP(UK)*
110992

ØEmms J L *BDS*	10696
ØAshkan-Whatley F *BDS*	140497
ØDobbie V A *BDS*	231298
Edmondson J J *BDS MFGDP(UK)*	
	40199
ØMcLaughlin M M	150899
Riddick I A *BDS*	11200

Captains

ØPratt A C *BDS*	50296
Gillespie J R	10796
Yip B H W *BDS*	30796
Willey D A	300497
Bhara H S	110797
Rahman A Z M M	110797
ØRamage S L	110797
McElhinney G J *BChD*	210997
ØVan Heerden L	111097
ØCarson M *BDS(GLAS)*	190698
Budworth R M *BDS*	250698
Fildes T G	250698
ØParry J S *BDS*	10798
ØVoss K M *BDS*	60798
Dilworth T M	130798
Lowrie A P *BDS*	130798
ØRoberts A V	130798
ØBatey G F *BDS(Hons)*	170798
Clover M J	170798
Harmer S G	170798
Watson W P	280699
King M	300699
Davies B J B *BDS*	70799
Ranns N J *BDS DGDPRCS(Eng*	
	70799
Bunting A J *BDS*	120799
Dufty J R *BChD*	120799
Mishra S B *BDS*	120799
ØTaylor R S G *BDS*	120799
Witton R V *BDS*	120799
†Breeze J	10999
†Steen I T J	291199
†Macnaughtan M T	11299
ØFox J A *BChD*	120600
Furze D S	280600
†Du Plessis J A	100700
Fulford N J *BDS*	100700
ØPatel M S	100700

Smales A J	100700
Woodsford D V	100700
Nowak M J S *BDS*	120700

2nd Lieutenants

ØCopestake S J	20799
ØAnderson E L	90799
††Francis J P	90799
ØHedley C	90799
ØCerajewska T L	170700
††Crockard P A	170700
ØEdwards S H	170700
††Gibbs N G B	170700
††Greaves S E	170700
ØRoberts J E	170700
††Usmani R	170700
††Woodward D J	170700

Majors

ØIngram S J *BDS*	270600
†Murphy E F *BDS*	30700
ØDoherty M *BDS*	50700
Siddiqui S J *BDS*	250700

Captains

ØHodge S C *BDS*	10696
Gamble S R	40796
ØLearmonth D	10896
Hyslop J R	131296
Maciver C	100797
Jones D	110797
ØLee J J *BDS*	110797
ØLawson C T *BDS*	300698
Moores G C *BDS*	170798
†Edwards S A *BDS*	20500

2nd Lieutenants

††Palin B J	10999
††Lindsay R K	170700
††McLean A P	170700
††Twamley M	170700

INTELLIGENCE CORPS

A Union rose within two branches of laurel surmounted by a crown; below the laurel a scroll inscribed
"Intelligence Corps"
"Manui Dat Cognitio Vires"

Regimental Marches

Quick March . . . ."The Rose and the Laurel"
Slow March . . . ."Trumpet Tune (and Ayre)"

Agents . . . . .Holts Branch, The Royal Bank of Scotland plc

Corps Headquarters . . . . .Chicksands, Shefford, Bedfordshire SG17 5PR (Tel. 01462 752340)

Alliances

Canadian Armed Forces . . . . .Canadian Forces Intelligence Branch
Australian Military Forces . . . . .The Australian Intelligence Corps

Colonel in Chief . . . . .Field Marshal *HRH The Prince* Philip *Duke of* Edinburgh
KG KT OM GBE AC QSO

Colonel Commandant . . . . .Maj Gen J P Kiszely *MC* 181000

Brigadiers

Springfield E P O *CBE BA(Hons)*
  FIMGT psc hcsc(J) 300691
Messervy-Whiting G G *MBE FIMGT*
  MIL rcds psc(a) jsdc *(A/Maj Gen*
  130300) 300693
Holtom C G psc 300698
Kerr J G *OBE QGM MA* sq 300698

Colonels

Wardley M C *BSc(Econ)Hons*
  psc(GE) I 300695
ØWalthall F A *OBE BSc(Hons)* rcds
  psc† 300697
Cronin M J *MA MIL* psc(GE) I* I
  300698
Everson P F *OBE* psc psc(J) 300699
Hill M K *AIL* sq IES I* I 300699
Campbell-James J *BA(Hons) CGIA*
  psc† 300600
Andrews R I H *OBE* sq jsdc 311200

Lieutenant Colonels

Webb H P (SL) sq *(L/Col 131296)*
  300688
Morrison J P sq jsdc 300692
Payne G S *BA(Hons)* sq 300693
Sanderson C *MBE BA(Hons)* psc(a)†
  (A/Col 141200) 300693
Lawton C P psc(GE) I* 300694
Kett R E sq 300695
Levack W D M *MBE* sq 300695
Stevens T E *BA(Hons)* psc 300695
Charters D S psc 300696
Suggit J R *BA(Hons)* psc 300696
Fox N R H *OBE* psc 300697
Russell M S *BSc(Hons)* sq aic jsdc
  300697
Terrington C J L *MA* psc 300697
Duncan E R *BSc(Hons)* sq jsdc
  300698
Fox P L D sq 300698
Hubberstey N J psc† 300698

Pedley N C *MBE BA(Hons)* psc
  300698
Bullivant G *BSc(Hons)* psc† 300699
Hopkins M J *MA MBA* sq 300699
Keightley M D *MBE* sq 300699
Lincoln S G psc 300699
Walker J W *BEd(Hons) DipEd MIL*
  sq IES I 300699
Walters H O *MBE BSc(Econ)Hons*
  psc† 300699
Watts I F *MIL* sq IES I 301299
ØFelton L G *BA(Hons)* psc† †
  300600
Franks A H T *MBA MIL* psc I
  300600
Le Fevre G R *MA* psc† 300600
Tomlinson T C *BSc(Hons)* sq
  300600
Perrey A D psc 300900

Majors

Dysterre-Clark N F *BA(Hons)* sq
  300985
Cox P L *BA(Hons)* sq I* 300986
Millar W G E *BA* sq(w) ais
  300990
Jefferies I D *MBE BA(Hons)* sq
  300991
Banner G T E *BSc(Hons)* sq 300992
Miller I J *BA(Hons)* sq 300992
ØRoberts M R *BSc(Hons) MIL* sq I*
  PC *(A/Lt Col 270301)* 300992
Penry D *BA(Hons) MSc(Econ)* sq
  300993
Tunnicliffe I P sq 300993
Bird C B *MA* sq I 300994
Fairclough G J *BSc* sq 300994
Marshall R D *BEM* sq 300994
Britton N J *MSc* psc psc(J) 300995
Edwards P W D *MA MSc* psc(J) †
  300995
Hallas M J *BSc(Hons) MA* psc(J) †
  (A/Lt Col 241100) 300995
Hazel J M E *BA(Hons)* sq 300995
Hockenhull J R *MBE BA(Hons)* psc†
  300995
Snedden S E *BA(Hons)* sq 300995

Whiteley J *BA(Hons)* sq 300995
Wreford P R F 300995
Eggleton S I J *BSocSc* psc psc(J)
  300996
Fynn M A N *BA(Hons)* sq 300996
Ingram P J *MBE BSc* psc(J) 300996
ØMcCutcheon K A psc(J) 300996
Mutter N R sq sq(w) 300996
Nash M J R *MA* psc(J) † 300996
Nichol H W *BA(Hons)* 300996
Rawdon-Smith R J 300996
Baker N A psc(J) 300997
Barrow A G 300997
Morrill R I *MA BA(Hons)* 300997
Orr R K *MA MRIN* psc(J) 300997
Bliss P S *BA(Hons)* 300998
Deans R 300998
ØFord J P *BEM BA(Hons)* sq
  300998
Mainstone J R *MSc* 300998
Miller R A 300998
Park A J 300998
Hawker M *BA(Hons)* 300999
ØMalone V A J *MA(Hons)*
  MA(Hons) I 300999
Marriott A C J 300999
McGreavy E P 300999
ØMills D J *MA(Hons)* 300999
Rudd J S 300999
Small A L *BA(Hons)* 300999
Williams S J 300999
Clarke M F *BA(Hons)* 300900
Easter P L *BSc(Hons)* 300900
Hanson M A D 300900
Herring D M *MBE* 300900
Jee S P 300900
Jones D G S 300900
Kite B D A 300900
Marshall A A *BEng(Hons)* 300900
Warwick S J *BA(Hons)* 300900

Captains

Tomlyn M T H *(A/Maj 271100)*
  10494
Stern A D *BA(Hons) (A/Maj*
  060900) 60894

ØHodgson J BA(CombHons) (A/Maj 140800) 10495
Roughley J P BEng(Hons) (A/Maj 141298) 130495
ØKirman C L BSc(Hons) MSc 141295
Tuppen N H BA(Hons) 60296
Ormiston C J (A/Maj 310100) 110296
Darling S M 80596
Clark P J BA(Hons) 110896
ØHanby T A BA(Hons) 110896
Pearce A L MA(Cantab) 131296
ØGalbraith F E 120298
ØHenderson-Lea S H BA(Hons) (L/Maj 271100) 120298
Brown J E LLB(Hons) 160698
ØDe La Rue S N LLB(Hons) LLM 160698
ØCrichton F G LLB(Hons) 100299
Fewson G BA(Hons) (L/Maj 010800) 100299
Huston A J BA(Hons) 100399
Evans G J BA(Soc)Hons 140699
ØWoodhams E L BA(Hons) 140699
Roberts S L MA BA(Hons) 131099
Kell N A BSc(Hons) 90200
Winter A J BA(Hons) 90200
Bavin M A BA 130600
Statham C D BA 130600
Wilkinson R D BSc(Hons) 130600
ØCoulson S MA 101000
ØJanes A C BA(Hons) 101000
Jones M H BA(Hons) 80201
ØMayo A I R 80201

Lieutenants

Brett T D 161297
ØMoore K A BA(Hons) 100298
Morris J C MEng(Hons) 140698
ØFletcher K L BA(Hons) 100898

2nd Lieutenants

†Vowles R J 80996
††Murphy M J 60998

Regular Category Late Entry Officers

Lieutenant Colonels

McNamara D A MBE 50600

Majors

Gillion G P H MBE 300991
Withey T D 300992
Ackers G S MBE 300993
Garnett D W QGM sq 300994
Lynch-Staunton R A C MBE sq 300994
Firth S J BEM 300995
McCreath D W 300995
Moodie A J 300995
Skipper J S sq 300995
Power R A J sq 300997
Adams G B I 300999
Day A R BA(Hons) 300999

Captains

Warren T C H BEM 310595

Barbour A R I* I (A/Maj 310100) 100696
Rowles N W 110797

Technical Duty Officers

McMullen T M MBE Lt Col 300699 220786
Richardson P A MBE sq Lt Col 300699 220786
Knought G A MBE BEM sq Lt Col 080998 281087

Special Regular Officers Late Entry

Majors

Thain C P 300996
Atkinson J A 140797
Curtis P R BEM 300997
ØSykes J L 300998
Tuck A 300999
Ferguson J J 300900
Massey S J BEM 300900
Moyles D MBE 300900
Williams J C MBE QGM 300900

Captains

Anley D V 210194
Lynch T A BEM (A/Maj 060499) 70795
Harris A F BEM (A/Maj 100101) 290796
Holman A R 251196
Sturney M J (A/Maj 260500) 100397
ØLoughborough H M MBE 10497
Whiteoak R MBE 300697
Bunten R W 300797
Graley S A 80997
Baigent I F 10498
Blake S S MBE 10498
Crawford G J 10498
Garton S R BEM 10498
Jacobs J P BEM 10498
Lybert J QGM BEM 10498
Pearce G S MBE BEM 10498
ØWalshaw M BEM 10498
Miller K 80498

Intermediate Regular Officers

Captains

Probert P R AIMGT QSS QTM aws 111195
ØPillar S E BSc(Hons) (L/Maj 041200) 270896
ØLomax D 10198
Thomas S J BA(Hons) 160698
Proctor M C 260299
Bacon M J 90200
ØDuesbury N A BSc(Hons) 101000

Lieutenants

Mullin C MA(Hons) 300696
Fairweather N L BA(Hons) 161297
Cloke R J T BEng(Hons) 90899

Short Service Late Entry Officers

Majors

Butler J P Grad I I SE IES 300995

McKenzie R QGM 300996
Walker S L 300997
Whiley P D MIMGT 300997
Veale J S MISM 300998
Brighten M D MBE 300999
Dilley M A 300999
Hodges R M 300900

Captains

Addy G M 260694
Edwards R N MBE 100696
Buck S J MIMGT MIL I 290796
Chapple M G 10498
Davie B (A/Maj 240100) 10498
Denton M J 10498
Evans J G 10498
Evans A E (A/Maj 010101) 10498
Fearon J C 10498
Harding A J 10498
Jones D S BSc 10498
Keating P J 10498
Lamb J C 10498
Thompson R A W 10498
Williams P G BSc MIL 10498
Steadman J M 80498
Abercrombie L A I (A/Maj 071100) 280498
Lamb C R 110598
Acott R C QGM BEM 190698
Carpenter R J 190698
Comerford I P BSc 190698
Simm L 111298
Southam N J 10499
Langhorn D G 90499
Murray T J 90499
Potter R S 90499
Rooker A D 90499
Worsley A P 90499
ØRoberts N J 260499
Tester J E 40699
Clapham M P 120799
McDill P J A 20999
Thirsk M R 161299
Hellawell G J BSc(Hons) 30200
Kennedy P R 70400
Atkinson J 90600
Jenkins C J 90600
Loughborough I M 90600
Gore C N 70700
Russell S J 70700
Skyner W 70700
Tait R K BEM 70700
Davidson E 200800
Keeton A T 150900
Riley J W 150900
ØBrittan S L 80101

Short Service Officers

Majors

Gray D C 191298

Captains

Woolmer J M H BA(Hons) 100299
Green M A 220899
Haseldine A J 121099
ØSimpson J BA(Hons) 90200
ØGreasley E H BA(Hons) 130600
ØStocker A L BSc(Hons) 80201

Lieutenants

ØColeman L K *BSc(Hons)*   120297
Cadman M A *BSc(Hons) MSc*
                              100298
Hadley W R *BA(Hons)*   100298
ØAllingham C S J *MA BA(Hons)*
                              140698

Hiscock J J *BA(Hons) BA(Hons) MA*
                              140698
ØEmmett M G *BA(Hons)*   100898
Owen A R *BSc(Hons)*   141298
Stanworth T E *BSc(Hons)*   141298
ØAllen R L *BA(Hons)*   90299
ØBromage A H *BSc(Hons)*   90299
Balfe S P *BA(Hons)*   130699

ØRoberts L N   130699
Whitaker C *BSc(Hons)*   90899
ØThompson S J *BSc(Hons)*   131299

Short Service Volunteer Officers

Captains

Strangways R G   251189

280

ARMY PHYSICAL TRAINING CORPS

Crossed swords surmounted by a crown

Regimental March

Quick March . . . . .Regimental March of The Army Physical Training Corps ("Be Fit" words from "Land and Sea Tales" by Kipling)

Agents . . . . .Lloyds Bank plc Cox's & King's Branch

Corps Headquarters . . . . .Headquarters APTC
Trenchard Lines, Upavon, PEWSEY, Wilts SN9 6BE
(Tel: Upavon Mil Ext: 5159)

Colonel Commandant . . . . .Gen Sir Jeremy MacKenzie GCB OBE 220297
Commandant . . . . .Brig R M Wilde CBE 240100
Assistant Commandant . . . . .Lt Col R A Steel OBE 040598

		Parker T *MBE Maj 300989*	40685	Wood R A	10498
Majors		Steel R A *OBE DipPhysEd DipRGRT*		Johnson G	140498
Horn I A *MBE* sq	300993	*MCSP SRP MILAM* sq *Lt Col*			
Maccunn H R C	300997	*121298*	40685		
		Pickering K *BEM* sq *Maj 300991*			
Regular Category Late Entry			240687	**Short Service Late Entry Officers**	
Officers					
Majors				*Captains*	
Baggaley D *MBE BEM*	300993				
File A *MSc DipPhysEd MSRG MCSP*		**Special Regular Officers Late Entry**		White C E *BEM*	10498
	300993			Sheppard A G	20498
Watkins P A *MBE (A/Lt Col 170101)*				Coulthard R M	80698
	300994			Dupree B J	50199
Huffen D	300995	*Captains*		Peters D	50199
Mellor I J *BEM*	300996	Billings A *(A/Maj 110400)*	60595	Bacon M D	10299
Morgan W B *CertEd*	300997	Robinson C S *BEM*	20496	Phinn A D	10499
Challinor N	300998	Shaw M P *(A/Maj 140800)*	60996	Williams R	120499
Wood J E *BEM*	300998	Dolan J C *(A/Maj 110199)*	120497	Alhaji S D	40100
Davies G L *QGM*	300999	ØHiggs S L	290997	Scott D C	100300
Martin E	300999	Annis M J *MBA DipM DMS*	10498	Hughes P J	40400
Wilson R J	300999	Bryan D C	10498	Roderick G	280400
		Chapple A J *BEM*	10498	Fowle A	260500
Masters at Arms		Colclough M K	10498	Appleby P	310700
		Edwards K P	10498	Willetts A S	280800
Captains		Holmes W J	10498	Carter G S *MM*	41200
Hepton S J *BA MCSP* sq *Lt Col*		Jones G B	10498	McDonald K M	41200
310598	40685	McCuaig D D	10498	Shaw I A	111200

QUEEN ALEXANDRA'S ROYAL ARMY NURSING CORPS

The Cypher of HM the late Queen Alexandra combined with the Dannebrog, the whole within a laurel wreath inscribed with the Corps motto "Sub Cruce Candida" surmounted by a crown. On the lower portion of the wreath a scroll inscribed "QARANC"

Regimental March

Quick March	"Grey and Scarlet"
Agents	Holts Branch, Royal Bank of Scotland plc, Lawrie House, Farnborough, Hants
Corps Headquarters	Headquarters Army Medical Services, London Road, Camberley, Surrey, GU15 4NP

Alliances

Australian Military Forces	The Royal Australian Army Nursing Corps
New Zealand Army	The Royal New Zealand Nursing Corps

Colonel in Chief	HRH The Princess Margaret *Countess of* Snowdon *CI GCVO*
Colonel Commandant	Col I M Leith Macgregor *RRC* 010400

Colonels

McEvilly B C	*ARRC RGN*	300697
George K	*RRC RGN*	150399
Botting F G	*ARRC MIMGT RGN*	100300

Lieutenant Colonels

Quinn J D F	*RGN*	300696
Bale L	*RRC RGN RM*	300697
Bate M J	*ARRC BA RGN RNT RCNT DipNEd*	300699
Spencer W J	*RRC BSc(Hons) RSCN RGN sq*	300699
Wood V F	*BSc(Hons) RGN RM sq*	311299
Gunter P V	*RGN*	300600
Thomas M L	*MSc RGN RM sq*	300600

Majors

McMillan J M	*OND RGN*	270784
Quickfall M A	*ARRC RGN*	10986
Gac S J	*RGN*	160888
Webster S L M	*ARRC RGN RCNT*	81288
Davy K R	*RRC RGN*	180889
Edgar E M	*RGN*	50790
Mills D P	*RMN RGN RNT RCNT*	271291
Greed V J	*RMN RGN*	130592
Jenkins D A	*MA MSc RGN RNT DipN DipNEd*	260592
Wright L A	*RGN sq*	71292
Sokolow P J	*ARRC RGN*	10193
Payant K	*ARRC RGN EN(G)*	240293
Foulkes S K	*RGN*	260993
Cornwell T	*RGN sq*	91193
Childerley P	*RGN*	120694
McDougall P J	*RGN*	200195
Kefford C M	*RGN (A/Lt Col 290101)*	150295
Bush S J	*RRC BA(Hons) RGN sq*	300395
Radford G I	*RGN*	140296

McMachan T L	*ARRC RGN*	300696
Reavell G L	*RGN sq*	300696
Horsfall M	*BSc(Hons) ONC RGN D P S N*	311296
Jefferies C L	*ONC RGN*	311296
Finnegan A P	*DANS RMN RGN*	110497
Bates D C	*ARRC BN DANS RGN*	210797
Williams A M	*BA(Hons) RMN RGN*	11097
Jones N O	*ARRC RMN RGN*	71197
McCulloch J R	*RGN*	230798
Bettaney P E M	*DMS RSCN RGN RM*	160899
Jolly A A	*ARRC RMN RGN*	160999

Captains

Duffy C	*RGN EN(G)*	250896

Special Regular Officers Late Entry

Majors

Gilbert J	*RGN*	180898
Neblett C H A DE L	*MSc RMN RGN EN(G)*	121098
Collins T	*RGN*	70200
Macdonald P F	*ARRC RGN*	180900
Berry A A P	*RGN*	131200

Captains

Wallace M J	*RGN (A/Maj 030400)*	40791
Kenward G	*A&ENCERT*	20896
Roden M A	*RGN*	111296
Lines L D	*RGN EN(G) (A/Maj 010700)*	131296
Clark J	*RGN*	11197

Intermediate Regular Officers

Majors

Bellwood M	*RMN RNMS RGN RNT*	160790
Robinson A K G	*RGN*	111093
Millar J E	*RGN RM*	81293

Webber A C	*ADM RGN RM*	81293
Icely Brown A	*CMS DN RMN RGN D*	30594
Cotterell J	*RGN*	300696
Greenwood S P	*RGN*	300696
Bardell L M	*RGN EN(G)*	311296
Barr A M M	*ARRC RGN D P S N*	311296
Holman M L	*ONC RGN*	311296
Jones S A	*RGN RM*	311296
Morrison D M	*RGN EN(G)*	311296
Pollard R J	*RGN*	311296
Searle G	*RGN*	311296
Taylor G	*RGN*	10197
Hayhoe K M	*RGN RM*	140497
Reavell R H	*ONC RGN*	270697
Irvine K J	*RGN RM*	230798
Murphy J	*RGN RM*	230798
Sweeting K	*RNMH RGN*	230798
Wells B P	*RGN*	230798
Thompson-Wells N A	*RGN*	180898
Darby R I	*OND RGN*	91198
Durham D	*RGN*	291198
Earnshaw N M	*RMN RGN*	270699
Crosbie P	*RGN*	50899
Walker G A	*RMN RGN*	110999
Costigane A	*RMN RGN*	251299
Duncan T	*RSCN RGN RHV*	140200
Jones W H	*DANS OND RSCN RGN*	150300
Godkin Y T	*RGN*	290300
Archer S	*ARRC RGN*	110400
Harrison D E	*RGN*	140400
Bernthal E M M	*RGN RM*	210400
Brown C M	*RGN RM*	50700
Lubbock J	*RGN*	220700
Doyle J A	*RMN RGN*	160800
Woodhouse S	*RGN RM*	200800
Francis S	*RGN*	240800
Whitley B	*RMN RGN*	270800
Taylor T A B	*RMN RGN*	110900
Palframan A M	*SRN SEN*	111100
Simmons S I	*SRN RGN*	91200
Kingdom D	*RGN*	271200
Hill D A	*RGN*	311200

Captains

Shephard C S	*RSCN RGN*	160493

Adam L S *ARRC RGN (A/Maj 100200)* 180993
Phillips E *RGN* 181093
Bowman-King B *BSc(Hons) RSCN RGN* 261193
Fuller J A *RGN* 261193
Hearle G *RGN* 130394
Lakeman A *RGN* 240494
Philpott A E *RGN* 300494
Williams A R *ARRC RMN RGN* 10694
Turner L M *RGN* 250694
Benton A S *RGN* 300894
Eldridge R *RMN RGN* 260195
Davies T J *RGN* 40795
McCourt A L *ARRC RGN* 170696
Williams J C *DipHE RGN* 250700
Wright K *RGN RM* 260700

Short Service Late Entry Officers

Captains

Penney T D *RGN* 220392
Raymond P H *RMN RGN* 230493
Benson A H P *ARRC* 220995
Marshall J N 220995
Tristham P E *EN(G)* 251095
North G A *RGN EN(G)* 251295
Smyth A T *RGN EN(G) D P S N* 111296
Sutton B *RGN EN(G)* 90597
Charlton A M 90697
Fairclough W 40897
Farmer A E B *ARRC RGN* 170897
Tovey P P D *RGN SEN* 30898
Michael G L *MRSH RMN RGN* 110998
Pickford Y P *RGN* 21198
McKay A T 61198
Corner S J *RGN SEN* 141298
Gibson P L 60699
Ford C A *RMN RGN* 130899
McCarthy D L 150899
Watson N D *RGN* 240999
McKenzie E C *RGN* 220500
Taylor M J 130600
Smith A G 160101

Lieutenants

Dean A W M *RMN* 290896
Rowsell A M 80399

Short Service Officers

Majors

Burnett P A *RGN* 171200

Captains

Martin G *RSCN RGN* 121296
Chambers C A *SRN SCM* 180992
Fox E A 200293
Spice S *RGN RM* 80393
Atkinson B G *RGN* 200393
Bradburn D J *RSCN RGN* 201193
Marshall C S *RGN* 50294
Tyrrell M A *RSCN RGN* 150294

Disney-Spiers P S *RGN EN(G) GICN* 110394
Archer S L *RGN* 170894
Clare C J *RGN RM* 81294
Reily-Jones L R *RGN RM* 60295
Lintonbon L J *RGN* 170295
Thorogood J M *RGN RM* 250295
Rogers C A *RGN EN(G)* 60395
Grant A L *RGN* 130395
Verma B J *RGN RM* 90595
Jones C 220995
McDonnell C *RGN* 271095
Pilgrim J M *RGN* 11195
Pratt V M *RGN* 261195
Akers V J *RGN* 180496
Woods J M *RGN* 80596
Shaw P M *RGN FETC* 160896
Sewart M R *RGN* 111196
Searles T N *RGN GICN* 150197
Williamson F J 160297
Manson P J *RGN* 220297
Neilson P K 80397
Kiernan M D *RGN* 300597
Edwards E C *RGN* 70697
Hall G S *RGN* 10797
Fenby T 190897
Dodds R L *RGN* 131197
Lancaster A J *RGN* 151297
New G E J *DN RGN* 171297
Forsyth P M A *RGN* 271297
Lightfoot E H *RGN* 80298
Bluhm H J 210298
Robinson A J 190398
Bateman S E *GICN* 300498
Jackson P M 300498
Findlay S 220598
Lowes C L 40698
McGhee F *SRN* 130698
Trehane G 130698
Humphries D J 180698
Kelly C J 210698
Bryceland M D *RGN* 230698
Manley A J *RGN* 280798
Harding J 310798
Garner K P 150998
Campion B H *RGN REMT* 240998
Robertson I 21098
Bremner L *BSc(Hons) ADM* 141098
Davidson S G L 201098
Tippett M D *RGN* 201098
Reidy P *DipN* 301098
Crawford J A *RGN* 81198
Owens A M 31298
Andrews C Y 80299
Vannan S L *RGN* 100299
Dalzell S L *CertHEd* 180399
Viveash S G *RGN* 10499
Cruickshank K L *RGN* 120499
Rothwell S M J 190499
Quinn H M *MSc RGN* 230499
Whitley S 250599
Ives K E *RGN* 290599
O'Reilly J E 10699
Sloane-Mather R J *BSc(Hons) RGN* 40799
Bunn C L *RGN A&ENCERT* 110799
Jordan C D *BA(Hons)* 130799

McKay M L *DN* 160799
Sharland S 170899
Stokes E 120999
Shuck S W 200999
Tippett J *RGN* 280999
Phelps C M *RGN EN(G)* 171099
Povey M T 201099
Grieves T J *RGN* 11199
Bradley I E C 150100
Grant K M 170200
Winder H S 210400
Marshall R B *RGN* 280600
Bailey J *RGN* 10700
Le Quelenec B T 10700
Ibbotson K J *BNURS RGN NDN* 80700
Duffy R C 240700
Merchant V F 240700
Ricketts K A 210800
Gardner A L *BSc(Hons) BA(Hons)* 30900
McKelvie E J *RGN* 80900
Beatty S M *B Sc (Hons)* 90900
Maloney K J 230900
Hawkins S B *DipHE RGN* 290900
Stevens C A C *DipHE(RN)* 81000
Winterbone H J *RGN* 91000
Shelby-James J L 231000
Sheppard A 311000
Croser P 181100
Henderson L R *BSc(Hons)* 191200
Williams S *RGN* 191200
Wigelsworth K L *BMedSci* 10101
Morgan L I *BNURS* 80101
Skinner T D 230101

Lieutenants

Bowes-Crick E J 171195
Tunney J 191196
Brownhill S E 260197
Templeman K M 200297
Blair S P R *RGN* 10497
Donald M *BSc(Hons)* 100497
Penfold T R 190497
Murana D E *DipHE* 60697
Orman C A 80697
D'Arcy J P 160797
Brockie A F 260897
Hornsby C L *RGN* 290897
Cassidy P 30997
Gray D J *RGN* 30997
Beaumont K A 231097
Berridge R D 231197
Knott S L *RGN* 261297
Phillips C A J 240198
Frith Z *BSc(Hons)* 260298
Jenkins D J *BSc(Hons)* 250498
Morris N J *BA(Hons)* 210898
†Berski M S A 160200
Hines S E 160200
†Chamberlain C W *RGN* 200900

Rec Res (RARO)

Majors

Srinivasan J *ONC RGN* 80591

CORPS OF ARMY MUSIC

Corps Headquarters . . . . .Kneller Hall, Twickenham, Middx TW2 7DU
(Tel: 020-8898-5533 Fax: 020-8893-8746)

Torrent M J *LTCL LGSM* psm *Maj*
300995   140493

Regular Category Late Entry Officers

Majors

Chatburn A R *BA ARCM* psm
                                                300997
Owen R J *ARCM* psm   300998
Jones G O *MBE ARCM* psm 300900
Meldrum C R *LRSM ARCM ARMCM*
                                                300900

Captains

Shannon P D *MBE BA* psm   100696
Robertson D D   psm   141196

Directors of Music

Hills P E *FLCM* psm *Lt Col 090699*
                                                  20187
Smith S J   *LRSM ARCM* psm *Maj*
  300994   161187
Kingston G A   psm *Lt Col 270600*
                                                  81287

Special Regular Officers Late Entry

Majors

McElligott I D *ARCM*   300900

Captains

Peaple I R *LRSM* psm   60694
Clark P R *ARCM* psm   150295
Taylor J W *BA(Hons) BBCM ARCM*
  ALCM psm   220496
Rodger G D   290496
Burton D *ARCM* psm *(A/Maj*
  080500)   30596
Gray C C *BA(Hons) ARCM* psm
                                              200696
Cresswell D W   psm   110796
Keeley E H *ARCM* psm   10498
Murrell P L   psm   10498
Wassell B   10498

Short Service Late Entry Officers

Captains

Barnwell S C   psm   10498
Pennington R *MISM* psm   10498
Young J R   psm   200798
Arnold T D   191098
Milgate D J   180299
Hopla R W   280299
Morgan N P   151099
Goodwin P   291099
Cooper T J   140100
Knox A   280100
Clegg G E   30300
Stredwick P *LRSM ALCM*   100300

Directors of Music

Hatton K *BA(Hons) FTCL ARCM*
  psm   110496
Hicks C E   90596

SECTION IV

TERRITORIAL ARMY

ROYAL MONMOUTHSHIRE ROYAL ENGINEERS (MILITIA)

The Prince of Wales plume, cornet and motto *'Ich Dien'*, surmounted by a crown, on either side of the plume the letters 'R' and 'E', below a scroll inscribed *'ROYAL MONMOUTHSHIRE'*

Hon Colonels . . . .*HRH The Duke of* Gloucester *GCVO*
Col A F George *TD* 311296

		Washington D *TD BSc* sq(V)	10596	Scrutton M *BEng(Hons) ARSM*
		Smith C J *TD*	310399	200401
Colonels		Browning M C	140899	
		Woollaston D M	10400	
Coulson M G *OBE TD BA(Hons)*				*Lieutenants*
FRICS tacsc sq(V)	250398	*Captains*		Glyn-Roche J R	310592

Washington D *TD BSc* sq(V) 10596
Smith C J *TD* 310399
Browning M C 140899
Woollaston D M 10400

Captains

¶Lawes B D 311086
¶McGrath K W 210488
¶Wright D S 80888
Stead J 10690
Carter J M sq 300990
Reed M B *BSc* 10192
Mann S J 161194
Clarke T P *BEng(Hons)* 290796
Pritchard A C *BSc(Hons) CMS*
10998
Pavey M M W 131297
Morrisroe C M *BEng(Hons)*
MIChemE 310199
Windram A D M 10999
Brown J P 21299
Jones D A 91000
ØElliott-Hunt C R *BSc(Hons)* 11200

Scrutton M *BEng(Hons) ARSM*
200401

Lieutenants

Glyn-Roche J R 310592
†Morshead H M 10197
Spencer S M 270994
ØHill J L 30898
ØHill L S 61098
Dorrington C J 280100
Brittain G R 130600
Lavelle E J 310101

2nd Lieutenants

†Evans T O 150697

Quartermasters

Henderson B *MIEETE* Capt 190291
Littleford J G Capt 010493
Troke P J Capt 110996
Morris R Capt 61197

Colonels

Coulson M G *OBE TD BA(Hons)*
FRICS tacsc sq(V) 250398

Lieutenant Colonels

Thompson I C *BSc(Hons) PGCE*
tacsc sq(V) 10900
Hoyle R A *TD•• BA AHA* tacsc
11100
ØPride J M *TD BSc(Hons)* 30101

Majors

Hennessy H *TD•* sq(V) 130587
Down K H *TD BSc(Hons) CEng*
MICE MIHT tacsc 10191
Turner C D *TD BA(Hons)*
DipPhysEd PGCE 311091
Charles J E *TD BSc MCIOB* tacsc
291191
Smith J W G tacsc 131291

THE HONOURABLE ARTILLERY COMPANY

Artillery
An old fashioned cannon with a scroll above inscribed 'HAC'
and a scroll below inscribed *'ARMA PACIS FULCRA';*
the whole surmounted by St Edward's Crown

Infantry
A grenade with monogram *'HAC'* on the ball

"South Africa 1900-02"

The Great War _ 3 Infantry Battalions and 7 Batteries of Artillery _ **Ypres 1915-17, Somme 1916, 18**, Ancre Heights, **Ancre 1916, Arras 1917, 1918**, Scarpe 1917, 18, Arleux, Bullecourt, Pilckem, Polygon Wood, Broodseinde, Poelcappelle, **Passchendaele**, Amiens, Albert 1918, Bapaume 1918, Drocourt-Queant, Hindenburg Line, Epehy, St Quentin Canal, Cambrai 1918, Selle, Sambre, **France and Flancers 1914-18**, Piave, **Vittorio Veneto**, Italy 1917-18, Rafah, Egypt 1915-17, **Gaza**, El Mughar, **Jerusalem**, Jordan, Megiddo, Sharon, Damascus, Palestine 1917-18, Aden.

The Second World War _ Bourgebus Ridge, Antwerp, Le Havre, Rhine, North-West Europe 1944-45, Knightsbridge, El Alamein, El Hamma, Sbiba, Thaia, Tunis, North Africa 1941-43, Sicily 1943, Cassino II, Coriane, Senio, Italy 1944-45.

Regimental Marches

Quick March	.British Grenadiers
Slow March	.Duke of York
Canter	.Bonnie Dundee
Trot	.The Keel Row
Walk	.Duchess of Kent

Regimental Headquarters . . . . .Finsbury Barracks, City Road, London EC1Y 2BQ
(Tel: 020-7382-1543)

Alliances

South African Defence Forces . . . . . . .Transvaal Horse Artillery

Captain General . . . . .THE QUEEN

Colonel Commandant . . . . .Gen *Sir* Alex Harley *KBE CB* 300698

Hon Colonel .Lt Col J M Ferguson *TD* 010799

Master Gunner within HM
Tower of London . . . . .Lt Col J M Ferguson *TD* 010799

Colonels

Lalor S F N *TD* tacsc	10796

Lieutenant Colonels

Ferguson J M *TD BA(Hons)*	250696
Clarke G R *TD* tacsc	11198

Majors

Vyvyan-Robinson P D C *TD*	11191
Brigden D *TD*	11093
Lovell W J *TD*	241095
Murphy R S T	161096
Garrett S C	171096
Baldwin B *TD•*	11097
Caie A D C	71098
Briggs S C	300499
Treasure N A G	11299
Gabb A H S *TD*	61200

Captains

Maitland-Jones G H *TD*	11093
Emus W M	10795
Osborn-Smith B R *MBA*	171096
Russell M N G	10497
Leighton J O	71098
Pickersgill A T	71098
Trenwith S J V	71098
Summers J M H	220599
Murray M F	100699
Marment C V	11299
Sallitt W T B *BSc(Hons)*	41000

Lieutenants

Barnes S M	41193
Bobjerg-Jensen P C	30196
Forsyth J A	170697
Halliday S J R	151097
Small A N	301098
Mackinlay D	80599
Holmes C M	311099
Deane M B	10200
Chorley J P	260500

Pritchard J H	20800
Woellwarth N H	150900

2nd Lieutenants

†Clark P W J	10899
†Marten A C	10899
†Ranson A J	10899
†Collis R W N *ARICS D P S N*	
	40600
†Fordham C J	40600
†Robinson J A	40600

Quartermasters

Bain R	*Capt* 251094
Parkes J R	*Capt* 050298
Tregear M J	*Capt* 010898
Strofton T M C	*Capt* 240600
Watts S A	*Lt Col 141197* 10900

Directors of Music

Swift R G *LRAM LTCL ARCM* psm	
	280790

YEOMANRY OF THE ROYAL ARMOURED CORPS

Colonel Commandant Yeomanry . . . . .Col J E B Hills *TD DL ADC* 091299

The origins of the Yeomanry Regiments now included in the Royal Armoured Corps are as follows:

THE ROYAL YEOMANRY

The Royal Wiltshire Yeomanry (Prince of Wales's Own)
The Sherwood Rangers Yeomanry
The Leicestershire and Derbyshire (Prince Albert's Own) Yeomanry
Kent and County of London Yeomanry (Sharpshooters)
Inns of Court and City Yeomanry
Westminster Dragoons (2nd County of London Yeomanry)

THE ROYAL WESSEX YEOMANRY

The Royal Wiltshire Yeomanry (Prince of Wales's Own)
The Royal Gloucestershire Hussars
Royal Devon Yeomanry
The Dorset Yeomanry

THE ROYAL MERCIAN AND LANCASTRIAN YEOMANRY

The Queen's Own Warwickshire and Worcestershire Yeomanry
The Staffordshire Yeomanry (Queen's Own Royal Regiment)
The Shropshire Yeomanry
The Cheshire Yeomanry (Earl of Chester's)
The Duke of Lancaster's Own Yeomanry (Royal Tank Regiment)

THE QUEEN'S OWN YEOMANRY

The Queen's Own Yorkshire Yeomanry
The Ayrshire Yeomanry (Earl of Carrick's Own)
The Northumberland Hussars
The Fife and Forfar Yeomanry (Scottish Horse)
North Irish Horse

THE ROYAL YEOMANRY

Regimental March

Quick March . . . . .The Farmer's Boy

Locations and Affiliations

RHQ . . . . .Chelsea
A (Royal Wiltshire Yeomanry (PWO) Squadron . . . . .Swindon . . . .The King's Royal Hussars
S (Sherwood Rangers Yeomanry) Squadron . . . . .Nottingham . .The Queen's Royal Lancers
B (Leicestershire and Derbyshire Yeomanry (PAO)) Squadron . . . . . .Leicester . . . .9th/12th Royal Lancers (POWs)
C (Kent and Sharpshooters Yeomanry) Squadron . . . . .Croydon . . . .Household Cavalry
W (Westminster Dragoons) Squadron . . . . .Chelsea . . . . .Royal Tank Regiment

Role Affiliations . . . . .The Royal Scots Dragoon Guards (Carabiniers
and Greys)
The Queen's Royal Lancers and Royal Tank
Regiment

Honorary Colonels

Royal Honorary Colonel . . . . *HM* QUEEN ELIZABETH THE QUEEN MOTHER

Deputy Royal Honorary Colonel . . . . *HRH Princess* Alexandra *The Hon Lady* Ogilvy

Honorary Colonels . . . . .Gen *Sir* Jeremy Blacker *KCB CBE* 011197

A (Royal Wiltshire Yeomanry (PWO)) Squadron . .Lt Col J G Peel *TD JP DL* 010595
S (Sherwood Rangers Yeomanry) Squadron . . . . .Col J C V Hunt *OBE TD DL* 011094
B (Leicester and Derbyshire Yeomanry
(PAO)) Squadron . . . . .Brig H W K Pye 010992
C (Kent and Sharpshooters Yeomanry) Squadron .Lt Col J G Y Radcliffe *TD OBE* 010100
W (Westminster Dragoons) Squadron . . . . .Gen *Sir* Jeremy Blacker *KCB CBE* .011197
Royal Yeomanry Band (Inns of Court and
City Yeomanry . . . . .Maj *The Rt Hon The Earl of* Limerick *KBE DL* 050393

	Alderson A B	10196	†Howell T	50200
	Shepherd-Smith B H	10496		
Colonels	Hodson M	20796	*Quartermasters*	
Radcliffe J G Y *OBE TD•• MA* tacsc	Niekirk A P C	260796		
100800	Guinness D E M	10996	Livingstone J A *Capt 020893* 310784	
	Rhodes C E R C	10697	Blake P J *Capt 010492* 250293	
————	Norton A C P	61097	Falshaw R *Capt 250597*	
	Ross-Wilson A W M	10198		
Lieutenant Colonels	Turner D B *BA*	50198		
Sutcliffe R W H *BA(Hons)* tacsc	Moss J D *TD BA(Hons)*	120198	*Lieutenant Colonels*	
10496	Dempster K R	10199	Cameron E G *TD LLB(Hons)* tacsc	
	Astbury N R W	10499	10101	
Majors	Cullen B T	10799		
Lee R T *TD• LLB(Hons)* tacsc	Appleton G R M U	30500	*Majors*	
50683	Douglas M R	11100	Morley J	11200
Bennie C H A R *TD*	70990	Brooks A P	120301	Oxley J A G	10401
Brooks-Ward S H	11195			
Marsh R D *TD*	200396	*Lieutenants*	*Captains*	
Cann M J A *BA(Hons)*	180497	Lykke-Dahn N P	40389	ØFrampton-Hobbs E C *BSc*	31194
Bonser G	100597	Davey P M	270592	McLennan Fordyce D	130496
Szembel N	100597	Strong A P C	100495	Woodall W R *BA(Hons)*	110896
Smith A M *TD*	51097	Russell J E	300495	Mason R C S H	10499
Raschen H D *BCom*	201097	Cadogan C A E	100197	Foster J F	10800
Gambles J E J *BSc(Hons) ARICS*	Melville P C F	150699		
10199	ØWrangham T G	30899		
Attenborough G B J *BSc(Hons)*	Tilbrook J R	270999	*Lieutenants*	
310300	Burr J L W	231099	Reid D J *BSc(Hons)*	130492
	Legh Smith R R	10200	Zank D T	310796
Captains	Phillips R L G	140101		
Hewlett M S J	11192		*Quartermasters*	
Davies D J	21193	*2nd Lieutenants*	Brown R W G *Capt 120696*	
Sayer C J	121293	Wilson A	210591	Wood A J *BSc(Hons) Capt 040497*	
Leighton J	140194	Starkey E T W	130699		
Nall R G A *TD*	11194	Blake C J	170799		

THE ROYAL WESSEX YEOMANRY
Locations and Affiliations

RHQ . . . . .Bovington
B (Royal Wiltshire Yeomanry (PWO)) Squadron . . . . .Salisbury . . . . .The King's Royal Hussars
C (Royal Gloucestershire Hussars) Squadron . . . . .Cirencester . . . . .The King's Royal Hussars
D (Royal Devon Yeomanry) Squadron . . . . .Barnstaple and Paignton Royal Tank Regiment
A (Dorset Yeomanry) Armour Replacement Squadron . . . . .Bovington . . . . .Royal Tank Regiment

Role Affiliations . . . . .The Royal Dragoon Guards, The King's Royal Hussars and
Royal Tank Regiment

Honorary Colonels

Hon Colonel . . . . .Lt Col J G Peel *TD JP DL* 011100
B (Royal Wiltshire Yeomanry (PWO)) Squadron . . . . .Lt Col J G Peel *TD JP DL* 010595
C (Royal Glocestershire Hussars) Squadron . . . . .Lt Col D R Ayshford-Sanford *TD DL* 011199
D (Royal Devon Yeomanry) Squadron . . . . .Capt *The Rt Hon the Earl of* Devon *DL* 250599
A (Dorset Yeomanry) Armour Replacement Squadron . . . . .Lt Gen *Sir* Timothy Granville-Chapman *KCB CBE* . . .010497

	Cherry J T	10498	Ford J H	10899
	Attwell D G *BA(Hons)*	11198	McFadzean A W	150500
Colonels	Utting D W *LLB(Hons)*	11099	Mountain I W *BEng(Hons)*	20101
Chamberlain O J H *TD• MRAC*	Morgan J D H *TD*	151200		
FRICS tacsc	10197		*Lieutenants*	
Hodson A D F *TD BA(Hons)* tacsc		*Captains*	McLaughlin S P	230595
	10497		ØWildish J D *BA(Hons) DipM*	
———	¶Hoddinott A J	40285	*MCIM*	21095
	Fowle C S *BSc(Hons)*	20688	¶Pearce C H	291097
Lieutenant Colonels	Mills R G	111090	Perry M A	301097
Maitland J A C *TD* tacsc	10199	Ashton-Johnson P J *TD*	290792	Caldwell B H *BSc(Hons)*	21198
Ranson L C A *TD*	20999	Baker N L	231192	Furlong M T	40699
	Gourlay R	110493	Bennett A R	150699
Majors	Bathurst The Honourable	10497	Machray R J	291099
Rothwell M J R *BA(Hons) ARICS*	Long P M	90497	†Geraghty M D	21100
tacsc	40196	Doyle-Davidson C M S *BSc(Hons)*		
Ponsonby R C *TD* tacsc	111196		10897	*2nd Lieutenants*
Kelly N J F *BSc(Hons)*	150697	Marsden M M W	170997	†Gilruth A H C	40600
Adams B J tacsc	90398	Fisher G J	120898	†Ehlas M *MEng(Hons)*	310800

THE ROYAL MERCIAN AND LANCASTRIAN YEOMANRY

A Mercian Eagle topped by a Saxon Crown superimposed upon a Lancastrian Rose below the Duke of Lancaster's Coronet

Regimental Marches

Quick March . . . . .The Light of Foot
Slow March . . . . .Scipio

Locations and Affiliations

RHQ . . . . .Telford
A (Staffordshire, Warwickshire and Worcestershire Yeomanry) Sqn . .Dudley . . . . .The Queen's Royal Hussars
B (ShropshireYeomanry) Squadron . . . . .Telford . . . . .1st The Queen's Dragoon Guards
C (Cheshire Yeomanry) (Earl of Chester's)) Squadron . . . . .Chester . . . . .1st The Queen's Dragoon Guards
D (Duke of Lancaster's Yeomanry) Squadron . . . . .Wigan . . . . . .The King's Royal Hussars

Role Affiliations . . . . .The Queen's Royal Hussars and Royal Tank Regiment

Colonel in Chief and Honorary Colonels

Colonel in Chief . . . . .THE QUEEN

Honorary Colonel . . . . .Maj Gen R W Ward *CB MBE* 090296
Honorary Colonel Designate . . . . .Brig *The Duke of* Westminster *OBE TD DL* .140501

A (Staffordshire, Warwickshire and Worcestershire Yeomanry) Sqn . . .Martin Dunne Esq *JP* 010400
B (ShropshireYeomanry) Squadron . . . . .Capt D U Corbett .011096
C (Cheshire Yeomanry) (Earl of Chester's)) Squadron . . . . .Maj *The Lord* Hawke *TD* 010498
D (Duke of Lancaster's Yeomanry) Squadron . . . . .Lt Col M Steiger 010201

Colonels

Seccombe The Hon Philip S *TD FRICS* tacsc 11299

Lieutenant Colonels

Leigh D L *TD*• tacsc 10400

Majors

Widgery E F *TD*•• tacsc sq(V) 10386
English J R S 10587
Skirving M T *TD* 230191
Hill N L tacsc 10193
Maclean J H S *MRAC* 70595
Swayne D A *TD* 10196
Hall G R 10898
Miles C P C *TD* 21198
Cook W J 10499
¶Wilkinson L 10499
Palmer N S 10401

Captains

Hutchings S W 110190
Caddick-Adams A P *TD BA(Hons)* 11294
McBride J *BEM* 300995
Compston J R 10697
Morley J 190997
Villar J G 190997
McEwan M D 61097
Parry R H *BSc(Hons)* 61097
ØCooke A M *BA(Hons)* 11197
Evans S J 191297
Ledsham C J *BA(Econ)Hons* 10298
Elwell C W E 10498
Murphy M R 180598
Lindsay J M E 10400
Tamlin J C 10500
Garrety M J 131100
Sadler R 131100

Lieutenants

Harvey R L *BA(Hons)* 280490
Keramatian D D 40891
Harrison G N 230693
Pipe M G 80894
Sugrue B B 101096
†Hodgkinson C M 230798
Hartshorne RG *BSc(Hons)* 71297
Bragg T W H 101198
Wilkinson M N 20299
Bankes W N W 20899
Bulmer M 20899
James D 70999
Hilsdon J 140600
†Frith K W 80201

THE QUEEN'S OWN YEOMANRY

A fox on a scroll inscribed 'QUEEN'S OWN YEOMANRY'

Regimental March

Quick March . . . . .D'ye Ken John Peel

Locations and Affiliations

RHQ . . . . .Newcastle upon Tyne
Yorkshire Squadron . . . . .York . . . . .The Royal Dragoon Guards and
The Light Dragoons
A (Ayrshire (Earl of Carricks Own) Yeomanry) Squadron . .Ayr . . . . .The Royal Scots Dragoon Guards
D (Northumberland Hussars) Squadron . . . . .Newcastle upon Tyne . .The Light Dragoons
C (Fife and Forfar Yeomanry / Scottish Horse) Squadron . .Cupar . . . . .The Royal Scots Dragoon Guards
B (North Irish Horse) Squadron . . . . .Belfast . . . . .The Royal Dragoon Guards and
The Queens Royal Hussars
Role Affiliations . . . . .Household Cavalry, 1st The Queen's Dragoon Guards,
9th/12th Royal Lancers (Prince of Wales's), The Light
Dragoons

Honorary Colonels

Royal Honorary Colonel . . . . .Maj Gen *HRH The Prince of* Wales *KG KT GCB AK QSO*
ADC 170600

Honorary Colonel . . . . .Col E C York *TD DL* 150698

Yorkshire Squadron . . . . .Lt Col R E Howard-Vyse *TD JP DL* 110397
A (Ayrshire (Earl of Carrick's Own) Yeomanry) Squadron . .Maj P N B Kennedy *TD DL* 010297
D (Northumberland Hussars) Squadron . . . . .Lt Col A G Gibson *TD* 141097
C (Fife and Forfar Yeomanry/Scottish Horse) Squadron . . . .Capt J Gilmour *TD DL* 011197
B (North Irish Horse) Squadron . . . . .Col D M Christie *TD DL* 010598

	Thornton-Kemsley I S *TD HDA*	
	DipFBOM	21193
	Assheton The Honourable tacsc	
Brigadiers		11294
Westminster The Duke Of *OBE TD*	Malcolmson J C	120597
DL tacsc 170100	Tougher N C tacsc	61097
	Golden J N *BEng(Hons) MICE*	
Colonels	*ACIArb* tacsc	200999
	Illingworth J H	101099
Glazebrook N C *TD* tacsc 10400	Moss J C *TD BA(Hons)*	10800

Lieutenant Colonels
Callander R *TD•• FRICS* tacsc 270192
Lewis P J *TD ED BA(Hons)* tacsc 10698
Royds J C *TD MBA DMS MIMGT* tacsc 11099

Majors
Prince-Smith J W *BSc(Hons)* 10291
Boyes J *TD* 11092
Roads C G W *TD BSc DipM* aic 41192

Captains
Graham S J M *BA(Hons)* 290192
Dickson D S P sq 40396
Reynard C W 10197
Chrisp A H R *MA(Hons)* 10597
Potter N W E 10797
Foster R L S 50498
Carrick-Buchanan A D T 130698
Forbes J W C 270998
Costello S W D *BA(Hons) MA PGCE* 90699
Carrick C P *BSc(Hons)* 10799
Halford-Macleod A A R 11000

Lieutenants
Findlay I R 220894
Macfarlane S M 51295
Clark S M G 40896
Linehan A D *MA* 261196
Clark M J M 60897
McLuckie A J 10298
Williamson T G 100998
Prinsloo T J 10599
Mortimer D 150699
Parker P G *LLB(Hons)* 310100
Montgomery S J 130600
Oriordan P D *MA* 70900
Crump J T 310101

2nd Lieutenants
†Pennett M T 10600
†Kyle J W 20700
†Lock G W J 150700

Quartermasters
Boast L T *Capt 011198*
Barker T C A *Capt 310301*

294

ROYAL REGIMENT OF ARTILLERY

Hon Colonels ....Brig D E Radcliffe *OBE (Hon Col 101 (Northumbrian) Regt RA (Volunteers)*...................................... 111099
Brig A S Ritchie *CBE (Hon Col 100 (Yeo) Regt RA (Voluteeers)* 170201
Brig W B Stevens *MBE MC (Hon Col 104 Regt RA (Volunteers) ret pay*............................... 010197
Brig R L Styles *(Hon Col 106 (Yeo) Regt RA (Volunteers) ret pay* 010799
Col J M Steele *CB CBE TD DL (Hon Col 105 Regt RA (Volunteers)* 010199
Col M J E Taylor *CBE TD (Hon Col 103 Lancashire Artillery Volunteers Regt RA (Volunteers)* 011092

Brigadiers

Thomson J R *TD BA(Hons) MBA MIMGT MCIM* 310300

Colonels

Partridge W M J *TD•* tacsc 11298

Lieutenant Colonels

Fletcher-Wood C *OBE BA(Hons)* odc(AUST) psc 200989
Blair J M G *TD LLB(Hons)* tacsc 10794
McCracken W A *MBE MC* sq 290196
Watson R L *BA(Hons)* 300196
Shaw W E psc† 40396
Ash R F *BSc(Econ)Hons* tacsc 10197
Wilson R W *TD* tacsc 70197
Kinloch J A B tacsc 140297
Burton R *TD ACMA* tacsc 150897
Comport C E *TD•* tacsc 10997
Lemon W J *TD BA* tacsc 11197
Taverner A I psc† 311298
Bryson G R *LLB MA* tacsc 10799
Gray A J *BA(Hons)* psc† 11099

Majors

Bucknall R M *TD•••* 10279
Mount P *TD••* 180983
Westlake-Toms J S *BSc* sq G(a) sq(w) 11084
Thompson P G N *TD• FCIS* 11284
Hancock R D *TD•• NADC(V)* tacsc 50285
Heap P *BA(Hons)* 10885
McIntosh C R G *BSc(Hons)* psc† 131085
Frank A R *MBA* psc† 70186
Smyth P C *TD• BA(Hons)* tacsc 10187
Skillman D J psc 191087
Hearn C *TD•• MSc* tacsc gsd 10788
Manson F P L *TD• MBA FCCA* tacsc 270788
Boyce P J *TD• BSc* tacsc 240988
Lincoln-Jones C sq 300988
Wardrop A D G(y) 281088
Robertson S A *TD MA(Arch) DipArch RIBA ARIAS MIAA* 160189
Wilson T G GT(Y) 180189
Mills R J *TD•* 40389

Tatton H M *TD• BSc* tacsc 40389
Logan K S *BSc(Hons)* tacsc ae G(a) 300989
Hawkes M H 131089
Haggerty J H *TD BEd* 120290
Chambers C J *TD•••* 10390
Downham R E *TD•••* 10390
Nuttall P J *TD* sq(V) 120890
Paget D W *TD* 181290
Cowell-Smith P E ph 50291
Docherty J S 10491
Brown P K *TD•* 20791
Gibson B G *TD• FInstLEx* 251091
Mitchell L C *TD• ATD* tacsc 190192
Hutt R W F *TD BSc DipPROPIN FRICS AMRSA* tacsc 170392
Paine M C *BSc(Hons) PGCE* G(a) sq(w) 211092
Barrington Brown C *MA MBA* tacsc G 10493
Whyte N F 10493
Griffith J D *BSc(Eng)Hons MSc ARSM* dis 290593
Salloway P C *TD BSc* tacsc 50993
Pointet D A J *BA(Hons)* psc 41093
O'Connor M J *TD•* 251093
Stormonth R J G 11193
Farrell R P 10394
Bolton-Clark J ndc sq sq(w) 80494
Constable J C *TD BSc* tacsc 10994
Walker G J 151294
Jones I *TD ACMA MIMGT* 10195
Joslyn M A G(a) 300195
Sadler S N S *TD* 200395
Lonsdale I D *BA(Hons) BSc* 70595
Comport C A *TD•* tacsc 90795
Wilson I A *TD• MSc* 310795
Middleton D *TD* tacsc 10895
Horton D C 300995
Watson K A tacsc 131195
Robinson S C *MA* 11295
Weston M I *MInstAM* 10196
Dowdney N J *TD•* 50396
Gough A J E *TD PhD MRSC* 50396
Winchcombe J P *BA(Hons)* 50396
Hare S J *TD FCIS MIPM MIMGT FCIPD* 10496
Shepherd P H *TD DCR(T)* 10896
Fox J S *TD BSc(Hons) PhD* 11296
ØForbes L M *TD BSc(Hons)* 10397
Hitchman S C *TD* tacsc 10397
Berendt P R *AIMGT* 10597
Llewellyn G J *TD* 10597
Routh C A 10198
Evans H M *TD* 90198
Forbes A J G *MA* 10498

Higgins J R C 10498
ØSadler L J 60498
Russell A L V *TD* 10598
Bailey B J *TD* 300698
Gwizdala J P A *BA* 300698
Humphrey D A *TD MA CPhysMInstP CPhys* 300698
Jefferson I D *TD• BA(Hons) BSc* 300698
Kerry-Williams C P 300698
Walker T N C 10898
Sinclair W G 300998
Gault K J 151298
White G *TD DMS* 10499
Bulmer D C *BA(Hons)* 190699
Williams D G *BSc(SocSciENCE)* 230799
Dufley D J 11299
Simpson N H *TD* 120100
Auckland-Lewis J C *BA(Hons) DipM* 80200
Tough S G *BA(Hons)* 80200
Copland I D *BA(Hons)* 10300
Sparks J N *BSc(Hons) AMIEE* 10300
Ellett S 10400
Crosby A pi 190500
Kirkwood S A 10600
Ross I L J 10600
Rogers A G 150600
Forbes J B C *LLB(Hons) Dip L P* 10101
Hefferman D J T 10301
Ewings D A *TD* 10401

Captains

Thompson H E G *TD•* 230285
Price S L *TD* 10685
¶Baldwin K W *TD* 70486
Cookes H N *TD* 20686
Koss R A 10886
¶Wilson B K 201086
¶Thompson R C A 10187
Hutton J M *BEM* 11089
Privett R J 11089
Mulkern T P 21089
Tynan W J 301089
Mackenzie C A 311089
Sweeting D A *BA(HonsCantab)* 51189
Taylor J A B 241189
Reed C D 10190
Knox D E *MA* 10390
Compton J R E *BSc(Hons)* 10990
Holley D B 221290

Clark P *TD* 200591
Hilton K A *BEng* 90192
Lea I A 10492
Abrahart F J 290492
Leadbeater R J *BSc(Hons)* 11092
McLachlan I H 301192
Walters R C *TD* 190193
Chakravarti P 10293
Sim H D 100293
Mannings K M *MBE* 40893
ØBradnam L D 170893
Inness C H P G 210893
Scholes L 170993
ØLaverty J W 200993
Aldous D P *MIMGT* G sq(w) 21193
Davey J R 21293
Smith R V *BSc MCIBSE* 10194
Suthers J W D *TD* 10194
Gray J J M O *TD* 70194
Glass R J *BSc* 220194
Haslam P W *BA(Hons)* 190394
Doyle P 100894
Chaffe R R *BSc(Hons)* 140894
ØServaes J *BA(Hons)* 291094
Whiteley M *TD* 100495
Merrylees A G *BA(Hons)* 70595
Cochrane A 290595
ØFaux W 160695
Varvell S K *BA(Hons) MSc* 10895
White P B 10895
Wood A W 110895
McKeown P B *BEng* 21095
Towers J M 91095
Littlejohn D A 211095
Garstang P J 291095
ØFeatherstone N *BSc(Hons)* 101295
McDonnell L F 250296
Sloan A S T 130496
Armitage B *MBE MILOG* sq 200496
Morgan S J 10596
Ward F N *BSc* 10696
Persse T G 30696
ØRandall R A 250696
Willett E P 150896
Copley A G 11196
Murray S A *LLB(Hons) DipLP* 11196
Holme D W 251196
Cunningham A M 11296
Reid S F *BSc(Hons) PGCE* 101296
Vallack P A 141296
Taylor L J 10197
Moore H N *TD BA(Hons)* 10497
Griffiths S C R 30497
McCartan J M 260497
Fisher J R 10597
Haywood C D *BA(Hons)* 90797
Thorburn A R 160797
Hatton P 11097
Hudd B G 131297
Grant S G 10198

Bishop D M *BA(Hons)* 120298
Curtis C P 10398
Every A J *ARICS* 10398
ØStinson H M 190398
Boyd W C 10498
Oldershaw I 90598
Cleverly J S 260598
Thomas G H B 260598
Lucas B 10798
Winton P D 10898
Nield S H 10499
ØTook S V 10499
Taplin D J 20899
Adamson B 11099
Allen J C 11199
McFarland J 251199
Seward R H P 40100
Eaton S D C GT sq 50100
Smith A C 100100
Mistry R C 130200
Pender J A 160200
McGrath W H 100400
Halliday W S J 120400
Obre L J M *BA DipTechEd CertEd* 120400
Smith M C *BA* 280400
King R A 10500
Pennett T W *BSc* 10700
Jackson R M 40700
ØBrinton J E 140800
Haigh P A *BEng(Hons)* 10900
Primrose I C *MA(Hons)* 20900
Hamlett R 11000
Maclellan D 11200
Thurley M R 121200
Cranston R S 10401
Whalley M J 10401

Lieutenants

Griffin J 120792
Smallwood A M 20892
Brown N J 230593
Pinnell L J 61093
Owen P D 260194
Latham S 270994
Hemstock N T *BA(Hons)* 21095
Anderson B J *BA(Hons) CertEd* 61095
Watson J A 191095
Strugnell J J 51295
White D W 161096
Snowden S 300397
Searle J P 10697
Megaw G P 180697
Lynass T J 200697
Lavender T 70997
Casely B G F *BA ACIVS* 40298
Fleming A J F 150698
ØWylie S A 20798
Tarr C J 70798
Griffith D S C 20898

Craig R R 40898
Falloon A 30998
Norris J E *BSc(Hons)* 280998
ØFirmstone I J 300199
Tancock S C 310199
Saunderson B 20599
†McKeown D J 250599
Maher C M 20899
Reynolds S A 30899
Fraser S K S 80999
Anders D 71299
Flint R W 100100
Porter R D 300100
King A J 110200
Brougham M J 160200
Timmis J P *BSc* 10500
McKibbin N J R 140600
†Crabtree S 240600
Poulten D J 10800
Joyce D S 20800
ØHarris N M 260900
Munafo M R 260900
Gilbert H F 11200
Auty J B 121200
†Munro D J 301200
†Wheeler C I 170101

2nd Lieutenants

†Witts J R 281294
ØKnight A V 280997
ØDown S E 200798
Browne G E 270998
ØWiles S N J 10899
ØMackenzie S K 260999
†Burton M S 201099
†Greaves D M 270100
†Robson M A 40600
†Way A M 40600
ØParnham H L 10800
†Bazley A J 60800
†Kennedy R D 60800
†Waldron-Lynch T 60800
†Carey T L 11000
†Parker E M 11000
†Clarke D M 61000
†Griffiths R R 11100

Administrative Officers
Captains

Paterson K R *MISM* 300990

Quartermasters

Watkins J V *TD   Lt Col 010797*
170592
Fletcher F D   *Maj 160796* 010793
Connor P   *Capt 040898*
Morrison M W   *Capt 010400*
Corrigan J J   *Capt 100500*

CORPS OF ROYAL ENGINEERS

Hon Colonels .... Air Marshal *Sir* Malcolm Pledger *KCB OBE AFC* .... .030897
Brig G A Hewish *MBE* .... .080892
Gen *Sir* John Wilsey *KCB CBE ADC Gen* .... .011092
Maj Gen J A J P Barr *CB CBE* .... .281093
Maj Gen R Wood .... .140794
Air Chief Marshal *Sir* Richard Johns *KCB CBE LVO* .... .291194
Lt Col R B Hawken .... .010496
Col J R Hennessy .... .011296
Sir Richard Nichols .... .240497
Sir Clive Martin *OBE TD DL* .... .140799

Colonels

Pagan C W *MBE TD• BA(Hons) LLB(Hons) FRSA FIMGT WS NP* tacsc 10487
Gardiner C A *TD QVRM BSc* tacsc 10497
Barker W R *TD BSc(Hons) CEng MICE* tacsc 10498
Gowen S *TD* tacsc 10600

Lieutenant Colonels

Goodwin R A C *TD• BSc(Hons) MICE MIHT MIMGT* tacsc 81086
Daniell I M *BSc(Hons) MA FRSA MIPM* psc 300692
Rigby C S *MBE TD•• BEd MIMGT LRSC ACP* tacsc 150995
Murfin R W *TD•* tacsc 301095
Brookes E J N *TD• BA(Hons) MA (EURING) CEng FIMechE* tacsc 11295
Braden S A *TD BSc(Eng)Hons* tacsc 10796
Cheetham S *MBE TD•• BSc FPWI* 311296
Hawgood B J 210197
Willis A J *TD BSc(Hons) MSc (EUR ING) CEng MIQA AMICE FIMM MIMM* tacsc 10497
Walker H *TD* tacsc 280997
Smith A M *TD• CEng MCIWEM* tacsc 10498
Charlesworth J tacsc 10299
Waters D I *TD FIPM* sq(V) 10499
Stretch C J *TD• BSc(Hons) MBA* 11099
Darley S J 10400
Squibb S M *TD* tacsc 10400
Brown R H *TD BSc(Hons) MBA CEng FICE FCIT FPWI CDipAF MIMgt* 10401
Salmon A J *TD MA MICE* tacsc 10401

Majors

Stephens J M *TD• CEng MICE* tacsc 10981
Park D A M *BSc(Eng)Hons MBA CEng MICE* tacsc C 130885
Irvine T D *TD BSc CEng MICE* tacsc 11285
Ward I *TD BSc(Hons)* tacsc 30287
Evans D W *TD BA(Oxon) MA MBA* tacsc 140287

Kermack J A *TD BSc(Eng) AMICE* tacsc 20188
Metcalfe S *TD• BSc(Hons) CEng MICE MCIWEM* tacsc 151088
Randall T M *BSc(Eng)Hons* sq 31089
Anderson E G *TD BSc CEng MICE* 10190
Smith L M *TD BSc(Hons) PhD CEng FGS MICE MIStructE* 300690
Waddell C Q O *TD* tacsc 20791
Newcombe R H J *TD BA(Hons) PGCE* tacsc 10891
Anderson W G *TD FRICS* tacsc 120192
Macewan L N A *OBE FIPURM* sq 11092
Gay P A *TD BSc DMS* 51192
Willmott E P *TD* tacsc 81192
Hamilton R A *TD BSc(Hons)* 10293
Jackson D A *MIPlantE MIMGT P* sq(V) 280593
¶Downey G P 10693
Mauer P J *TD* tacsc 10693
Cooper R A N *TD* tacsc 10793
Critchlow C *TD* 11093
Purvis E J *TD BSc(Hons)* 301093
Holland R T *TD* 10294
Mann G C *TD• MChS* 110394
Brownrigg T G *BSc CEng MICE* 10494
¶Davis J W 10494
Eaton J C *TD BSc(Hons) FGS MIHT AMIGeol* 10494
Redgate T C W *TD* 10494
Cosgrove G B *TD BSc(Hons) (EUR ING) CEng MICE AIExpE* 40694
Johnson I A E *TD BSc* 280894
Burridge N *TD* 60994
Hickman S J *BSc ARICS* 10195
Larmett E F *TD MIAS MIBC* 130195
McLean A J *BSc(Hons)* 10495
Hinchliffe R G 20995
Rice S *BSc(Hons) FRICS ACIArb MInstCES* 201095
Somers R M *BSc(Hons) CEng MICE MCIWEM* 10196
Webb L E S 10196
Field D G 10496
Maybin F J *TD* 10496
Finnie M G 60796
Elvidge R D *TD BSc ARICS* tacsc 310796
Smith T F S *TD BSc(Hons) GRADRSC* 10896
Chadwick B M tacsc 11196
Pugh M C 51196

Langley G E *CEng MIStructE* 10497
Facchini M A *TD BSc(Hons) MIFST* 60497
ØNelson C *TD* 60497
Webster I *TD MBA MIMGT MIBC* 190597
Englishby C J *TD* 10797
Foote M B 200797
Kinsville-Heyne C L 240797
Wilkinson K *BSc(For) MBA MSc* 10897
Welford C J tacsc 61097
Lee C A 10298
Henwood E C 10298
Salmon P F E *BEng(Hons) IEng FIHIE SVY(pr)* 10398
Bell A T *BSc(Hons) MICE* 10498
Hann M *TD* 10498
Robinson D *BSc(Hons) FRGS MBIM MHSM* 10498
Coulter A A *TD BSc PGCE* 210498
Young T W 230598
Coleman S J 240598
Shallcross A D M tacsc 250598
Taylor S D *TD* 300698
Rowlands L J *TD* 10199
¶Clarke P 180199
Finnen A J *MBE* tacsc 140499
Snelling B G *TD BSc(Hons) (EUR ING) CEng MICE* 230499
Edwards A A *TD MBA DMS MIMGT* tacsc 10899
Harris D S jsdc 220999
Wood A C 91299
Queen G T *BSc* 70100
Hill A P 10200
Ryan A J G *TD BSc(Hons) DipArch* 10400
Moult J *BSc(Hons)* 10600
Cooper A J *BSc(Hons) MIFM* 291100
Fisk P A 31200
Syme D R 31200
Dow R I L *BSc(Hons) CGeol* 220101
ØTownson C 010301

Captains

¶Coveney R A G 160479
¶Godsmark R J 70679
¶Batty B 60581
Ratazzi I G 140683
McAlinden B P 10486
¶Walton T J 10486
¶Kennedy P W 10487
¶Duncalfe J A 210188
¶Moreton A R 111088

Heyes T P O *TD*	11289
Robinson E E *MBE*	50290
ØKitson E J	10390
Hills P R	270690
Baldwin B R	11090
Gibson A J G	71190
Blades J	10291
Lee J	130491
Denning W T	60891
Cotter W J	160891
Kelly G J *MBE*	120991
Gavin J J *TD*	11091
Parnell M H	11091
ØShell A P *TD BSc(Hons)*	11091
Sach J R	240392
Foong K Y *TD*	10492
Amy R F *TD MBA MIMGT*	10592
Mitchell P D	10892
Hartney J H	10193
Hurd D T	10293
Ritchie D	260493
Headridge E R *TD*	190693
Tennuci B S	150793
Houlston J	140893
Lang J M	110993
Taylor G J M *TD*	10194
Baldwin E	10294
Connelly V	10294
Hargreaves C R	10294
Hunt R J	10294
Smith T S	10294
Williams J G	10294
Owen G S	250694
Beesley G G *TD*	260794
Hudson R J R *BEng(Hons)*	80894
Baldwin D J	11094
Rattray J	191094
Sheridan D A	30195
Nathanail C P *BA MSc DIC CGeol*	10495
ØPeden E A	110495
Carter M P *BSc(Hons)*	130695
Ware D R J *BA(Hons)*	150995
Curtis M D *BSc(Hons)*	31095
ØLloydlangston C E *BA(Hons)*	101095
Lancaster J M *BSc(Hons) MBA MIExpE*	161095
Huxley-Wright E F *BEng(Hons) MICE MIStructE*	171095
Griffin S C *BSc(Hons)*	201095
Farenden R W	11195
ØWilkes K	11295
Osborne M J *BEng(Hons)*	121295
Chapman D	180196
Beckett D B *BSc(Hons) PhD FGS CGeol*	10296
Corbett A J	10296
Balsillie A F	10396
Mawer N P *BSc(Hons)*	100396
Wilson J M *BSc(Hons) MA DMS*	100396
Southway C	210396
Dunn G A	130496
Hutchinson S R	150496
Mackenzie I D	20696
Scullion S F	120696
Stewart J D *BA(Hons)*	170696
ØMcNee M	210796
ØSimpson S E	290996
Bage S J	11096

Graham D W *BSc (EURING) CEng MICE*	11096
McRae W	21196
Moody N G *BEng(Hons)*	91196
Sanderson P A *MBE*	10297
Smith S P	10397
Baines M L	10793
Evans H D	10497
Letties G T	10497
McKnight J T	10497
Oliver M G *BEng(Hons) AMIMechE*	10497
Rosborough P	10497
Walton T	10497
Gray M J	110497
Adam J R G	230697
Doust A J *BA(Hons)*	130797
Parfitt K D	90897
Leach R A	210997
Smyth A M G *BA(Hons)*	61097
Oldfield A J	301097
ØBrown J A *MEng*	161197
Owen M D	40298
Eaton J W	80298
Baker D M	60398
Edmondson C	60398
Powell A N *BEng(Hons) CEng MIMechE MIEE*	60398
Rae J A M	10498
Baldwin M I *MEng(Hons) PhD*	10698
Ward S	10698
Lewis R	90698
Pavey M J	10798
Callingham P J	50798
Price J D	180798
Clarke R M *BA(Hons)*	10898
Barclay D J	40998
Durham S M	40998
Craft A P	70998
Phillips P C W	11098
Keddie M A *BA(Hons)*	121098
Holman J N	241098
Handley R	251098
Gapper R A	301098
Norman D *BA*	301098
Wilson N S	61198
Turvey O G	11298
Roden P A	310199
ØCouser C A *MA(Hons)*	10499
ØPalmer R T J	10499
Bell J M	180499
Biggins K J	180499
Manning J G	10699
Martin D A	40699
Warner D C	250699
Parsons V	10799
Brown S D	190799
Blow D B *BA(Hons) BArch*	10999
Shreeves M J	60999
Gordge N M	70999
Starling D J	70999
Willmott D	70999
Man C C L	221199
Thompson J M	120100
Nugent D S	10200
Rudd A R *BSc(Hons) MSc PhD*	10200
Holdsworth D A	70200
Elliott S J	80300
Thorneycroft G H *MBE*	90600
Ladbrook M B *BSc(Hons)*	70700

Wilcock C M	300900
Forber D	11000
Savage P	10101
Mitchell W T	80201
Keogh D P	10301
Gray D *BEng(Hons)*	170301

Lieutenants

Pidgeon H A	250590
Winter R S	250193
Keeley D J	11194
Cairney S	130695
Waters A N	180695
Easton T	210596
Finch S M	30897
†Shackel C	60997
Page A M B	111297
Foulkes I D	270298
Deppe P J	10898
Black G P	30898
Clarke A S	100898
ØVenables S J	10998
Armstrong P	101298
Livesey J R *BScEng(Civil) MSc(Eng)*	10299
Rowe P D	10299
Beecham M J	280599
Hughes R D	10699
Dixon J	130699
ØYeomans L	140699
Pitts N C	150699
Freemantle P R	20899
†Gibson P	51199
Gregson G M *BEng(Hons) MICE*	181299
†Hay I T N	50200
†Hambrook J N	200500
†Speigt G	200500
ØEyre C	260900
Robbins N E	260900
Craig A G	51100

2nd Lieutenants

†Bush G K	41294
ØBosanquet L E	60895
Dare C R S	161095
Morrison P	180497
Arthern R J	280997
†Hanley D J	280997
White T H L	241198
†Carroll J J *LLB(Hons)*	10899
Donnelly C T	10899
†Hall D	10899
†Harding S P	10899
Ibbs D P M	10899
†Pilbeam A D	10899
Schofield S J	260999
ØBrown M D	40600
†Elmer P G	40600
ØJeffery T C	40600
†Cobbett G	20700
†Riley M F W	20700
ØSharpe E J K	10900
†Gray P A	170101
†Kehoe A G	180201

Administrative Officers

Captains

Stinchcombe D J	271195
Jurgens D	30796

Quartermasters

¶Hall A J   *Capt 021186*   11077
¶Lucas J   *Capt 030486*   81181
Schofield R *MBE TD   Maj 110595*
                                      110583
Hobley R A *TD   Lt Col 010498*
                                      50983
¶Baron G W   *Capt 020886* 80184
Howle L *TD*   *Capt 080184*
Barker M J A *IEng AMICE FPWI*
   Maj 010497   150285
Collins K J *TD•   Maj 010197*
                                      80487
Brankston R *TD*   *Capt 010897*

McCallin E J *AIOP   Capt 010497*
                                      10490
Shillito C L   *Capt 100690*
Middleton J A *Maj 010499*   11290
Lumley G J   *Capt 071091*
Bulmer A   *Capt 011191*
Reddy A   *Capt 101092*
Poll D C *TD• BSc(Hons) CEng*
   MICE MIMunE MIHT   Maj 110300
Zygmant P J *MIMI AMIRTE TEng*
   Maj 010499   10493
Webb P J   *Capt 260593*
Hedger G M   *Capt 141093*
Garner E   *Capt 010194*

Azzopardi M   *Capt 100298* 190195
Gaze D A   *Capt 160696* 201095
Green R I *MIExpE   Capt 010496*
Giles P A   *Capt 030996*
Gwilliam G R W   *Capt 181096*
Roach D B   *Capt 220597*
Taylor A J   *Capt 060997*
Scott G D   *Capt 060198*
Stuttard D   *Capt 100298*
Crane W   *Capt 200798*
Saunders C R   *Capt 290300*
Curtis G M   *Capt 010700*
Scholey A R   *Capt 010101*
Clark N P   *Capt 170101*

299

THE ENGINEER & LOGISTIC STAFF CORPS RE (V)

c/o R3 Halton House, 20-23 Holborn, LONDON EC1N 2JD
(Tel: 0207-831-6563 Fax: 0207-405-7047)

Commanding Officer . . . . .Col G O Whitehead CBE BSc CEng MICE 160101
Hon Colonel .Lt Gen A D Pigott CBE MA 280201
Acting Adjutant . . . . .Col R M Stancombe BSc(Eng) CEng FICE ret pay 010194

Colonels

Whitehead G O *CBE BSc CEng*
  MICE   261095
Laing *Sir* Martin *CBE MA*
  FRICS   180697
Urwin R J *BSc PhD FEng*
  MIEE   170299
McAlpine *Hon Sir* William *Bt*
  FCIT FRSE   230699
Chartres F R D *BSc CEng MICE*
  MIGeol FGS   251199
Stancombe R M *BSc(Eng) CEng*
  FICE Eurlng MIMGt   210600
Bateson P A *BA CEng FICE MCIT*
                            280201
Rouse M J *BSc CEng*   280201
Sheaves P A *BSc CEng FIEE*
  FCIBSE   280201
Webber H P *BSc CEng FICE*
  FIMgt   280201

Lieutenant Colonels

Day R T *BEng FICE FIWEM*
                            300992
Scott K D *BSc CEng FICE*
  MIStructE MIHT MHKIE 180697
McLaughlin R T P *MA MSc CEng*
  FICE FIStructE   250298

Webb J F T D *BSc CEng FICE*
  FIHT FHKIE FIEAust   051198
Hutt B C *BSc(Hons) MEng PhD*
  FCIBSE MIEE MIMechE MInstE,
  MConsE   230699
Hindle D J *BSc MSc DIC CEng*
  Eurlng FIMM   251199
Lazenby T *M CEng FIChemE*
  FInstPet MSc   251199
Howarth G G *BSc CEng FICE*
  FCIT FRSA   251199
Williams K *BA(Hons) FRSA* 251199
Taggart H G R *MSc CEng FIPlantE*
  FInstPet MIMgt MIOSH
  RSP   230300
Doughty S J *BSc CEng MICE*
  FIHT   210600
Robinson R W *BSc(Hons) CEng*
  MICE   210600
Alexander W J *FEng FIMinE*
  FIMechE   280201
Armitt J A *CBE FEng FICE* 280201
Canadine I C *PhD BSc CEng*
  MIChemE FILog   280201
Duff A R W *FCIT MIHT*   280201
Hunt R J BA *MBA FILog*   280201
Jones S A L*VO BSc FRICS*   280201

Majors

Welton M W *BSc CEng*
  MICE   190297

Shaw M R *BA MSc CEng FCIBSE*
  CMath FIMA CPhys MInstP
  MBCS   180697
Russell B C *MSc FICE MIStructE*
  FRSA   250298
Baxter J *BSc(Hons) CEng*
  FIMechE FRSA   170299
Drury J V P *MA(Cantab) DipArch*
  RIBA FILog   170299
Fletcher A *BSc CEng*   170299
Schlegel W *CEng MICE*   230699
Steedman R S *BSc MPhil PhD*
  CEng FICE FRSA   230699
Wickens P J *BSc CEng FIStructE*
  MICE   251100
Belcher C J *BA FCIT*   230300
Bolsover G W *FIQ*   230300
McWhirter R   230300
Templar B S *BA(Hons)*   230300
White K G *MA FRSA FIFP*   210600
Banyard J K *BSc(Eng) FCGI FREng*
  FICE FCIWEM ACIArb   010900
Bishop M W *FRICS FCIOB*   010900
Eaton J C *BSc(Hons) MIHT FGS*
  CGeol TD   010900
Pullan K   010900
Thompson N C *CBE CEng FICE*
  FIStructE   010900
Brettel P D *BSc CEng MICE* 280201
Welsh S M *MBA*   280201

ROYAL CORPS OF SIGNALS

Hon Colonels . . . . Maj Gen W J P Robins *CB OBE* 011097
Col A C Cunningham *TD* 190399
Professor P Toyne *DL FRSA* 010299
Sir Ronald Norman *OBE* 010596
Col B N T Foxon *OBE TD* 010799
Col A E M Hall *TD DL* 010190
Brig W H Backhouse 010195
Maj Gen A H Boyle *CB* 010497
Maj Gen J D Moore-Bick *CBE* 220600
Lt Col A J Cramsie *DL* 030590
Vice Admiral *Sir* Geoffrey Dalton *KCB* 010398
Col J R Hensman *OBE* 250795
Sir Nicholas Bonsor *Bt* 010800
Brig J H Almonds 270297
Richard Marriott Esq *OBE* 010796
Brig A P Verey *QVRM TD* 011100

		McConnell D C *TD*	130985	ØHubbard J E *TD CertMGMT MISM*
		Burnage J F sq	150386	170495
Brigadiers		ØMillar C F B *TD• MA* tacsc		ØShepherd S R N *TD•* tacsc 10595
Verey A P *TD• QVRM* tacsc	10397		10486	McCappin T R tacsc 160595
		Evans A T *BSc(Eng)Hons MSc CEng*		Baker M A *TD BA(Hons)* 10895
Colonels		*MIEE* psc† dis TEM	300986	Vardy D J *MSc* dis 10995
		Macgillivray A C W *TD* tacsc		Houston W B *TD BSc* 11195
Acda P W *TD• ADC* tacsc	21192		10587	Appleton R I 161295
Foxon B N T *OBE TD• ADC MSc*		Maxwell E P *TD BSc(Hons)*		Lansdown M W *BSc(Hons) ACA*
tacsc	10293	*MIEx(GRAD)* tacsc	11087	291295
McLay D *TD•* tacsc	11293	Penfold P F *TD* tacsc	151288	Hall I T tacsc 30196
Bruce-Smith K J *TD•• BA(Hons)*		Harvey D A *TD BSc(Hons) PhD*		Miles G *TD* tacsc 30196
tacsc	130596	*DipEd GRADRSC* tacsc	120289	Sawyer R S H *TD* 10296
Henderson I G *OBE TD•• BSc*		ØPayne J C *TD BSc(Hons)* tacsc		Parkes N G *TD• BEng(Hons) AMICE*
MSc(Econ) tacsc	30498		10689	50396
Laurence C J *TD••• BVSc* tacsc		Puddy I G *TD BSc(Hons) GRADIMA*		Pell S L *BSc ARICS* 150796
	10899	tacsc	310789	Robertson H J *TD* 10996
Davenport R *TD BA* tacsc	170100	Lambton J A *TD*	10690	Palmer S P *TD* 11096
		Crawford D A *BA(Hons)*	60790	ØSutherland C R 11196
		ØTuhey R K *TD BA(Hons)*	10591	Jackson M *TD* 100397
Lieutenant Colonels		Scott R J	40991	Baker S J 10497
Kirby J E F *OBE* odc(AUST) psc		Cornish A J *TD BSc(Hons)* tacsc		Flanagan K M *TD BA(Hons) CISEM*
osc(ZIM)	101188		171291	120497
Buston R *TD•• LLB(Hons) MIMGT*		Geddes J F *TD LTCL* tacsc	60292	Tomlinson D T *TD* 10597
tacsc	10494	Munson D G *TD BSc(Econ)Hons*		Webb M A P *BA(Hons)* 10597
ØHarrison L F *TD MA* tacsc	10796	*ACA*	10892	Carmichael J 100597
Lapsley A C C *TD•• QVRM* tacsc		ØAston H A *TD BA(Hons)*	10992	Smith M 230697
	71096	Willmott P N *TD BSc(Hons) FRGS*		Heaton C D tacsc 280797
Beacom N C *TD* tacsc	101096	*MRTPI*	10992	Cummings M O 11097
Whittle A J *TD• BA* tacsc	130697	Miller J W D *TD BSc(Hons)* tacsc		McAneny B 11097
Hornsby G S *TD*	10997		11292	Sowerby B M *TD BEng(Hons) CEng*
Crackett J *TD MA(Hons) CEng*		Ferguson A *BSc(Hons) ACIB*	70193	*MIEE* 81097
MIMechE AMIEE	10398	Grindrod A M	200193	ØScott-Foxwell S E 11197
Gilfether B P *MBE TD*	11098	ØFarquharson F *TD BSc MCSP*		Blyth E M *TD* tacsc 10398
Potter S J *TD BSc ARICS* tacsc			10493	Aitken P 10498
	10399	ØMcClean J C *TD• BSc LRSC PGCE*		ØReed S K *BA(Hons) DMS* 10498
Brown W D L *TD• MSc*	10700		10493	Sixsmith D E 10498
Wenlock P D *TD BSc(Hons) ACMA*		O'Beirne M J *TD* tacsc	10793	Fraser-Brenchley M R 10598
tacsc	11200	Holman M S *BSc(Eng)Hons*	10893	Lynch H 70301
Malik S C R *BSc(Hons) PhD*	20201	Kelly R J *TD*	11093	McCormack D M 20998
		Hogan J E TEM	270194	Lankester T J R *ASCA FCMA*
		Holt R L sq(w)	10394	300998
		Fitzgerald S J	10494	Bowden R J *TD BSc(Hons)* 121098
Majors		Weir D *MBE I** sq(w)	270694	Lenton R B 131098
Cartwright M J	110397	Pyman J F *TD*	300894	White M *TD* 151098
Tydeman J D *BSc(Eng)* sq(w) adp		Fallows J W *TD*	11094	Marshall E J H *BA(Hons)* 171198
	190380	Ahern J P *TD*	11294	Shirley W J 121298
Bosley M J *TD•• BTech(Hons) PhD*		ØClegg P J *BA BSc(Hons)*	181294	Bergin E W 10199
	11281	Duggan J R S Q *BA(Hons)*	40195	Smith A D 230199
Williams P sq	310382	Fern J	240295	Jones C L *BSc(Hons)* 10299
Davis R E C *TD BSc(Hons) FSMC*		Moore A J L *BSc(Hons) ARICS*		Davison M F L *TD•* 10499
FBOA tacsc	161282		10495	Tillotson C F *TD* 90499

301

Ward R C 10599
Sleigh D J 280699
Foulkes D J *BEng(Hons)* 300999
Tallents C S 110100
Atkinson M G P *TD• BA* 80200
Gregory J D *TD* 80200
Russell J A 100400
ØEngland J C *LLB(Hons)* 80800
Nilsson F *CISEM* 210900
Duffy-Penny K J 240900
Titheridge D A 80101
Prince D A 160101
Crilly A F 10301
Ballantyne A 10401
Cosgrove M 10401
Orr-Cooper S J *TD CISEM* 10401

Captains

¶Naismith W J A 260179
¶Jordan J 111083
Donald N *BEM* 171285
Lane W G *TD BSc(Eng)Hons AMIEE* 10486
¶Frost J W L *MBE ASTA* 20786
Atterbury R S 30887
Etheridge B J 90887
Wilson J J 120888
¶Kinghan C *MBE* 190988
Brough D 110589
Evans M D *TD BSc(Hons)* 11089
Scott K 61089
McCourt L D 220790
O'Gorman P W P 300790
Yates L 130990
Gleeson M F *MBE* 300990
Farmer J R *BA MICD* 240391
ØCole M L 240491
Homewood C E 270491
Lavery K S 10691
Goddard D J 30691
ØThornber K 280691
Salvoni R C P 10791
Bryson A C 110791
Jones S M 140791
Murray I E 150791
Byrne J F *MISM* 250791
Cullen J M 20891
Glover T W 10991
Manley J I *TD BA(Hons) MPhil* 10991
Webb J P 10991
Campbell P 150991
Theakston P A 60492
Rustidge K S *TD* 10592
Stone R D 10792
Brown G A 130992
Robertson C D 111092
ØDouglas D G 261092
ØDuncan L H *TD* 11192
Cooper D S *MBE* tacsc 21192
Bruce A A *BEng BEng(Hons)* 131292
Pitman G D 141292
Carr W K 10393
Calvert I R 110393
Baker A G 160493
Hopkins A C D 130593
Edwards C W tacsc 80693
Downey G N 20793
Sherburn K 150793
Knowles J D 91193
Whelan G M 190194

Gibson D A 10294
Sheldon R J 40294
Carr L L 20394
Baker P M 10494
Tarrant D Z *MISM* 10594
Wadley I W 30594
Key R L *BSc(Hons)* 120594
ØMcGrellis J A 200594
Cox N P *BEng(Hons)* 30894
Bewsher R G G 141094
Tuke R W M 311294
Hallas D 40295
Jennings G 260395
ØMcClung M T *BEd(Hons)* *DipTEFL* 10495
Glover S C *BA(Hons)* 240495
Hayes P K 150595
Loveys J R 230595
Siggs N L *MSM* 230595
Dods D M 10695
Pepper A D 10695
Shankland B 20695
ØAitken S L *TD* 260795
Pitt T M *LLB(Hons) LLM DipLP NP* 10995
James B 90995
Houghton A S 180995
Duffy R J 91095
Dick T 231095
ØDodd J M 291295
ØKirby W J *BSc(Hons)* 20196
ØCowie J E 10296
Tierney A D J 150296
Taylor P A 10396
ØGriffiths D G 10596
Gordon D *BSc* 10696
Belbin R H 230796
ØLankester C M *BEng(Hons) MEng* 200996
Baker J P 11096
Fowler-Smith P H *TD* 311096
Ong S T 101296
Welch N B 10197
Kirkham S C 10397
Davidson R I 40397
Piechota M 70397
ØLockhart J A *BAcc* 170397
Middleton S M *MA* 170397
Cox M S 10497
ØBird R K 170597
Bryden M 200697
ØStreete S L *MSc* 10797
Samways P J 270797
ØHope D S 10897
McCann G J 10897
Carter M R *BEng(Hons)* 300897
Jordan L T *BEM* 300997
Thompson A R *TD BSc* 11197
Adams P J 71197
Finch M J 71197
ØSwain A R *RGN* 11297
Dillon A A *BA(HonsCantab) MA(Cantab) AMIMechE* 70198
ØHook M D L *RGN RM* 100198
Symmons J A 150298
ØBallagh J M 240298
ØEmpson R M 10398
Mason S 10398
ØSwift B E 40398
Barker K A 240398
Fletcher A J 240398
ØGalli A P *BA* 300398

ØWood P J 20498
Pearson J D *BA(Hons) BArch(Hons)* 10698
Sanders W H C 10698
Anstiss G S 200698
Walker S R 10798
Shayler S A 130798
Whalen A P D 50898
Giles C S 140998
Wood M 180998
ØSheriff V J 280998
Edwards D W *BA(Hons)* 51098
Dixon W S 171098
Woods T A 11198
Jeffries T *BSc(Hons) MSc* 271198
Walshe J W 31298
Wopling J N 121298
Wayman S C 161298
Quinn A J 60199
ØJames C A *BSc(Hons)* 10499
May S A 30499
Craig I 10799
Feasey E D 10799
Howe D M 10799
Uhomoibhi J O 20799
ØTaylor L *LLB DipLP* 260799
Brimer A M *BEng(Hons)* 210999
Bamber C T 11099
Rowson S A 41099
Whitehouse P 41099
Lamb A T *BA(Hons)* 261199
Rance A S 291199
¶Ponton T M 21299
ØWilkinson E S *BA(Hons) PGCE* 230100
Brogden A B 10200
ØPollard E A 310300
Smith L D A *BSc(Hons)* 10400
Ong E J *BSc BSc(Hons)* 10500
Moses D E 100500
Ayre P W 210500
Clout S H 220500
Hudson S 10600
ØMiddleton-Powell R 90600
Smith S A 90600
Spence E J 50700
Jones P R 10800
Kelly M J 30800
ØLodge J H 150800
ØMcLaughlin A M *LLB(Hons)* 10900
Schofield M R 10900
ØHoward J L 230900
ØBulley P H 240900
Cassell I F *BSc(Hons)* 300900
Lewis C C 300900
Moseley C R 300900
Whalley A E 300900
Evers A K D 11000
Reid P C 11000
Skinner B J 11100
Rodgers A C T 61100
Edwards P 111100
†Moore D J 181100
ØDaly C L R 301100
Kendall J R 301100
ØMurison C L 301100
†Pringle J E 301100
White A L *BSc(Hons)* 11200
McFarlane A D 10101
†Cockburn A N 10301
†Watson P D L 10301

Lieutenants

Marshall A S	100788
Dinan M J *BA BBS*	30401
ØHopkins R C	40891
ØWilliams S E	271091
Brindley C W H	10893
Donnithorne N C	10893
Cranston R D	310794
ØReardon L A	270994
Lysak A E D	180696
ØHunter S L	300696
Weir M B O	10796
Donegan P T	310796
ØFitzpatrick E A *BL*	60896
ØBowes J B	61096
Watts M C *BA(Hons)*	201096
ØJeffreys Z S	20597
Evans S	150697
Henderson A	180697
Smith M P N *MA(Hons)*	10897
ØDrennan A S	30897
Jenner S A	40897
Macsween S A *BA PGDA*	40897
ØMcArthur J J	280997
Milnor D J	280997
Ackroyd J L	21097
Ciaralli-Parenzi A	21097
ØGreen S J *BSc(Hons)*	101197
ØFerry J S	10498
Lowther A D	230798
ØHanlon K M	30898
Hook R I R	30898
Hughes C A	30898
ØSidwell S E *BA(Hons)*	10998
Weir E G M	280998
†Knight P A	11298
McDowell S P *BSc(Hons)*	10299
ØStalley J	100299
Fensome J T	230499
Sturt A M R	260599
Macmillan N R	140699
ØWilliams A H	140699
Wilson D J H	270699
Oliver J P	20899
Burgess S J	270999
Middleton-Powell A J	270999
Ukpai P	280999
Kinvig C R	131099
Bailey J D	251099
Downing A L *BSc(Hons)*	311099
ØCropper-Mawer R B	21199
ØHillyard E J	121199
Black J S	51299
Peploe A J	170200
†Banner R J	170500
Kennedy A	130600
Kane D J	140600
Cropper J L	10700
ØLawrence J E M	10800
Migallo N P G	10800
Woodhams R M	20800
ØKeegan R	10900
Howes T C *BEng(Hons)*	20900
Williams K A	40900
ØCox L	310101

Browning J C	40201

2nd Lieutenants

†Ewart D J	10893
ØDempsey T	11096
ØSkillman C R	51196
Abbott D	180597
ØSpeakman D C	50898
†Carter D S	270998
†Longcake M J *BSc(Hons)*	270998
ØCaldwell D M	11098
Dickey G F	111198
†Grant D S *BEng(Hons)*	20299
†Taylor G A	130699
†Denning P M	10899
Galloway A	10899
†Zazzi M D L	10899
Durtnal S J	260999
†Reynolds N J A	260999
ØRiberzani L E	280400
†Ambler D G	40600
†Beaumont D W	40600
†McEvoy L	40600
ØYarrol C M	40600
†Baker G B	40800
†Manickavasagan R	60800
†George H G	11000
†James S A	11000
†Hubbard J S	130101
ØPounder B L	180201

Administrative Officers

Captains

Miles W V	10786
Mason G J *BEM*	90196
Pengelley T J	20796
McGowan M M *MBE*	220796

Quartermasters

Evans W F *TD•••*	*Maj 280492*	
Watson D J *TD*	*Maj 110296*	131187
Watts A	*Capt 120490*	
ØStrachan M A *TD*	*Maj 010999*	10690
Minshall P J	*Maj 091299*	131090
Butler C	*Maj 010299*	150592
Newbery A	*Capt 210892*	
Hall R E W	*Capt 221192*	
Fraley D M	*Capt 281192*	
Payn C S	*Maj 260900*	130193
Barber J R *TD•*	*Maj 311095*	50393
Howe B C	*Capt 110893*	
Macguire N J M	*Capt 211093*	
Corfield P B	*Capt 171293*	
Shaw A D P	*Maj 011099*	10194
Southey F R *TD*	*Capt 010489*	140394
Thomas D	*Capt 150494*	
Cooper M F	*Capt 100594*	

Winterson T R	*Capt 191094*	
Trayers D *TD• BA CertEd (FE)*	*Maj 040888*	11194
Hattersley J M	*Capt 270196*	130295
ØTraylen B M *TD*	*Maj 010292*	10495
Mather A M	*Capt 040595*	
Carroll P L	*Capt 110995*	
Gillespie C M	*Capt 031095*	
Brownlee I P	*Maj 180799*	161195
Logan R P *MISM NEBOSH*	*Capt 041295*	
Wyper W F	*Capt 141295*	
Jones D H	*Capt 150296*	
ØSuddens P C	*Capt 220396*	
Riley J	*Capt 240596*	
Sirr K	*Capt 240596*	
Taylor H C	*Capt 070696*	
ØWard T J	*Capt 010996*	
Granitza M A	*Capt 240996*	
Stanley M J	*Capt 220197*	
Parr D B	*Capt 270197*	
Finlay R E	*Capt 290197*	
Giles AC	*Capt 100397*	
Ruthven W P	*Capt 010497*	
Dempsey J P	*Capt 050298*	
Walker C	*Capt 160598*	
Shelley G S	*Capt 010898*	
Potter A J	*Capt 180998*	
Campbell M	*Capt 181099*	
McGiveron P J	*Capt 181099*	
Payne B	*Capt 011199*	211299
Loveridge R R	*Capt 130500*	
Milsom S P	*Capt 160500*	
Meddeman M J	*Capt 040800*	
Anderson K N	*Capt 160800*	
Jephcote R A	*Capt 160800*	
Knowles P E	*Capt 011100*	
Masson A	*Capt 051100*	
Mustoe M J B	*Capt 071100*	

Technical Officers in Communications

Fredericks P A *TD*	*Maj 190295*	50784
Thomas I R *TD MSc*	*Maj 310394*	271084
Corrie D J *TD BSc(Hons) DipTM CEng MIEE TEng*	*Maj 011197*	10387
Long J	*Maj 171199*	171187
Dawes C M	*Capt 310388*	

Traffic Officers

Lingard J R *TD*	*Maj 010494*	280885
Walker P J	*Maj 011198*	221186
Haldane J	*Maj 100696*	81288
Swann D A	*Maj 171296*	210290

THE SCOTTISH DIVISION
COMPRISING
52nd LOWLAND REGIMENT
Walcheren Barracks, 122 Hotspur Street, Glasgow G20 8LQ

Upon a Saltire, a thistle within a circlet inscribed *NEMO ME IMPUNE LACESSIT*

Regimental March

Quick March . . . . .Scotland the Brave

Hon Colonel . . . . .Col J P Wright *TD TAC SC* 010799

51st HIGHLAND REGIMENT
Queen's Barracks, 131 Dunkeld Road, Perth PH1 5BT

Hon Colonel . . . . .Brig I A Sim *CBE TD* 010799

Colonels	Campbell C H *BSc FIBMS AIBMS* tacsc	210596
	Pollock R D M	270796
Wright J P *TD•* tacsc 10497	Grant H	10996
d'Inverno J G *TD LLB DipLP WS*	Wilson J L N tacsc	100297
tacsc 30200	Glancy D C *TD LLB DipLP*	60597
	Tait K M	210997
	Wood W M *LLB DipLP NP* tacsc	
Lieutenant Colonels		11097
	Murray R M *BA(Hons)*	10398
McKen G *MBE TD•* tacsc 40893	Doyle R *MA* tacsc	220398
Kelly J L *MBE BSc(Hons)* psc†	Clinch D F C	150798
280794	Elliott G W S	10998
Young R M D *TD••• LLB MIMGT*	Williams A M *TD*	120100
NP 201196	Sweetman R J H	80200
Downie A F *TD BA BSc* tacsc	Banks A J *TD BSc(Hons)*	11000
260197	Maclean-Bristol C B M *MA(Hons)*	
Hudson N E *TD• BSc(Hons) PhD*		11000
tacsc 10798	Jones A G M *LLB MA DipLP*	
Macdonald M 10799		10101
Burns S W *TD* tacsc 10101	Anderson J L	20101
	Jennings D J	10201
Majors	Maclellan J C	50201
Steuart-Corry M C *TD• MBA DMS*		
DipM tacsc 180682	*Captains*	
Edmunds D F *TD•* 11085		
Trevillion E A *TD PhD MRSC*	¶Thomson R	10486
11086	¶Moody F J *MBE*	170686
Robinson R H *TD•• BA M A (Oxon)*	¶Macdonald A	151287
ACIB 10788	Cruickshank R M *TD LLB Dip L P*	
McLeod G tacsc 10888		10590
Prentice P C *TD•* NADC(V) 11189	Auchterlonie J H	291190
Simpson D G sq 291086	Adams G G T	11290
Tosh G C *TD MA(Hons) MSc* 10488	Cabrelli P	301091
Milroy C J A *TD BSc MPhil CEng*	Catto A G *AMIEE REMT FIDIAGE*	
MICE MCIWEM 10190		10392
Doherty D J *TD IEng* 210391	Sutherland K G *BScEng(Civil)*	
Keating J A *TD* 91091		10492
Doyle J *MBA AMIEIE* 231191	Bollen S J R *BSc*	150992
Macdonald I D *MBA* tacsc 11092	¶Beveridge A	161186
Couser G R 181092	Hermitage B	40693
Carroll P J *TD BA* tacsc 30393	Bennett A S	10993
Fisher D B 160394	Sinclair M *BSc(Hons) CEng MIEE*	
ØDavies C M M tacsc 190494		130993
Macleod M M *TD• MBA* tacsc	Williamson J J *BA(Hons)*	60894
80794	Bateman S H M	11195
Lee W G *TD* 270295	Steele D R	60196
Thomson M G *TD BSc DipEd MEIS*	Stacey G A P	190196
201095	Ogilvie M P	140596
Connor K J tacsc 201295	Graham D R	10996

Edwards M A	210796
Hood R J G	181196
Hussain Z	300197
Coull C A	30197
Rorie P A *BD*	10297
Macfarlane A C	30397
Scroggie E F R	150997
Cherry B W	11097
Vicca M J *MA(Hons)*	10198
Smith D A	60298
Macgruer I	10498
Allan J M T	160698
ØBoyd A H	190698
Kennedy A J	190698
Stimpson D G	190698
Knox D	280599
Clark S	91099
Tookey J E *BTech(Hons)*	30900
Crosby D J	20101
Aitken R I	10201
Henderson J B	50201

Lieutenants	
Dunbar A P	40896
Whitley F A *BSc*	40896
Hume K A	250996
†Munro J A M	180497
Kay P	260597
Macdonald M M	180697
Gaston G H	150797
Woodley J A	300698
Sharratt B C	150898
Hunt J M *BSc(Econ)Hons*	10299
Henderson D S	110399
Fitzpatrick R J W	10599
Barker R J	10799
Corrigan G J	30899
Combes J C H	310100
Towler G H W	10200
Blair A	110400
†Kerr S J	20500
†Pope E A	20500
†Jack C D	20700
Campbell A I	20800
†Hitchings B J *AFM*	261000
Colville A J	310101

2nd Lieutenants	
†McKellar J A	40891

ØMackey R E	10298
†Corkerton T A G	20898
†Ellison R B	20898
†Keen A W	20898
†Hall A H	40600

Quartermasters

Banks W G	*Maj 100899*	10191
Clayton J W	*Capt 021193*	
Blackstock D M	*Capt 080796*	
McDonald P C	*Capt 081097*	

Cockerill H   *Capt 010694*

Administrative Officers

Captains

Restall D A	40697

THE QUEEN'S DIVISION

COMPRISING

3rd (Volunteer) Battalion The Princess of Wales's Royal Regiment
Leros TA Centre, Sturry Road, Canterbury, Kent CT1 1HR

Hon Colonel .Col J R G Putnam *CBE TD DL* 010799

The London Regiment
TA Centre, 27 St John's Hill, Clapham Junction, London SW11 1TT

Hon Colonel .Maj *Sir* Paul Newall *TD DL* 200495

The East of England Regiment
Blenheim Camp, Newmarket Road, Bury St Edmunds, Suffolk IP33 3SW

Hon Colonel .Brig M E Browne *CBE TD DL* 010799

Colonels	Burns R G *MBE TD* tacsc	50493
	Cserjen R L	20893
Chissel A D *TD* tacsc 10194	Long R L H *TD•* tacsc	71093
Storie-Pugh P A D *MBE TD ADC*	Neame M Q *BSc(Hons)* tacsc	30194
tacsc sq(V) 10494	Davidson J M tacsc	280994
Jackson R M *BA(Hons)* psc† 10497	De Planta De Wildenberg F M G	
Argent C L *TD FCA ATII* tacsc	*BA(Hons)* tacsc	10994
10797	Randall M D	131194
Easton N P *QVRM* tacsc aic 231000	Windmill S M *TD BA(Hons) MBA*	
———	tacsc	20395
	Wright N M *TD* tacsc	240595
Lieutenant Colonels	Fairbanks Weston A D *MIMGT*	
	MIPR tacsc	170795
De Hochepied Larpent A L D *OBE*	Chaytor R A *BA(Hons) DMS* 10196	
BSc(Hons) psc 300689	Ayling K S *BA(Hons)* tacsc 280596	
Colville R M L *TD* tacsc 80492	Cook D J	10996
Gill H N D tacsc 140496	Carr L *MISM*	30996
Duff A N sq 10197	Wheaton R A *TD*	181296
Ffitch N A *TD* tacsc 10497	Frost A J	260197
Auld C J D *TD• BA* tacsc 10497	Lane B K E *MBE*	270397
Turner N H *TD* tacsc 10899	Milward A J	10597
Simpson G C tacsc 180899	Plowman S J F	10597
Guthrie A P *TD• BSc(Hons) FRICS*	Tusa J H A *TD*	10597
tacsc 10400	Monk P C T	180797
Mooney J P *BA(Hons)* tacsc 10400	Young S G	260797
Straughan G tacsc 10101	Brown N M P *TD*	31197
	Fraser-Burton S	41197
Majors	Paling N J *TD BSc(Hons) PhD FRES*	
	tacsc	181297
Raybould J L *TD•• DipRSA* 10282	Petersen T J *TD BSc ARICS* 10498	
Petrie A G *MA MDA DipEd* psc	Smith A D	10498
MDA 300982	Trott C V	250598
Roche T O G *TD* tacsc 10785	Muir G I *TD•*	300698
Pratten J N 281085	McEwing J G	141298
Ross J H D *TD• sq(V)* 10286	Mogg D K *BA(Hons)*	120399
Blyth G L *TD sq(V)* 10487	Shaw G B	140999
Frere-Cook S A C *MBE*	Brothwood P J *BSc(Hons)*	210999
BSc(Eng)Hons psc† 91287	Atkinson R G	171099
Rankin-Hunt D *MVO TD• sq(V)*	Clements R M S	71299
150789	Ladd J A P	10400
Livingstone D A *TD* 230290	Googe M	130500
Ferguson G R W 230890	Dawber D W *BSc*	220900
Hurman M J 90890	ØBlack R L	91000
Lopes J D *TD BSc* 171090	Law S H	11100
Kemp I D *BA* 30191		
Redfern J A *TD* tacsc 190291		
Liddell-Grainger I R P 10591	*Captains*	
Scott J *TD BSc(Hons)* tacsc 70991		
Matthews T J C *TD* 20192	¶Nolan T S	11282
Tutt R E *TD* 11092	Parker J C	10185
Turquand J N *MIPM MIPD* 11292	¶Mears C N *BEM*	210188
Clapham N G *TD•* tacsc 150393	¶Reeve C F	180388

Keating R J J	11188
Cunningham M A	240789
Gilfoyle J T	231289
Cottrell P A	260390
Elliott O C *TD BA(Hons)*	10291
Pratt J C	200491
ØHaughie S C	11191
Mackenzie G J *MA(Hons)*	10192
Jones I R sq aic	21092
Thurston P D	200493
McCaig D J *MBE*	300993
Smith P L *BEM*	21193
Humphreys J J F *BSc(Hons)*	101193
Nicol D S *BSc(Hons)*	20495
Hussey S D	150495
Woodburn S E *MBE*	260495
Fairbairn S R	20695
Fortune R F	40795
Lawn D J	10995
Watson S R	191195
Griffin M S J *BSc(Hons)*	41295
Windibank M P	41295
Wong A Y L	30396
Harrison R D F *BA(Hons)*	80396
ØTrustram Eve C F *BSc(Hons)*	
	10696
Sutherland N J *BA(Hons)*	231096
Bulley J R W	10197
Yardley A J G	10197
Blake M P	10497
Overton M A J M	10597
Ladds R W E *BEng(Hons)*	130597
Plews D A	10797
Thompson G P	220797
Webber D J E *TD*	260997
Fahy B M	11197
Rowney M R *MIMGT FISM*	11197
Ronald C N A *BA(Hons)*	11297
Smith T M B *BA(Hons)*	80398
Layzell A	10998
ØBrodie C E *BA(Hons)*	21298
Hunter J H	171298
Woods D N	261298
ØFry H P	310199
Anglin G W	190299
Wishart A S	190299
Lowe S F W R B	270299
Bennett J F	240399
Debenham A J	280699
Butlin M J	10799
Hall R P	10799

Brackley F P D *BA(Hons)*	10799
Brudenell K G	10799
ØHeron A J	10799
Morgan C J	10799
Lincoln P M *BA MEng*	10999
Smith A C *TD*	210999
Bond A T	11299
Wake S J C	91299
Sommerville D J	10100
Spiers K E	10100
Smith T D *MBE*	150700
Thompson T C	10800
Harris A K *BA(Hons)*	11100
Stott I J	220201

Lieutenants

Gothard M D	261191
Shaw R A *BSc(Hons) A(Mus)LCM*	270394
Campbell H A *MA(Hons)*	180695
Lloyd M J	41095
Greengrass J A	101295
Blott J P *BSc(Hons) BSc(Hons)*	170796
Manfield N C	60897
Shackleton J F	101297
Todd K S	210694

Massingham C M	40896
Williams M G	40896
Moss A M *BA(Hons)*	40896
Sparks J R *BA(Hons)*	90996
Moth A S	30897
Hebberd T G	280997
Litjens D H J	21097
Wellman S *BSCComb(Hons)*	21097
Garrett G N	181097
Haden N D *MBChB*	21297
Preeston H G	111198
Irwin-Parker T J	20899
Wood R J	30899
Rock R M	140399
Panton C J	20899
Copeland R J	10200
Lyons L D	10200
†Rogers R G	200500
†Sackree I M	200500
Althorp J R	20800
ØGlazebrook S F	20800

2nd Lieutenants

†Seddon J A	11195
†Lorriman H D J	40896
†Axcell J P	41297
†Ross McNairn J E	140698

†Strickland G M H *BA(Hons)*	
	270998
†Chamberlain L A	130699
Lawrie P J	10899
†Taylor M C	10899
†Bromwich K M	260999
†Sutton B	260999
†Ardley S	20700
†Howle G C A	60800
†Campbell C C	40600
Lowther S	170797
Griffn T V	200500
†McGarry S F	180201

Administrative Officers
Captains

| Lynch J J | 180692 |
| Allen R J | 20997 |

Quartermasters

French G W *TD Capt 240988*	
	11092
Hitchings G A *TD Capt 010999*	
Smith G G *Capt 010492*	

THE KING'S DIVISION
COMPRISING
The Lancastrian and Cumbrian Volunteers
Kimberley Barracks, Deepdale Road, Prreston PR1 6QB

Hon Colonel . . . .*Lord* Shuttleworth *JP DL* 010799

The Tyne-Tees Regiment
The Gilesgate Armoury, Gilesgate, Durham DH1 1JR

Hon Colonel .AVM A F C Hunter *CBE DFC DL* 010799

The East and West Riding Regiment
Minden House, Wakefield Road, Pontefract WF8 4ES

Hon Colonel .Brig G B Smalley *OBE TD* 010799

Brigadiers	Hodgson P M tacsc	11093
	English R M *TD*	151193
Smalley G B *OBE TD*••• *ADC ACIB*	Hampson P T	20994
tacsc 10497	Lodge M A *BA(Hons) BA(Hons)*	
	MIMGT MCOLLP tacsc	300994
Colonels	Simpson P A tacsc	11094
	McFarlane I tacsc	101094
Tovey W J *MBE TD*• *BA(Hons) MSc*	Byrne E L	111094
tacsc 10395	Radford A M *TD*•• *BA(Hons)*	20395
	Donaldson K S *BEd(Hons)*	11095
	Edwards R T *BSc(Hons)*	131195
Lieutenant Colonels	Pendlebury-Green J *BSc(Hons)*	
Lamb M E *TD*•• *BSc(Hons) MEd*		131195
MRSC tacsc sq sq(V) 10492	Williamson J G *TD*• *BA*	50396
Harris C T J *TD*• *BA(Hons)* tacsc	Ronaghan T W A	111196
300994	Simpson P A	91296
Tasker D *TD JP* tacsc 50195	Potts C W *TD*	10197
Biegel M P *BEd* tacsc 10296	Rhodes D K	10197
Hopkins D E *TD*• *BA* tacsc 10498	Davies P A *BSc(Hons)*	10397
Glover M J *BA(Hons)* psc(CAN)	Goodall A J P	230497
10499	Jones H M R	10597
Scott C M G tacsc 10600	Banks I C tacsc	10198
	Kelly I G psc(CAN)	120198
Majors	Miller A M	290498
	Miller A M	10798
Holland W F *TD BSc(Hons)* tacsc	Clarke P S *TD*	70998
101083	Moss S *BSc(Hons)*	270998
Evans N R H *BA(Hons) MA* psc†	Hughes J G	10199
10585	Handford S J	260499
Chandler A P *TD*• sq(V) 220386	Irvine D P G *BSc(Hons)*	10699
Hayward K C *TD*• *BA(Hons) PGCE*	Baird D R *MSc*	10799
PGCE 10486	Quegan P E *LLB(Hons)*	10999
Hilton P J *TD*• *BA(Hons) PGCE*	Hopper S J *BSc(Hons)* tacsc	40700
10487	Senior J W	170700
Morgan S J N *BA(Hons)* psc 300987	Loudon C A M	10101
Hudson P J *TD* tacsc sq 220988		
Brennan D *TD*	40190	**Captains**
Gallacher C A *TD*	260190	
Edwards H G *TD BA(Hons)* tacsc	¶Hopper J A	260483
310190	¶Baxendale H	190488
Crompton G R *TD MA MA(Econ)*	James M P *TD LLB(Hons)*	90189
DipEd 10990	Coatsworth S J *BSc(Hons)*	70490
Buczko P D *TD BA(Hons)* 181290	Sutcliffe J K G *BSc(Hons)*	290490
Milner K G *TD*	10191	Johnson J C	291090
Stonebridge J M *TD BSc(Hons)*	Smith P G	10391
PGCE tacsc	10191	Hey B	81092
White J R C *LLB(Hons) SIE(DIP)*	Barker P J	140193
tacsc	170392	Atkinson B	110893
Beech N *TD*• *BA(Hons)*	10293	Corrin R P	261093
Dowson A S *TD BEd(Hons)* 210993		

Whitworth L K *QGM BSc(Hons)*	
	61193
Page B *BEM*	20394
Bradley M	10495
Wilson R I *BSc ARICS*	80495
Topliss I R *BSc(Hons)*	250695
Hoggarth P A	160995
Coughlin J J	200995
Hutton M D	231195
Johnston T B *BA(Hons)*	10196
Ledger A P	261196
Foster J J L	161094
Townsend I C	130597
Barnes C S *BA(Hons)*	240298
Springham A K	70498
Hunter M K *BSc(Hons) DMS*	10598
ØHalstead C A	190698
†Mossop A	190698
¶Urwin I E	10798
Albon K	251098
Makinde D B	190599
Haworth W *TD ACII ALIA(DIP)*	
tacsc	10799
Watson M R *LLB(Hons)*	10799
Machin I	101299
Brearley R T L *BEng(Hons)*	10300
Howard C E	10500
North C G D	310500
Cotterill A M S	11200
Rutherford A *BEng(Hons)*	10101
Cameron J A E	180101
Curry S P M	10401
Potter C A S *PhD DSc MRSC*	10401

Lieutenants	
Harold N A *BEng(Hons)*	20892
Norton A T *BSc(Hons)*	191093
Proctor D A	31193
Scott P A C	231094
Crook K N	140895
Wickett G H	21095
Hargreaves J D *BA(Hons)*	30897
Monteith K I	10298
Johnston S W	10398
Mode A J	40898
Cornick D J	61098
Mackay P D	81298
Pudney G	150699
Trimble J A	10799

Huddart R J	20899	†Devine M B *BEng(Hons)*	130699	*Administrative Officers*
Dowdall D M	30899	Derby A J	10899	
Brooks R N	260999	†Greaves J C	10899	*Captains*
Brown N E	10200	†Strickland T O	10899	
Routh S A	280400	Oakes R	260999	Nichol J S
†Heap G P	300800	Johnson C M	10400	Noble B
†Kenny N D J	300800	†Bates A S	40600	
Palmer J N	310101	†Bolinbroke A K	40600	
Saunders R A	310101	†Dodd J D	40600	*Quartermasters*
		†Hall M P	40600	
2nd Lieutenants		†Hebditch D J	40600	Scullion P *TD* Capt 010592
		†Newiss S P	40600	Woodhouse J M *Maj 010401*
†Randle M J	40896	†Blanchard A E	101000	
†Tribe P D	150697	†Davies S D	180201	McBride G W *Capt 010297*
†Gallon J C	310199			

Nichol J S 90988
Noble B 10291

Woodhouse J M 10494

309

THE PRINCE OF WALES'S DIVISION

COMPRISING

The West Midlands Regiment
Wolseley House, Fallings Park, Wolverhampton WV10 9QR

Hon Colonel . . . . .A E H Heber-Percy Esq *JP* 010799

The Kings and Cheshire Regiment
Peninsula Barracks, O'Leary Street, Warrington WA2 7QS

Joint Hon Colonels . . . . .Col I Paterson *OBE TD* and W A Bromley-Davenport Esq *JP DL* 010799

The Royal Welsh Regiment
Maindy Barracks, Cardiff CF4 3YE

Hon Colonel .Capt N Lloyd-Edwards *RD JP* *010799*

Brigadiers	
Holmes E R *CBE TD•• ADC MA*	
PhD tacsc hcsc(J)	180294

Colonels

Brady G E *TD* tacsc   50893
Sneath D R *TD MA(Cantab)* tacsc   231294
Jones N A *TD•• BSc* nadc(V) tacsc   10295
Bateman R P   tacsc   11295
Thomson J A J *OBE TD BEd(Hons) MSc CertEd* tacsc   60498

Lieutenant Colonels

Mason C R   311089
Beard N R *TD* tacsc sq(V)   80493
Shadbolt J W C *TD•* tacsc sq(V)   10794
Bramble I *TD RIBA* tacsc   11294
Durant S A *TD MIPD* nadc(V) tacsc tacsc   130495
Fausset M C *TD BSc(Hons)* tacsc   10796
Boden M J *TD LLB(Hons)* tacsc   10497
Protheroe C *TD•* tacsc   10497
Walton A C D *MBE TD* tacsc sq(V)   140498
O'Donovan D T   tacsc   11198
Bell S M J *BA(Hons) MA* tacsc   11299
Rock S E J   tacsc   10301
Spragg M E *BA(Hons)* tacsc   10301
Jones M P *BSc(Hons)* tacsc   10401

Majors

Garlick N P   tacsc sq(V)   220581
Titley R K *BA(Hons)* sq   261181
Rayer W F   10384
Ranson M B *TD•*   170384
Machin R E *TD BA(Hons) MSocSc*   171285
Leedham S C *TD•* tacsc   10386
Thomas J A *TD•* tacsc   20589
Venus A A   120989

Wort J C *BSc(Hons)*   241190
Kent H N *TD BSc(Hons) CEng MICE*   240191
Hockedy M E   10192
Mann C E J *TD*   100292
Varley J H *MBE* psc   11092
Clarke N L   151092
Roberts C D *TD*   10493
Mereweather I T *TD*   190993
Jones M W *BA(Hons)*   41193
Hiles R G *BAcc MIMC*   10694
Gay N S *TD*   10794
Green G S   180994
Marshall A W *TD*   161094
Gibson M   11194
Johnson A *TD* tacsc   11194
Higgs S C   tacsc   10495
Gumm I R *BSc(Hons)*   250895
Mann N G *BSc(Hons) PGCE*   11095
Ellis S E H *BA(Hons)* tacsc   141195
Halsey S A   tacsc   11295
Pritchard S D *BA(Hons)* sq(V)   11295
Upshall I R *TD•*   130496
Wong A L   tacsc   20696
Angel A N   10796
Turner A J *BA PGCE*   130796
Murday J P M *BSc(Hons) MBA*   60197
Winterbottom A *TD*   100397
Thomas D J *TD LLB(Hons)*   10497
Williams L T   110497
Coombes N A *BSc(Hons) MSc ATP MRSC PGCE EURCHEM* tacsc   200597
Wotton P J *TD MA(Hons)* tacsc   10498
Hughes R G *BEC*   90498
Allen T H   90598
Collie M D   10698
Houlston P S   10698
Snape D K *TD ABIAT*   281098
Bull C F J   110199
Johnson A M *BA(Hons)*   10499
Tolan J *BEd(Hons)*   10699
¶Taylor R L *TD*   10799
Yardley I J L   180700
Williams D A   10999

Phillips D K T *BA*   80400
Arden-Davis S F *TD BSc(Hons) MBA*   10700
Sheppard N J   160700
Shepherd R F D   11100

Captains

¶Wilding J   20983
¶Goldman D J   170983
Hall-Wilson T F S   261083
¶Earl J A G   11187
¶Ditchfield R   170789
McCartney W N   51089
Maund M   tacsc   70990
Pickering T E *MBE ARCM*   10591
Attwood R   261091
Oak D M   10192
Farmer C J O *BEng*   211292
Hann T G *TD*   10493
Jones A V *MIMGT*   281093
Buckley J W   250194
Challis C P J   10694
Bartlett G J P *TD*   10894
Rainey M W   10295
Forrest D C *MBE*   40598
Boswell R J *MBE*   150595
Rowe E C   120895
Tyson J   220895
ØBudd L A   10995
Edmonds B W *MBE*   300995
Boulter M K *BSc BSc(Hons) PhD*   10296
Crook D R   80396
Bridge M R   210596
Fenton M R   300996
ØCorminboeuf D   51296
Bennett M T *BA(Hons)*   10497
Jones R E   10497
Adams N A   190597
Wildgoose S J *BEng(Hons)*   200597
Mulingani P C   160398
Idziaszczyk M *BSc(Hons) MBA*   10798
McConnell A G   10998
Wibberley C R   140998
Brancher A C   160998
Smith R   180499
Adams S J   10799
Richardson J   20799

310

Alcock H J 10899
Richardson S H E 180100
Barrell A J 10300
Till J 10500
Porter R S *BA(Hons)* 140600
Ferguson A 150900
Hurst J 150900
Flynn P L 11000
Willis P J 11000

Lieutenants

Cassidy D P 71092
Fox R J *BA(Hons)* jssc 11294
Owen P F R R 60895
Middle C J 51295
Feehan P G L 100696
McCarthy D A *MBE* 60996
Cuttle F G B 21096
ØDavenhill A K G *BSc(Hons)*
 10197
Moses J C 180697
Roberts C J 180697
Goodbody R M 170398

Motte D 190598
Jones T I 51098
Glentworth N 61098
ØBrown H J 10499
Oldcorn D T 150699
Mudukuti K M 20899
Tait J R A 200899
Johnson P J 60400
†Bromiley J 270900
French N W R 270900
James I L 310101

2nd Lieutenants

†Bedford J D J 101295
ØLynch J L 20898
†Thornton A J 270998
†Howe C C 130699
Skates S P T 130699
Cvetkovic L 10899
Harris J B 10899
†Rose W K C 10899
†Thomson D A J 10899
†Wong C 10899

†Collinson A P 260999
Hamilton I D 300400
Paul M R H 10500
Evans D L 40600
†Mottershead R 60800
†Holmes B S 11000
†Watson J G T 11000

Administrative Officers
Captains

Williams E D *DCM* 230792
Ford R J *MBE* 70497
Ireland G F 30997

Quartermasters

Davies A J *MBE Lt Col 010497* 180585
Campbell R *Maj 011297* 10192
Carty C G H *Maj 010997* 150193
Talbot E K *Maj 011098* 270196
Banks M A *Capt 050300*

THE LIGHT DIVISION

COMPRISING

The Royal Rifle Volunteers
Brock Barracks, Oxford Road, Reading, Berks RG30 1HW

Hon Colonel . . . . .Lt Gen *Sir* Hew Pike *KCB DSO MBE* 010799

The Rifle Volunteers
Wyvern Barracks, Exeter, Devon EX2 6AE

Hon Colonel . . . . .Gen *Sir* Mike Jackson *KCB CBE DSO* 010799

The Royal Irish Rangers

4th (Volunteer) Battalion The Parachute Regiment

Colonels	Ainsworth P H P tacsc	10597
	Blackburn K F *TD BSc(Hons)*	
French T G *OBE TD• ADC* tacsc		10697
11094	Addyman N J S	170797
Abrahams S A G *TD•* tacsc 10499	Reynolds J K *TD BSc(Hons)* 310797	
Smith G S *TD BSc(Hons)* tacsc	Greenwood H J	10997
10999	Sturrock C G F	10198
	Napier M	140498
———	Johnson R J S *Ed*	170598
Lieutenant Colonels	Partridge R J	10698
	Truman G C tacsc	210798
Sawers I J psc	300491	Bartlett S W	11198
Hastings S J *TD MBA MSc ARICS*	Holden S F	70399
tacsc	11294	Clark S L *BSc(Hons)*	20699
McCourt R L *BA(Hons) MSc*	Evans T G	10799
psc(IND)	10496	Jenkins T P *TD*	20600
Chapman S C *TD* tacsc 10497	Malloch J C	180900
Guest R J *TD* tacsc 10198	Chisholm A C	90201
Trelawny A R psc 10700		
Butson P R *TD* tacsc 10101	*Captains*	
	¶Lundie A	100287
Majors	Frolish R A *TD*	10690
Vyvyan G J T *TD* tacsc 100685	Griffin D R	140890
Latter M J *TD••* *BSc CPhysMInstP*	Stewart-Smith G	21291
CPhys	11085	Ellis S L	10394
Ottowell C M S tacsc 300986	ØCave J A *BSc(Hons) PGCE* 80492	
Conroy W F *TD•* tacsc 21286	O'Brien P E C *MCIT* t 120992	
Carney A	10189	Fry E W	11092
Downey T J *TD BA(Hons)* 10189	Stanger R E	191292
Daly M A *TD*	10289	Gillingham D J	10393
Miles I D *BSc(Hons) FCA* tacsc	Wragg J M	130793
280289	Taylor G W	210793
Coia J M *TD*	10490	Osullivan P A	21293
Haldane G E *BA ACCA ACMA*	Dowle J A *BSc*	10194
240590	Casson-Crook P A J	20194
Coulon M D tacsc 220690	Vaughan P T	10494
Griffiths P D	11092	Ogden A	10694
Hill S T *TD* tacsc 10493	ØHaggerty B S	211094
Poe A D	10493	Ulmann C T	10495
Jones C S tacsc 80493	Smith R B *BA(Hons)*	50795
Light T D psc 281293	Hutchinson M C	150895
Browne R P ph 110394	Skliros J M	150895
Russell-Brown E *TD* 110394	Baker H K	220895
Blanchard G K G 291094	Winkel Von Hesse-Nassau F W C P E	
Johnson I C *TD CertEd* 111194	*MA(Hons)*	130995
Stables D A *TD* tacsc 10195	Littlejohn M	151095
Marvin A M D *TD BA* 10495	Walker J A B	161095
Prosser S J	21195	Robson W H	161195
Wilkinson S E *TD* 10496	ØLittle C	200296
Petchey C R F *TD* 190796	Wheatley S P	90696

Baker H J	170796
Gill A S	11096
Gilfedder F G	111096
Jarrett M H	101296
Norris A C P	161296
Crewe-Read S D	50797
Corcoran G J	10997
Tomczyk A J *BEng(Hons)*	240198
Wilson G J	180398
Collyns R M	10598
Elton E S O *LLB(Hons)*	20598
Rogers D J	190898
Vandaele-Kennedy R A	200998
Groves C R W	11198
Simonite R J	40199
Wells M J	70399
Price A D W *BA(Hons)*	200399
Wood P G	10599
Caseman M C *CertEd*	141099
Harper T J *BSc(Hons) MA*	10300
May D *BA(Hons) DipTEFL*	140500
Smith S	40900
Payne J R W *BA(Hons)*	141100
Cox G N	271100
Maxwell-Batten D M	10201
Bates C J	120301
Lieutenants	
Robinson N J	10893
Crew R S L	60895
Legon W E *BEd(Hons)*	20496
Turner C E *BA(Hons)*	280497
Haslam J R A	10597
Littlewood R S	11198
Roberts A M	150699
Leevers J N	310100
Scott-Hyde M S	10400
Parsons C G	270900
Hathway R P	310101
2nd Lieutenants	
†Oakley J D	30897
McIlwaine T L U	311097
Brandreth B X	20898
Arter R	10899
Von Savageri C S	10899
†Fleming L C	260999
†Harmsworth P A	260999
Quertier J	260999
Salisbury M	260999

†Sparks G   180201

†Toomey J C *BSc(Hons)*	260999
Scadden M A	10300
†Thynne P T	40600
Griffin X L *BA(Hons)*	10700
†Dicks M J	20700
†Freer S J	180201

Administrative Officers

Captains

Wroe D	210588
Luxton P C *MBE*	210597

Quartermasters

¶Jacobs R F	Capt 181287	50182
Phipps A W	Capt 010698	
Roper T J	Capt 211190	
Wilson-Hutton-Stott T H *MIExpE*		
	Capt 010400	
Lane C J	Capt 021100	
Atkinson J E	Capt 171090	10191

THE ROYAL IRISH RANGERS
4th/5th Battalion the Royal Irish Rangers (Volunteers)

Hon Colonel . . . .*The Rt Hon Viscount* Brookeborough *DL* 050197

		Fallis J E *TD*••	20482	Weir G J	10296
Lieutenants		Herron N H *BEd(Hons) DipEd* tacsc		Lyttle J O M *BSc(Hons)*	10796
Hudson M	130600		290887	Wood D W	190597
		O'Rourke C H *MA* psc	240890	Gracie D L	60898
		Owen R D J R *TD*••	170392	Smith M P	131298
Extra-Regimentally Employed		Nicholl J W tacsc	10994		
		Lyttle W D J *TD BSc(Hons)*	110994		
Lieutenant Colonels		Milliken J W *BEng*	160998	*Lieutenants*	
Telford R J *TD• BEd* tacsc	10494	*Captains*		Johnstone D A	230693
Phillips S J L *TD BSc(Hons) PhD*				Latus G R	20800
ATII tacsc	10498	¶Anderson J	160979		
Majors		Hill R J	180492		
		Johnston W G	110595	*Quartermasters*	
Farnan M G *MBE TD• BSc(Hons)*		Speers M A	10196		
AFIMA	10479	Dunn A M	10296	Glass G	*Capt 010196*

314

THE PARACHUTE REGIMENT

Hon Colonel .Col B M De L Cazenove *TD* 4 PARA(V) 310799

Colonels

Power J C *TD•• BA(Hons) MRCGP
MIEE FIEETE CDipAF FIMGT* rcds
hcsc(J)   10495
Campbell D J *FCIS FIMGT MIPR*
psc aic   311298
Ackroyd C E H *TD RD*   250900

———

Lieutenant Colonels

Hodges N P *TD MIPM* tacsc   11189
Tanous C D W *TD••• MIPR* tacsc
                                              10195
Kemp F C *FRGS IEng MIHT MIET
FCIPD* psc   150595
Cave S D *TD• BSc(Hons) PhD
CBiolMIBiol* tacsc   40396
Bowden P L *TD• BSc(Hons)* tacsc
                                               61296
Munro R T I tacsc   10498
Quarendon B L *TD•* tacsc   11100
Evason P C   10401

Majors

Whitley P J *TD*   10586
Harris-Ward L *MBE TD* tacsc 10287
Turner S V *TD*   11087
Bellairs S J *TD•* tacsc   10588
Skinner P N *LLB(Hons)* tacsc 30289
McFadyen D Y A   11089
Stott T *TD BEd(Hons) DipHE*
                                              10792
Osborne J *TD*   10992

Nichols M J   20395
Young P J sq(V)   90495
Brown R H   310396
Jordan W M *TD*   30896
McAuslan I A   300996
Bird D W S   40298
French H G *BSc(Hons) MSc* tacsc
                                             11098
Harwell D S   10299
Humphrey P R M *TD*   10799
Reynolds D J   291099
Burrows N J   10100
Beckett M A   10200
Porteous C J *DipTechEd*   80200

Captains

Goldspink R I   280182
Crowther N M   110184
¶Tosh T   10983
¶Collier G   290184
¶Cotton M P   270687
Ratcliffe L *TD*   100392
Duff H M   61192
Channon I P   280993
Howe S J   231193
McMillan B A   161293
Petersen M J   110594
Southall D T L   101294
Merrylees J W   10595
Neil A J L   10595
Newman J M M   100996
Macauley D A   60497
Manfred M   20797
Mahoney K J   170897
Witty B T *BSc(Hons)*   280897

Copcutt N R   11197
Meredith J C *DCM*   10198
Okeefe K F   270198
Wharton T A F   240398
Mitchell P T   280199

Lieutenants

Lovegrove P M *BSc ARICS* 180695
Horne A P *BSc(Hons)*   120696
Phillips S M   120696
Clarke A J   250996
Pilling L D   300698
Ross K S   30898
Porter N J   40898
Duncan D R   40299
Winter G Q   150699
Nelson M C   210699
Eves G   310101
Purdon G J   310101

2nd Lieutenants

†Owen R M   130699
Ingledew J W   10899
†Shorter N A   40600
Newcombe S   60800

Administrative Officers
Captains

Smith C A W   240397

Quartermasters

Boyle F   *Capt 300999*

315

ARMY AIR CORPS

7 Regiment Army Air Corps (Volunteers)

Hon Colonel .Col *The Duke of* Westminster *OBE TD DL TACSC* 010196

Lieutenant Colonels	
Slessor A J R *BA(Hons)* psc ph	
	290399
Beaver P E	10800
Majors	
Manning G *TD* ph	10491
Stewart B P B *BA(Hons)* ph(i) ph	
	300992
Terry M C ph	300993
Green M A *TD* ph	230594
ØRobb A J *TD*	10694
Lawrence C sq ph	10396
ØStudholme P S *BA(Hons)* tacsc	
	250896
Hampton C M F *TD* ph	10697
ØNewcourt A F M *TD BA(Hons)*	
	70399
Gordon D S *BA(Hons) MA*	11299
Gordon A D ph(i) ph	101200
Captains	
Skinner D J sq ph	201269
Moore T D *MC* ph(i) ph	20573
Taylor-Roberts A B sq ph	251173
Hyde-Smith C S psc ph(i) ph	
	290474

Sample M W ph	310776
Holden R E	240377
Abbott F P *TD* ph(cfs) ph	280477
Leslie J psc(PAK) ph	300777
Twist R W *BA(Hons)* psc† ph	
	280878
Gilderson R P D ph(cfs) ph(i) ph	
	50279
Munro R M sq ph sq(w)	
	40479
Talbot N *BSc* ph tp	40879
Evans I C ph	60879
Hodgson R P	110280
Chinneck P J E *BM DAvMed DIH*	
AFOM ph	180482
Salisbury J	270983
Adams-Cairns I M ph	250484
Woods J D ph	90784
Gill C ph	150984
Aungiers R G ph	180685
Sheldrake R G *TD* ph	290486
Jarvill M K ph	20187
Hennah R D *BSc(Hons)* ph	250687
Sapper M *BSc(Hons)* ph	141287
Mitchell A E M ph	130688
Fergusson A *BLE* ph(cfs) ph(i) ph	
	80888
Fortune D V ph	11190
Bacon G A *MBE BEd* pl	270191

Pratt J C R ph	250391
Grogono J G B	220292
Morley C J ph	100392
King M A	140492
Dalgliesh J D A	160892
Bell I J ph(i) ph	20992
Roche P J ph	240393
Woods D R C ph(i) ph	290393
Cox B J *AFC* ph(cfs) ph(i) ph	
	10493
Morgan J V	170593
Ashwell M ph	10893
Shafto J R ph	70993
Deer A L ph	301093
Short R J K ph	141293
Dann N C *BSc(Hons)* ph	230194
Wood R H ph	60694
Neil R A	180894
Banham R V	170795
Walker D A ph	11195
Markey W R	81295
Bather N W	191295
Shoobridge I *AFM*	220296
Kennard J L ph	60698
Fanshawe W D ph	20300
Lieutenants	
Snell I M	240595

ROYAL ARMY CHAPLAINS' DEPARTMENT

Chaplains to the Forces (3rd Class)
ranking as Majors

Hughes A Rev *TD•*	200982
Herve J A Rev *TD BA DPS PGCE*	11282
Blakey S A Rev *BSc BD*	310883
Grey R T Rev *TD BA*	250784
Barclay I C Rev *TD MA MPhil MTh*	180385
Hathaway D A G Rev *TD•*	260286
Sutch C D Rev *TD•*	160486
Crawley D Rev	30986
Wilkinson S E Rev *TD BA(Hons) CTH*	30986
Taylor J P Rev *TD*	201287
Scott J P Rev *TD BA(Hons) MA DipTh*	11288
Forsyth A R Rev *TD BA MTh*	160289
Latimer D Rev	240389
Pugh J H Rev *RMN CTS SEN*	141189
Douglas A V Rev *BEd*	161189
Punshon K Rev *TD MA JP*	50591
Payne R S Rev	120691
Thomson J M A Rev *BD THM*	170792
Warwick I C Rev *BD*	50992
Calder R P Rev	171292

Wall N J Rev	90493
Ward W E Rev	10593
McVeigh S Rev	30793
Smith K R Rev	70993
Godfrey S H M Rev	120194
Fayle D C W Rev *CertEd CTH*	120494
Butt W A Rev *MIMGT MRIP MRIRM*	200594
Francis P T Rev *BA(Hons) CTH*	170894
Thompson J I Rev	11194
Hamilton J F Rev	260195
Chester M Rev *BA(Hons)*	250895
Stone P J Rev *BA(Hons) MA*	10196
Van Os S W Rev *BA BD*	290496
Darbyshire B Rev *BA*	120696
Fanning P N Rev *BA(Hons) BD CertEd*	280896
Buckley D R Rev	121096
Kerr P T Rev	201196
Sutton J J E Rev	200997
Kinsey L Rev *BD*	50298
Reindorp D P E Rev	280298
Humphreys J R Rev	10698
Bearn H W Rev *MA DLO*	90499
Bloxam-Rose S F Rev	160799
Farmer S J Rev	30300
Eaton D A Rev	220400
Freeman K F Rev *BSc(Ed)*	170600
Ingham A W Rev	80900

Chaplains to the Forces (4th Class)
ranking as Captains

Jackson R B Rev	230491
Dent R W Rev *BA CertEd*	290791
Jennings J P Rev *BA(Hons) CTH*	151093
Blewett T J Rev *BA(Hons)*	190695
Hope C H Rev *MA BA(Hons) FRGS*	31195
Whitehead P C Rev	81195
Grainger I Rev	130396
ØLewis R V C Rev	50896
Cuttell J C Rev	10297
Myatt F E Rev	10497
ØWinfield F J L Rev	220797
Parker P V Rev	11197
Burke C M Rev	90698
Craven C P Rev	170798
Robertshaw J S Rev	10898
Herbert D A Rev	10998
Lowe A Rev	150499
O'Shea R J Rev *TD*	220599
Callan-Travis A Rev	10699
Gamble I R Rev	70200
Gullidge P M N Rev	70200
Lodwick S H Rev	70200
Cook S Rev	60300
Henwood G R J Rev	170700

THE ROYAL LOGISTIC CORPS

Hon Colonels Territorial Army . . . . . . .Mr D E Rayner *CBE* 010492
Maj Gen C E G Carrington *CB CBE* ret pay 020992
Maj Gen M L Wildman 030293
Col N A Johnson *OBE TD* 040493
Mr B E Toye *JP* 260494
Col A E W Stormer ret pay 290694
The Rt Hon The Baroness Chalker *of Wallasey* .010195
Brig M W Betts *CBE* ret pay 010495
Brig R M Bullock *CBE* ret pay 010495
Col C J Constable ret pay 010495
Brig R H T Kirby *CBE* ret pay 010495
Col I W B McRobbie *OBE TD DL* 010495
Lt Col D K Helm *MBE TD* 130695
Col D S Hall *CBE TD* 010895
Mr T W Boyd *DL* 200995
Brig C B Telfer *CBE* ret pay 241195
Brig R N Lennox *CBE* ret pay 010196
Col P S Walton ret pay 010196
Lady Victoria Leatham *DL* 010496
Maj Gen J D MacDonald *CB CBE DL* ret pay 010796
Maj Gen D L Burden *CB CBE* ret pay 010896
The Rt Hon A B Baldry *MP* 011096
The Rt Hon Sir Malcolm Rifkind *KCMG QC* .021196

Colonels

McRobbie I W B *OBE TD•• DL*
tacsc 270791
Hughes M J N *TD•• BSc* tacsc
160493
Astbury J *TD• BSc* tacsc 211194
Morrow E M *TD••• FCIPD* 10497
Sheen M J *TD BEd MA FRSA* tacsc
10499
ØOliver D M *TD DipPR(CAM)*
MA(Hons) MIMGT MIPR tacsc
31299
Hood R A *TD• PhD* tacsc 250700

Lieutenant Colonels

Shawley G J *TD•••• * tacsc 10484
Hughes R D L *TD••• BA(Hons)* tacsc
10488
Lees T *TD• MA MIMGT MILOG*
tacsc 10689
Waite-Roberts E G *TD•• ACIB* tacsc
11191
Brewer N *TD• MA MCIT MILOG*
10792
Smith M L *MBE* 10493
Laird R J *TD BSc(Hons) MIMechE*
CDipAF MIPC NADC(V) tacsc sq
31094
Hambleton R C *TD•* tacsc 71194
Aindow P J *MBE TD• GRADIPD*
MIPD JP 10495
Bonney N A *TD* 10495
Castle R C *MIMGT MILOG MIPD*
MILAM 10495
Watt W A *TD•• BA ACII* 10496
O'Brien T N *TD* tacsc 50397
ØCampbell-Hayes C M *TD• BA ALA*
tacsc 10497
Hamilton A A D *TD• BEd CertEd*
FISM tacsc 10497

Wilmshurst N R *MSc MCIT MILOG*
sq t 10497
Whittaker J F 11197
Aickin R M *TD• BSc(Hons) PhD*
MRSC ACII tacsc 11297
Caley K L *LLB(Hons)* 10498
Ettinghausen S L *BSc MIHT* tacsc
10498
Mathias D A t 10498
Williams R G psc(a) 150998
Hawkins J H A tacsc ato 10499
McCoig M J *TD• ATD DipAD MCIH*
10499
Stanford G F *TD* tacsc 10499
Whittaker T P *BA BSc(Hons) MBA*
10499
Page R C *TD MBA DMS MIMGT*
10799
Sykes J P *TD* 10799
ØPitt L J *TD* tacsc 120999
Barnes A F *TD BSc(Hons) DPODM*
DipHSM tacsc 10400
Roberts P J S *TD* 10400
Sanders D A *TD BA BSc(Hons) PhD*
CEng MIEE tacsc 10400
Bingham K K 10900
Palmer D M *TD MCIM* 10900
Goulding N W S *TD MSc* tacsc
11000
Robinson M J *TD BEd DipEd*
CertEd CertMGMT CertEd
11000
Wilkinson N W *TD MBA* tacsc
10101
Deighton P *TD* 10401
ØKing E J *TD•* tacsc 10401
Limb M S *TD FRGS* tacsc 10401

Majors

Kennerley P M *RD FRICS* 141075
Burton D R *TD•••• ACIB* tacsc
10179

Dempster I F *TD••* tacsc 10479
Betts G A *TD MIMGT MILOG*
MLIA(DIP) sq 300980
Davidson A *BA(Hons) CertEd*
121081
Tillotson G *BSc(Hons) MIExpE*
psc(a)† ato 80182
Budworth G M sq 10482
Neville I H R sq lcc t 210682
Kane D J *TD•• MIPD* 21082
Naysmith P A R *TD•• ACIB* tacsc
11183
Baker P W *TD* tacsc 130185
Butler J M *TD• MSc PhD* tacsc
10585
Sutherland A D *TD•* 210585
ØCarnson S F *TD• BA(Hons) FRGS*
ALA MIINFSc tacsc 10686
Williamson P *MBA* psc ato o
150786
Naqvi R H *TD• LLB(Hons) MIMGT*
tacsc 10187
Beevers C A *TD ACIB* tacsc 20487
Miller A J *MSc MCIT MILOG* sq t
270487
Coggon S H *TD••* 81087
Chapman J M *TD• FCIT MILOG*
11287
Woodland N *TD• BSc(Hons) MIPD*
10488
Appleton N I F *DipTPM PGDA* sq t
120488
Cooper C J *TD* 10688
Thwaite M C *MIMGT* S s 50788
Duffell C G *TD•• BSc CEng MICE*
MIHT 11088
Jones I E *BA(Hons) MSc GRADIPD*
AIMGT FISM MIPD sq
11088
McKay F *TD• MIIA* 10489
ØMorters J *TD• BA(Hons) MSc* tacsc
10489
Smethurst C R *MSc GRADIPD* ato
im 80689

Green M F T *BSc(Hons)* tacsc sq(V)	80190
Carter B W	10490
¶Hunt J	10490
Lane R *TD BA FCII* tacsc pi	10490
Smith R J *TD• MSc IEng FIMI FCIT MILOG FIDIAGE MIMechIE*	10490
¶Pether M J o s	50490
Mahanty A *MBE MBA MSc* psc(CAN)	21090
Cloke S R	11290
Kings A F	20191
Parry S J *MSc* im o pi	260191
ØArmstrong F C *TD BSc(Hons)*	10491
ØBarker S A *TD BEd(Hons) MA*	10491
Cockbill P J *TD*	10491
Inman D T *TD• MIPR*	10491
Forsythe D M *UD* tacsc	300491
Markwick T A	120891
ØJoyner S M *BSc(Hons) DPS* tacsc	11091
ØBuchanan C M	11191
ØBensaid K E *TD MA VetMB MRCVS* tacsc	11291
Stead K *TD•* tacsc	170392
Waller G R *TD• MICM*	170392
Schofield V T *TD*	10492
Owsley R M *MBE*	30592
Cameron D J	10493
Wilmowski W P *TD•*	10493
Fox R J *BA(Hons)* tacsc	50493
Goble E *TD*	50493
¶Ryan M J	50493
Browne N P *TD* tacsc	120793
Owen C L *BSc(Hons) MSc CEng* ato EOE sq(w)	150793
Logan A D *TD*	161093
Wilson J D tacsc	311093
Dixon S G *TD•* tacsc	11193
Hassall M J *TD*	270294
Cowan N *TD•*	280394
ØCarson S M *TD• BSc FRICS FCIArb*	10494
Davison G M *TD•• FCIT*	10494
Poole D N J *TD• BD MA FRGS MIL I*	10494
ØStocks J R *BA*	10494
Taverner J H E *TD BSc*	200494
Cinnamon R *TD BSc(Hons) AMIMechE MCIM*	300494
Holder E R *TD* tacsc	210694
Adams M *BSc(Hons)*	10994
Evans N G *TD FIBMS*	11194
Gray J D H	21194
Little M R *BA PGDA* sq t	81194
Terheege T R *TD*	270395
Allwood R J *TD*	10495
Liddle T S	10495
ØTudor S J *TD ALAM*	10495
Whitty W J *TD•*	10495
Young R F *TD*	10495
Halus K F *TD•* tacsc	20495
Macnab C *PGDA* t	300995
Kitney W R tacsc	61195
Creedican P J W	251195
Austin W J *TD* tacsc	201295
Nisbet K R *TD*	10196
Gritton M J D ato	290296
Buckingham M B J	10496
ØChambers K *BSc(Hons)*	10496
Jones T F *TD BSc(Hons)*	10496
Parrott D W *TD BSc(Hons)*	10496
Underwood J S *TD*	10496
ØWilkinson C M *TD*	10496
Ciotti M *PGDA* t	60696
ØSmith S D *TD GRADIPD*	10896
Arnold R L	60197
Seal T J tacsc	220197
White I A	30297
Moynham D *TD BSc(Hons) LRSC*	310397
Coleman S J	10497
Easton D	10497
Fidgeon M C	10497
Goddard A C	10497
Hankinson I C *BEd*	10497
Keyte S J	10497
Louis D J *MBA*	10497
ØMcParlin P I *TD DipEd CertEd*	10497
Thorpe J	10497
Herriott M W *BSc(Hons) MIMGT FHCIMA*	10697
ØStonehouse S A *TD BA(Hons) DipAD* tacsc	120697
Fergus W	10797
Randall P N *TD*	181097
Bennett S W *TD MBA* tacsc	11197
Urquhart D S *TD BA(Hons) MSc MCIT*	21197
St John C J	101197
Baldry I R	11297
Tween K N ato	10198
Waterston A J	10398
Fraser Ker N	290398
Hoad A S	10498
McDonnell I M	10498
ØShaw A M *TD MA*	10498
White M F *TD BSc(Hons) MBCO*	10498
ØThomas C M J *BSc(Hons)*	300698
ØWatt J C *BSc(Hons)*	300698
Cairns P S	111098
Harris R C A	100199
McBride C *TD*	140299
ØFalcon A H *BSc(Hons)*	270299
ØAllen J P *BEd(Hons) DipTEFL AIPD*	10499
ØCattermull J A *BA(Hons)*	10499
Lucas J D *TD BSc ABIAT*	10499
Parsons M P *TD*	10499
¶Everitt M W	10799
Morris C P	10799
Scales J A	10799
Dickinson S B	10899
Colligan B M	101099
Fenton C A	181099
Barron A G	151199
Holt N C *TD ACIB*	10200
ØChadderton Z	80200
Doherty P J	80200
ØMorgan K S s	80200
ØParry S A	80200
Forbes A	280200
Gallagher J P	310300
Price B S *DipTPM BSocSc(Hons) PGDA* sq t	90400
Burn R *TD*	240600
O'Connell P	260600
Cobbett W P	150700
Martin N F *DPH*	150700
White J *TD* tacsc	150700
Sainsbury D J *TD*	170700
Kabia I S	10800
Baldwin B J S A	10900
Hurley I M *MBE DipTPM PGDA* sq owc t	171000
Ashley D A	271000
Kekewich H C	121100
Higgs J H *BA(Hons) MA* jssc	10101
Scott D H	270101
Barnes S C P	70201
Bilton R W *BSc(Hons) ARICS*	10401
Blake R T	10401
Carey T	10401
Carson A	10401
Duff M T	10401
Handyside J pi	10401
Macdougall N S I *BA*	10401
Macpherson G R *BSc MITSA DTS*	10401
Mitchell S J	10401
Puckey D J *BA(Hons)*	10401
ØSnell C M *MBE BA(Hons) PGCE*	10401
ØWilson L M *TD*	10401

Captains

Tuhey K M F *TD• BA(Hons) MINSTAMDip ACP PGCE LCGI*	10678
Ritchie B D *MSc* dis ato im sq(w)	160981
¶Orr R	300182
¶Gill P J *MBE MIMGT*	160982
Lawson D N sq	300982
French D J *TD MBA*	10483
¶Thompson A T	160583
Saer J M H *MILAM* qs	21183
Wallace A R *QGM* ato o sq(w)	61283
¶McCorkell J *MBE*	21185
Hill S G	231286
¶Rowley J	250687
Edmonds P S pi	10188
Price J R *TD•*	10388
Young A	170388
Stevens N J	270488
Stanley J J	90788
Rayer J E	210788
Taylor P S ato	200289
¶Collins J	10389
Barwick G P *TD*	10489
Jones W *TD MICW*	170689
McFarling P S	11289
Johns K I	250190
Simpson M *MBE*	310390
McArthur A *TD•*	180490
Fairclough T H	20590
ØDixon F M *TD BA(Hons)*	80990
ØClubley S T	10291
Quinn K A	230491
Dean A J	10591
McBain A F	50591
Alexander S C	140691
ØHackford A A *BSc(Hons)*	190691
Pascoe J M	220891
Allport A	280991
Tarr E J	110192
Vooght C	160192
ØStevenson J A *MHCIMA*	220192

Ashburner D J	30392
Bullock R H	10492
Lay S J *BSc(Hons)*	10492
Nicholas W H M	10492
Ward J P *TD BA*	10492
Aveyard B	120492
ØForbes L M *BSc(Hons)*	90892
Brooks D	50992
Parrott W J *MA ACA*	110193
Boles R F	10393
Harrison P A	10493
Young P	10493
Collinson M N J *BA(Hons) MISM*	
	50493
Everton M W *MBE*	50493
ØHall F J *TD BEd(Hons)*	50493
ØEdwards S P J	60493
Parker N B	90493
Scott D C	10693
¶Standen K *MBE*	210693
Heyes S M *BSc(Hons) CEng*	
MIMechE	300693
Hill K A K	240793
Chapman C M	10993
Francey P D	11093
McGrath P T	141093
ØCrozet C P	221093
ØBankier K F	11293
Harrison S	31293
Waddington A I	51293
Gorringe E G A	160294
Rayson S W *TD BA(Hons) MILOG*	
	90394
Greenough K C	280394
Harrison M A *BA(Hons)*	70894
Holmes C M	10994
Pearce A T	60994
Bedford B S J	50195
Briggs G E	90195
Croft A P	100195
Davies R J	10295
Strickland A J	130295
Windas W R	310395
Curtis C	10495
ØGardner V C *BA(Hons)*	20495
Gaudoin J P *ACIB*	200595
Thomas H A D	200595
ØFerguson M A *TD*	10695
Egan S B	11095
Batty P	31095
Gough A C	231095
Messervy S M *BSc ARICS*	11195
Baker N G *ABIAT*	181195
ØFitton J A	191195
ØPanton S I *BSc(Hons) MA DipLA*	
ALI	121295
ØRasor J L *BA(Hons)*	151295
Moore A C	30196
ØBrowne K L *BSc*	140196
Gilbard P S	10496
Newman S	10496
ØParsons K L	10496
Riches S M	10496
Turkington W J *BA(Hons)*	10496
Fox J D	300496
ØLack S L E L	210596
Driver I M	10696
ØSymon R C *BA(Hons)*	290896
Conrad S J	130996
Cutler G D	191096
ØTerry R J	11196
Walker S D	11196

Jacobs R R	211196
Forsyth W	100297
Hall J E	30397
ØLaughton S E *BSc(Hons)*	100397
Macintosh N C	10497
Roberts I R	10497
Soutar I	10497
Cave J O	10597
Dugan D R	10697
Miller K C *BA(Hons)*	10697
Walsh C J	10797
Griffiths P	70897
Broadbent R J R	210997
Bolton G A	11097
ØThompstone D J *jssc*	161097
ØLawrence C L	11197
Metcalf G J	31197
Gotobed P M	271197
Withers R G	10198
ØRanson J L	50198
Evans S P	310198
ØByers S J M	10298
Bruce S D	100298
Schermuly A C	100298
Wilcox J J	160398
Brough F C	10498
Black G	10598
Draisey G M	70698
ØFoden-Ellis A C	290898
McLees S D	11098
Charlton K D *BEng(Hons) MEng*	
	221098
Smy G B	81298
McSpadden R M	201298
Boyle S	70199
ØBryan H J	300199
ØDixon C A	10499
Lee A C S	120599
Sykes C J	200599
Henderson D A	10799
Ward A G S	10799
ØThrower C H *BSc(Hons)*	160899
ØEdwards H R	10999
Matthews T J *CertMGMT LCGI*	
	10999
Morris W G	10999
Bradley D F	160999
Drain S E	11099
Johnstone R J M	61199
Grinton I	90100
ØGlasswell N *BSc(Hons) MSc*	
	150100
Layton M E	10400
O'Driscoll W	10500
Platt A A	100600
Drewett S P *BSc(Hons)*	150700
ØMcGill F C	210700
Ramsden P A	11200
Byers G A S	21200
Montgomery J S	21200
Afendoulis P S *TD AMILOG*	111200
Harley S D	310101
Gomes L L *TD*	10401
Reynolds A G	10401

Lieutenants

Dorins H L	151287
Archer G R H	160288
Malaure R S *BSc(Hons) PhD*	
	220588
Marshall J P	120789
Macleod I	50890

Crichton R J	240692
Aitchison C I	131092
ØChandler L	130793
Boucher B C	40893
Hallett T D	170993
Adams J C O	31193
Kiehlmann M H *BSc*	51293
Jones V S	200294
Clubley B M	220594
Scrivens L A *BSc(Hons) ARICS*	
	50694
Smith S G	150795
Moran F B	60895
Roberts C J	101195
Young I A	10696
Warrack C A S	300696
ØKirkbridge K D	310796
ØWoodman S	310796
Tremelling R T *BSc(Hons)*	220297
French A G	80497
Collier G L	210497
Larard M F	10697
†Heal G D	50697
Urding R	160697
Bell P M	60897
Kempson G E *BA(Hons)*	21097
Brown N	101297
Lewthwaite J D	50698
ØEvanson-Goddard L F	300698
Stewart J C	300698
Harris D F	70798
McGuinness A	30898
Little A	40898
Schofield N L	40898
ØSharp B A	130998
ØEdwards A C	181198
†Gray A J	41298
†Daddow M P	120199
Lupton R T	120199
Theobald W P	50399
Aitken A M	150699
Evans D J	150699
McCarthy K J	30899
Thomas C K	30899
†Fraser R G	170999
†Jepson D J	270999
ØSapwell C J *BSc(Hons)*	161099
†Punshon D E	51199
Bouttell C D	110100
Morfitt S J	110100
Richardson A M	110100
ØWilson J *BA(Hons)*	260100
Gane T I	140200
ØGardner L P	10300
Smith N T	290300
Atkins M	10400
Hill C A	10400
†Gill M J	280400
†McNairn M S	150500
Lydon J J	140600
†Beaton A D	210700
Allen A H *BA(Hons)*	20800
Wing B D	20800
†Driscoll P S	40800
†Keenan I *BEM*	150800
†Stephenson W N	150800
†Thomas P N	220800
†Mitchell G A *BEM*	130900
†Hinton A	81100
†Pountney N D	81200
†Deck M D	181200
†Hilton J *MBE*	251200

Paget D W	310101	
†Ward M	140201	
†Thornley K	260201	

2nd Lieutenants

†Harper G	60895
†Russell K R	141197
ØKendrick R L	20798
Filewod T E	80998
Jackson B J	270998
Worrow S D	10199
Aikman D A	130699
†Greenway I J	140699
Hardy G W	10899
ØCranshaw A J	260999
†Goodwin I R C	260999
†Hike C L	260999
†Cooney A M	60800
†Eagers A M	60800
ØGraham A L *BEng(Hons)*	60800
†Gibbs A	11000
†Farrar R	31100
†Ord C	50101
†Bennett A P	180201
†Constance S	180201

Administrative Officers
Captains

Lynch J F	60193
Moreton P P	90993

Ravera A T G	110196	
Cook L L	20797	

Quartermasters

Kelly J R *TD• MCIT Maj 080894*		
		130584
Jarrett K J	*Capt 291084*	
Eden R	*Lt Col 010499*	180585
Milne A	*Capt 090386*	
Bradley M *TD Maj 010497*	200887	
Hunter W J *BEM Maj 111296*		
		10888
McEwen T A G	*Capt 150988*	
Kane R	*Maj 041096*	81288
Warke R N	*Maj 220697*	221288
Smith D S *TD Capt 030389*		
Jones I T *MISM MILOG ASPS*		
	Maj 290797	310389
Roche M J *Maj 201197*	180989	
Burns A A *QGM MIExpE*		
	Maj 260697	10390
Terriza G J *Maj 120798*	10490	
Fowles R G *Maj 290399*	41090	
McGrath P D *Maj 060899*	51290	
Walsh P M *DMS Maj 101298*		
		101290
McKnight R A	*Capt 010591*	
McDowell R J	*Capt 120591*	
Wilson T C *HCITB-INSTR*		
	Maj 221198	140691

Reece K F	*Maj 280201*	
Howard M	*Maj 121098*	10192
Anspach A J *MHCIMA Maj010589*		
		20192
Gallagher D J	*Capt 130392*	
Halsall A J	*Capt 010492*	
Robinson G	*Capt 104922*	21200
McCarthy D J	*Capt 111192*	11092
Wilson D G *TD• Capt 010193*		
Dunn A M *MLIA(DIP) Capt 050493*		
Rowles G R	*Capt 151290*	60493
Connolly J	*Capt 060395*	
Banyard P F	*Capt 120495*	
Beatty I A	*Capt 240795*	
Cahill M	*Capt 121095*	
Austin F	*Capt 140196*	
Whatley J N	*Capt 070296*	
Marlow M D	*Capt 230596*	
Oflanagan A F	*Capt 010696*	
Blowers T	*Capt 270696*	
Cooper J H	*Capt 180697*	
Rowe M P	*Capt 151197*	
Downey J O	*Capt 211197*	
Docherty E A	*Capt 280298*	
Lovell D	*Capt 080598*	
Moore I	*Maj 020199*	10199
Swift P M *MBE ato Maj 241100*		
		10199
Bingham C R	*Capt 010299*	
Maguire B C	*Capt 010400*	10499
Dalby D J	*Capt 010200*	

ROYAL ARMY MEDICAL CORPS

Hon Colonels . . . . .Col J Egan *OBE OStJ TD* 010395
Brig *The Rt Hon The Lord* Vivian 010495
Col P J F Baskett 010196
Col L J Hipkin *TD* 011096
Col C M Gwynn *OStJ TD* 010997
The Honourable Neil Turner 101097
Mrs K E Thomas *JP DL* 110598
Col D W Herring *TD* 010898
Lt Col J A Dunbar *TD* 191098
Col D J L Carson *OStJ TD* 080299
Prof *Sir* Miles Irving 010399
Brig G R B Jones *OBE TD* 290499
Brig M J Ratcliffe *OStJ* 011099
Brig M H Daley 290500
Maj Gen *Sir* Iain McKay-Dick 201200

Colonels

Bremner A D *TD QHS MB ChB DCH DObstRCOG* 21179
Jones J J *TD• MB ChB* 300983
Young C J *TD MSc MRCOG MRCS LRCP FRCOG* tacsc 11185
Jones G R B *OBE TD•• QHP MB BCh FRCPEd MRCS LRCP* 11188
Newsome D A *TD• MB ChB MRCP(UK) FRCP* tacsc 11089
Feggetter J G W *MB BS FRCS* tacsc 60491
Walker N J P *OBE TD MB BCh BAO MRCGP MICGP* tacsc 10791
Chandler G P *TD••• MB ChB FRCOG* tacsc 61092
Cox C W F M *TD• MB BS FRCSEd MRCOG FRCSED* tacsc 61093
Gallagher P *MB ChB BSc FRCS* tacsc 61093
Murphy R J *TD MB BCh BAO DA DRCOG* tacsc 61093
Smith M F *TD••• MA ChM MB BA(Hons) FRCSEd* tacsc 10194
Young J R *TD• MB ChB FRCS DLO* tacsc 20194
Herring D W *TD•• QHS MBBS FRCS FRCS(Eng)* tacsc 10794
ØJohnston H M L *TD MB BCh BAO FRCA* tacsc 250695
Robertson B *TD• MRCS LRCP* 10995
Robertson I G *OBE TD•• MD MBChB BSc FRCOG* tacsc 11095
Freeman J W *TD QHS MB ChB MRCP MRCP(UK) FRCA* 11096
Mixer P R *TD• MB BS MRCGP DCH DRCOG* tacsc 111196
Maguire M J *TD• MBBChir BA FRCP* tacsc 40197
Bowler G M R *TD MB ChB FRCA* tacsc 10297
Paterson R M *MBChB* 290897
Gill K J *MBChB FFARCSEng* tacsc 10199
Wignall J B W *MB ChB BSc* tacsc 80299
ØHeber M E *TD•• MD BS MRCP MRCS FRCP* tacsc hcsc(J) 10500

Lieutenant Colonels

Roberts J D A *MRCS LRCP MIMGT* 290180
Stanworth P A *TD••• BM BCh FRCS DCH* 10782
Shepherd W F I *TD• MB BCh BAO FRCSEd DO* 10483
Hawkins T J *TD•• MB BS FRCA DA* tacsc 161283
Johnson M K *TD• MB ChB FRCA* 10884
Stenson K *TD MB BS MRCGP MRCS LRCP DObstRCOG* 130884
Ryan J M *MCh MBChB BAO FRCS* 120185
Wilson C R M *TD••• MB BS MRCPsych DPM* 40385
Hamilton J B *TD MB BCh BAO FRCSEd* 311085
Murray D P J *TD BA MRCP(UK) DipVen CMS* 10286
Tallents C J *TD MB BS FRCS LMCC DO* 51286
Cove P *TD• LRCP LRCS* tacsc 61286
Sherriff H M *MBBCh FRCSED* 80187
Ducker D A *TD MRCP* 10787
Evans D H C *MB BS FRCA DObstRCOG DTM&H* 291087
Reid A R *TD MB ChB DIH MFOM* 11287
Ireland B J *TD•••• MB BCh BAO MRCGP DA DObstRCOG* 10688
Hedges J R *MB BS MRCS MRCGP MRCP(UK)* tacsc 301088
Rosenberg B C *TD• MB BCh BAO MRCOG DObstRCOG* 10189
Whiting B H *MB ChB MRCGP DRCOG* 30289
Olver J J *TD MB BS FRCA* 210289
Macintosh K C *TD• MB ChB FRCA* tacsc 10389
Peyton J W R *TD• BSc(Hons) MD BCh BAO MRCP(UK) FRCSEd* tacsc 10589
Ghosh A K *TD• MB BS DTM&H DipVen* tacsc 10490
Capps S N J *TD• MB BS BSc FRCS* 311090
O'Callaghan E G *TD MB BCh BAO DObstRCOG* 311090

Housam G D *CD MBChB BA(Hons) FRCP(C) FRCA* 60491
Moore J W A *MB BS DRCOG* 131191
Brooman I C *TD FRCGP* tacsc 61092
De Mello W F *DipIMCRCSEd MB BS DA DRCOG FRCA* 260293
Matthews S J E *MBBS FRCS LRCP FRCSED* 10893
Hamilton A J *TD• MB BS FRCS FRCSEd FRCOG LRCP* tacsc 61093
Thomson N S *TD MB ChB MRCP* tacsc 11193
Goulbourne I A *ChM MBChB BSc FRCSED* tacsc 10794
Nag S K *MBBS* tacsc 11194
Waterworth T A *MBBS LRCP FRCS(Eng) MRCS* 21095
Jowitt M D *MRCS LRCP DA* 111195
Randall P J *TD PhD MBBS BMedSci BSc FFARCSEng* 71295
Scott J N *MRCP(UK) MRCPsych FRCPED* 71295
Khan F *MBBS FRCSI LRCP* 310196
May A R L *TD MB BS FRCSEd* 50396
Gilbert P H *MB BCh MRCGP DCH DRCOG* tacsc 10896
Whitton A D C *TD MBChB DRCOG MRCGP* 11096
Ashton J R *MB ChB FRCSED* 71196
Godby C *TD MBChB DRCOG* tacsc 71196
Parnell C J *MB BS FRCA MRCS LRCP* 211296
Bhatnagar D *TD MBBS FRGS MRCPath MRCP* 10197
Ryan P G *MB FRCSED FRCS(Eng)* 10197
Robinson A D T *TD MBChB MRCPSYCH* tacsc 10297
Deahl M P *TD MBBS FRCPSYCH MRCPSYCH* 10397
Palmer R J *BS FRCA MRCS LRCP DA DObstRCOG DRCOG* 10497
Williams R J W *TD MB ChB DPM FRCPSYCH* 10497

Black A J *MB BCh BAO MRCP(UK)* tacsc 10797
Chambers T L *MB BS DObstRCOG FRCPI FRCP FRCPED* 11197
Chand D *MD MBBS DMRD FFR RCS IRE* 11197
Logan J I *MB BCh BAO FRCP FRCPED* 11197
Massam M *TD MB ChB MRCP DCH* tacsc 11197
Haworth E *TD MB ChB MRCP(UK) FRCP* tacsc 10498
Lowe J W *TD MBBS MRCP(UK) FRCPath MRCPath* 10598
Lowe D 150598
North R F *MBChB MRCGP DRCOG* 20798
ØEke A J *MB BS* ph 10898
Hicks I R *MB,BS,BA,DA,MCSP, MCSP,MRCGP,LRCP,MRCP(UK), DRCOG,FFARCS ENG,FRCA,M* 11098
Bennett J D C *MA MB ChB BSc DCH FRCS(Eng)* 131198
ØHamilton A F M *MBChB DRCOG* tacsc 261198
Cope A R *MB BS FRCS MRCS LRCP* 11298
Rew D A *TD MBBS* 11298
Rawlinson P S M *MBChB BSc MIMunE MRCPath MRCP* 71298
Laurence A S *MD MBBChir FFARCSEng* 70299
Tamin J S F *TD MBChB MRCGP DRCOG JCHMT MFOM MIOSH* 70299
Richardson F J *MBChB FRCSED* tacsc 150699
Fok P J *MA MBBChir BA FRCS(Eng)* tacsc 80999
Ward G *MRCS LRCP FRCSED* 11299
Taylor D M 10100
Baker B C *MB ChB MRCGP* 110200
Shieff C L *MBChB FRCSED FRCSE(SN)* 80300
ØAckerman S *MBChB DRCOG FFARCSEng* 100500
Moles I G D *MBBChir MRCGP* 10700
Hayward A P *MB BS MRCGP DRCOG* tacsc 260301

Majors

Dineley G *TD•••• tacsc* 190469
Bell J R *TD• MB ChB FRCSEd* 300377
Frewin T H *TD•• MB ChB MRCS LRCP* 70977
Bishop R *TD• MB ChB* 160878
Reid R J S *MB BCh BAO DRCOG MICGP* 310779
Messing H J *TD• BM BCh DCH DObstRCOG* 150480
Haines D H *TD MRCS DRCOG BDS MRCGP* tacsc 120680
ØCurrie F *TD• MB BCh DRCOG* 10481
Akhtar M J *MB BS FRCPsych DPM DTM&H DipVen FRCPSYCH* 300481

ØBlackburn A M *MD MA MB BChir BA(Hons) FRCP* 240781
Levack I D *TD MD ChB FRCA* 130881
Hedley G S *MB ChB DRCOG* 131081
J ayatilaka M N D P *MS(OBS&GYNAE) MBBS MFFP FRCSED MRCOG* 170382
Groves R C C *MB ChB MRCGP DRCOG* 160982
Cave-Bigley D J *MB BS FRCS LRCP* 61182
Kocan M K *MBChB FFARCSEng* 300183
Mikhael M S H *DEAA MB BS FRCA* 240483
Jenkins J H *MB BS BSc MRCPsych MRCS LRCP* 140983
Dwyer P A *RGN RCNT* 191283
Boreham J J C *TD MRCS DRCOG* 190184
Misra G K *MB ChB* 30284
Hardie R J *TD•• MA MRCP(UK) MD FRCP MRCP* tacsc 10884
Greaves D N J *TD MB ChB DRCOG* 51284
Hannam R C *TD MRCS LRCP BDS* 20585
Dixon C G *MB BS MRCGP DObstRCOG* 200186
Shorten W W J *MB BCh BAO MRCGP DCH DRCOG* 10886
Jackson R G *TD MB ChB MRCGP DRCOG* 71186
Goddard J M *MB BS MRCP(UK) FRCA* 181186
Hirani A *TD MBBS* 30387
Pope A J *TD BSc(Hons) MD MBBS MD(PAED) FRCSED FRCS(Eng)* 210487
Finch M E *MB ChB MRCGP DObstRCOG DObstRCOG DRCOG* 260587
Fram R F *MSSCh MBCHA FISM AIIRSM* 150787
Rai B S *FPCERT* 181287
Giddins G E B *FRCSED FRCS(Eng)* 90188
Weller R M *TD MBBS LRCP FFARCSEng MRCS* 140188
Denton M *MBChB DRCOG* 220388
Hadden W A *BAO FRCSED* 40588
ØO'Sullivan E M *MB BS FRCR MRCS LRCP* 200588
Miller J E *TD MB ChB DA DRCOG DTM&H FPDip MRCGP* 10888
ØKerr M 150888
De Lusignan S *MBBS B Sc (Hons) MRCGP DRCOG* 10988
Aston N O F *MChir MB FRCS LRCP* 30988
Paine S L *FISM JP* 300988
ØYates J *MRPharmS* 300988
Dendy R A *MB BS MRCS LRCP* 41188
Walker S J *MB ChB FRCSED* 10189
Ahmed K *TD MBBS* 170189
Jones-Owen P W *TD MSc FRSH ABPSS MBSECH DCP CPsychOL* 10389

Andrews G M *TD• FIBMS* 10889
Morton I N *MB BS ACLS FPDip MRCGP* tacsc 80889
Purdy G M *MB BCh BAO MRCP(UK) FFARCSIrel* 60989
Knock M A R *MB ChB FRCSEd* 290989
Ewart I C *MB BS* 141189
Volkers R C *MB BS FRCS LRCP* 201289
Gallamore R A J *MRPharmS* 40590
Rajagopal C *MRCGP DCH* 60690
Bellamy D C *MB BS MRCGP* 290690
Bhala B B *MBBS FFARCSIrel* 111090
Firth D A *TD MSc MB ChB MRCPsych DCH MRCPSYCH* 311090
Shrestha K L *TD MBBS MRCPSYCH* 311090
Robinson M J *TD BA MRCS LRCP* 31290
Rahman A K M R *TD MBBS LRC PLRCS LRCPS DORCPI DTM&H DRCOG FPCERT JP* 10391
ØMuttrie P *MB ChB* 100591
Cromie A J *MBBCh* 110691
Hall A W *TD MBChB FRCSED FRCS(Eng)* tacsc 10791
Raja A U K *TD MBBS FRCS(Eng)* 10791
ØHunter-Rowe C K A *TD LRCSI DRCOG* tacsc 310791
ØHeath K J *MBBS BSc FRCA* 10891
Cumiskey F *TD SRN RGN EN(G) BTA* 30891
Morley R *MBBS FRCS(Eng)* 41091
Rai P K *MBBS DCH* 281091
Mahoney P F *TD MBBS DA FRCA FFARCSIrel* 11191
ØDoughty H A *DipPath MB BChir MRCPath* 10292
Bish D M *TD AIBMS* 140292
Clifford A D *MB ChB MRCGP DRCOG* 210392
Strange F *RGN* 60492
Jenkins D M *MB ChB* 200492
Martin M J *MBBS* 10592
ØCampbell B E C *MB BS DRCOG* 80592
Thomas P D *MB BCh* 20792
ØBest W A *MB ChB* 10892
ØPhillips S L *MBBS FRCS(Eng)* 10892
Unwin T A E *MBBS MRCGP* 10892
Scott J A *TD•• MA MB BChir MRCGP DObstRCOG* tacsc 11092
Sharma R C *TD MB BS* 51092
Kelsey C R *MSc MBBS MRCS LRCP MRCP* 230293
Martin S A *ChB* 10493
Sunderland G T *MD MBChB BSc FRCPS(GLAS)* 40693
McEwan G D *MBBCh MRCGP DOBS* 280793
Simons G D *MBBCh BAO LRCP* jsdc 30993
Hugh C C *MRCS LRCP* 80993
Turley J F *MBBS* 270993

ØCross H A *MBChB BMedSci*
DRCOG 11093
Huitson I *RMN RGN* 11093
Fielding P D *BM DCH MRCGP*
131093
Ashok C K *MBBS* 251093
Hockram P J 21193
Sarkar P K *MAO MBChB DRCOG*
MRCOG 21193
Weppner G J *MPhil MBBS*
MRCPSYCH 191193
Morison D D *TD AIBMS* 11293
Lovell M E *MBChB FRCPS(GLAS)*
FRCS(Eng) 10194
Mason C M *MBChB MRCGP* tacsc
90294
Clough D G F *MBChB* 170294
Callaghan N J *LMSSA* 230294
Ishak M K *MBBCh MRCOG*
DObstRCOG MRCOG 230294
Mackey C J *MB BS* 70394
Smith A E *NDN RMN RGN* 290394
Sparks D L *MSRG MCSP SRP*
40494
Byers M *DipIMCRCSEd MBBS DA*
DRCOG MRCGP DRCOG 300494
Ternent T *MBBCh DIH AFOM*
DRCOG 230594
Duckett J R A *MBChB MRCOG*
10894
Mathew M C F *MB BS* 10894
ØStableforth C F *MB ChB FRCA*
10894
Penman D G *MBBS FPCERT*
MRCOG 100894
Stack J J *BA(Hons) RMN RGN RNT*
260894
Guy P S 10994
Templeton P A *MBBCh BAO*
FRCS(Eng) 260994
Sheikh J H *MBBCh BSc MRCP*
251094
ØLewis C L *MBChB MRCP FRCR*
121194
ØSommerville I K M *MBChB DLO*
181194
Studden M C H *MCIEH* 11294
Harrison P M *MD MBBS B Sc*
(Hons) MRCP 10195
Smith M P 210395
ØHaendel A E G *TD MCSP SRP*
100495
Hill J C *MBChB DMRD FRCR*
10695
ØTilsed H R *MBChB FRCS(Eng)*
220895
Hunter R W *MBBCh B Sc (Hons)*
11095
ØDuff C H *BMBCH FPDip MFPHM*
FFPHM 271095
Pape S R *RMN RGN* 61295
Hammond J S *MBBS FFARCSEng*
10196
Mellor I *MBChB FRCSED* 10196
Buxton N *MBChB FRCSED* 250196
Evans G A *MA MBBChir* 90296
McGeehan D F *MBBCh FRCSED*
130296
Anderson I *MBChB MRCGP*
DRCOG 260496
Ramsbotham S E *MBBCh MRCGP*
170596

Myint K *MBBS DO FRCSED*
140696
Bracegirdle A P *MBChB DFFP*
MRCGP DRCOG FHSA FHSA
280696
Hamilton-Davies C 10796
Macleod J *MBChB FFARCSEng*
FRCA 50796
Manickarajah P *FRCPS(GLAS)*
LRCP FRCSED MRCS 70796
Gray P J *MA MB BChir BA FRCSED*
F C OPHTH 250796
Neil J M *MBChB BSc(MED) FRCA*
250796
Pringle A J *MBChB* 10896
Henderson Slater J D E 160896
Chadha J C *MBBS (D T M)* 210896
†Haynes I G *MBChB FRCS(Eng)*
50996
Morrison P A *MBBS FFARCSEng*
200996
Eslea-Macdonald P A *TD* 230996
Pincott R G *MBBS AKC* 260996
Boyd J J *TD* 11096
ØThomis S P *TD• BPharm*
MRPharmS MCPP tacsc 140297
Sandhu P S *MD* 190297
Bonfield C D V *MRSH DN RGN*
EN(G) REMT 10497
ØCadwallader D K B *TD• MIPM*
MECI 10497
McGrath L T *PhD MSc FIBMS*
10497
Eaton D 10597
Yu L F *MBChB MRCP* 140597
Calder J D F *MBBS* 10897
Watson A J M *MBChB BSc(MED)*
120897
Broadman L A *TD* 10997
Nelson P 140997
ØCardwell M E *MBChB* 161097
ØHartington K 11297
Mughal M M *ChM MBChB*
FRCS(Eng) 11297
Maclaren R E *MBChB* 41297
Gray D C *MB ChB* 200198
Banerjee B *MBBS* 10298
Cunningham R S *MBChB DA*
50398
Edgecombe K A F 140498
Williams D J *MBBS FRCS(Eng)*
160498
ØMarshall C A *MBBCh BAO DFFP*
MRCGP MRCOG D C C H 20898
ØPitt E S *MBBCh DFFP MRCGP*
DRCOG 50898
Duff P W *MB ChB DObstRCOG*
81098
Gregson R E *DipEH* 221198
Steel C N *DRCOG* 21298
ØDuggleby K J 10199
Allan J 10299
Morton P C 10299
Bone R G *IEng MIMechIE* 170299
Henman P D *MBChB* 100399
Mathewson K G *MBChB DRCOG*
FRCGP 100399
McAuley J *MBChB ACLS DA(UK)*
DFFP DRCOG 100399
Rigby R C *BMedSci* 100599
Byrne M J P 10699
Singh S *MBBS FFARCSIrel* 280699

Wilson D I *MBBS FRCS(Eng)*
250799
Harrop M 11099
George R J *MBBChir BA(Hons)*
FRCA DCH 61099
Kovar I Z *MBBS* 111099
Keoghane S R *MBBS FRCS(Eng)*
11199
†Crooks M P *MBChB DA(UK)*
MRCGP 91199
Heller D R *MSc MBBS DTM&H*
MRCP MFPHM 261199
Hay The Lord *MBBS DA(UK)*
21299
Walker C P R *MBBS DA(UK) FRCA*
21299
Cooke J C *TD* 51299
Klava A *MBBS* 10100
Pine R C *MBBS LRCP FRCSED*
MRCS 10100
Maxwell-Armstrong C A *MBChB*
FRCS(Eng) 50100
Bruen S M 10400
Cruickshanks D R *MChS DPODM*
10400
Anandan C W R W 170400
Moran J C *TD DipEH DMS* 190400
Kay A R *MBChB FRCS(Eng)* 150600
Strivens V G sq G(ss) 190600
Lynch M R J *MBChB* 290600
ØTreharne L J *MBChB* 20800
Redmill D A *MBBCh* 90800
ØCalder S J *MBChB* 110800
Lockey D J *MBBS* 11000
ØHaywood J *MBChB MRCGP*
11100
Dyke T N *MBChB MRCGP DRCOG*
FRCSED 201200

Captains

Dinnig A W
Whyte P 120681
Hall D L 80881
Mullen C P 240881
¶Barron D J 50284
Donnelly A G 190484
Evans J E F 60185
Dixon W T 280685
Willmott P D 60286
¶Thomson P J 30486
Coker T M 40486
Lequelenec A C *MBE* 40187
Craig G R *BM MB MRCP* 270687
Cox Q G N *MBBS FRCSED*
FRCS(Eng) 10787
Kerr G R *MBBS* 130987
Potter K G 10488
Sharp R S 140588
¶Keary M E *MIPlantE MISM*
110888
McGhee T D *TD* 200888
Short A D 10789
Willatt J M G *BA(Hons)* 10889
Irlam A C *BSc DCH DRCOG*
MRCGP DRCOG FFARCSEng
290989
Exley B M 30390
Galbraith B A *BSc AIBMS* 100990
Rickards C *MD BMBCH MRCP(UK)*
121090

Curphey A R G *MBChB* 151100
Gundabolu S S R 151100
Smith P R *MBBCh* 281100
Taylor R A 11200
Murray J M A 71200
Lavalee P J *MBBS* 121200
Smith S T *MBBS BSc DRCOG*
DA(UK) MRCGP FFARCSEng
151200
Yasin K M 211200
Newton D 30101
Mutalik C *MBBS MRCS* 100101
ØBracebridge S P *MBBS BSc*
MRCGP 170101
ØDutton J A E *SCM MBBS FRCR*
140201
ØCavanagh S A 210201
Lacey J F 10301
Mackenzie Ross R V *MB BChir*
20301

Lieutenants

Lavine M J *TD MB BS MRCS LRCP*
210785
ØReid S 31195
ØBurns L J 221295
ØEvans L A 60396
Willcox M S 120396
ØHall E C *MCSP* 160896
ØGregor N K 90197
Clements R M 190297
Dowey L C 190297
ØAnderson C L *DCR(R)* 40497
Davison P 230797
Nolan S C 250997
ØLeadon K L *RGN* 111097
Hanlon T R G 51197
Williams M E 301297
ØLindsay F E M 20498
†Barnard J B 170798
Hudd A P 170798
Moncaster M G 120998
Buglass R J 131098
Millarvie A J 170399
Dudill W P *MRPharmS* 30599
Holland A J 10699
ØLamb J M 110699
Smith M A 110699
Carter M I 150699
Coleman J J 290699
Melley C R 60799
ØFaun C 110799
†Douglas B M J 160799
†Parker S M 190799
Russell S J *MBBS* 190799
ØWilliams J W J 200799
Kirkpatrick P I *PhC MCPP* 290799
Russell P *CBIOLMIBIOL* 290799
ØScott L M 290799
Davidson B G 150999
ØCrooks L D 290999
ØRedmond R M 290999
Tucker S M 191099
Howley L J 101199
ØBrownhill C 11299
Harding N 71299
ØKent H G 71299
ØNelson S R 71299
Robinson R W L *MCSP* 71299
ØSmith T A 71299
ØHampton D 81299
Raju T 131299

Clark P I C 300100
Barker A P 250200
ØRiley D L 30300
Cockcroft M G 150300
ØWray C L 170300
ØPresswell A C E 100400
Devlin S *FRSH MCSP* 110400
Gentile G 110400
ØLatham V M M *MCSP* 110400
ØMcLenaghan J R *MCSP* 110400
Shardan A M *MCSP* 110400
ØHogg M H *MRPharmS* 120400
Jones G J M 120400
ØSharp J *PhC MRPharmS* 120400
Telford M L *MRPharmS* 130400
ØIllingworth S *MCSP* 200400
ØBlair B A 100500
Maddock I D 100500
Briant-Evans T W *MB BMedSci ChB*
10600
ØBuller V I *DCR(R) DCR(MU)*
40600
Shaw S J *MCSP* 140600
Giles R J 220600
ØCousin R M *MB ChB* 40700
Rahman I A 40700
Heslop L M 100700
Sarkar S N 100700
ØLogie H M A 110700
Sheddan G T 110700
†Humble S R 120700
Roberts M D *MRPharmS* 120700
ØHalliday T K Z 170700
ØFair S M *MBChB* 190700
Johnson C J D *MBChB* 190700
ØOliver J C *MBChB BMedSci*
190700
ØPlunkett E K *MBChB* 190700
Khoo K T J *MBBS* 200700
Moseley G D *MBBS* 200700
ØTapp M L *BMedSci* 200700
Dunbar J A T 210700
ØTaghizadeh R 250700
ØWhite A L *MBChB* 10800
ØGoodchild L M *BSc* 160800
ØMarshall E 160800
Lazenby P 300800
ØCatesby C E *BSc SRP* 130900
ØChattle A R *BSc MCSP* 130900
ØGrey L A 130900
ØLavery K 130900
ØGregory H J 270900
Daking R J 111000
Wood M *BSc* 111000
ØStarkey K J *SRMLT* 191000
ØLamki L *DCR(R)* 211000
Ooi S W *MBChB* 211000
ØWattie H B *MRPharmS* 211000
ØWood R M 251000
ØBushell C *BSc* 151100
Tang A P 151100
Bakere H G *MBBCh* 161100
Savage S J *DCR(MU)* 161100
Whitehead G P *CPSM MCSP* 61200
ØStapley J C *FCSP* 10101
Richards S P *DCR(R) DCR(MU)*
100101
ØWoods S M *MRPharmS* 170101
Eyre J R *MBChB* 260101
ØOrange S J *MCSP* 310101
Mann R C 140201
Jones M G *BSc MCSP SRP* 150201

2nd Lieutenants

ØPerry S J C 30497
Mayall S G 230797
†Casserley R H 310797
ØCousens L C 50997
†Bowdler G R 250398
ØCastille S N 250398
†Clifford D P 250398
†Devadson D S 250398
ØKirbyrobertson L A 250398
†Philpott M C 250398
†Goff I 150498
†Macfarlane G T 20898
ØPhuah M W 40898
†Soo F Y 40898
†Khoo T H 120898
ØGeraghty A K 131098
†Carrothers A D 251198
ØWilliams H S 251198
†Holliman D 190599
ØHelbren E L 130799
†Sigera S R 240899
ØNagra I 230999
†Riddell L M 261099
†Proctor P 101199
†Waller M D 101199
†Baird J 171199
†Coulson J M *BSc ACLS* 251199
†Millar T M 11299
†Patel S D 11299
†Smith I G 11299
†McComiskey M H 61299
†Grocock C J 71299
†Bourne J T 81299
†Din S U 81299
†Warburton M S 81299
ØJacobsen N L 200100
†Puxty A 290100
†Roberts C E S 260200
ØHarvey M 80300
†Nayar R C R 80300
ØHawes R S 150300
†Hyams J B 150300
†Biggs M J P 60400
Mather R C 140400
†Reaveley M D 230400
ØTownsend O C 140600
ØNguyen P T L 300600
†Galappathie N 50700
†Raju H 50700
†Green C A 120700
ØBraid J J 90800
ØJackson L 130800
†Read P N *BMedSci* 150800
ØChettiar T K V 270900
†Holmes M E 270900
ØMarchand C L 270900
†Newton-Ede M P 270900
ØDwyer S E 191000
†Brown D R 211000
†Dean F K M 211000
†Chinery J P 251000
ØHart S M *BMedSci* 251000
ØAmos K J 151100
†Green T E W 301100

Pharmacists

Majors

ØMalins D R *TD MRPharmS*
70689

326

Latty A J *TD• MRPharmS* 311289
McCarthy C A *TD BSc MRPharmS*
110198
Mawhinney W M *BSc MIPharmM MRPharmS* 11200

Captains

Inman J S *MSc MRPharmS* 80789
Seth G V *BSc PhC* 10193

Majors

Shepard G J *MBBCh FRCSED*
10896
Sweet D G *MBBCh* 10896
Pool R W *MBBS* 10197
Nesbitt I D E *MRCP FRCA* 30897
ØKhoo S M *MBBCh* 10498
Reed M R *MBBS* 10898
Gardner S G *MBBCh* 10299
ØSutcliffe R C *MA MB BChir DRCOG* 10299
Bruce A S W *MBChB* 10899
ØWarr C A *MBChB* 10899
Taylor M A *MBBCh BAO FRCS(Eng)* 10800
Rennie I M *MBBCh BAO* 90800

Captains

ØJackson S E *MBBS* 20891
Fon L J *MBBCh* 10892
ØAkhtar S *MB* 10893
Mangar S A *MBChB* 10895

Administrative Officers

Majors

Dugdale T B *TD••••* 10277
ØAtherton I *TD•* 240786
Hudson F D B *TD CertEd* 10489
Gutkowski J A *RMN RGN* 240190
Dixon J *TD* 171290
¶Rowan D 150492
Kirk W T 30393
Connolly B *TD•* 10693
McAllister E J *TD* 10693
Leeson P J 10494
Funnell M J *MISM MRSH SEN*
300494
ØBone L K *TD••* 10396
Mackenzie R 10998
Gidman C M 241099
Hamilton A T *MBChB DRCOG*
10301

Captains

Kane L 120274
Stoddart L R I 100275
Naylor J D 170978
Lambert W A *TD* 310880
¶Booles R L D *MBE* 130583
¶Frost P J 71283
¶McSweeney D J 20784
¶Barley A K 10884
Crompton W *ABSC* 10487
Smith B A 160390
ØClash M A 40691
Wenban D I *TD BEng(Hons)* 100691
ØChater L J *EN(G)* 140991
Martin J A 170991
ØWalker M A 50492
ØFreeman E A M *TD* 11092

ØColeman M V 121092
Marshall P *TD* 11192
ØLodge J M *CertEd* 10593
Hatch R 240693
Dunn C 10494
ØMcKenzie M F 280694
Hunter G D 20196
Gordon D 40296

Lieutenants

Leek D J *MISM* 101188
Haden W J 10894

Nursing Officers

Majors

Young B *TD• MIMGT LHA RGN MHSM* 290786
Earl D N *TD• NDN RMN RGN RNT DNTC FETC* 80886
Brown K *TD RGN RMN* 250589
Goodman L G *TD RMN RGN*
61090
Gardiner J E R *RGN RNT RCNT CertEd* 10491
Little T G *RGN* 281191
Nicholls C F *RMN RGN* 220192
Goodship D A C *DN RMN RGN*
281093
Jones T N *RMN RGN* 80194
Lilley R *RGN* 290695
Siddle R G *TD RMN RGN* 210995
Herbert J M E *TD RMN RGN*
201095
Barrie A S W *TD RMN RGN* 10196
Morris J G *RMN SRN* 10900

Captains

Atkin R S *TD B Sc (Hons) RMN RNMH RGN RNT* 90685
McLean A *HVCERT RMN RGN RM*
310189

Technical Officers

Majors

Harris D A *TD• BA TDCR* 10483
Griffin J 100585
Armstrong C I *FRSH MRIPHH MCIEH MIOSH* 11086
Windsor A M *TD• MCSP SRP*
10387
Broadbent A N 51187
ØGoodall D M *PhD B Sc (Hons) FIBMS* 10389
Phimister D A *TD MSc FIBMS*
10389
Rutherford I C *TD MPhil MCSP DipTP* 10889
Elliott M B *TD MCSP SRP* 10190
Karran G P *TD•• FIBMS* 10190
Kennedy J H *TD* 30290
Copland B D B *TD MCSP* 180490
Davies D E *TD CBiolMIBiol AIBMS*
241090
Atterbury N G D *DipEH* 230791
ØMorris R O *MBBS DRCOG*
10893
McKinnon A J *TD MS BSc FIBMS*
200494
Munson K M *MCSP* 280494
ØDockray L *B Sc (Hons)* 10295

Henry W S *TD DipEH* 10995
McLellan J H *TD* 311295
Brice J S *TD MCIEH AMIOA*
10496
Faulkner P J *DCR(R) D R I* 10496
Barnett M J 10596
Lewin I *TD HDCR(R) SRR FETC*
240796
Fisher J *TD MCIEH* 280996
Ward G *TD HCITB-INSTR* 231196
Adair L S *TD* 10197
Willis R J *MCIEH* 10297
Moore D *TD FIBMS* 10497
Mead A J C *FIBMS AIBMS DMS*
10697
Chapleo R A *FIEH* 140697
ØHibbs-Owen D *TD MCSP SRP*
10797
Jordan R *MISM AMASMC REMT ASPS* 10797
Rea W H *TD CRP TDCR FETC*
100498
Helmrich C I 11198
ØPrice H E *TD FIBMS* 120599
Birbeck R P *MCSP* 30899
ØWoodhouse J A *MCSP* 201299
Lawson P M *B Sc (Hons) MCIEH*
270100
Kelly J A *FCSP SRP* 100200
ØBurns A V *MCSP* 250600

Captains

Bartholomew R K *FIBMS* 140289
Soar R H *FIBMS* 140289
Jackson M *FIBMS AIBMS* 230192
Nash S G *TD MSc FIBMS AIBMS ABPI* 140292
Mehta N V 120792
Pace J W *DCR(R) SRR* 10193
ØRhodes A S 10195
ØDarley M A *TD MSc* 10195
ØMillband J E 281095
Mathieson A *BSc* 11196
Fullerton M G 10198

Non-Medical Officers

Captains

Terrett W H *TD• BEd* 10193

2nd Lieutenants

†Kenny S E *MB ChB* 111288
†Davies P L 20389

Quartermasters

¶Smith J *Maj 231182* 221174
Winter J T *Capt 300491* 121180
¶Wilson H M *Capt 010487* 10181
Curry-Peace F *TD• Maj 130894*
130882
¶Rossi D R *MBE Maj 180693*
160983
Beesley B E *TD Capt 010196*
61283
¶Doherty J A *BEM MInstAM MISM MIWO AMIWO Capt 030484*
Macdonald I *Capt 020484* 20285
Ternent E *Capt 020486* 100686
Carter C R *MISM Capt 030983*
220387

Farrugia W J   *Capt 291187*
Motion J A J   *Capt 150187* 170289
Samuel P D *TD* *Capt 130876*
                             11189
Beveridge D L *Capt 300994* 300690
Franks M J   *Maj 210100*
McBryde J B H *Capt 210691*
Talbot R N   *Capt 140991*
Berry A S *REMT* *Maj 300899*
                             170192

Davis L J *MISM DipM MInstSMM*
   Maj 130300   130392
Chapman L B   *Capt 240692*
Willis D L *ACMA FETC MAAT*
   Maj 090600   20393
Lewis D *TD* *Capt 301095*
Straney R A   *Capt 310196*
Goodall S J W   *Maj 010400* 21296
Baxter P   *Capt 010797*
Proctor P S   *Capt 090598* 10598

Burt E E   *Capt 050300*

Administrative Officers

Nash N T   *Capt 060185*   150190

Technical Officers

Hall C R *TD• FIBMS AIBMS*
   Maj 221185   290875

CORPS OF ROYAL ELECTRICAL AND MECHANICAL ENGINEERS

Hon Colonels . . . . .Col M W Whyman *TD* 010495
Col D W Forrest *TD* 010398
Col G R Illingworth *TD* 010498
Col R Lucas 010499
Lt Col J R Steele *TD* 010499
Lt Col J S Evans *TD* 010800
Col T G E Gillanders *TD* 010800

Colonels

Illingworth G R *TD••• ADC*
BSc(Eng)Hons MIMechE tacsc
sq(V)   10495
Gillanders T G E *TD•• BSc(Eng)*
MSc FIOH tacsc   10498
Harvey J L *TD BSc(Hons) CEng*
MIMechE tacsc   170301

Lieutenant Colonels

Evans J S *TD• BSc CEng MIMechE*
MCIBSE tacsc   11192
O'Hanlon J L *BSc(Hons) CEng*
MIMechE MIEE MInstMC tacsc
  10495
Wood A R *TD• MA CEng MIEE*
MIMGT tacsc sq(V)   10197
Griffin R M *MSc CEng* tacsc   10397
Mifsud V J *TD• MA PhD AIMGT*
AIL tacsc   10397
Young W M *TD• BSc(Hons) CEng*
MIMechE MCIBSE tacsc   10699
O'Leary W J *TD AMIMI AIRTE*
tacsc   250999
Pickard P W *TD* tacsc   10100
Ewens A J *TD BSc(Hons) MSc(Eng)*
(EURING) CEng MInstMC CertEd
  10400
ØAttlee *The Countess TD BSc(Hons)*
MILAM tacsc   10101
Manson S H *BSc(Eng)Hons MBA*
CEng MIEE MIRTE CDipAF
me sq(w)   10301
Szabo C L W tacsc   10401

Majors

Garden B *TD••• BSc* tacsc sq(V)
  10480
Broad P E *BSc(Eng) CEng MIMechE*
me sq(w)   70281
Huxford G G *TD• BSc(Hons) DMS*
tacsc   10486
Bayliss M W E *MA CEng MIMechE*
me   60187
Dobbie D M *TD BEng(Hons) MSc*
CEng MIMechIE tacsc   310387
Haxell J P N *TD• BSc(Hons) PhD*
DIC MRSC   10989
ØMantle E *BSc(Hons) MIEE DMS*
tacsc   11192
Stuart P M *TD* tacsc   81293
Grime I S D *TD* tacsc   40494

Cooke A G *BSc(Hons)*   180594
Taylor J C *TEng(CEI) AFSERT*
  10894
Plater A *IEng AIRTE MIMGT* 31094
Atkinson D C   71194
Bennett A R tacsc   10495
Littlewood P R *MBE* sq   10495
Roberts I M *BA(Hons) DipEngMAN*
MISM   10495
Turner M S *DipEngMAN*   10495
Cunningham W   240795
ØCran A A W *BSc(Hons)* G(ss)
  151295
O'Regan J *TD*   191295
Booth R C *MSc AMIMechE*   80296
Reeves J E A M *TD• BEng(Hons)*
DMS CEng MIEE   170296
Greaves L P   10596
McDougall R J   230996
Lavery S S   10297
Boulton G G   61097
Thomas E J *FETC*   101197
Sower P   10198
Moreman S *TD*   160198
Atkins L *IEng FSERT FIEIE*   10498
Attlee J R   280498
Kumik P C *BSc(Hons) CEng MIEE*
  10798
Davies A *BEM*   111098
Platt C   231098
Beggs V   131298
Simpson M A *TD*   40199
Graves P M   60499
Ward J S *TD BSc(Hons) PhD* 60499
McMillan D W *BEd(Hons) MBA*
  10699
Edwards T *BEng(Hons)* tacsc 200699
Ingram E   10799
Potter K G   10799
Kelly P B *MIMGT AIIRSM* 270899
ØGregory-Evans C Y *BSc(Hons)*
PhD   110999
Storey P T *BSc IEng FIEIE*   11199
Truluck V S *MISM*   21299
Evans H G *BEng(Hons)*   80200
Salisbury C S *BEng(Hons)*   80200
White S R *BEng(Hons)*   80200
ØCooper J M   10400
Crow G F   10400
Hearty K P   160600
Orpin B P *BEng(Hons)*   10900
Simmons P H   231000

Captains

¶Heath I C   130787
Besant M A W   10189
ØBurgess F M *CEng MRAeS* 60389
Creek N B M   10890

Hinton S G B   91090
Hallam T J *TD*   80791
Lindsay T   21191
Allcock K E   10292
Southall S   290492
Cooper G L *BEng(Hons) AMIEE*
  40592
ØRolland I A   20692
Goodburn S E   200892
Gardiner N PC   180293
Fairlamb A W *MISM MCIPS* 10393
Woodcock D C   150493
Oldfield P *MIRTE*   10793
ØAitken J K E *BEng(Hons)*   80893
Duncan R W L   10993
Rolfe P C   50394
Jackson D M *BEng(Hons)*   10494
Gill A W *BEM*   190494
McEntee N P *AMIRTE*   10594
Daly J J   120694
Quirk R J   120994
Williams C J   150994
Edmond P J *BA(Hons) MA(Hons)*
AIIRSM   41194
Fitzhugh R R   141194
Ferguson G   10195
Meeson G V *BA(Hons)\MA PGCE*
  10495
Lowe S D *BEng(Hons)*   230995
Ashdown P R *BSc(Hons) MSc*
  11095
Holmes-Jefferd V C   11195
Atkinson P   10196
Bowman T A   170296
Williams D J   290396
Hughes I M   10496
Paterson W B   10496
Shotton G   10496
Thornton R   11096
Senter D M *IEng MIMechE*   10297
Lawson A A P   260397
ØBrown H K *BEng(Hons) AMIEE*
  280697
Tollerfield P G *MEng CEng*
MIMechE   280697
Wheelans C N *BEng(Hons) MBA*
CEng MIMechE   10997
Winspeare A R   191197
Walton A   11297
Needham R J   31297
Harrow M   71297
Gilmartin S   10198
Sochon G J   10198
Windsor P F   80198
Campbell A   10498
Dowling J W *MIMechE*   10498
Wright M A   10498
Reeder W   70498

Simpson R S	270498	
Dorman K F	11198	
Butcher H M *BScEng(MECH)*		
	10199	
Crawford T H W	10199	
Legg C A *BEng(Hons)*	190499	
Hardman D A	300699	
Prince C W	300699	
ØCreek G E *BSc(Hons)*	160899	
ØKiggell J L	140999	
Lewis P H	10100	
Pinchard P G	10500	
Thompson P	10600	
Calder N J *BSc(Hons)*	10700	
ØEarl R L	10900	
Black A *BEng(Hons)*	300900	
Carmichael A P	11100	
Pallett B C	10101	

Lieutenants

Quinn L E *BEng(Hons) MSc(Eng) PhD*	21095
ØKnowles E	40896
McBride D	40297
ØRoberts H M	10597
Macpherson N D	31097
Woollett J P	160698
Basey K A	280698

ØWilson E D *BEng(Hons)*	280998
Furber R S K	151198
†James S D	151198
Sim M	60599
Oakes K J	110699
†Taylor P J	110699
†Tomsett D J P	110699
†Clubley S M	120699
Hunt S C	140699
Hopkirk R B	60999
Busher M *BEng(Hons)*	11299
ØHughes S A	310100
Stephenson M	10200
†Donnelly S R	130500
†Kelly P W	130500
†Mermagen C G	150500
†Leeke M B J	230500
McGrath B D	140600
Atchison N H *BEng*	70700
†Mackinnon D K	190700
Harris D J	10800
†Kilsby N I	160800
†Townrow G	160800
†Donoghue G F	20900
†Vidler D L	240900
†Goodfellow G C *IEng*	61100
†Dorling I J	171100
†Sellers G J	171100
†Brotherston M	251100

†Griffiths M F R	251100
†Boland C	91200
Morgan C N	40101
ØKinrade H M *BEng(Hons)*	310101

2nd Lieutenants

Rhymer S J	131097
Agathangelou A J	10799
ØMacleod J L	11099
†Francis M D	40600
†Johnson W R	11000
†Bockle M A	180201
†Creighton S	180201

Administrative Officers

Captains

McCombe R C	160989

Quartermasters

Anderson A E	*Capt 030998*	10488

Electrical and Mechanical Assistant Engineers

Laska F A	*TD Maj 020496*	221185
Mawdsley R L	*TD• Capt 010487*	

ADJUTANT GENERAL'S CORPS AND PERSONNEL SUPPORT BRANCH

Majors

Storey J W   MBE TD••• MIPlantE
  FCOMA JP   231078
Garrett K   TD   160780
Wilson C G   111080
McLean I S   TD•• tacsc   10183
ØHoward K M   TD   10584
Parsons R S   TD• ACIB   160389
Quayle S   TD• CISEM   10689
Kyle I H   TD   20789
Jones N L   TD•   50190
Young K J   MInstAM   80290
Davis J A   BEd   170290
Chown J D B   TD BSc AIDPM
                              10390
ØLarsen-Burnett E C A   TD
  BEd(Hons) sq(V)   10490
Franklin D   300990
¶Haslam M J   90691
ØDaly U M   TD BSc   10492
Mutch J   TD   10592
Walton P R   10692
Boardman R   TD   11292
Masters N H   TD•   280293
Jones R J R   TD   81093
Northover M A   TD ACA   140194
Lindsay A   TD ACIB   10494
Garner G K   TD   90794
ØWilde L M   BA(Hons) tacsc 160894
ØRanson A M   TD• tacsc   20395
Norris S F   TD   80495
ØThompson J L   TD BSc(Hons) MSc
  PhD PGCE   11095
ØRichards A E   TD•   10297
Anderson T W   90897
Cornwell M J   OBE MIMGT sq
                              20997
ØJacobsen F M E   BSc(Hons) 10198
Vince C P   TD tacsc   10198
ØEdington F A   30198
Buckley L J   250298
Boulter S C W   10498
Howse K J   30798
Kiely J M   sq(V)   30898
Clark H D   sq   141298
Playford R F   MBE BA FIMI FIE
                              10499
¶Bartaby R C   MBE   10799
¶Colclough A J   10799
Ebbens V D   MBE   10799
Midgley S A   TD   10799
Robinson J   10799
Gee P A   110799
¶O'Hara H F   181099
Quinn J   10100
¶Ross M   MBE   10100
¶Wall M J   10100
¶Turnbull H A   310100
ØLittlejohns R R   BSc(Hons) 80200

Harding E J S   sq   20700
Nixon J R   10800
Farnsworth D   310800
Quain R P   TD   41000
Carroll J P   21100
Jenkins R J   10301

Captains

ØMatthews R   BSc(Econ)Hons
                              90581
Thompson F T   TD• BA   40983
¶Kirkham J W   110385
¶Bennett D M   130885
Martin J   280187
Hawcroft R L   11287
Hebbert C M   sq   121288
Martin G M   30389
ØRogers M E M G   TD• CMS CertEd
  DMS   10689
ØDavison S   BSc(Hons)   220889
ØHill J L   TD   10989
Fish E   MILOG   10190
Pearson M   10390
Leese S W   TD BA(Hons) MISM
  MIPD   110390
Green D M   MInstAM MISM MIIA
                              20890
Olney M   TD   71090
Eyres D   BA(Hons) ACIB   10491
Bender M K   160792
Coward D M   IEng AMIRTE MISM
                             151092
Williams T C   10393
Hardy M A   80693
ØBiegel A E   BA(Hons)   100693
Bolam B E   230693
Lupton C R   220793
ØStone R A   80893
Mann P G   310893
Eva R F   31093
Blackford G J   TD ACIB   121293
Carey R J   10294
Simpson B F   10294
Martin K R   20394
Whittingham A M   TD   10694
Hawkey P   180894
Green T P   10994
Shakespeare M W   40994
Whitehead M H   181194
Gwilliam D J   10295
McConway K   BA(Hons) AINSTAM
                              10695
ØFauguel F E   200695
Dobson R M   80995
Atwal S S   120995
ØOldroyd-Campbell S L   291095
Bowes A R   91195
ØMay M   30396
Jones P D   FInstAM   40496
Twilley J G   10596

ØHoldom D M   210696
Fryer P   241196
†Brittle S W   ACIB   10297
Pennicott C J   220297
ØWilkinson S R C   201097
Hodson E   10198
Orejda H A   10298
Staley C C   10698
ØEvans J   BA   190798
ØMohan S A   TD• LBIPP MECI
                             311098
Scarfe I   141298
Freeland C N   BSc ASVA   191298
ØDominguez L L   10799
Cope C J   140799
ØLambirth S J   140799
ØGraham D A   190799
James S J P   20899
Anderson G M   100899
Middler J   140899
Hudson J D   80999
Littler P G   80999
Bridgen P R C   230999
Fitzgerald A M   11099
Ainscough M T   201099
Jackson M E   281099
Fraser G   81199
Csernikovics C   50300
Young R J   220300
Sneddon I   290400
Pope D J   10500
Murray E P   290500
Butcher A E   10600
Cole A G   10600
Reynolds J   230600
Lock K R   MISM   11000
Newman C G   161000
Allison M R A   20301
Lawson M D   MISM FIAB   20301
Butcher M C   80301

Lieutenants

ØRussell S L   131196
Wilson R   31098
ØRichardson J   161298
ØBarclay T A C   80599
ØMercer A J   121199
ØRussell A M   111200
ØWoodgate L   50101

2nd Lieutenants

†Powell S D   170600
†Williams J H   40700

Quartermasters

Emerson J W   Capt 090395

ADJUTANT GENERAL'S CORPS (ARMY LEGAL SERVICES)

Majors		Captains			
Girling R A *LLB(Hons)*	270598	London J F J	190398	Coles R M F	180498

ADJUTANT GENERAL'S CORPS (EDUCATION SERVICES)

		Syme D C *MA I* I*	221187	Westaway D A *MBE PGCE MIEIE*	
		Hazel D F *BSc(Econ)Hons MA*			100899
Majors		*PGCE MIPD*	300990		
Jackson W M W *MBE* sq I*	300676	Joseph A *BA DTFLA MIL I* I*		*Captains*	
Thomas G J *AMBCS* ph sq(w) adp			210191	Gardner F R	140394
	91082	Tittmar H-G *TD•• BA(Hons) PhD*		Bielecki S	10497
Fec Z M *BA(Hons)*	60384	*DSc AFBPSS ABPSS CPsychOL*		ØHardy G V *MBA*	141097
Johnston J D *MA ADVDipEd AIMGT*		*MBISC*	10493	Holmes C S	10498
MIPD LCGI I	60586	ØCoulthard S P *MBE BSc(Hons)*			
Zaremba-Tymieniecki M W *TD*		*PGCE* tacsc	130695	*2nd Lieutenants*	
	10986	Pirozzolo M G	261197	Makhzani A	40600
Beaumont M P *CertEd*	21186	ØDando J A	50498	Newland D P	40600
		Sekunda N V	260499		

ADJUTANTANT GENERAL'S CORPS (RMP)

		Aitken M G P im	10200	ØMacleod L J	131098
		Payne N W	230301	Donoghue J M	10799
Lieutenant Colonels				Gifford A P	10799
Johnston H C *TD* tacsc	10300	*Captains*		Gill N J	10899
		Bealey D G *BA(Hons)*	10490	Holden R J M *BA(Hons)*	10600
		Hallam C S M *TD*	260491	Majchrzak Z A	140201
Majors		Stephens M A *TD*	10192		
Grubb J M A *TD BA* sq(V)	210989	Graham J	50493	*Lieutenants*	
Driver P J *TD*	10890	Greenoak J	170493	ØDennes N J	10599
Gray J W *TD*	11090	ØMcLean P C	80693	Gable J K	180699
Hurley K B	20391	ØHastings J A	10793	Bateman M A	190500
Fothergill S D *AMIMI MIRTE*		Kemp R	10793	McCartney R J	20800
	10891	Walker J P	10793		
Glover E M	300991	ØBugdale R	10794		
Mudford R J *TD• MSc RMN RGN*		Spurling G L	10794	*2nd Lieutenants*	
tacsc	11192	Murphy D M	270794	ØLloyd C E L	10899
Payne S G *TD•*	10794	Tallis R	10495	†Salmassian D	10800
Baker E D tacsc	91196	Crabb N	90497	†Sparkes K A	60800
Kilby R B hcsc(J)	10497	Atkinson P A	180697	†Bolwell S J	11000
Bogle J S L	300997	Doyle P	10797	ØDias S	11000
ØWood S M *BA(Hons)*	291099	Ellson J V	171297		

ROYAL ARMY VETERINARY CORPS

Hon Colonel .Brig A H Parker Bowles *OBE* ret pay 010195

ØWood A J *BVSc MSc MRCVS*
40691

Lieutenant Colonels	ØBowen L J *BVSc MRCVS*	240795	*Captains*	
Koder P C *Ed BVMS MSc MRCVS*	Huey R J *MVB MRCVS*	10196		
CBiolMIBiol tacsc 160490	ØWood L S *BA VetMB MRCVS*	170996	Harris D M *MRCVS*	260397
			Morgan E R *VetMB MRCVS*	50997
Majors	Cooke G R D *VetMB MRCVS*	10497	ØArculus S L *BVMS MRCVS*	90298
Carver J F A *BVetMed MRCVS*	Storrar J A *DVM MRCVS*	10398	Farland M G	10499
310790	Rose I R B *BVMS MRCVS*	10499	ØRose Larner J F	10499

SMALL ARMS SCHOOL CORPS

		Ryan J M	301294	*Quartermasters*	
Majors					
Harverson A	300990	*Lieutenants*		Henderson R	*Capt 120195*
Silk R	301092	†Omeara T J	220700	Sayers R	*Capt 190696*

ARMY PHYSICAL TRAINING CORPS

Lieutenants
Goodall S	30496
†Virgo P	191197

ROYAL ARMY DENTAL CORPS

Colonels

Harrison A *TD•• PhD BDS*
FDSRCSEng   311289
McAllister H K *OBE TD BDS*
MGDSRCSEng DGDPRCS(Eng tacsc
270699
___

Lieutenant Colonels

Alston F *TD• BDS DOrth* tacsc
50981
ØLithgow Smith D K *TD• BDS* tacsc
10487
Brace D M *TD BDS* tacsc   41189
Cuccio J J *BDS* tacsc   61092
Hudson G M *TD• BDS* tacsc   61092
Willey D L *TD• BDS* tacsc   180794
Jackson P D *TD BDS FDSRCPS*
tacsc   10499

Majors

Patton D W *TD MBBS BDS*
FDSRCSEng FDSRCPS FRCSED
tacsc   10775
Parkinson A D *TD•• LDS*   290876
Hale L R O *MSc BDS FDSRCPS*
GLAS DOrth   170981
Revington P J D *TD MScD MBBS*
BDS FDSRCSEng FRCS(Eng)
50182
Caen A J *TD•• BDS*   10282

Nelson M V B *BDS DGDP(UK)*
250784
Maceachen W R J *TD BDS*   270187
Graham D B *MCDH BDS DDPH*
CMS   260288
Griffiths J *BDS*   240888
Goldthorp W F *TD BDS*   41088
Tyrer G L *TD BDS*   61088
Marshall I R *BDS*   290591
Evans D R *BDS* sq(V)   261191
ØHudson S M *BDS DGDP(UK)*
tacsc   70492
Jervis P N *BDS LRCP MRCS*   10293
Leggate I P *BDS*   180393
Mayor P J *BDS*   80695
Lowe M J *BDS*   80597
Rowe C A *BDS(Hons) LDS LDSRCS*
300597
Kennedy D W G *BDS FDSRCPS*
110997
Curtis G   310198
Cromie C J *BDS*   120598
Reid S C *BDS DGDPRCS(Eng*
80299
ØWilliams J R *BDS*   220700

Captains

Bhattacherjee A J   231098
Patel S R   231198
Minchella L C *BDS*   101199
Coventry J P A   190100
Kirk N J *BDS*   200100
ØWatson L C   290500

Maguire G R   310500
Megahey P W L   310500
Jones I L   290600
Crutchley R J *BDS*   20800
Kelso S S J *BDS*   50900
Stanton I *BDS*   140301

2nd Lieutenants

Harris S A   121297
McClean K D   130700

Lieutenant Colonels

ØMountford C L *BDS(Hons) TCERT*
tacsc   10199

Majors

McVicar I H *MBBS BDS*
FDSRCSEng FRCSED FRCS(Eng)
10490
Lloyd C J *BDS FDSRCSEng*   20793
Clark J A *MBBS BDS*   230294
ØEdwards S E *BDS*   200494
Richardson S *BDS*   10694
Robb N D *PhD BDS FDSRCSEd*
140994
Dickson R D B *BDS*   201094
ØSoszko J B J *BDS*   40196

Captains

Walters B P W *BDS*   150191

INTELLIGENCE CORPS

Hon Colonel . . . . .Col R G Kaye *TD LLB QC* 001099

Lieutenant Colonels

White R M *TD•* tacsc	10791
Wiskin M C R *TD* tacsc I	10791
ØGuzkowska M A J *TD MSc DPhil*	
AKC tacsc	10897
Smith P *TD• MA*	160798

Majors

Orford K J *TD BSc(Hons) PhD*	
FRAS CPhysFInstP sq(V)	10982
Fearn J N *TD• BSc(Econ)Hons*	
MCIM pl	11184
Thorpe M T tacsc	20188
Walker D J *TD•*	40288
Jay A C *TD BSc(Hons)* NADC(V)	
tacsc I sq(V)	11188
Cullimore J S *TD*	10691
Huxford R J A *BA(Hons)* I	10392
Nicholson P R *TD*	10894
Carr C R I	11295
Rudd I R J *BSc(Econ)Hons*	190196
Taylor G D *TD•*	10197
ØNorthwood-Smith L A *TD*	10497
Philipps R D psc	10497
Millington R A	10198
Macleod M L	10499
Miller S N *BA(Hons)*	10899
Weale A J *BA(Hons)*	80200
Fullerton P	10400
Jones R D	10600
Cresswell K P	80201
Stanley P A	230201

Captains

Devere D A L *TD•*	10478
Lawrence F E *MA*	170181
Butler G N A R *BSc(Econ)Hons*	
	240183
¶Herring A J	110984
¶Black A E *MBE* I	51184
McCarraher C F *BA(HonsCantab)*	
BA(Hons) MA(Cantab) MIL	190686
Roe J N *MA*	20886

Rollins A *BEd(Hons) MA MIL*	
TCERT DipRSA	70988
Strachan N A *TD* tacsc	161188
Bryant T P M *BA(Hons)*	291290
Haley K J	50591
Maclellan I S	301091
Gregory E	181291
Deamer S C *TD*	10292
Cooper K S *BPhil CertEd*	10392
ØPhilipps M C *BSc(Hons)*	60392
Kennedy S D *BA(Hons)*	10393
Snell G S	160493
Tong T Y	130693
Carlarne J S	80893
Peatfield G *BEM*	141093
ØDalton J M	10594
Boughton M P R	110794
Harrison M G	10295
Redwood J E S o	10395
Holley W L *CertEd (FE)*	311095
Forbes W A	10196
Morton N P K	110296
Lyons J M	10396
Keating G J ph	10496
Wilson R J	10896
Wallen P J	10996
Smith G R H *BA(Hons) MA FRGS*	
	11296
Whitney A K	11296
Scheer A D	10197
Cheshire N R	10297
Wilson D G *DMS*	70297
Wakelam D E	90297
Koenen C A J	10497
Jenkins P J L	30497
Thornbury P C	120597
Brittan R B *BA(Theol)*	70997
Ikin D G	260898
ØTempleton K E	11098
ØAllen D M	231098
ØSummers C R *BA(Hons)*	111198
ØCarter A L	10399
ØEvans T	10499
Prideaux G A	61099
Evans W M	161099
ØClayton A L	191099
Bashir N	10600

Hodkinson R A J *BA(Hons)*	10600
ØMottram P B	10600
Truelove J M	10600
King R J	10700
Farquharson I M	11100
ØGreen C J	11100
ØMcGregor J E	11100
McInulty P I	11100
Page E A	11200
Saunders A G	10101
Thompson J	10101

Lieutenants

Walker G R	220189
Bradshaw R	260593
ØBostock E M	250994
Lennard A J *BSc(Hons) MA*	41294
ØDerouet C J	180296
Van Spall C	130397
Duarte T E	50298
Locke C J *BCom*	10899
†Owen R	50899
Forsyth C A J	280999
ØTeesdale K E	81099
Clarke B S	91299
ØCross C L	150100
Hutchinson N V	20200
ØYoung J E	50200
Ingram R J	180200
Roberts J P	10300
Robbens A V I	10400
ØHalpin L B	130600
ØMobbs A J	11000
Malik M H	151100
†McCracken I H	90301

2nd Lieutenants

ØMawby B A	250994
ØMcCreath V H E	180298
†Walker C N	41298
ØBrown S G M	180199
Walker T E	10399

Quartermasters

¶Hamill J P	*Maj 011195*	260587

QUEEN ALEXANDRA'S ROYAL ARMY NURSING CORPS

Colonels

Quayle S N *TD MBIM MRSH RGN RCNT* 10597
Clouston A *ARRC TD• QHNS(TAOF FR) BSc(Hons) RGN RCNT* tacsc 10498
Kennedy R M *TD RGN RM* 51299

Lieutenant Colonels

Scotton C *TD RGN* 61092
Young M A *TD• MTD RGN RM* 61093
McEvansoneya S *TD RMN RGN CertEd (FE* 71293
Jenkins L J *TD OHNC RGN FETC* 10494
Bailey P *TD RGN* 180794
Bandy M *RRC RGN RM* tacsc 10495
Saunders W P *TD RGN RNT* 10495
Smith E R *RGN RM* 20497
Jones D A *TD BA(Hons) CertEd FRSH RMN RGN CertEd* 11097
Bell C M *TD RGN RNT RCNT* 11197
Davis J E *TD QVRM RGN* 11197
Stead W L *ARRC TD CMS RMN RGN* 10598
Norris O E *RGN RMN* 11298
McArthur D J *TD RGN RMN RGN* tacsc 10999
Higham C J *RMN RGN* 11299
Dixon S M *MSc DN HVCERT FWT(HV) RGN RM FETC MHSM* 10400
Broomhead J A *TD RGN* 10600
Spires K A *TD BA RSCN RCNT* tacsc 10600
Davies V *TD ONC RGN* 11000
Worley P A *TD RGN* 11100
Ridout C E A *RGN* tacsc 10401
Walmsley R A G *OHNC RGN* 10401

Majors

Rutledge A A *TD•• RGN RM RHV* 60479
Parsons V R *TD• HVCERT RGN DOHN* 160981
Powell J M *TD••• RGN* 41181
Young C A *TD NDN RGN RM* 10782
Ritchie D E *TD• RGN* 301082
Cuming E *TD RGN RM RCNT* 60583
Waller C *TD BA(Hons) RMN RGN RNT RCNT* 100883
O'Brien S H *TD• RGN DOHN* 10284
McWhinnie L P *TD• RGN OHNC* 180484
Pocock P A *ARRC RMN RGN EN(G)* 80584
Mackenzie D A *TD• RGN REMT* 301284

Carroll S J *TD• RGN* 130185
Williams B *TD• MEd DN RMN RGN RNT RCNT* 180185
Spires K A *TD BSc(Hons) DN RGN RM RNT RCNT* 110985
Shanahan B H B *TD HVCERT RGN RM* 250985
Howorth H M *RGN* 101085
Hempton J A *TD RMN RGN* 181085
Pointon T *TD RMN RGN* 30986
Baker J C *TD• RMN RGN RNT* tacsc 270986
Pringle M T *RRC TD• RGN RSCN RGN RM* 11086
Green M *BSc(Hons) RMN RGN RCNT* 70187
Morley J M *HVCERT RGN RHV DipHV* 60387
Barnes L J *RMN RGN* 10587
Fagan P *TD• BSc(Hons) ADM RGN RM* 270687
Handbury N K *TD• MN DN RNMS RGN RNT RCNT* 60887
Knowles D *TD• RGN* 201087
Terry M H *TD DN RGN RNT* 131187
Casey J E *TD MA MEd DN HVCERT RGN RM RNT CertEd FETC* 130288
Averty J T *HVCERT RGN RM* 250288
Kelly V A *HVCERT RGN* 280388
Dunn R J *OHNC RGN RGN OHNC* 10488
Davies A *TD• DPSN RGN RM* 30488
Hubbard K E *TD RMN RGN* 130788
Hubbard R D *RGN RM CertEd* 250888
Hunter C *TD DN RGN RM FETC* 150988
Humphries B B *RGN* 230289
Carey-Harris J *TD• CertMGMT RGN RCNT* 280389
Deery E L *TD• RGN RM* 300589
Johnson A *TD RGN RCNT* 310589
Cowling H E F *TD RGN OHNC* 90689
Lee M C *TD RGN RM* 70789
Osborne B M *TD• BSc(Hons) RGN* 260789
Munro-Watson M *TD NDN RGN* 220989
Jeffery W R *TD DN RMN RGN* 11189
Wilson L *TD OHNC RGN* 211189
Berry A E *TD RGN RM* 11289
Duffy C A *TD RGN* 311289
Myers U D *BSc(Hons) DN RGN BTA RNT RCNT DON* 311289
Dorrington P J *RGN* 100190
Barker J W *RGN RM* 190190
Tarleton E A *TD• HVCERT RGN RM CertEd* 10290
McHale H *RGN* 220390
Seth-Kosoko V M *TD BSc HVCERT ONC RGN FETC* 240490
Jones N D *RGN RM* 10790

Verow K J *TD RGN* 200790
Lee-Munson G R *TD HVCERT RGN* 230790
Walbridge P J *RMN RGN* 10890
Johnson B *TD NDN RGN FETC DMS* 110890
McClure C *TD RGN RM* 261090
Stephens S *TD DN MTD RGN RM FETC* 80291
Karran S E *RGN RM NDN* 150391
Barr D M J *TD• DMS RGN* 280391
Kennaugh A *TD OHNC RGN RM* 10491
Cefferty M R *TD RGN RGN RM* 230491
Murphy S *TD• RGN EN(G) A&ENCERT* 310791
Dart A *ONC RGN* 190991
Cheung S N *BEd RGN RNT RCNT CertEd* 111091
Strong P G *TD BA MSc RMN RGN RNT* 161091
Burgess P A *TD BA(Hons) MA RGN RSCN* 281191
Goorwappa L *RGN RCNT* 51291
Nicholl H M *RSCN RGN RM* 151291
Pert C *HVCERT RMN RGN* 171291
Mitton C *BN DN OND RGN* 50192
Whittaker C *TD BSc CertMGMT OHNC RGN* 210192
Rajabally A *BEd(Hons) DN RGN* 200292
Boyd J B *RGN* 220292
Harbinson S M E *TD BSc(Hons) RSCN RGN* 110392
Latimer A M E *OHNC RGN RM* 10492
Hunter P *TD RGN RNT RCNT FETC* 20492
Wall M *TD BEd(Hons) RGN RNT RCNT* 130592
Ash P E *RMN RGN* 260592
Scott C *TD BSc(Hons) DPSN DN RGN CertEd* 250692
Rickard N A S *TD BSc(Hons) MSc RMN RGN RNT PGCE* 140792
Halliday M E *TD HVCERT RGN RM FETC* 31092
Baston J J *TD RGN* 81192
Parkin E J *TD BSc(Hons) RGN SEN* 11292
Henderson J M *RGN* 41292
Richardson D M *TD RGN* 151292
Clewley D J *RMN RGN RM* 80193
Conibere M P *NDN RGN RM* 200193
Mear J E *ONC RGN NDN D P S N* 220193
Ryan E A *TD RGN* 250193
Hollins G M *TD RGN* 110393
Worby E M *RGN RM FETC* 150393
Robertson-Bell D M *RGN* 10493
Thomson T B *TD RGN* 100493
Colley J E *HVCERT RGN* 70593
Evans A E *TD HVCERT RGN RM* 60693
Whewell C A *MTD ADM RGN RM* 220693

Edwards A J *RGN RM*	11299	
Fink V L *RGN RN(T)*	11299	
Harrison S K *SRN*	11299	
Harrison-Bond I *RGN RM*	11299	
Hulme A *MSc RGN RM D P S N*	71299	
Jivan N *RMN RGN RM*	161299	
Evans C A H *RGN*	281299	
Quinn J *RGN*	20100	
Orpen M A *RNMS RGN*	180100	
Neave D I *RMN RGN*	10200	
Wilson M M *RGN A&ENCERT*	10200	
Maltby G M *RGN*	30300	
McMillan C S	60300	
Rooney C A *RGN*	10500	
Smith J S *RGN*	10600	
Ackroyd D L *RGN*	70600	
Martin L J *BA RGN RMN*	80800	
Millar J T *RGN RM*	110800	
Powell V C *RGN*	110800	
Marshall J L *RGN RM*	310800	
Hughes P J *RSCN RGN RM RHV*	20900	
Davidson E A *RGN*	11200	
Edgar S A *RGN*	11200	
Harper E J *RGN*	11200	
Johnson J *RGN RM*	11200	
McCloskey A G *RGN RM*	11200	
Milne G M *RGN*	11200	
Wilcox S *RGN*	11200	
Dennis R W *RSCN RGN*	21200	
Simm H *RGN*	201200	

Captains

Tuitt S G *RGN*		
Wilkinson B *RGN*	201283	
Chatwin D H *RGN*	250585	
Lucey P J S *RGN*	10985	
†Paden E O *SRN RGN RM CertEd (FE)*	100386	
Warwick D *HVCERT RGN*	31086	
Hillsdon P J *TD• OND RMN RGN*	20487	
Doran S E E *OHNC RGN*	290987	
Denchfield J *TD RGN RM*	201087	
Brunskill R A *SRN RGN*	80188	
Den A *RMN RGN FETC*	200488	
Baynton J G	250588	
Kirk K H *NDN RMN RGN REMT*	70788	
Lawless S L *RGN SCM*	20888	
Malcolm A *RGN*	80888	
Kemp J A *HVCERT RMN RGN*	261088	
Burlingham F J *RGN NNEB*	71288	
Gallacher S W F *RGN RMN*	250489	
Makepeace J *RMN SRN RGN*	110889	
Madill J C F *RGN*	131189	
Powell G *RGN*	270290	
Keenan E O *SRN NDN*	30390	
Calleja Y G *RGN*	160390	
Rose C A H *RGN*	10490	
Westwood J C	210590	
Goldsmith R A *RGN*	200890	
Wilson J A	181090	
Vertue M J *RGN REMT*	91190	
Fisher M A	201190	
Andrews M E *RGN*	90191	
Hickman A *RGN*	60291	

Tuckett S B *RMN RGN*	170591	
Anscomb S J	10691	
Govier I M *BN DN RGN*	60891	
Snaith H *RGN*	140891	
Bailey R *DN RMN RGN*	61291	
Ormiston C J *RMN RGN EN(G)*	141291	
Walgate J *OND RGN*	220192	
White K J *RSCN RGN*	300192	
Kelly C T *EN(G)*	310392	
Conlan C P A	100492	
Dickinson A M *RGN*	90592	
Shirley L	60892	
Worthington L J *RGN RM*	200992	
Mortimore J E *RSCN RGN*	191292	
Baxter S E *RGN*	70293	
Hambleton R *RGN RM*	80293	
Brown V E	230293	
Kelly F R *RGN RM FPDip*	80393	
Spicer C J *RMN RGN A&ENCERT*	130393	
Malby A D *RGN*	200393	
Knight D *RSCN RGN*	250393	
Rice C *RGN*	10493	
Jamieson W D C *RGN SEN*	70593	
Jones O C	190593	
Wilding J *BN RGN EN(G)*	290693	
Kelly J C *RGN RM*	20793	
Anthony J *RGN*	310793	
Chorley W E *BSc(Hons) RGN EN(G)*	280893	
Kendrick M I *RGN*	50993	
Laing D M *RGN RM*	100993	
Evison S E *RGN*	41093	
Graham L S *RGN A&ENCERT*	81193	
Jayes J A *RGN RM*	231193	
Anderson T *RGN*	151293	
Gray C *DipHE RGN*	10194	
Frazer N T *ARRC RNMH RGN*	170194	
O'Connor P A *RGN*	230194	
Hayes J E *RGN*	270194	
Noble D *ADM RGN RM*	80394	
Earl C N *RGN*	190394	
Williams K R *RGN*	260394	
Allen N H *RGN*	10494	
Johnston J I *RGN*	80494	
Hornby W S A *RGN*	290494	
Jones C *RGN RM*	300494	
Bond A C	40694	
McCann J F *RMN RGN DOHN*	180694	
Young S A M *ACLS RGN*	300694	
Stewart S A *BSc RGN*	20894	
McClure J *RGN*	220894	
Green D R	300894	
Woodcock P P *CertEd RGN*	30994	
Ford J A	110994	
Cleary A C *RGN*	180994	
Caughey A L *RGN*	81094	
Lingard J *RMN RGN*	301094	
Tisshaw C C	71194	
Kelleher M S *RGN*	221194	
Bradbury J E *RGN*	10195	
Smith M J *RGN EN(G)*	60195	
Byers A E M *RGN*	140195	
Purvis H E *RGN*	140195	
Brown C J *RGN*	10295	
Mulholland L M *BA ACLS RGN*	190295	
Snaith S *RGN*	280295	

Fleming M F	120395	
Worrall J A *RGN RM RHV*	220495	
Crane A L	120595	
Mitchell J *DOHN*	160595	
Batten J P *RGN RM*	210595	
Armstrong B P *RMN RGN*	120795	
Donaldson C I *RGN*	140795	
Owen A J *RGN*	140795	
Gilchrist N J	200795	
O'Neill G *RGN*	200795	
Horrocks K J	20895	
Adair M E *RGN*	130995	
Galluccio P	270995	
Keith B L *RGN*	11095	
Pashley J A *BSc DN RGN*	11095	
A&ENCERT	11095	
Cater T	51095	
Clarke C J *RGN*	111095	
Neal A J *RGN*	211095	
Riddick K A	301095	
Kemp A *RGN*	11195	
Feeney T R *RMN RGN*	31195	
Feeney L A *RMN RGN*	31195	
Evans J L *RGN*	251195	
O'Donnell I D M *RGN*	161295	
Shahid S H	90196	
Chapman R	130196	
Harper S L	140196	
Jones C M *RGN EN(G)*	210196	
Owens S K *RGN*	260196	
Kelly S A *RGN*	200296	
Smith E A W G *BA(Hons) MSc RSCN RGN*	260296	
Pennant S B *RGN NDN*	110396	
Horne A J	120396	
Dawe C A *RGN*	200396	
†Thomson E J J *RNMS RGN*	200396	
McDonald G *RGN*	10496	
McCormick C *RGN*	40496	
Macdonald S M	190596	
Cooper N A *RGN*	250596	
Donaldson D F T *RGN*	40696	
Mulryne J *RSCN RGN*	70696	
Rand J *RGN DipN*	100696	
Atkinson J S *RGN*	240696	
Porter D E *BSc(Hons) RGN RHV DipHV*	10896	
Monteith R *SRN*	80896	
Stewart G A *RGN*	80896	
McDonald I	130896	
Harthern D H *RGN*	250896	
Jones M C	40996	
Kyzer K E	110996	
Deal L A *RGN*	180996	
King S E *RGN*	270996	
Peel R H *RGN RM*	71096	
Fountain S A	181096	
Morris A *RGN*	151196	
Orr H A *RGN*	41296	
Finnigan G P *RGN*	131296	
Merchant S A E *RGN RM*	60197	
Cooke J *RSCN RGN*	90197	
Parnell C M *RGN NDN*	170197	
Griffith I	180197	
Docherty A W *RGN*	230197	
Nicol S M *RGN*	120297	
Robertshaw M J *RGN*	150297	
Ferguson J K	220297	
Clephane A J	270297	
Phillips T K *RGN*	160397	
Myers A J	200397	
Johnson J D	10497	

Quigg S *RGN D P S N SEN* 10497	Day K E *DN RGN* 110498	Shearer M D *BSc(Hons) RGN*
Eastwood B A 30497	Arnell E *BA(Hons) RMN RGN*	281198
Jones S 70497	120498	Allingham H S F *DipHE RMN RSCN*
Kelly J *BSc(Hons) BSc(Hons) RGN*	Carr E *EN(G)* 180498	*RGN RHV* 301198
RM RHV 70497	Vogan E M 220498	Atkinson W R *RGN* 61298
Anderson W R *RGN* 250497	Banks P J *RGN* 20598	Mott D *RMN* 61298
Pickering F M *RGN RM* 270497	Oneill M B *BSc(Hons) RGN* 30598	Sions J P M *RGN A&ENCERT*
Furey P M *RGN* 20597	Sowney R *RGN EN(G)* 30598	61298
Ashton R H *RGN EN(G)* 130597	Mears G O *RGN EN(G)* 50598	Kirk J 71298
Jackson A L *RGN* 130597	Frederick C E 70598	Lindon-Davies S M *RGN* 131298
Winslade K E 310597	Tams Gregg J S 150598	Wardle J H *BA(Hons) RGN* 231298
Micklewright S *RGN* 30697	Haydock A M *RMN* 170598	Rogers M D 261298
Randall L H *RGN* 80697	Taylor D M 210598	Andrews A J *RGN RM* 10199
Ohanlon J 120697	Campbell D F A *RGN RM* 240598	Rowley A J *BSc DN RMN* 60199
Clayton S M 130697	Green J A *RMN RGN CSS* 240598	Haylett W *RGN* 90199
Bell S M *RGN* 210697	Lewispowell M C *RGN* 270598	Lim T C U *RGN* 170199
McGonnell A *RGN* 250697	Anthony S L *RGN* 10698	Moore K H *RGN* 170199
Poulter A F *RGN A&ENCERT*	Fittock O *RGN* 40698	Robinson K E *RGN RM* 170199
260697	Gritt A J *RMN* 40698	Pyper D M *DN* 220199
Connor J M 30797	Ford C A *RGN* 140698	Topham J A *RGN* 310199
Guest P *RGN* 70797	Hall S M *RGN* 140698	Jones V 10299
Lee Roffe E J *RGN* 40897	Charters E A *RGN* 270698	Ryall M J *RMN RGN* 140299
Carr M D 70897	Pye M J *RGN* 270698	Haddock D L 190299
Merry S E 180897	Griffiths M A *RGN RHV* 290698	Semple M *RGN* 210299
McGhee S J A *RGN D P S N* 200897	Kelly A *RGN* 290698	Haynes D *RGN* 220299
Bull T *RGN* 220897	Wink D M *ONC RGN* 290698	Royle A P 230299
Webster L J 290897	Brown P S *RGN* 10798	Cameron F J *RMN* 260299
McKee T H 10997	Harris J M *RGN RM* 50798	Saunders M J *RGN* 40399
Smithson W J *RGN* 30997	Baker N *RGN RM* 120798	Tregaskes T A *RGN* 50399
Coombs A E 190997	Hill S M 140798	Stanley A L *RGN* 90399
Muir D C *BSc(Hons) RGN* 250997	Boorer S 150798	Owers R A *RGN EN(G)* 100399
Layfield C *DipHE(RN)* 181097	Ashdown L M 170798	Rickers D *RGN EN(G)* 250399
Bell J R 191097	Rosewall L J A *RGN* 180798	Fisher A J 70499
Fievez A 191097	Mitton C 290798	Rudd S J *RGN* 100499
Bacon A C 221097	Eldred V J *RGN* 310798	Stewart J A *RGN* 30599
Staveley I A *RGN RCNT* 221097	Roden M L *RGN* 10898	Simpson A 60599
Jeys M C 301097	Storey A C *RGN* 30898	Ansell D M *RGN* 90599
Snow V 311097	Jones T A *RGN DOHN* 90898	Ritchie J A *RGN* 100599
Eastwood-Dunwell C 41197	Platt S E *RGN* 90898	Hall P J *RGN* 210599
Cook J A 11297		Osborne-Smith L *RGN* 240599
Preston R E *RGN* 91297	Beaumont J M 140898	Everington S R 300599
Angus J 151297	Trotter M P *RMN RGN RM* 140898	Reeve L A 80699
Burns E 151297	Lamont T B *RGN* 150898	Coltman M H F 100699
Fraser J M *RGN RGN* 151297	Lancaster T 190898	Colver C F J *RGN* 130699
Fry L E 151297	Robinson N M *RGN* 220898	Crutchley J R *RGN* 130699
Fry H M 151297	Edwards J M *RGN RM* 240898	Thorneloe J C *RGN* 140699
Smith J *RGN* 151297	Hooper D R *RGN EARCH D P S N*	Pugh A J *EN(G)* 150699
Beale H E 281297	240898	Tan A *RGN RHV SEN* 230699
Bullock G *DipHE(RN)* 10198	Reynolds S C *RGN* 60998	Moore M M *RGN EN(G)* 40799
Bullock N *RGN* 10198	Dudley M J *RGN* 100998	Poole H J 80799
Busby D *BSc RGN* 10198	Craster A *RGN* 130998	Boyd A J *RGN* 100799
Kirtland R K *DipHE(RN)* 10198	Burrow A R *RGN* 280998	Johnston L F M *RGN RHV* 130799
Thompson A P *RGN* 10198	Hagerty A J *RGN DipN* 280998	Moore J *RGN* 200799
Young J F *RGN* 70198	Burgess P J *RGN* 21098	Crabb R R *RGN* 240899
Worthington B *DipHE(RN)* 120198	Fothergill J M 51098	Warren R V *RGN* 280899
Davis J E *RGN RSCN* 140198	Redican A L K *RGN* 51098	Gallimore J *RGN* 290899
Allwood D M *RGN EN(G)* 150198	Thompson M M 121098	Titley H N *RANA RGN RGN*
Adams A M 190198	Allinson A 161098	40999
Willis L M *RGN* 190198	Bandy G W 181098	Rollison F M 60999
Mohammed-Newnham P *RGN*	Davies V R *RGN RM* 191098	Couldrick J *RGN* 80999
240198	Hughes L J *RGN* 191098	Young N F *BSc(Hons) DN RGN*
McKirgan C M *RGN RM* 260198	James J P *RGN* 191098	100999
Lathan L T *RGN* 90298	Primrose L *RMN* 211098	Davies C A 91099
Wilson P F *RMN* 140298	Burke D D 281098	Rowlands M T 111099
Cordingley N L *RGN* 280298	Hornby J *RGN* 31198	Burt D K *DipHE RGN* 141099
Fitzpatrick A 30398	Cole H D *FIPI RMN* 151198	Mina P *RGN* 241099
Brehany J *RGN* 100398	Marlow S A *RGN* 151198	Darby P *RSCN RGN* 251099
Krysinski H L *RGN* 110398	Ferguson J W *RMN* 161198	Burns H P *RGN* 21199
Smales J I *RGN* 150398	Otoole J A *DN RGN* 161198	Hogarth D 41199
Cross D J *RGN* 170398	James D J 181198	Lewis C A *DN RGN* 91199
Harris E M 40498	Williams S M *RGN EARCH* 241198	Alfrey G L 121199
Spencer I H *RMN RGN* 50498	Macaulay I M *RGN* 281198	Cooper S D *RGN* 281199

Fitzpatrick B C *RMN RGN*	91299	Winter J M	110895	Racheva K A *RGN*	40797
Turner S C *RMN*	91299	Middleton K E	140995	Stewart K S M	50797
Blair K M *RSCN RGN*	131299	Plant C B *BA(Hons) RGN*	250995	Douglas A R *RGN*	60797
Thompson K L *RGN*	151299	Stearn D S J *BA(Hons) RGN*	91095	Geddes D J *RGN*	110797
Cook S E *RGN*	201299	Lennox I R *BSc(Hons) RGN*	191095	Proctor J C *RGN*	110797
Worthington B S *RGN*	10100	Bowden R E *RGN*	31195	Leworthy K E *RGN*	120797
Ireland J L	90100	Davies A J	81195	James S *RGN*	20897
Middleton M M *RMN*	110100	Baxter A J	91195	McConaghy A D *RGN*	70897
Birmingham L *RGN*	190100	Williams D	251195	Riley C *RGN*	70897
Cowie I J	240100	Wawrysz H *RGN D P S N*	81295	Gilmore K	280897
Thompson S *RGN*	50200	Tolton R J *BSc(Hons) DN RGN*		Ekoku L M *RGN SEN*	20997
Butler C L *BSc(Hons) DipEd*	250200		140496	Daive F L *RGN*	40997
Butler S J *BSc(Hons) DipEd*	250200	Heath R S *DN RMN*	200496	Ball J *BA(Hons) RGN*	190997
Carter S D *BSc RGN*	10300	Godfrey J A	260496	Ferry J	200997
Keisel A W *RGN*	10300	Meeks C *RGN*	270496	Cooper P J *RGN*	220997
Miller D N	10300	Van Hotson S R *RGN*	20596	Wilson K *BSc(Hons) RGN*	220997
Hillery A L *RGN*	40300	Hill P J *RGN*	140596	Bell J C	270997
Cana A M *RGN*	70300	Davies L *RGN*	60696	Truelove C J *RGN*	290997
Grieves N J *RGN*	140300	Foyle J E *RGN*	60696	Lees D J *RMN*	11097
Harris S L *RGN*	200300	Smith M E *RMN RGN*	80696	Lane B J *RGN*	61097
Jackson D M	200300	Draper J *RGN*	150796	Harrison-Diver V *RGN*	91097
Sealey L	200300	Collery M D	200796	Sharpe R M *DN RGN*	101097
Gallagher N P *RGN*	270300	Williams G W *RGN*	90896	Greaves R	111097
Ball H C *RGN EN(G)*	310300	Kenyon M T *RGN*	280896	Rutter J *RGN*	181097
Taylor D L	110400	Hume D J *RGN*	10996	Fernie H I *RGN*	201097
Lewis C A *DN RGN*	260400	Webb M A *DN RGN*	20996	Hugill D L	211097
Guinan S A *RGN*	280400	Newton C R *RGN*	90996	Priestley J *RGN*	231097
Parry A	220500	New A J J *RGN*	150996	Hawkins S M	251097
Tabbinor S A *RGN*	310500	Hargreaves K *RGN*	260996	Hinkin J *RGN*	261097
Bull K S *RGN*	120600	Smyth P J *DN*	270996	Burns S E *DN RGN*	51197
Stevens L J *RGN*	130600	Dove G K	101096	Thompson D N *RMN*	51197
Porter C M *RGN*	180600	Swallow F L *RGN*	161096	Flannery G	101197
Liston J L	200600	Bunn M R *RGN*	171096	Buttriss S P *RGN RM*	141197
Browning C *RGN SEN*	260600	Gray C R *RGN*	241096	Hall K *RMN*	161197
Gazeley A *DN RMN RGN*	40700	Colquhoun T S	41196	McGrath O M *RGN*	221197
Smith D L *RGN*	250700	Godfrey R *DN RGN*	51196	Dugdale D *RGN SEN*	71297
Sullivan S G *RGN*	310700	King D A *RMN*	51196	Holland R L *RGN*	171297
Barker T A *RGN*	150800	Warr P M *RMN*	101196	North T M *RSCN RGN*	171297
Colville R L E *RGN*	160900	Aylett D J	181196	Smith C T *RGN*	191297
Martin P J *RGN*	101000	Clark V G *RGN*	231196	Wardle M S *RGN*	201297
Evans D J	211000	Williams L *RGN*	261196	Clarkson G J	211297
Harris G M *RGN*	81100	Sturgeon M M	171296	Andrews S *RGN*	40198
Stubbs M P *RMN RGN*	181100	Donkersley E F *RGN*	241296	Buchanan H J *RGN*	60198
Rennie I L *EN RGN*	261100	Hopkins B N	291296	Brown H *RGN*	200198
Crow E M *RGN*	131200	Harrison J C *DipHE BA(Hons) RMN*		Green D L M	210198
Richardson J E *RGN SEN*	261200		311296	Jude U M *RGN*	220198
Kidd S P *RGN*	280101	Chick D *RGN*	100197	Loveday I J *BA(Hons) RGN*	230198
Wright C J *RSCN RGN*	10201	Collins S L	170197	Morris K *RGN*	310198
Tierney L E *RGN*	70201	Young A C *RGN*	180197	Hill G R *RGN*	30298
Powell J J *RMN*	90201	Snowden M A *RGN*	240197	Long M C	110298
Purdie R M *RGN*	260201	Chadwick S C *RMN*	250197	Martin K *RGN*	280298
Moore I *RGN*	190301	Tuckett W A *RGN*	250197	Odams E T *RGN*	60398
Christie G A *RGN*	310301	Ramsey G R *RGN*	290197	Donegan S L *RGN*	160398
		Evans S L *RGN*	120297	Symington A J *RGN*	270398
Lieutenants		Coombs E J	160297	Foxall K J *RGN DipHE(RN)*	300398
Franklin H J *BSc(Hons) RGN EN(G)*		Pickering D A *RGN*	90397	Broad P E	10498
	120187	Colledge-Quinn D L *RGN*	100397	Brannan C *RGN*	60498
McNab G *RGN*	20691	Jackson E *RGN*	130397	Fievez C E *RGN*	210498
Bell A M	80693	Stratton E K *RGN*	240397	Sira S J *RGN*	270498
Sumner D F	101093	Goldsmith P *RGN*	250397	Lloyd E J *RGN*	290498
Jones C A *RMN RGN*	131093	Bloomfield J M *BSc(Hons) RMN*		McWilliam C *RGN*	230598
Dagless E J	200494	*RGN*	280397	McAlister B A *RGN*	10698
Evans M H	20594	Barnard S A	310397	McClelland S *RGN*	170698
McInerney C A *RGN*	230894	Brear J A *RGN*	60497	May J T *RGN EN(G)*	280698
Young W J *RGN EN(G) SEN*	311094	Jones J M	130497	Shorrock V E *RGN EN(G)*	30798
Downes N R	180195	Richardson Y *RGN*	160497	Power C M J *DN RGN*	60798
Howes A D	10495	Vollam J P *RGN*	300497	Crawford C A *EN RGN*	150798
Matterson G *RGN*	80495	Banks C	30597	Muldoon P B *RMN*	250798
Pickin R V	100695	Anstock J S *RGN*	250597	Turner J E P *RGN*	60898
Saunders H D *RGN SEN*	120695	Brazendale S P *RGN*	180697	Skellon S F *RGN*	240898
Wragg Z P *RGN*	180695	Dargan P A *RGN*	180697	Smith V J *BSc(Hons) RGN*	260898
Vesty R A	90895	McCleery I A	200697	Jackson C S *RGN*	290898

Harper S 10998
Hird J A *RGN* 30998
Watson C A *RGN EN(G)* 50998
Wonacott S L *DipHE RGN* 60998
Hodgkinson G *RGN DipHE(RN)* 70998
Williams R J *BSc(Hons) RGN* 70998
Haigh M A 140998
Atkins J 210998
Smith P J D *RGN* 260998
Braithwaite J A 51098
Cummings L A *RGN* 61098
Berrow P 231098
Edwards N P *RGN* 231098
Ferry G W 31198
Harris C C *RGN* 311298
Cosgrove D A *RGN* 40199
Ullmann A J *RGN* 40199
Abernethy I D *RGN* 20299
Murfin S J *RGN* 220299
Margison S *RMN* 270299
Dewa A *RGN* 10399
Babb P L 80399
Wright B L *RGN EN(G)* 90399
Neale H W *DN RGN* 150399
Peat R J *RGN* 150399
Anderson J C *RGN* 180399

Hayward S J *RMN* 50499
Shelley A C *RMN RGN* 50499
Pugh Y D C *OHNC RGN EN(G)* 280499
Johnson T *RGN* 30599
Miskin L J *RGN* 150599
Evans R V *RGN* 230599
Ridpath M A *RGN* 120699
Halsall J *BA(Hons) DipEd DN RGN* 10799
Sedgwick H J *BSc(Hons) RGN* 170799
Hill E G *BSc(Hons) RGN* 190799
Bateman J M 70899
McGee A *DN RGN* 160899
Milburn S *RGN* 290899
Hollis J K *RGN* 300899
Speight L *RGN* 300899
Eccles R J *RGN* 60999
Gittins C G 120999
Hamilton D E *RGN* 120999
Hobbs A P *RGN* 170999
Hallam D J *RGN EN(G)* 180999
Moore J A *RGN* 210999
Jarymowycz J D *BA(Hons) RMN RGN* 230999
Petite S A *RSCN EN(G)* 91099
Yardley R G *RGN* 101099

Garland S E *RGN* 181099
Harrison N G *RGN* 221199
Thompson P *RGN* 260200
Williams R E *RGN* 280200
Woods R J *RGN* 130300
Lee D A *RGN* 200300
Samson T A *RGN* 200300
Burne P *RGN* 220300
Dutt R *BA(Hons) MA RMN* 280300
Mackey C A *RGN* 80400
Henderson S A J *RGN* 240400
Mackie I M *RGN* 10500
Gould P *BA(Hons) RGN PGCE* 240600
Cowan I *RGN* 280800
Gallagher C M A *RGN* 280800
Todd W B *RGN* 280800
Dixon A J *BSc RGN* 180900
Moyer S L *RGN* 180900
Scott A *RGN* 180900
Ridley J 250900
Tobin R C C *RGN* 270900

Quartermasters

Phillips J O   *Capt 251199*

OFFICERS' TRAINING CORPS

ABERDEEN UNIVERSITIES
Hon Colonel
Brig M S Jameson *CBE* 101296
Commanding Officer
Lt Col R J Carrow RGJ 300798

BIRMINGHAM UNIVERSITY
Hon Colonel
Mr R R Taylor *OBE RSJ JP and Lord LT of West Midlands County)* 280297
Commanding Officer
Lt Col S L Naile RE 240898

BRISTOL UNIVERSITY
Hon Colonel
Maj Gen B M Lane *CB OBE* 041187
Commanding Officer
Lt Col R G Dixon RET 070497

CAMBRIDGE UNIVERSITY
"South Africa 1900-01"
Hon Colonel
Lt Gen *Sir* Edmund Burton *KBE* 010593
Commanding Officer
Lt Col A J Tabor LD 070797

EAST MIDLANDS UNIVERSITIES
Hon Colonel
Brig P I B Stevenson *CBE* ret pay 170689
Commanding Officer
Lt Col N F W Hile RA 030898

CITY OF EDINBURGH UNIVERSITIES
Hon Colonel
Field Marshal *HRH The Prince Philip Duke of* Edinburgh *KG KT OM GBE AC QSO*
Deputy Hon Colonel
Rt Hon Sir Malcolm Rifkind *(KCMG) QG OBE* 291298
Commanding Officer
Lt Col S M Bargeton BW 200299

EXETER UNIVERSITY
Hon Colonel
Lt Gen *Sir* Richard Swinburn *KCB* 010694
Commanding Officer
Lt Col C E I Beattie RGJ 010997

GLASGOW AND STRATHCLYDE UNIVERSITIES
Hon Colonel
Col J R Thomson *TD ADC*
Commanding Officer
Lt Col G R Bryson RA 160101

LEEDS UNIVERSITY
Hon Colonel
Col A C Roberts *MBE TD DL JP* 261190
Commanding Officer
Lt Col G H Hony *MBE* RGBW 110897

LIVERPOOL UNIVERSITY
Hon Colonel
Prof D A Ritchie 050201
Commanding Officer
Lt Col M J Atkinson *TD* Kings(V) 310397

UNIVERSITY OF LONDON
Hon Colonels
HRH The Princess Royal KG KT GCVO QSO
Brig A G Ross *OBE* 310199
Commanding Officer
Lt Col N M Holland RE 230398

MANCHESTER AND SALFORD UNIVERSITIES
Hon Colonel
Brig(Retd) E C W Morrison *OBE* 010398
Commanding Officer
Lt Col M J Glover 4 QLR 010499

NORTHUMBRIAN UNIVERSITIES
Hon Colonel
Col *The Duke of* Westminster *OBE TD DL* 010196
Commanding Officer
Lt Col J A F Howard KRH 310397

OXFORD UNIVERSITY
Hon Colonel
Gen *Sir* Roger Wheeler *GCB CBE ADC Gen* 100300
Commanding Officer
Lt Col A F Matheson of Matheson, Little Yr, COLDM GDS 310398

QUEEN'S UNIVERSITY BELFAST
Hon Colonel
Col J A Creaney *OBE TD DL QC* 011293
Commanding Officer
Lt Col N P Gallier *MBE* GH 280998

UNIVERSITY OF SHEFFIELD
Hon Colonel
Col R J Elliott *TD DL*
Commanding Officer
Lt Col C V Clarke KRH 310398

SOUTHAMPTON UNIVERSITY
Hon Colonel
Maj Gen Martin Spencer White *CBE DL*
Commanding Officer
Lt Col C E H Ackroyd *TD* PARA(V) 181296

TAYFORTH UNIVERSITIES
(St Andrews, Dundee and Stirling)
Hon Colonel
Maj Gen A F Irwin *CBE* late BW 311297
Commanding Officer
Lt Col C M Lavender *MBE* RGBW 310399

UNIVERSITY OF WALES
Hon Colonel
Brig W E Strong 010196
Commanding Officer
Lt Col C J Finch PARA 150897

GENERAL LIST

Colonels

Kingscote M J F   sq jsdc   190597

Lieutenant Colonels

Usher R L   tacsc   10198
Bell R D   10898

Majors

Patchett J M *BA(Hons) PGCE* sq   300980
Howell D V *LLB(Hons)*   190383
Rogers J S *TD*   40484
Walker D M *MBE BSc(Hons) MICE* tacsc   101186
Maxwell J G *TD• BArch BSc(Hons)*   40789
Grice R I *TD* tacsc   10490
Hames K S sq   220690
Batchelor J K   101190
Le Marchand R P G   10493
Shepherd A *TD*   10194
Falkowski J P M *TD*   140195
Gallier S M *BDS*   70295
McNeil D R *TD MEng*   10695
Bruce Of Crionaich A A B R tacsc   10796
Walker T *TD* tacsc   51096
Goldstein S R tacsc   10197
Fraser W S *BSc(Hons)* tacsc   230197
Gwynn P P J   230197
Howie E M *TD• BSc(Hons)*   300698
Facer R P T   181198
Torbica M   231198
Sinclair J S   10999
Fox C   270300

Captains

Cousins R F M *BSc(Eng)*   250481
Gardiner A W M   100881
Goulding T J   110183
¶Smith H J   10583
¶Watts D S   161183
Taylor T A *TD BSc(Hons) CEng MIEE*   310584
Clarke S R   10285
King S R C *BSc* psc†   10385
McGill W M *BEM*   10486
Shugar N A   120488
Phillips N G *TD BSc(Hons) DN RGN*   10788
Parsons E G *TD• JP* tacsc   10189
Howard V M *MBE*   210689
ØMetcalfe K L tacsc   11189
Bramall W T   91189
ØNeil C R   60690
Butterworth C M   11090
Larsen L   160191
Backhouse R   100691
Brown J   11091
McClurg H W *BSc(Hons)*   10292
Hooper R J   270292
ØHoldsworth C *BA(Hons)*   120492
Morgan A S   280892
Dickson W N   51192
Hatton D B W   260693

Nilan J L *TD*   260693
¶Gregory M   210793
Matthews S R S *BSc(Hons)*   10993
Dinmore A J   10994
Merritt J H *BSc(Econ)Hons*   40994
Mawer J *MISM AIIRSM*   51294
Nattrass D H   81294
Knowles G W   140195
Raybould M J   10295
Winkley C H *BSc(Hons) MIPD*   130295
Anderson I R *BA(Hons)*   230295
Leigh R   200395
ØCranwell-Child S A   50495
Weir J M *BSc*   60495
Dean B J *LLB(Hons)*   110995
Russell J A A   11195
Winrow B W   11295
Shilliday M A   10696
Wills A E J *TD*   10796
Sims A E   10896
Colbeck G   160896
Colquitt P A   10996
Morran A M   250497
Acton F S *BA(Hons)*   60797
Buchanan C R   10997
Bristow M J   10198
Broomfield R P   100298
Jewell K C   10698
Verrier M J   10698
ØSteven W A   50698
Martin H P B   270199
Cowen M *LLB(Hons)*   10299
Talbot-Jones P D   10200
Charlton D G   270300
Brown R   90700
Pitchforth B W *MBE*   40900

Lieutenants

ØSharich C   250994
Harley S J   50995
Newby D W   260396
Laughton N A D   60897
Fernandez P M   11097
Francis-Jones M C   70298
†Connors T J   150498
Moloney J A   270798
Harvey P H C *BSc(Hons)*   181098
ØVenn K J *BA(Hons)*   311099
Whiston C E   50200
Skipworth P H   140600
ØDe Maria S L   10700
Hassell N R   160700
†Coughtrie S W C *LLB(Hons)*   180800

2nd Lieutenants

†Fitzgerald N E
†McKeown A P   270386
†Cox R W M   240690
†Woods A W   50890
†Heslop P R   71090
†Brindle J B   240691
ØBootherstone A E *BEd(Hons)*   240592
ØBlackshaw J M   20892
ØSaunders E M   20892

ØCampion L C *BA(Hons) MA*   291192
ØHarvey A J   150393
ØHennessey K A   230593
†Eddy H J W   10893
†Range G E   10893
†Reekie E J R   260993
ØBailey V E   270394
ØWilliams H M   310794
†Middleton T F   110195
†Tidy H G A   70795
†Squire R J   21095
†White F G *BEng*   21095
†Warren J W J   91195
†Hawley T P   170196
ØFalcon K E   300696
ØNorriss K E   110896
†Deas G D *MA*   61096
ØDonaldson S J *BSc(Hons)*   61096
†McAllister D G *BEng(Hons)*   61096
†Weller M R   61096
†Cook M C   181096
†Shepherd J T W   71196
ØHeaton J R   111196
†Sharma R   181196
†Archibald C E   241196
ØGuy J M   11296
†Steevenson S D R   120797
ØWoolley C J   210797
†Cahill R W D   30897
ØCuthbert L M M   30897
ØWard J L   30897
†Whitfield A H N   30897
†Fraser E A   260997
ØNeil G P   270997
†Lee C J   280997
†Leeds D A   280997
†Lipscombe S J   280997
†Sainsbury I S S *BSc(Hons)*   280997
ØSundt A G   280997
†Tregoning J S   280997
†Hellier C R S   300997
†Fletcher J R   111097
ØDavis C N   121097
†Wilson R S   121097
†Holt A P J S   161097
†Akerman A J   311097
†Worthington L   31197
†Martin B R   51197
ØThompson R J   131197
ØRadway C E H   141197
†Menzies R I   181197
ØCarslake R J   31297
ØSweeney R J   91297
†Hanbury-Bateman P W   151297
†Walker C D   251297
†Capron T E H   271297
†Greet-Smith R J   301297
†Fries C A   240198
†Robertson S M   10298
ØRichards E E   150498
†Richards R H   150498
†Paterson I J   10598
†Irwin S P   140698
ØPitman T E   140698
†Simcock R J   140698
†Atkins R J   20898

ØCampbell K E	20898	†Chisholm A R T	260999	†Palmer D P	60800
ØCorcoran G A	20898	†Cobb G R	260999	†Phillips R D T	60800
†Delaney N	20898	ØDeakin V E	260999	ØReay T V	60800
†Hayes G M	20898	†Dutton S P	260999	ØRobinson E C *MA(Hons)*	60800
ØMcCaferty L F	20898	†Evans C A	260999	†Rose D J	60800
†McEwan R N *Bsc(Hons)*	20898	ØGates S J	260999	†Waddell R A	60800
†McFall J M	20898	†Gaw G	260999	†Wales D J R	60800
†McGivern R	20898	†Goldhawk M J E	260999	ØHaworth K J	90800
†Ross M J	20898	†Hook A W L	260999	†Chalk A M	10900
Scarlett P J R *BSc(Hons) MSc*	20898	ØHoppe R L	260999	†Brember I D	230900
†Smith I M	20898	†Hutchinson G	260999	†Nash	250900
†Sykes C R	20898	†Lamont I	260999	ØGray L J	300900
†Walshaw D E C	20898	ØLove H J *BSc(Hons)*	260999	†Bendall T E	11000
ØJohns P M *BSc*	60998	†McDougall P R	260999	†Cadwallader P N	11000
†Perry T D	160998	†McLenaghan C J	260999	ØChristodoulou T L K	11000
†Chelmick T H	270998	†Potter M R	260999	†Clarke C S	11000
†Coates M D	270998	†Reeves A S	260999	ØCox N B	11000
†McConnell J F	270998	ØRickard C	260999	†Crook R	11000
†McFadzean A J	270998	†Rigby S C	260999	†Crosbie M A	11000
†Mitchell J	270998	†Stanger G A	260999	ØFindlay G K	11000
†Parnell D D	270998	†Stead O J	260999	ØGarthwaite R F	11000
†Roberts J E	270998	†Temlett P J	260999	†Gill M P	11000
†Sylvester-Thorne A N	270998	†Turner J G	11099	ØHook G E R	11000
†Whitley A M	270998	ØHerbert M A	221099	ØHorton R E	11000
†Wigham A D	270998	†Banks J H G	10400	†Irvine W W W *BA(Hons)*	11000
†Hunt D M	61098	ØMoss J E	10500	†Jones M S	11000
†Blake B J	301098	†Aickin R G	40600	†Matthiae T L	11000
†Payne D M L	301098	Boulton A J	20700	ØMcLean A M	11000
ØTimmins N M	71198	†Broughton S C	20700	ØRudd L M	11000
ØParsons E C	101198	†Edwards C D C	20700	†Rule A J W	11000
†Graham P L	201198	†Farrelly C D	20700	ØShambrook S L	11000
ØWoods J M	11298	ØHughes A H	20700	ØTyrrell A M	11000
ØTaylor K L	61298	†Sumners M W	20700	†Badcock D L	21000
†Ashworth J E	301298	ØWest S J	20700	†Lyon J D	21000
†Barnett O J	301298	ØWoodward R M	20700	†Miller J E P	21000
†Joyce G P	20199	†Young S J	20700	†Harris J M	41000
†Lynch P J	310199	†Allchurch M N S	60800	†Johnson B D	51000
†McCullagh M	310199	†Babbington J M	60800	†Kempson E R	51000
†Brewin P E	210299	ØBarr J E G	60800	†Berry N G	71000
†Palmer A D	130699	†Buckley C A	60800	†Sanders P R	171000
†Barraclough C D	10899	ØByers D R	60800	†Harvey J H	181000
†Boyle J E R	10899	†Carpenter T R A	60800	ØHall E J	231000
†Burrell R	10899	†Clifford E P	60800	ØStanley L J	251000
†Castleden J D	10899	ØCook O C L	60800	†Heyes G M T	261000
†Cochrane C M	10899	†Dyer G R	60800	ØBarrett S E J	281100
†Edgar S J *LLB(Hons)*	10899	†Gammon J G *D P S N*	60800	ØLyons L J	10201
†Espie G	10899	†Grimditch A	60800		
†Kemp T J	10899	ØHallett C J *BA(Hons)*	60800		
†Smith R D	10899	†Harty A J S	60800	*Administrative Officers*	
ØStoy H J	10899	†Kent A W	60800	*Captains*	
†Smith N J H	260899	†Maclay A I	60800		
ØLeyland A J	110999	ØMain K J	60800	Veitch B	10487
†Andrews M A	260999	†Mansell A J	60800	Russell A *MBE sq*	20897
†Benn G H	260999	†May T P	60800		
†Bethune R M	260999	†McAvan J O	60800	*Quartermasters*	
†Bull P H	260999	†Millington E J	60800	Hallewell P J *Capt 010400*	
ØCampbell F M	260999	†Oosterveen G M	60800		
†Carter P L	260999	†Pajger S D	60800		

SECTION B
COMBINED CADET FORCE

Captain General . . . . THE QUEEN

ABINGDON SCHOOL
Majors
Earle J C
Lyon S R
Captains
Carson D J M
Lieutenants
McLean-Inglis A R
Ocock S P
2nd Lieutenants

ADAMS GRAMMAR SCHOOL
Majors
Thompstone B S
Captains
Davies I
Davies T E
Shaw A A C
Lieutenants
Skeate M W A
2nd Lieutenants
Weyers D St J

ALLEYNS SCHOOL

Lieutenant Colonels
Jones E M D
Majors
Tickner D J
Captains
Wilkinson D J
Lieutenants
ØPurvis C
ØCowan N L
2nd Lieutenants
Price I M R

AMPLEFORTH COLLEGE

Majors
Corbould M
McLean V F P
Lieutenants
Stewart R M
2nd Lieutenants
ØMulligan S M

ARDINGLY COLLEGE
Majors
Wolley D W
Captains
ØMacKay K L
Pitt J D
Lieutenants
Kerr G J
2nd Lieutenants

ARNOLD SCHOOL
Lieutenant Colonels
Ashcroft J B
Majors
Captains
ØCarroll B A
Lieutenants
ØAllen J
ØPritchard L M
2nd Lieutenants
Treharne A J
Crowther A

AUDENSHAW GRAMMAR SCHOOL
Majors
Twigg J A
Captains
ØDean C E
Lieutenants
Andrew R
Tilling A R
2nd Lieutenants

BANCROFTS SCHOOL
Lieutenant Colonels
Bromfield J G
Majors
Stephens P G
Captains
MacLeod A P
Lieutenants
ØGust T B
Watkins G E
ØPrescott-Morrin H J
2nd Lieutenants

BANGOR GRAMMAR SCHOOL
Lieutenant Colonels
Captains
Culbert J W
Lieutenants
Titterington J T
ØCrawford L E
2nd Lieutenants
ØBoyle K A
ØMilligan J G

BARNARD CASTLE SCHOOL
Majors
Kean S
Captains
Lieutenants
Nicholson M H
Konstacka L
2nd Lieutenants
Hudson M M
ØTucker Z I V

BATLEY GRAMMAR SCHOOL
Captains
Dawson G
Lieutenants
Gott P H
Renolds P N
2nd Lieutenants

BEARWOOD COLLEGE
Majors
Bisset J
Captains
Owen J P
Hooper R L S
Ryall R P
Lieutenants
ØSmith C
2nd Lieutenants

BEDFORD SCHOOL
Majors
Matthews R G N
Lieutenants
ØMilton P E

BEDFORD MODERN SCHOOL

Captains
Beresford R H

Lieutenants
ØLockwood S J

2nd Lieutenants
ØMoody A J

BERKHAMSTED SCHOOL

Lieutenant Colonels
Charnock F

Captains
Mowbray R K

Lieutenants
Cato T
Dobson P E
ØWalsh S A

2nd Lieutenants
Simpson D H
Ridgley G C

BIRKENHEAD SCHOOL

Majors
Gill S M

Captains
ØRowley C H

Lieutenants
Wiltshire R G

BLOXHAM SCHOOL

Lieutenant Colonels
Fletcher-Campbell C

Lieutenants
Parker P V

BLUNDELLS SCHOOL

Majors
Homer I

Captains
Brabban D H

Lieutenants
Berrow A J R
ØSmith F M

2nd Lieutenants
ØGillan E J

BOURNEMOUTH SCHOOL

Majors
Bowen A J

Captains
Mcaulay H

Lieutenants
Kewley G J

2nd Lieutenants

BRADFIELD COLLEGE

Lieutenant Colonels

Majors

Captains
Maynard A M
Urquhart K B

Lieutenants
Lee D

2nd Lieutenants
Carlier C A
Gillies D H
Goodwin M K

BRADFORD GRAMMAR SCHOOL

Majors
Burnett S P D
Stoney I M TD

Captains
Ratcliffe P

Lieutenants
Hicks D M
Wilson A R

2nd Lieutenants

BRAMDEAN SCHOOL

Captains
Cowley A D *MBE*

Lieutenants

BRENTWOOD SCHOOL

Lieutenant Colonels
Retford L G T

Majors
Carr N J
Thomas G
Brown J R

Captains
McCallum K I R

Lieutenants
ØHarris K E
ØMillward T J
Nuttall R N

2nd Lieutenants
McSkimming G J
Innocent M L
ØTaylor G G

BRIDLINGTON SCHOOL

Captains
Kneller B G
McKenna P J

Lieutenants

2nd Lieutenants
Middleton B S

BRIGHTON COLLEGE

Captains
Radojcic S

Lieutenants
Turnbull D U
ØArcher M J

2nd Lieutenants
Dahl J

BROMSGROVE SCHOOL

Majors
Hayward T R M
Stephens R E W

Captains
ØHayward G S

Lieutenants
Maund C P
Johns A R

BURY GRAMMAR SCHOOL

Majors
Rylance R J

Captains
Newton P G

Lieutenants
Phillips A A
Bishop D A
Robinson L W
Hone M J

CALDAY GRANGE GRAMMAR SCHOOL

Lieutenant Colonels

Lieutenants
Farnworth P D

2nd Lieutenants
Davies I M

CAMPBELL COLLEGE

Lieutenant Colonels
Grant D E

Majors

Captains
Cathcart H
Quigg S D
Semple J W D
Stevens A D

Lieutenants
Dermott P T
King J T C
McKinney H J
Oldfield D S
ØThompson K E

2nd Lieutenants
ØMoore S A
Johnston S J

CANFORD SCHOOL
Majors
Culley D P
Owen M A

Captains
Bartlett M A

Lieutenants
Hooker R H J
Baugniet N R
Blan S J

2nd Lieutenants
McCarroll S A

CATERHAM SCHOOL
Majors
Atkin M J

Captains

Lieutenants
Bage I
Du-Toit P C
ØStumbles P J

2nd Lieutenants

CAWSTON COLLEGE
Captains

Lieutenants

CHARTERHOUSE SCHOOL
Lieutenant Colnels

Majors
Sergison-Main J

Captains
Kenyon S

Lieutenants
Fielder S P
Kitt R M C
Reid C L

2nd Lieutenants

CHELTENHAM COLLEGE
Lieutenant Colonels
Wright I D

Majors
Cox S H
Trythall P J A

Captains
Reid C L

Lieutenants

2nd Lieutenants
Bullock S F

CHICHESTER HIGH SCHOOL
Captains
Sambrook J O

Lieutenants
Graham R S

2nd Lieutenants
Jones M T

CHRIST COLLEGE BRECON
Lieutenant Colonels
Crockett R J

Majors

Captains
Vickers M *BEM*

Lieutenants
ØTill J L M

2nd Lieutenants
ØMorrell C M

CHRISTS COLLEGE, FINCHLEY
Lieutenant Colonels
Walden J I

Majors

Captains
Cliff J N
Fuller B W
Davies G A
Waller R J

Lieutenants

2nd Lieutenants
Jacobs R C
Dearing A P

CHRISTS HOSPITAL, HORSHAM
Lieutenant Colonels

Majors
Smith A

Captains
Mason S
Gunning A M

Lieutenants

CHURCHERS COLLEGE
Captains
ØEaton C

Lieutenants

2nd Lieutenants
Page K R M
Parrish M

CHURSTON GRAMMAR SCHOOL
Lieutenants
Green C G

2nd Lieutenants
Wood J C

CLAYESMORE SCHOOL
Majors
Smith S A

Captains
ØBillington S M *M BSc*

Lieutenants
Middle C R

2nd Lieutenants

CLIFTON COLLEGE
Majors
Cross R C

Captains

2nd Lieutenants
Scaife M
Warn K W

COLFE'S SCHOOL
Majors
Cherry C J

Captains

Lieutenants

COLLYERS 6TH FORM COLLEGE
Captains
Caudwell W G

Lieutenants
McDowell D B

2nd Lieutenants
ØTodd J P

COLSTON SCHOOL
Majors
Waters S W A

Captains
Dawson K
Scarll T J

Lieutenants

2nd Lieutenants
ØScarll A A

COWES HIGH SCHOOL
Captains
ØMead E F

Lieutenants

348

CRANBROOK SCHOOL

Majors
Green C G

Captains
Allison A C

Lieutenants
Cossins R A P
Swinburne D A
ØTaylor J A

2nd Lieutenants

CRANLEIGH SCHOOL

Majors
McConnell-Wood T I

Captains

Lieutenants
Staley C N
Sutcliffe D C
Young S A H

2nd Lieutenants

DANIEL STEWARTS AND MELVILLE COLLEGE

Lieutenant Colonels
Caton P A

Majors
Hamid M Z

Captains
Cairney J E

Lieutenants
Burns R
ØLewis C I
Mitchell G W

2nd Lieutenants
Witherspoon A N
Shepherd S W
ØMcIntosh J D

DEAN CLOSE SCHOOL

Lieutenant Colonels
Burrows J R J

Majors

Captains
Reid A J

Lieutenants
ØCarmichael C F
Waring N L
Williams G T

2nd Lieutenants
Young A K P
Edmond L C
ØMosley N A

DENSTONE COLLEGE

Majors
Menneer R C

Captains
Duncan A R J
Lieutenants

DOLLAR ACADEMY

Majors
Hendry J M

Captains
Collier G L
Stewart C A

Lieutenants

DOVER GRAMMAR SCHOOL

Captains
Peall M F J

Lieutenants
Wilkins W

DOWNSIDE SCHOOL

Majors
Pountney A H

Captains
Barrett N J
Pearce G G

Lieutenants

2nd Lieutenants
Leverage M G P

DUKE OF YORK'S ROYAL MILITARY SCHOOL

Majors
Alexander D W
Carson M B
English J H

Captains
Saunderson S S
Parsons D L
Pearce R J

Lieutenants
Bickerstaff A W
Broughton J R
ØDyer C J
Nunn A M

2nd Lieutenants
ØBelcher L S

DULWICH COLLEGE

Majors
Brownridge J P
Rutter G E

Captains
Jones R O

Lieutenants
Field R J
Howell J A R

2nd Lieutenants
O'Neill J M

DUNDEE HIGH SCHOOL

Majors
Spowart G W

Captains
Holmes D C
Steele R H

Lieutenants
Allen G H
Hulbert C E
McAdam C R
Tosh E J

2nd Lieutenants
Gifford M B
ØGeorge T M

DURHAM SCHOOL

Lieutenant Colonels
Burgess J A

Majors
Kern N G

Captains

Lieutenants
Hallam G
Wallace A R

2nd Lieutenants
Earnshaw G J

EASTBOURNE COLLEGE

Lieutenant Colonels

Majors
Hodkinson D J

Captains
Wynn A P

Lieutenants
Heale R E
Mathieson K I

349

EDINBURGH ACADEMY
Majors
Turner R G

Captains
Jack N J
Miller J E

Lieutenants

ELIZABETH COLLEGE
Lieutenant Colonels
Rawlins-Duquemin I J

Majors

Captains
Aplin B E H

Lieutenants
Smith M P

2nd Lieutenants
Mathieson K I

ELLESMERE COLLEGE
Lieutenant Colonels
Scorer J M

Majors
Clewlow M P
Hutchinson G

Captains
Richmond C D

Lieutenants
Blake N M
Gareh M T
Moir C G

2nd Lieutenants
Moir C G
ØHilton K B

EMANUEL SCHOOL
Majors

Lieutenants
McLean-Inglis A R

2nd Lieutenants

EPSOM COLLEGE
Majors
Hampshire M

Captains
Huxter E A
Scadding A G
Gill R
ØParsons D A

Lieutenants
Shephard P M
Postle J R W
Bucholdt C B
Corbett F C

ETON COLLEGE
Lieutenant Colonels
Cooper D

Majors
Prior R G

Captains
Wilcockson M L

Lieutenants
Land W M A
ØSaunders E M

2nd Lieutenants
Price D A

EXETER SCHOOL
Majors
Allen J D

Captains
Daniel A J
Poustle J D

Lieutenants
Daniel A J
Foster M W
Keyes N P L
ØStewart S L

2nd Lieutenants
ØWynn J C
Moon N W

FELSTED SCHOOL
Majors
Bartlett P

Captains
Lee C

Lieutenants

FETTES COLLEGE
Lieutenant Colonels
Orr J A *OBE*

Majors
Morris J J
Murray A F
Gillespie J W J

Captains
Kesterton P
Mather D F
Alexander A S

Lieutenants
Rogerson C D

2nd Lieutenants
Aidonis A

FOREST SCHOOL
Majors
Smith M J

Captains
Lewis J C

Lieutenants

2nd Lieutenants
Butt R D B

FRAMLINGHAM COLLEGE
Lieutenant Colonels

Majors
Myers-Allen M K

Captains

Lieutenants
Skitch R W
Wardle M A
Todd M J

2nd Lieutenants
ØRead F
Scarce R B
ØParson J-A

GEORGE HERIOTS SCHOOL
Majors
Copland I M
ØPeddie L J

2nd Lieutenants
Bain J
Meikle R S

GIGGLESWICK SCHOOL
Lieutenant Colonels
Mussett N J

Captains

Lieutenants
ØWood A L
Lawson M C
Thompson S

2nd Lieutenants

GLASGOW ACADEMY
Lieutenant Colonels
Littlefield R S

Majors

Captains
ØGilmour E A
Jeffreys A P

Lieutenants
McCallum C D
ØRiberzani L E

2nd Lieutenants

THE GODOLPHIN SCHOOL

Majors

Captains

2nd Lieutenants

Berry M W
ØRook-Blackstone S
ØStone S L

GORDONS SCHOOL

Majors

Robinson J A

Captains

Robinson D H
Kenyon S
Wilkinson D

Lieutenants

Short A W
Kenyon S
Norbron S J

2nd Lieutenants

GRESHAMS SCHOOL

Lieutenant Colonels

Peaver R H *TD MA MIL*

Majors

Heaney R G

Captains

Edwards A A
Flower N C
George R O
Moore S
Seaman J P
ØWalton K
Walton D T

Lieutenants

Ball N J
ØJones H C
ØMoore J E

2nd Lieutenants

Bartle G D

HABERDASHER ASKES SCHOOL (ELSTREE)

Captains

Tarpey J K

Lieutenants

Saddington N P
Yeabsley M I

2nd Lieutenants

HAILEYBURY COLLEGE

Majors

Monk P C T

Captains

Bishop R H
Johns P F
Bass R G
Strike V P

Lieutenants

Igolen-Robinson C E
Plewes N L M

2nd Lieutenants

ØGoble N L M
Oliver R D

HAMPTON SCHOOL

Majors

Xiberras M D

Captains

Bailey W N

Lieutenants

Hamm J D
ØMaguire J F

THE THOMAS HARDYE SCHOOL

Lieutenants

Hughes B M
Coles R K

2nd Lieutenants

HARROW SCHOOL

Majors

McKinney W J

Captains

Farrar-Bell C J
Stead M P
Davies J R
Luckett D A

Lieutenants

Jenkins G E

2nd Lieutenants

Howard A J
Patterson G

HELE'S SCHOOL

Lieutenant Colonels

Williams A G *MBE*

Captains

ØWard D C

Lieutenants

Damerell C J

2nd Lieutenants

HEREFORD CATHEDRAL SCHOOL

Majors

Matthews T A *MBE TD*

Captains

Payne C G

Lieutenants

Falshaw P J

2nd Lieutenants

HIGHGATE SCHOOL

Majors

Captains
Lunn N M

Lieutenants

THE HOWARD GRAMMAR SCHOOL

Majors

Wilson J D *TD*

Captains

Lloyd-Owen R A

Lieutenants

Collins D R
Loynes J T

2nd Lieutenants

Colthup P J
Morgan K

HULME GRAMMAR SCHOOL

Lieutenant Colonels

Coulton I T

Captains

Conreen D J
Galloway P

Lieutenants

Fearon S A

HURSTPIERPOINT COLLEGE

Majors

Gowans J A

Captains

Williams E M J

Lieutenants

Bowen G C

2nd Lieutenants

ØSimkin M D

IPSWICH SCHOOL
Lieutenant Colonels
Clayton R L

Majors

Captains
Anglim B J

Lieutenants
Hamlet P M

JUDD SCHOOL
Majors
Stowell G H

Captains
Noble A F

Lieutenants

2nd Lieutenants
Bull D J
Wyld J D

KELLY COLLEGE
Captains
Masters B T

Lieutenants
ØRankin E L

2nd Lieutenants
Ingram C P
Bell I

KELVINSIDE ACADEMY
Lieutenant Colonels
Geddes G

Majors

Captains
Gilliland A J
Macleod N G
Simpson D

Lieutenants

KIMBOLTON SCHOOL
Majors
ØCamp S E
Pepper M

Captains

Lieutenants
Buckley D P
Groom C L

2nd Lieutenants

KINGS COLLEGE, TAUNTON
Majors
Burton G C

Captains
Cole D J
Hart T K W

Lieutenants
Howard S M
ØPage F V
Sykes B

2nd Lieutenants
ØDenning M A

KINGS COLLEGE SCHOOL, WIMBLEDON
Majors
Grayson J T

Captains
Chambers M J

Lieutenants
Wharton P W
Lavender D J

2nd Lieutenants
Morren M S

KINGS SCHOOL, BRUTON
Lieutenant Colonels
Passmore M B

Majors
Hastings R C F

Captains
Chesney J P S

Lieutenants
ØAshton M
Ellis R S

2nd Lieutenants

KINGS SCHOOL, CANTERBURY
Majors

Captains
Franks M J

Lieutenants
Vye M J
Winrow-Campbell S J

KINGS SCHOOL, CHESTER
Captains
Robinson I H

Lieutenants
Elmore R D J
Williams H M

KINGS SCHOOL, GLOUCESTER
Lieutenants

2nd Lieutenants

KINGS SCHOOL, GRANTHAM
Majors
Barker D H
Brister P H
Dixon T E

Captains
Caulfield J L
Kirkby W R

Lieutenants
Barton N C
Thomas M J

KINGS SCHOOL, ROCHESTER
Captains
Gates S B

Lieutenants
Richter B W
Craggs D G

2nd Lieutenants

KINGS SCHOOL WORCESTER
Lieutenant Colonels
Davies S R

Captains

Lieutenants
Rudge M D
Featherstone N

KING CHARLES I SCHOOL
Majors

Captains

Lieutenants
Marrett R A

2nd Lieutenants
ØThomas J L

KING EDWARD VI GRAMMAR SCHOOL CHELMSFORD
Majors

Captains
ØOwen A

Lieutenants
Brown G P

2nd Lieutenants
Baggs A C

KING EDWARD IV GRAMMAR SCHOOL, LOUTH

2nd Lieutenants

Blakey K I
Hayday T E
ØKheng J M

KING EDWARDS SCHOOL, BATH

Majors

Brownrigg P A

Captains

Trim A

Lieutenants

KING EDWARDS SCHOOL, BIRMINGHAM

Majors

Captains

Collins T
Dewar D C

Lieutenants

2nd Lieutenants

ØAllhusen L E F

KING WILLIAMS COLLEGE

Lieutenant Colonels

Majors

Turner M W
Morton W D

Captains

Lieutenants

Gulland J R

2nd Lieutenants

KINGHAM HILL SCHOOL

Majors

Emberson A D

Captains

Fowler I W

Lieutenants

Mulholland S J

2nd Lieutenants

KINGSTON GRAMMAR SCHOOL

Captains

ØWright J E

Lieutenants

Hind J R
Markey M H

2nd Lieutenants

White T E J

KIRKHAM GRAMMAR SCHOOL

Lieutenant Colonels

Sayer F W

Majors

Scott I M

Captains

Hill A M
Gardiner S P
Miller T P
Crowther S

Lieutenants

KNOX ACADEMY

Majors

Macfarlane G L

Captains

Lieutenants

Smith R M

2nd Lieutenants

ØPeck S J

LANCING COLLEGE

Lieutenant Colonels

Lewis P E

Majors

Captains

Dell M P

Lieutenants

ØBailey L
Standage J E

2nd Lieutenants

LANGLEY SCHOOL

Lieutenant Colonels

Majors

Morgan G C
Ogden J N

Captains

Lieutenants

Skelton J L

2nd Lieutenants

Butt F P L

LEEDS GRAMMAR SCHOOL

Captains

Fuller K F

Lieutenants

Dickson J A J
Potter G S

2nd Lieutenants

LEYS SCHOOL

Majors

Captains

Fraser C I A
Brown M A

Lieutenants

Hill R A D

2nd Lieutenants

Silk R W

LINCOLN SCHOOL OF SCIENCE AND TECHNOLOGY

Captains

Savage D B

Lieutenants

Paddison N

2nd Lieutenants

McEwan L
Wieland P W

LIVERPOOL COLLEGE

Majors

Pickett D V

Captains

Davies A
Hildick B G
Corfe J D

Lieutenants

Blackwood I S
ØMiller L M
ØNuttall J

2nd Lieutenants

ØDavey P A

LLANDOVERY COLLEGE

Captains

Williams G C
Jennings C N H

Lieutenants

Price V A
Evans G R

2nd Lieutenants

Vaughan W T

CITY OF LONDON SCHOOL

Lieutenant Colonels

Woodhams F R

Majors

ØWoodhams J A
Clements M P

Captains

Lieutenants

Branch C H
Wilson A G
Woodhouse T S

THE LONDON ORATORY SCHOOL

Lieutenant Colonels

Captains

Mayers N M
Moore M R

Lieutenants

Western C D

2nd Lieutenants

Carabine J E

LONGHILL SCHOOL

Lieutenants

Ball J L
Johnson T D
Lonsdale P M J
Mayers N M
ØThomas R T

2nd Lieutenants

Burt D
ØBucklar S C

LORDSWOOD BOYS' SCHOOL AND SIX FORM CENTRE

Captains

MacIntosh N D

Lieutenants

Thurlow P D

2nd Lieutenants

LORD WANDSWORTH COLLEGE

Majors

Jackson R B

Captains

Owen D L

Lieutenants

Batten A P
ØMiranda De Carvalho M L

2nd Lieutenants

LORETTO SCHOOL

Lieutenant Colonels

Whait R P

Majors

Captains

Pryde C N
Spall C F

Lieutenants

2nd Lieutenants

LOUGHBOROUGH GRAMMAR SCHOOL

Lieutenant Colonels

Beazley H G

Majors

Jennings M R

Captains

Steele D W

Lieutenants

Burns J G
Crookes J P
Starkings D M
Taylor D M

2nd Lieutenants

Kerr G J

MAGDALEN COLLEGE SCHOOL, OXFORD

Lieutenant Colonels

Majors

Captains

Day J K

Lieutenants

Smith D L *MBE*

2nd Lieutenants

McNeile M T H
Curwood S J
ØHunter M H
ØRaw A M

MAIDSTONE GRAMMAR SCHOOL

Lieutenant Colonels

Smith L

Captains

Lieutenants

Dovey T H
ØRenn P J

2nd Lieutenants

Evans P J

MALVERN COLLEGE

Majors

Harriss F O

Captains

Lacey R G

Lieutenants

Smith R S D
Witcomb R G
ØPhillipson A

2nd Lieutenants

MARLBOROUGH COLLEGE

Majors

Cleminson N R

Captains

Conlen M
Cayley D W D

Lieutenants

Doyle G A

2nd Lieutenants

MERCHANT TAYLORS SCHOOL, CROSBY

Lieutenant Colonels

Irvine P A

Majors

Wallace I

Captains

Fitzgerald T J
ØKnaggs D
Slemen M A

Lieutenants

Lawrence D A
McKie I D
Toley R M

2nd Lieutenants

ØGonzalez M T
Husbands M C
Johnson A N K

MERCHANT TAYLORS SCHOOL, NORTHWOOD

Majors

Captains

Blight N G
Turner M

Lieutenants

2nd Lieutenants

MERCHISTON CASTLE SCHOOL

Lieutenant Colonels

Gill M C L

Majors

Captains

Russel R J
Selby J K
Syme D C

Lieutenants

Coull J C

2nd Lieutenants

354

MERRILL COLLEGE

Captains

Bruntell I J

Lieutenants

2nd Lieutenants

MILL HILL SCHOOL

Lieutenant Colonels

Bickerdike P S

Majors

Barnes H

Lieutenants

ØEvesham E J M
Ellen K V
Monaghan J R

2nd Lieutenants

MILTON ABBEY SCHOOL

Captains

Clapper M S
Hughes-D'Aeth W J

Lieutenants

Arkel N H M
Pugh M D

2nd Lieutenants

Phipps M A

MONKTON COMBE SCHOOL

Lieutenant Colonels

Majors

Findlay-Palmer I

Captains

Lieutenants

Herbert G P
Jameson D R
Smith J J
ØWales R L

2nd Lieutenants

ØWaddington A J

MONMOUTH SCHOOL

Majors

Captains

Spawforth G D
Dowling S
Christmas M R

Lieutenants

Adams D C
Dennis-Jones P

2nd Lieutenants

ØAlexander J

MORRISONS ACADEMY

Majors

Captains

Mair A W S

Lieutenants

ØO'Grady S M
Young G W

2nd Lieutenants

ØMair L M

MOUNT ST MARYS COLLEGE

Lieutenant Colonels

Jackson M P

Majors

Captains

Krlic M
ØHazelhurst G

Lieutenants

Kirrane G F
Mulkerrins A P
Thompson P S

NEWCASTLE UNDER LYME SCHOOL

Lieutenant Colonels

Pedder J A

Majors

Captains

George E M

Lieutenants

Preston D A
ØVarney A L

2nd Lieutenants

NORTHOLT HIGH SCHOOL

Lieutenant Colonels

Coleiro J

Captains

Hennah R D

Lieutenants

NOTTINGHAM HIGH SCHOOL

Majors

Clarke R J
Cleverley M T

Captains

Lieutenants

Quinlan T M
Spedding I P

2nd Lieutenants

OAKHAM SCHOOL

Lieutenant Colonels

Captains

Gutteridge S C D

Lieutenants

Miller S J
ØMeyrick C M

2nd Lieutenants

OLD SWINFORD HOSPITAL SCHOOL

Lieutenant Colonels

Dewar D G W

Majors

Captains

Day R E
Hudson S J

Lieutenants

Woods A E

2nd Lieutenants

ORATORY SCHOOL

Majors

Womersley R B

Captains

Harris J C
Topham N E

Lieutenants

Browne B W
Eastham M J
Upton R H

2nd Lieutenants

OSWESTRY SCHOOL

Lieutenant Colonels

Foster I C C

Majors

Captains

Evanson R G
Leonard R M

Lieutenants

OUNDLE SCHOOL

Majors

Captains

Sharp D
Dew D W

Lieutenants

Holstrom W F
King P S C
ØHolmstrom M A

2nd Lieutenants

ØBircher C S P

PANGBOURNE COLLEGE
Majors

Captains
Vasa A

Lieutenants
Brown R C M

2nd Lieutenants

PATES GRAMMAR SCHOOL
Lieutenant Colonels
Dray M J B

Majors
Woodall N J

Captains
Brunsdon R C
ØKidger K J

Lieutenants
Jones A J
Kidger K J
Wood D R
ØWoodall S

2nd Lieutenants

PERSE SCHOOL
Lieutenant Colonels

Majors
Roberts A J

Captains
Vodden H B G

Lieutenants
Burrows J C
ØHarris J
Wareing R

PLYMOUTH COLLEGE
Majors
Sillitoe C J

Captains
Sillitoe A S

Lieutenants
Scoins D J

POCKLINGTON SCHOOL
Captains
Tomaszewski N A

Lieutenants
Parsons D J
Milne M G

CITY OF PORTSMOUTH BOYS SCHOOL
Captains

Lieutenants

PORTSMOUTH GRAMMAR SCHOOL
Majors
Hunt J C A

Captains
Nials P E
ØSheldrick S J
Taylor W M

Lieutenants

2nd Lieutenants
Flowers C C
Sheldrick B W

PRESENTATION COLLEGE
Lieutenant Colonels
Moran T S

Majors

Captains
Luaces-Fernandez V J

Lieutenants
Morris A S J

2nd Lieutenants
Brown S C

PRIOR PARK COLLEGE
Majors

Lieutenants
ØSach D E
Trott R J

2nd Lieutenants
ØBlake C J

QUEEN ELIZABETH SCHOOL
Captains
Butler D

Lieutenants

2nd Lieutenants

QUEEN MARYS (THE VYNE SCHOOL), BASINGSTOKE
Lieutenant Colonels
Townend C M

Captains
Lock G D

Lieutenants

QUEEN MARYS GRAMMAR SCHOOL, WALSALL
Lieutenant Colonels

Captains
Law S J *BSc*
Maund A J

Lieutenants
Fudge I S
Champ R G
Anderson J S *MBE*

2nd Lieutenants

QUEEN VICTORIA SCHOOL, DUNBLANE
Majors
Silcox J R

Captains
Garden D
Onslow P S

Lieutenants

2nd Lieutenants
ØScott J

RADLEY COLLEGE
Lieutenant Colonels
Pollard R

Captains
Hearsey S E
ØJamset C
Jones S C I
Laidler P

Lieutenants
Weaver N J

2nd Lieutenants

RATCLIFFE COLLEGE
Lieutenant Colonels

Majors
Balmbra M G

Captains

Lieutenants
Strutt S M

READ SCHOOL
Lieutenant Colonels
Staves J *TD*

Captains
Gorse M

Lieutenants
ØBridgeford M L
ØPalmer C C *M C*
ØStrutt S M

2nd Lieutenants
Harper M R

READING SCHOOL
Captains
Scoble G T
Terry C J
Lieutenants
Hurst P F E
2nd Lieutenants

READING BLUE COAT SCHOOL
Lieutenant Colonels
Imeson J S
Captains
Brown J P
Reedman P A
Lieutenants
Selvester D H R
ØCard H M
Wadsworth M D
2nd Lieutenants
Lee A J

REEDS SCHOOL
Captains
Clapp I A
Hamilton D H
Lieutenants
2nd Lieutenants
Holdsworth M V

REIGATE GRAMMAR SCHOOL
Majors
Stephens P G
Lieutenants
2nd Lieutenants
Revell D N

REPTON SCHOOL
Lieutenant Colonels
Carrington C R
Majors
Wimbush M R H
Brown I D
Captains
Cox A A
Gould H G
Whittaker P
Lieutenants
ØNield S M
Scott T D H
2nd Lieutenants

ROBERT GORDON COLLEGE
Majors
Captains
Cowie K S
Lieutenants
Strang D J
Maitland M P
Morris D S
2nd Lieutenants
Spracklin C J

ROSSALL SCHOOL
Lieutenant Colonels
Majors
Evans N S
Captains
ØHolden P J
ØMarsh T
Lieutenants
Brooke F R
2nd Lieutenants
Eames D M
Riding J L

ROYAL SCHOOL, ARMAGH
Lieutenant Colonels
Griffiths M A
McCahon W E
Captains
Martin N W K
Maxwell R T
Lieutenants
2nd Lieutenants
ØNesbitt A
George T W

ROYAL BELFAST ACADEMICAL INSTITUTION
Majors
Stevenson H H
Todd B J
Captains
Wallace D L
Lieutenants
Laverty I J
Wilson R J
2nd Lieutenants
ØAndrews K L

ROYAL GRAMMAR SCHOOL, GUILDFORD
Lieutenant Colonels
Majors
Ross J A
Woolcott D J
Captains
Wilson S
Lieutenants
2nd Lieutenants
Rowland D

ROYAL GRAMMAR SCHOOL, HIGH WYCOMBE
Lieutenant Colonels
Hollingworth R G
Captains
Cunningham C J
Lieutenants
Boreham A
Rysdale G S
Rowe D R
2nd Lieutenants
Crook M S
Smith A F
Watson D A

ROYAL GRAMMAR SCHOOL, LANCASTER
Lieutenant Colonels
Thorn N
Majors
Captains
Rowe D R
Lieutenants
Storey R V
2nd Lieutenants
West R B

ROYAL GRAMMAR SCHOOL, NEWCASTLE
Lieutenant Colonels
Griffiths M A
Captains
Camm J L
Lieutenants
Barlow M R
2nd Lieutenants
Rothwell D A

ROYAL GRAMMAR SCHOOL, WORCESTER
Majors
Barnes T C
Captains
Wickson J L
Lieutenants
2nd Lieutenants

ROYAL HOSPITAL SCHOOL
Lieutenant Colonels
Majors
Surzyn P A
Godfrey M H
Captains
Barley S J
Lieutenants
Malone P P
Thompson L

ROYAL RUSSELL SCHOOL
Lieutenant Colonels
Green P W
Captains
Lieutenants
Parker R J
Lacey J D C
2nd Lieutenants
ØBoswell M J
Froy C D

ROYAL WOLVERHAMPTON SCHOOL
Majors
Beckett G W
Lieutenants
Bailey S M
Atherton A M
Sterling I
Toyne E M
2nd Lieutenants

RUGBY SCHOOL
Lieutenant Colonels
Ray R D R
Captains
McMenemey J D S
Lieutenants
Bartle J P
Heir J S
Longworth S A
Steele-Bodger H O
2nd Lieutenants
Byrne P A

RUTHIN SCHOOL
Majors
Lowry R C
Captains
ØWatts J
Lieutenants
2nd Lieutenants
Colclough J
Stazicker I

RUTLISH SCHOOL
Majors
Penny R J
Lieutenants
2nd Lieutenants
Parsons E G
Richmond A C
Schomberg J C

ST ALBANS SCHOOL
Majors
Woodsmith N A *BSc FSS*
Captains
Everitt K J
Lieutenants
ØMendes Da Costa L A
2nd Lieutenants
Webster D A

ST BARTHOLOMEWS SCHOOL
Majors
Patrick A
Captains
Hart M C
Lieutenants
Schofield M
ØParsons J L
2nd Lieutenants
ØEagles S
ØWright E C

ST BEES SCHOOL
Lieutenant Colonels
Payne A C
Majors
Evans J D
Captains
Hannah A J
Knewstubb J E
ØJohnston L A
Lieutenants
Elvin T M
2nd Lieutenants

ST BENEDICT'S SCHOOL
Lieutenant Colonels
Majors
Captains
Summerfield T J
Lieutenants
Rimington K
2nd Lieutenants
Bonfiglio J F

ST COLUMBAS COLLEGE
Majors
Captains
2nd Lieutenants
Ashmore J
Sapsford J

ST DUNSTANS COLLEGE
Lieutenant Colonels
Majors
Davis P F
Elliott R A
Captains
Austin R
Sharp A D
Lieutenants
Gordon D C
Osborne C J

ST EDMUNDS COLLEGE
Majors
Captains
Rivers S J
Lieutenants
Drew L M
2nd Lieutenants

ST EDMUNDS SCHOOL
Lieutenant Colonels
Barnard C D
Majors
Captains
Hawkins S R
Whitehouse D G
Hawkins G N
Hawkins M G S
Lieutenants
ØBarnard K M E
2nd Lieutenants

ST EDWARDS SCHOOL
Lieutenant Colonels
Anderson R A L
Majors
Johnston C J J
Captains
Nagle G
Lieutenants
Arnold S R
ØBudd J
Jolley P A
Yusaf A A
2nd Lieutenants
Shindler K J

ST IGNATIUS COLLEGE
Majors
East G A R
Captains
Crutchley M G
Lieutenants
Davenport K C

ST JOHNS SCHOOL
Majors
Jones R E
Captains
Noble P C
Seale B F T
Lieutenants

2nd Lieutenants
Plimsoll S
Scott A V
Tett J F

ST JOSEPHS COLLEGE WITH THE SCHOOL OF JESUS AND MARY
Majors

Captains
Hirst K J
Lieutenants
Friel P C J
2nd Lieutenants
Buck P J
ØRickard L
Vick S J

ST LAWRENCE COLLEGE
Lieutenant Colonels
Fletcher D E
Majors

Captains
Gill E B
Lieutenants

ST MARYS COLLEGE
Majors
Sullivan K
Captains
Rothnie N
Lieutenants
Bevan R W *MBE*
ØOverend A E M
2nd Lieutenants

ST PETERS HIGH SCHOOL
Lieutenant Colonels

Majors
Davey C M
Captains
ØOgden L R
Lieutenants

2nd Lieutenants

ST PETERS SCHOOL
Lieutenant Colonels
Majors
Captains
Lodge M
Lieutenants
Monteith M
2nd Lieutenants
Howman S
ØLowther A M

SANDBACH SCHOOL
Lieutenant Colonels
Ayres R J
Majors
Captains
Sykes K
ØMason N
Lieutenants
Richards S C
ØGoodman R
Mason J L
2nd Lieutenants

SCARBOROUGH COLLEGE
Lieutenant Colonels
Rowe K W
Majors
ØRowe G A
Captains
Mison L G
Lieutenants
Lucas J E
2nd Lieutenants
Wilson P J
ØFlower J A

SEAFORD COLLEGE
Lieutenant Colonels
Woodcock K R
Majors
Captains
Dunlop R C
Putnam A J
Lieutenants
ØFreeman K J
Smith A
2nd Lieutenants
Barnes D C
ØPointer K
Hodgkiss G E I

SEDBERGH SCHOOL
Lieutenant Colonels
Knowles P J N
Majors
Captains
Jeffries T
Lieutenants
Lewis A R
Fisher J E
Hobson I C
2nd Lieutenants
Brown P J
Wilson M D

SEVENOAKS SCHOOL
Captains
Bassett P R
Ford P
Penfold A R
Lieutenants
Hornsby P M
Kiggell J L
2nd Lieutenants
Coles E C
Hewson D I

SHERBORNE SCHOOL
Majors
Warren R M
Skinner M G
Captains
Lieutenants
Hatch A M
Tremewan S
2nd Lieutenants
ØClayton V A
Ricketts J R

SHIPLAKE COLLEGE
Lieutenant Colonels
Webb P J F
Majors
Captains
Cassells G
Lieutenants
Hose P G
Wilson D
2nd Lieutenants

SHOREHAM COLLEGE
Majors
Harrison G P
Captains
Lieutenants
Genders M J
2nd Lieutenants
ØSteere B J
ØClaydon K

SHREWSBURY SCHOOL
Majors
Gladwin J M
Kidson T
Captains
Scales P R
Lieutenants
David N P
Mostyn M A J
Wareing S

SIR ROGER MANWOODS SCHOOL
Lieutenant Colonels
Harlow R S *CFM*
Captains
Dean P G
ØGarvey J
Pashley H T

SKINNERS SCHOOL
Lieutenant Colonels
Majors
White C E
Holding A J
Wallace J D *MBE*
Fitzwater R W
Captains
Braggins P C D
Golding S B
Lieutenants
Neal P J
Smith M S
2nd Lieutenants

SOLIHULL SCHOOL
Lieutenant Colonels
Miller D R
Captains
Flood R N
Melling R J
Lieutenants
Leonard N W S
Bromley S D E
2nd Lieutenants
Coles J R G

STAMFORD SCHOOL
Lieutenant Colonels
Woolf G W
Captains
Bentley D J
Froggett G
Lieutenants
Earl G T
Tilling A R
Mills S J

STONYHURST COLLEGE
Lieutenant Colonels
Cobb J *MBE*
Captains
Oliver S J
Lieutenants
Barber A
2nd Lieutenants
Channing D B
ØParkinson J M
Stapleton P R

STOWE SCHOOL
Lieutenant Colonels
Cottam P V
Captains
Lieutenants
2nd Lieutenants
Brandt D G
Sewell P R

STRATHALLAN SCHOOL
Captains
Lieutenants
ØRick K S
2nd Lieutenants

SUTTON GRAMMAR SCHOOL
Captains
Ashworth S
Robinson C E
Lieutenants
2nd Lieutenants
Bhalla A
Collins P P

SUTTON VALENCE SCHOOL
Lieutenant Colonels
Parkinson C F G
ØWilkinson A F F
Captains
Miller B W
Lieutenants
Cooper D A
ØRankin E L
2nd Lieutenants
ØTragett P C
Walsh J R

TAUNTON SCHOOL
Majors
Pugh S E
Captains
Hill T J
Lieutenants
Kinnear D
Piper I D
2nd Lieutenants
ØArnold J M

THE PRIORY LSST
Captains
Savage D B
Lieutenants
McEwan L
Paddison N
2nd Lieutenants
Wieland P W

TONBRIDGE SCHOOL
Majors
Boucher S M
Captains
Cazalet F W G
Lieutenants
2nd Lieutenants
Brennan M F

TRENT COLLEGE

Majors
Barnett S D M

Captains
Dunford D A
ØFox R F
McGinnes A P
Shuttleworth P A

Lieutenants
ØPembleton-Brown C M
Phillips M C

2nd Lieutenants

TRINITY COLLEGE, GLENALMOND

Majors

Lieutenants
Allnutt M
Coffell J E
ØMcMeechan E D

2nd Lieutenants

TRINITY SCHOOL CROYDON

Majors
Thompson D M

Captains
Buckley M J
Geoghegan M P
Mazur P

Lieutenants

TRINITY SCHOOL OF TEIGNMOUTH

Majors
Elliott R J

Captains
Jones P

Lieutenants

2nd Lieutenants

UPPINGHAM SCHOOL

Lieutenant Colonels
Boston R A S

Majors
Worthington I R A

Captains
Spry-Leverton H H

Lieutenants
Allen W S
ØHorrex C A
Johnstone K G
ØOlof H M
Pattinson S J

VICTORIA COLLEGE

Lieutenant Colonels
Stockton R L

Majors

Captains

Lieutenants
Mourant C L E

2nd Lieutenants
Robbins A D

WARMINSTER SCHOOL

Majors
Burgess R

Captains
Strickland M

Lieutenants
ØArdrey S L

2nd Lieutenants

WARWICK SCHOOL

Lieutenant Colonels
Collis H E

Majors
Johnson P A

Captains
Reilly A J
Shield D J

Lieutenants
Newton W M

2nd Lieutenants
Bettison I
Jefferis T J

WELBECK COLLEGE

Captains
Clarke S

Lieutenants
Sparkes D

2nd Lieutenants
Daynes E

WELLINGBOROUGH SCHOOL

Majors

Lieutenants
Hellier J P
Moss G B
Roskilly N
Garfirth S

2nd Lieutenants
Hughes J H
ØWigg R J

WELLINGTON COLLEGE

Majors
Auger R C
Heddon E J

Captains
Adcroft H J
Head T J
Price J L

Lieutenants
Hutchinson C J
Oliphant-Callum C M

2nd Lieutenants

WELLINGTON SCHOOL

Lieutenant Colonels
Lungley D R

Majors
Hellier Rev J P

Captains
Salt A

Lieutenants
ØSalter H J
Toase S F L

2nd Lieutenants
ØDavey L

WELLS CATHEDRAL SCHOOL

Captains
Barnard J R

Lieutenants

2nd Lieutenants
Yates P A

WEST BUCKLAND SCHOOL

Captains
Dawson C H

Lieutenants
Clark D A
Clarke R
ØSharman D J
Minns W D

2nd Lieutenants

WHITGIFT SCHOOL
Lieutenant Colonels
Gibson P L
Majors
Smith K A
Captains
Johnstone R B
Mooney M J
Reddy A
Lieutenants
Range C
Frears M A
2nd Lieutenants
Collins S A
Hogben G A
ØJordan J

WILLIAM HULMES GRAMMAR SCHOOL
Lieutenant Colonels
Fisher D M
Captains
Jones M P
ØMatthews E L
Simkin A
Lieutenants
2nd Lieutenants
ØMilligan J A

WILLIAM PARKER SCHOOL
Captains
Lieutenants
Scott I
Spears R J
2nd Lieutenants
Moore M R
Meight R A
ØSillitoe D C

WILSONS SCHOOL
Lieutenant Colonels
Lyons D C
Majors
Edwards J R
Captains
Lieutenants
Ovens A J
2nd Lieutenants
Harper A K

WINCHESTER COLLEGE
Majors
Wallis M D
Brooks J S
Captains
Johnson A R
Lieutenants
2nd Lieutenants

WOODBRIDGE SCHOOL
Majors
Broaderwick R F
Captains
Bruce G B
Lieutenants
ØRichardson H V
ØSheperd C V E
2nd Lieutenants
ØKing L R
ØWilliamson N
Rickard L

WOODROFFE SCHOOL
Majors
ØWilliams J
Lieutenants
ØUnwin P J
2nd Lieutenants

WORKSOP COLLEGE
Lieutenant Colonels
Biddulph B C
Driver J A S
Majors
Captains
Farmer G T
Lieutenants
2nd Lieutenants

WREKIN COLLEGE
Majors
Savage A
Captains
Blakeway C I
Berry P
Lieutenants
ØJenkins M
2nd Lieutenants

WYCLIFFE COLLEGE
Lieutenant Colonels
Thomas W P
Majors
Rothwell P N
Captains
Lieutenants
Brightman C J
Crewe G E
Heir J S
2nd Lieutenants
ØThom M A G

YARM SCHOOL
Majors
Fox L
Crabtree S H A
Lieutenants
Doherty J R C
Headlam C
2nd Lieutenants
ØBaker J

ARMY CADET FORCE

Colonel in Chief . . . . .Field Marshal *HRH The Prince* Philip *Duke of* Edinburgh
KG KT OM GBE AC QSO

Cadet Commandant Scotland . . . . .Brig I S Taylor *OBE TD*

ANGUS & DUNDEE BN

County Cadet Commandant

Col K Simpson *MBE TD*
———

Deputy Commandant

Lt Col A D F MacLean *TD*
———

Cadet Executive Officer
———

Lieutenant Colonels

Majors

Cassidy A H
Dunn S
Gilbert J G
Hart D J
Jones G T
Quin N S
Roud S C
Thomson R G D
Turner S V

Captains

Fraser T
ØFindlay L
Gray B
Henderson L M
Jamieson J
Kilmartin W
Methven C J
Russell W C
Smith A D
Tanbini P A

Lieutenants

Aiken R
Chamberlain P S
Fotheringham I
ØRoud W C
ØRoss C M
Scott M P

2nd Lieutenants

ØBrown M R
Duncan I
McNaughton C P
Quin N S
Rae J S

THE ARGYLL AND SUTHERLAND HIGHLANDERS BN

Colonels

Ross D G

Lieutenant Colonels

Spowage A F
Fraser J M

Majors

Allardyce C G M
Bruce J H
ØCameron M
Clark M A
Ellis L
Hume B
Paterson F
Ritchie W M
Shaw D
Turnbull N

Captains

Baff J
Banks W G
Brooks A B
Campbell R D M
Gillies J
Holmwood I M
Hume B
Knowles T
MacDonald C
Middleton I
Turner S V
Wallace E B

Lieutenants

ØAllan S K
Dunn N L
ØFellows G B
Fellows R F
ØFrost N
Hubbuck C G
Hunter R
Keating J A
Kinsella R L A
ØLeeson-Cromar L
Lockhart R S
McAleese T
Milner P
Pearson W
Pollock R D M
Simm J A
Smith T B
Taylor J
Wylie R J

2nd Lieutenants

Clezy W K
Kerr G M

BEDFORDSHIRE

County Cadet Commandant

Col A Fairless *TD JP*
———

Cadet Executive Officer

Maj G N Taylor
———

Majors

Hugher B
ØMilnthorpe J E V
Terry P A
Seamark L J

Captains

Barden M *MBE*
Fitzpatrick I
Mansell A C
Phillips S
Reader B F
Walker D

Lieutenants

Clark C W
Dadd N J
Gaylor C P
Howard K I
Knapman D
Mason C R *TD*
ØMilnthorpe J E V
Odunsi L O
Ormston B
ØRobinson R
Stephenson A
Tearle R J
Thurgood M
Young J C

2nd Lieutenants

Birch J
Hampton A
Hearth J E
Hunter P J
ØMoorhouse V E

ROYAL COUNTY OF BERKSHIRE

County Cadet Commandant

Col P F Jolliffe *TD*
———

Colonels

Lieutenant Colonels

Majors

ØFurley S
Hawkins P
Laden D M
Oconnell T R
Sloper C D
Tearle B C

Captains

Gill A S
Frank P H
Hodgson A K
Hollister R F
Jeanes P A
ØKnight D R
Maidment T J
Oakley-Watson R J
Radusin B
Rogers W
Rogers A R
Simmonds R E

Lieutenants

Alway G M
Belcher P A
Brydon D P
Durden P J
Jefferies P
Lydon J J
ØPovey C S
ØPhillips L S
Rogers M
Spivey R J
Smith R P
Taylor P K
Williams O A

2nd Lieutenants

Allison P
Oakley S W
Reading S G
ØScott K M

BLACK WATCH BN

Colonels

Lieutenant Colonels

McRae J R *MBE*

Majors

Barclay I C
Halford-MacLeod A P L
McIntosh J A
Pover D B *MBE*
ØWinter A

Captains

Burns W D
Butcher N R
Forbes T
Malone J
Passmore M B
Scott M P
Taylor I

Lieutenants

Cockwell R L
Douglas K
France G

Kendall A
McCluskey M
Robb A R
Shaw D M
ØStoddart S
Stewart G
ØTruscott S
ØWelham E P

2nd Lieutenants

Lawson G
MacRae J R
Murdoch N A

CITY AND COUNTY OF BRISTOL

County Cadet Commandant

Col A Flint

———

Cadet Executive Officer

Maj W J M Taylor *MBE*

———

Lieutenant Colonels

Faulkner H M

Majors

Balliston-Thicke J
Cole P R
Goodfellow S P
John-Lewis M P
Scott M J

Captains

Bird M F
Buck D T G
Donaldson D S
Fitt R G
Gillman P A
ØGroom C A
Johns W A
Lynch G R
Newman G
Nock D B
Scull S J

Lieutenants

Brown G G
Cater M R
Farrance T C
Fisk I D
Gifford K J
Grainger D L
ØNicholson S A
Pearson R G
Richards J R
ØRoberts J L
Stamboulieh H N
Summers W T
ØThreader S D
Williams C B

2nd Lieutenants

Anstey S C
Lacey J D C

BUCKINGHAMSHIRE

Cadet Executive Officer

Maj B A Ford

———

Colonels

Howell-Pryce J B *TD*

Lieutenant Colonels

Weatherhead J A S *TD*

Majors

Carr M J
Chalfont M N
Shannon M L
Smart S W
Tyson-Woodcock P J E
Wallen R J
Williams L J

Captains

ØBayntun P R
Elliott R
Elsworth D V
Feeley P L
ØFurley S F
Houston M A
ØHunt A R
Jenkins L
Spiers A S D
Stocker A J
Welch K R

Lieutenants

Baguley J B
Blunt N J
Coulon M D
Cummings P E
Haynes R H
Kynaston L E
Mansi C D
Meads J R P
Morris A
Shannon T M L
Shearer J H T

2nd Lieutenants

Compton B J
ØLindner E C
Sale S H
ØWalker V L

CAMBRIDGESHIRE

County Cadet Commandant

Lt Col P R G Williams

———

Cadet Executive Officer

———

Colonels

Elsden C M

Lieutenant Colonels

Majors

Burch D P

364

Denson D S *TD*
Goude D G *MBE*
Knight M

Captains

Bliss R G
Gray B E
Kidman K P
Longmuir T M
ØNelson J H
Overy T B
Pilling L
Threadwell K G
ØThreadwell B L
Waldman C R
Watson J

Lieutenants

Badcock W C
Beautyman J C
ØCann N C
Criddle T M
Hayward B W
Herriot L E
Kester L M
Martin S C
ØMartin V R
Nicholls R W
Stacey S J
Steel D R
Swann S R

2nd Lieutenants

Barrett D W
Turner M A T
Ø Tyler E J

CHESHIRE

County Cadet Commandant

Col R A C Goodwin *TD*

Deputy Cadet Commandant

Lt Col D P Hickey

Cadet Executive Officer

Maj R H McC Shaw

Majors

Davenport G
ØDisley L C
Hatton P
Hickey D P
Kelly K
McSorley P N
Prescott P D
Shaw R H M C C

Captains

Disley M
Farrington K J
Firth P H C
ØJakeman M
Jones G O
Jones R
O'Connor T P
Sullivan P
ØThomas C A

Turner B A
Walker S F
Watts J
Welburn S

Lieutenants

Brown D F E
ØDaniels L J
Forshaw D S
Hartshorn P W
ØKarran S
Kelly S F
Mason J L
Matthews C
McGowan K C
Morris V A
Muir R A
Owen D
Sullivan P
Williams H M

2nd Lieutenants

Clarke N
Farrell P J
ØHammond S E
Hill G T
Hodson A B
Howard C
Manning S J
Snee C M

CLEVELAND

Colonels

Newton P J *MBE*
Charlton A W

Majors

Banks P
Connor M A
Hyde P D
Jackson J G
Paul R W
ØSkillen M M
Twinn M J

Captains

Carroll J W
Crossland G
Dauncey J
MacKenzie J S
Middleton P
Murray R
ØNicholson M J
Pygott A M
Short L
ØSteed A
Stephen K G

Lieutenants

Bell M W
Daniel E
Dillon F G
Forster S
ØForster V
Franklin J R
Fry A J
Gotts P W
Hunter D A S
ØHyde K
Jermy T E
Pallent S

Sexton D M
Shaw A T
Southall B
Wright R
Wood K

3 CDT BN THE ROYAL REGIMENT OF WALES

Cadet Commandant

Col J Wrangham *MBE TD*

Cadet Executive Officer

Maj R J Roberts BEM

Lieutenant Colonels

Davies J B
Dean C E
Toms G
Wardle P M

Majors

ØDavies-Jenkins S C A
Harris W H
Jeffreys K E
ØJones G H *MBE TD*
Martin D W
Martin G L
Thomas R W

Captains

Braham D
Brelsford K L
Donovan D
Downes G R J
Facey G P
Gullidge P
Howell I
ØMartin H E
Roblin R
Rundle H
Smith L E
Tasker D A
Thomas M J
Tugby F A
Ward C G
White P G

Lieutenants

Holder R A
Jones K A
ØLong C
Orpin P J
Rose A J
Thomas K R H
Tooze P D
Tucker G B

2nd Lieutenants

Cupples-Gruffydd D
Decarteret G A
Gulwell R R
Morris W
Pritchard G
Richardson M E
Ward J D

4 CDT BN THE ROYAL WELCH FUSILIERS (CLWYD)

Cadet Executive Officer

Lieutenant Colonels
Wood D J G

Majors
Bavister D B
Bracewell B F
Hewitt J E
Jones J E V
Jones F P
Lloyd H J
Mullis M C

Captains
Bowles J A
Holmes I G
Hudson F A
Marshall E
Meaby D A
Mountcastle J R
Pye R P
Thomas A W
Ward K G

Lieutenants
Hargraves M J
Hargraves N D
Hewitt J E
Humphreys J W
Jones R A
Jones G R
Lloyd D G
Marshall E M
Price G W
ØPeters C
ØPye C A
Rosedale L
Scarll T J
Williams D W

2nd Lieutenants

CORNWALL CDT BN LI

County Cadet Commandant
Col C Stenning *TD* Late R SIGS

Cadet Executive Officer

Lieutenant Colonels
Walkey P

Majors
Donnithorne L
Penn R
Wenmoth C

Captains
Baker M R
Cayzer G
Douglas A
ØMackrili C

Magor V
ØRoberts C

Lieutenants
Allardice J
Christophers G J
Duddart-Aberdeen J
French T G
ØGeach H
Hobbs K C
Scarrett D
Steer J
Veitch B
Wotton K

2nd Lieutenants
Christophers G J
Deakin P
ØFuller T A

CUMBRIA

Colonels
Diss M *OBE*

Lieutenant Colonels
Bennett J C

Majors
Ashton M R
Bell H J
Burns J H
Blackburn C
Casey G A
Fraser N C
Graham K
Ingram D G

Captains
Cooper R
ØGardias O A
ØIngram S
Jones A W
Langan J
Lockhart T
Parker A G
Whipp A D
Wilson J

Lieutenants
Chambers D S
Davidson M
Hall D B
Jackson D A
ØJohnston L A
Heffernan K F
Kell M R
Lewis A R
Marshall J A
Muller K K
Nelson M
Richmond A
ØSidorowicz C A
Sidorowicz S
Watson D W
Wylie R

2nd Lieutenants
Fahy S G
Lynch A P
Tuersley C E
Wilson J W

DERBYSHIRE CADET BN (WFR)

County Cadet Commandant
Col M S Cheetham

Majors
Bicknell T G
Boult J D L
Cumberlidge A
McCartney W N
Motteram E B
Porter-Parr K J
ØPorter-Parr A M
Spencer A A
Seeds C W
Palucci T A
Wilson J S

Captains
Burden T
Dean B A
ØDenny-Palucci S J
Matthews S D
Mawby J B
Murray D P J
Palfreyman R
ØThornley K J

Lieutenants
Barnes A
Chauntry D E
ØCheshire W
Hubbard J S
Hurst P W
Lang J A
Monk A R
Motteram E B
Simmons P C
Truswell K C
ØWilson L

2nd Lieutenants
ØHill L A
Hubbard J S
Rawlings A M
Reeve N T

DEVONSHIRE

County Cadet Commandant
Brig R S Tailyour

Lieutenant Colonels
Ley A J
Blencowe L J

Majors
Buller V
Candlish R H
Clapp D J
Emond G R
Loram R L
Lillicrap D T
Mellin D J
Waterworth D L

366

Captains

Anthony J
Ashton R E
Catchpole B O A
Fulford A R
Gayton T J
Howells D T
Keeling J B N
Lucas W C
ØMcDonald M P
Pritchard P H
Portlock M J
Ruane J A
Tucker F D *MBE*
Toogood E
Tatam S
Webber D R
Williams P D

Lieutenants

Barnes A R
Black P J
Bowen D H
Brace M S
Browne S V
ØChandler L
ØClark D A
ØCoombes C L
Edmunds D A
Hopkins K G
Husband W C R
Johnson J W
Julian G R
Martin J A
ØMolloy D R
Molloy E C
Puckey D J
ØRawlings H A
ØRussell S L
Smith K N
Squire D C

2nd Lieutenants

ØBland J
Brush D R
Hext D M
Kelly P
ØStevens W K
Sturges T M

DORSET

County Cadet Commandant

Col R P Steptoe

Deputy Commandant

Maj G J Davies

Lieutenant Colonels

Fox B I

Majors

Benneyworth N J A
Goodman R J
Morgan A P

Captains

ØBenneyworth J R

Oaten R C
Beswick R
Bishop A S
Buchanan R
Triggs A J BEM
Richards J H BEM
Pearce D C
Pearce D W
Frost S J
Garrett A R
Ireson R P
Letcher D J

Lieutenants

Davies A J
Guile N J
Heron G W
McMahon T W
Morgan A P
ØOaten M A
Reid M G
Scammell E A
Stevenson J D
ØTurner N J

2nd Lieutenants

ØRichardson T A

DURHAM

County Cadet Commandant

Col M P Colacicchi

Cadet Executive Officer

Maj M B Spence

Majors

Adams R M
Cartwright A M
Chaganis L A
Kitching B J
Leadbitter E G
McKenna M F
Oliver G R
Reeves J J
Scott M C
Spence M B
Tearney C

Captains

Avison B
Benson M R
Brown A P
Christer D A
Collins M
Curry A
Dobson R B
Goode J
Matthews C C
Mitchinson A C
ØNewham K E
Richardson W P
ØTwinn A C
Walden D

Lieutenants

Atkin M

Christie G
ØEdgar L A
Edgar M
Frary D
Lannon E
McCoy P
McDonough M
Peers A W
Pickering C
Raper P A
Rowland K D
ØStringer M E
Teder S H
Williams S

2nd Lieutenants

Askew J
Blackett A
Curry M
Foster N W
Halliday S
Hedley S S
Kidman G
Palmer T C
Parker K
Richardson W P
Roach M
Thornley P

DYFED

Cadet Executive Officer

Colonels

Lieutenant Colonels

Glover T G

Majors

Evans M E
Gwyther G D
Rees L
Rogers A R

Captains

Davies T A
Griffiths D R
Hadfield P
Horton B W J
Soady M
Spain M
Tune G A
Warner A J
Woods P H

Lieutenants

Clement D M
Davies I A
Harrison M J
Johns W P
ØLloyd N
Richards G J
Smith B

2nd Lieutenants

Evans D
John R D
Meaden C D

ESSEX

County Cadet Commandant
Col C A F Thomas *TD*

Deputy Commandant
Lt Col M I Wreford

Cadet Executive Officer
Maj A V Hughes

Majors
Boyce A H
Christian P A
Coffin I M
Fisher A A
Jones A R
Low B J

Captains
Atkins R J
Bishop L J
Davis M K
Foster C J
Goodwin R D
ØHenry I F
Holmes K W
Lambert B J
MacDonald I R
Ray D J
Rablin G C
Slater P A

Lieutenants
Annesley P S
Biegal M P
Davies S A
Disney M J
Edwards B T
Edwards S J
Foster P A
Fraser I R
Gafney S
Jones P R
Lengden M P
Smith D H
Wade P R

2nd Lieutenants
Lee P

GLAMORGAN

County Cadet Commandant
Lt Col R M Scott *TD*

Cadet Executive Officer
Maj W G Gulley

Lieutenant Colonels
Jones D J F
Welsh R J

Wrangham J

Majors
Davies E M
Dean C E
Harris R E
Harris W H
Harrison T
Martin G L
Thomas G H
Vosper K W *TD*
Wardle P M
Whitehouse B
White P G

Captains
Birch M O
Davies R P
Decarteret G A
Howell I H
Jeffreys K E
Jones G H
Martin D W
Tasker D A
Thomas R W

Lieutenants
Bean T R
Braham D
Brelsford B R V
ØDavies-Jenkins S C A
Davies J B
Downes G R J
Evans M L
Facey G P
Gill N M
Grant P E
Holder R A
Jones G H
Jones K A
Jones T
Leadbetter G
Long C L
Martin H E
Morris W
Mountcastle G
Mullings P J
Noake S R
Pritchard G
Richardson M E
Rose A J
Roberts R J *BEM*
Rundle H
Shaw S A
Thomas M J
Tucker G B
Thomas K R H
Tooze P D
Ward C G
Ward J D

2nd Lieutenants
Decarteret G A
Griffiths D S
Gulwell R R
Hopkins D P
Phillips J D M
Wareham P A

GLASGOW AND LANARKSHIRE BN

County Cadet Commandant

Cadet Executive Officer

Colonels
Neil P K

Lieutenant Colonels
Kelly J L *MBE*

Majors
Bissett A J
Bryce C R
Kerrigan J
Reade A N
Robertson R G
ØWatkins S

Captains
Abeledo B J A
Almond D
Canavan H
Coulter D S
ØLove E A M
MacKenzie I S
McCluskey D
O'Meara P E
Reynolds J
Robertson J

Lieutenants
Balfour D E
Buskie G
Clezy W K
Dunn K
Falconer W J
Hart W
ØLaird D M
Liddell A
Mathewson S
McIntyre R
McNamee A M
Mullen J F
Mullen J F
Stirling A
Thomson J

2nd Lieutenants
O'Reilly J
Robb C E

GLOUCESTERSHIRE

County Cadet Commandant

Cadet Executive Officer

Lieutenant Colonels
Bennett M E
Shaw J A

368

Majors
James M
Little M G
Lynett A M
Readstone D W
Titley G S

Captains
Canning P E
Cork J H
Gibbins D C
Hannam R C
Harrison M G
Noller W H
Rogers R J
Turley S J
Wise A G

Lieutenants
Bees C P
Bees M F
ØHarris J M
ØHemmings C M
Little A
Price K E
ØSealey C L
Shayle K A
Wain S J A

2nd Lieutenants
Brewster A L
Carmichael E J
Dyer R J
Millar A J
ØWain H M
ØThomson W J

GWENT

County Cadet Commandant
Col R A Melvin

Cadet Executive Officer
Lt Col P A Blagojevic

Majors
Bridgeman R L
Clifford C
Davies R M
John R B
Rooney J J
Ryan M J

Captains
Bridgeman M E C
Fulton-Forrest K P
Grey A J
Grey R
Gwynn G
Morgan G
Olson M
ØProbert L R
Syred R

Lieutenants
ØBudgen J C
Edwards P
Galloway N C
Gibbons C T

Holland A G
Jones A
Lloyd G H
Morgan O
McGuiness A
Noel-Smith M
Pritchard P G
Sharp G R B

2nd Lieutenants
Barnes H L
Duguid M
Evans W H
ØSnook J

6 CDT BN THE ROYAL
WELCH FUSILIERS
(GWYNEDD)

County Cadet Commandant

Cadet Executive Officer
_____

Colonels
Silverside T G W MBE

Majors
Binfield N E
Gibson J T A
Hughes M L
Hunt S B
Jones R C
Lewis E L
Williams D A

Captains
Jones A V
Jones R G
Lawson K
Lewis S L
Pagent B
Pell C A
Williams J C

Lieutenants
Beeland W P
Benneyworth A B
Greenwood T L
Hadfield J D
ØHardman J
Jones P A
Lally C W

2nd Lieutenants
Ross I K
Stuart J V
Thomas L

HAMPSHIRE AND THE
ISLE OF WIGHT

County Cadet Commandant
Col G J Shawley TD****
_____

Cadet Executive Officer
Lt Col M J Clutson MBE
_____

Lieutenant Colonels
Cloke J
Hogg T T
ØMarjoram V G

Majors
Bezant G R A
Bryson T H L TD OSJ
Colleypriest A V
Court B M
Day S K
Hawker P W
Huggett J W
Leather T C
Lewcock G D
Snell P J

Captains
Akers W H
Austin R C
Barker S J
Carey N P
Carter T P M
Curle L C
Dawes A L
Dudin J P
Ellis S L
Fagg B W
Ferguson I W
Faulkner B DCM
Fuller T E
Garman G T
Hadnett R G
Henwood E C
Horder M A
Moore R
Payne A J
Richter J F K
Rouse C T
Smith I W
ØTaylor M I
Tiddiman J R
Tutt R E
Vokes M G
Wright W G MBE

Lieutenants
ØBanks J A
Cameron-Ross K R
ØCarter R E V
Channon R J
Cheesman-Smith A T
Churcher R L
Clark P S
Deakin D J
ØGallimore L
Kerr A
ØPerkins J P
Randall D V
Rawlinson P A
Smith A L
ØSutherland J A
Tapsell P G C
Taylor M A
Thomas M A
Thomsett M D
Tutt R E
Wake Z L
Williams C J
Young A E

2nd Lieutenants

Adams A J
ØCollins S J
Daley J A
ØMacDonald M
Mills R H
Parker S
Sabin W J
Smith A C
Stirling A J

HEREFORD AND WORCESTER

County Cadet Commandant

Col I Bramble

Cadet Executive Officer

Maj J A Sandison *MBE QGM*

Lieutenant Colonels

Majors

Atkinson S
Biddle R
Davies D A
Gallivan R A
Martin A R E

Captains

Birch B J
Cater D M
Douglas A J W
Groves L B F
Hyde J P
Matthews N V
Twomlow C D

Lieutenants

Griffiths D W
Harrison R P
Hughes J T
Newbrook G T
ØPotter P A
Rainbow A W
Thorne W J
Wooles I

2nd Lieutenants

Hopkins M A
ØRudge S J
Stockham A C
Walker N J

HERTFORDSHIRE

Cadet Executive Officer

Maj P Barlow

Colonels

Wilson A S G

Lieutenant Colonels

Macleod I D

Majors

Murrell A F
Sharwood-Smith C H

Captains

Butts C S
Davey G W
Evans G
Ferguson I G
Furse A J
Griffiths A T
Guild J B
Gray M R
Grover K S
Hallows J M
Isaac E E
Kirby W
Rawlings K J
Singfield S R
Westley E P G
White S C

Lieutenants

Burnett K J P
Clark W G C
Dumbarton D R
Flinter A C
Gray B E
Gooch B G
Groom O H
Heal R
Hall W S
Humphrey Roberts D C
Jones R A
Mawer S A
Quinlan K T
Rivers S J
Yang J C Y

2nd Lieutenants

Burry W G J
ØGilbert J S
Outram D R

1st BN THE HIGHLANDERS

County Cadet Commandant

Deputy Commandant

McMaster W C

Lieutenant Colonels

Majors

Goskirk J L
Henderson A
Lobar P T
Lucas B P
MacBean M
MacLeod N
Morrison A W
Petrie A G
Ross D

Captains

Frizzell R S
Murdoch G

Woolley C

Lieutenants

Broadhurst S J
Burt L F
ØDouglas K
Gowans J W
Gray C L
Irvine R P
MacDonald D
MacDonald G
MacDonald M
MacKay A S
Marshall J
Paterson R M
Reid K J
Yates J S

2nd Lieutenants

Atkinson T P
Folley B
ØMackenzie S J
McLean N
ØMyers C E

2nd BN THE HIGHLANDERS

County Cadet Commandant

Lt Col S V Duggan

Cadet Executive Officer

Maj J D Beeton

Majors

Gatt F G
Gray J A
ØMason E A
Thow R G

Captains

Allan D
Mackie K W
Park J E
Shearer G
Smith D M
Torrance I R

Lieutenants

ØBerkin G J
ØGatt C H
Irvine R
Neilson D C
Ramsay J
Ross K R
Wilkie A J
Wood A A

2nd Lieutenants

Downs C
ØMurray L M

HUMBERSIDE & SOUTH YORKSHIRE

County Cadet Commandant

Col D Telfer

370

Cadet Executive Officer

Lieutenant Colonels
Wilson A
Garner D

Majors
Barrass A J
Bradford B A
Fuller D I CFM
Hudson W A
Newman P
Somers S J
Shepherd R E
Scrivens T
Turner S

Captains
Armstrong J N
Ball K H
Britchford G
Buckley D J
Cooper K
Cruddas M J
Eales B
Fletcher B T
Hastings P T
Harrison J M
Jackson M C CFM
Payne A D
Somers S J
Tunmore D J
ØTyrer M E
Tyrer E D
Wharam T
Birt C S

Lieutenants
ØAddison J
Ashby D R
Bourne A M
Britchford J M
Cowles R G
ØDavison E R
Dawson P
Desforges M
Flanagan S R
Froggatt-Smith I P
Harvey C
Leech M B
Lilly G P CFM
Maughan P T CFM
McGarva J N
Meares P S
Naylor L E
Parker S
Peka P B CFM
ØPrice E
Read N G
Rushby D A
Smith J R CFM
Summers R G
Smith J
Stafford C R
Wilson C W
Wood C J B *TD*

2nd Lieutenants
Charlesworth M J
Cunningham I

Green P A
ØLittle V K
Webb G D

ISLE OF MAN

County Cadet Commandant
Maj P D Glynn-Riley

Majors

Captains
Bennett P J
Charnley K

Lieutenants
Lawrence W J
Taylor C J

2nd Lieutenants
Champion S R

KENT

County Cadet Commandant
Col P Bishop *OBE*

County Cadet Commandant
Lt Col P T Troy

Lieutenant Colonels
Bellingham C M
Edgar N *MBE*
Riley R G

Majors
Ashman R D
Brooks T W
Gatter K A
Hatcher B
Hughes P R
Kennedy D W
Longbottom P J
Riley C M

Captains
Andrews M A
Bartlett G W G
Berry L G
Burns P M
Chittock B
Clarke J W
Dean S J
Duffield B M
Foster C G
ØHatcher J L H
Hunter C A
Masters K W
Pankhurst J A
Smith P H D

Lieutenants
Ashman A P
Bloor K J
Ellis G K
Freeman N

Goddard G H M
Harris C D
Mcdowell A
Jupp C
McNeil J
ØPellet P J
Rickard I M
Smith G J F
Whishaw K L

2nd Lieutenants
Adam J B
Bavin A J
Davis E W
Denton A
Coker M
Collins D R
Drinkwater S J
Harper P H
Masters G R
McDonnell M
McDowell A
Pankhurst S T
Pellett A D
Rathe J R L
Reid I W
Robinson D K
Searle R J
Twyman S P
Usher B

LANCASHIRE

County Cadet Commandant
Col E A Jolley

Cadet Executive Officer
Maj A G Wagstaff

Lieutenant Colonels

Majors
Birmingham P
Cheall H F K
Clegg L C
Davies J A
Doyle A
Stewart D J
ØTheobald J
Wallis M C
Watson S B

Captains
Brooke F R
Chakrabarti H P
Eskdale J R
Hacking J
Harrison C
Jones A D
Kennon H MBE
Mann D
Moss D C
Naylor P C
Paffard G F
Sibson J M
Smith C A
Smillie P

Storey R V
Tierney J W F
Toward G T

Lieutenants

Evans J D A
Gaskell T
Gledhill R
ØHarrison F
Heald K J
ØKennon M D
Kent W
Longden R M
Marshall D J
ØNapier K
Oak D M
Parsons H
Poloway M L
Smith R I
ØStewart W
Ward S J
Weighill R
Whittaker S

2nd Lieutenants

Assheton O
Mather G
Watters G T
Wilson R M

LEICESTERSHIRE, NORTHAMPTONSHIRE AND RUTLAND

County Cadet Commandant

Cadet Executive Officer

Maj D M Andrews

Colonels

Brunt J H *OBE TD*

Lieutenant Colonels

Holmes M D
Taylor G M
Wood A

Majors

Bazeley D W
Beirne M A
ØDavanna M J
Davies S
Desborough C S
ØHart S
Hurwood R S
Mills D F
Pickering J W
Poulton S J
Smith M
Ward J R

Captains

Ball A J
Bloor A G MBE
ØBradbury I M
Deegan A C
Derbyshire B
Dorey L J

Fleming P J
Greenwood P J
ØMachin A
McLean L M
O'Connor B P
Osborn J P
Richmond T E
Spry-Leverton H H S
Walton D P
Young C I

Lieutenants

Ashford G R
Boston E J R
Carroll P T
Davanna P
Davies S
Dobrowski J S
Doyle C B
ØFarrimond A R
Hubbard A S
James I
Llewelyn S J
Mander J R
McFarlane G J R
Murphy A E
Skingsley C L
Slessor B A
Slessor D T M
Walton I D

2nd Lieutenants

Bodycote P J
ØDorey S J
ØDoyle P J
ØDrinkall K
Flamson I

LINCOLNSHIRE

County Cadet Commandant

Cadet Executive Officer

Maj B Harrison

Colonels

Lieutenant Colonels

Dickinson R A
Larder D A

Majors

Carter R L
Dance T A
Dixon T E
McIntyre A D
Nguyen-Van-Tam J S
Ogg R M
ØOram M
Taylor N
Wakelin A F

Captains

Atkinson T H
Beever J R
Exley P P
Rowe J W K
ØTaylor W A
Vardy N E
Wells R J

Webber M A

Lieutenants

Adams M
Bird N J
Burrows M
Coleman M D
Condie R R
Eden D L
Elmer S P
Frere-Cook S A C
Jackson F V
Jones H C
Pearce-Hunt D A C
ØPearce-Hunt J A G
Rogers E H B
Smith M
Spraggins D M
Wilson R

2nd Lieutenants

Greenfield S
Maltby M A
ØOldfield M H
Overland M A
Scott D
Thompson C A
ØUpsall V J

GREATER LONDON (CITY OF LONDON & NE SECTOR)

County Cadet Commandant

Col G P Brown

Cadet Executive Officer

Lieutenant Colonels

Majors

Bryant M P
Coull C B
Crichton E M
ØFogerty J A
ØHorton L J J
Reith M

Captains

Hayman N R
Horner S M
Lammin D
Rynn D J
Williams N P
Zarych M

Lieutenants

Badruddin P
Brown A
Corbett D G
Cullinane J G
ØLowe V F
Johnson E G
Murphy-O'Kane N R
Robinson J M
Travers I P
Wallen R
ØWilliams W A

Woodward G W

2nd Lieutenants

Carter J E
Cope N H
Preston J J

**GREATER LONDON
(MIDDLESEX & NW
SECTOR)**

County Cadet Commandant

Cadet Executive Officer

Colonels

Salter A J D TD

Lieutenant Colonels

Cox F M F
Walker A C

Majors

Arthur K A
Collett R L
Denison A I
Jones R G
Murray P J
Newman G D

Captains

Bowden A P
Butlin C J
Caiger J F L
Collins D F
Cooper G K
Hart A V
Harwood D *MBE TD*
Hill K F
Johnson P
Lovelock M L
Traverse-Healy K T

Lieutenants

Axten A
Betancourt B
Burnikell B M
Perry H P
Bird J E
Caiger J F L
Chapman M B
Charlton M P
ØCollett J C
Davey A J
Draper P A C
Duncan M S
Gilby G M
Glenn K A
Hayes D L
Horridge A G C
Kamli G T
Lofts S
McBride A
McNaney T L
O'Sullivan J N
Pannell J D
Ryan M J L
Treasure A R
Walker P J

Wyatt P R

2nd Lieutenants

ØBoak D M
Cheasty J T
Hammond P J
Kayser P S
Hinks M
Mills P
Ricketts M L
Robinson B K
Wright S J

**GREATER LONDON
(SE SECTOR)**

County Cadet Commandant

Col M Sharp *TD*

Lieutenant Colonels

Annett J *TD*

Majors

Byrne P H
Cassidy S
Daniels B
Hitchcock D
Moore G
Philpot D
ØWilson E

Captains

Chudha S
Goddard K
Hennell L
Martin R
Neville M
Nicholls G
Rayment J
Reynolds A
Sellers D
Stiff P
Taylor D
Wilson D

Lieutenants

Brown E
Burton T
Collings M
Fabian M
Handley W
ØHennell L
Lucy T
Munday J
Rowe T
Steele D M
ØTaylor L
Thomas P
Thomas S
ØWarren P

2nd Lieutenants

Comyns D L
Ewen R W
Fish G M
Petit M G
Rayson T
Ryan M A

Smith D
Shearn D

**GREATER LONDON
(SW SECTOR)**

County Cadet Commandant

Col D Leech

Cadet Executive Officer

Lieutenant Colonels

Lee J

Majors

Casey W
Hamilton J
Joannou B
Joannou J
Purse J M
Sabey B

Captains

Buckley M J
Butcher D
Crowhurst C
ØFahey A
Fahey T
Hull J
Moore M W *TD*
Riches J M
Sokolowski E
Tunesi J

Lieutenants

ØAllen T
Benedetti S
Butten R M
Chaplin S
Clarke J P E
Edwards R
ØFoster-Delve C
Gaden A T
Hay K
Moore R H
Newton G
Whiteley J

2nd Lieutenants

Butten R M
Dadley J E
Dodson P C
Harrison P D
Salmassian D
Shaun R S
Stevens A

LOTHIAN & BORDERS BN

Cadet Executive Officer

Maj R A Ross

Colonels

Percy W R V TD

373

Lieutenant Colonels
Thomson R

Majors
Anderson M
Cook R H
Dougherty A D
Oag W G
McGarvey D D
Peacock W H
Thomson B J

Captains
Andrews E
Bainbridge J
Coulter A B
Jackson G R
Love G
Rae W
Ridgway G E
ØRoss C A
Scott G
Turnbull P D

Lieutenants
Anderson D W
Babington D
Bogan S L
Campbell J M
Cassidy R A
Connell K J
Dickson C B
Donaldson G
Goldstein B
Hill J M
Jordan A J
MacFadyen P R
ØMacFarlane C G
Mason R P
Rogers D B
Stevens W
Tonner R J
Tully D M

2nd Lieutenants
ØCarpenter K A
Cook A
Joyce R J
MacDonald P A
Millar K R
Rogers A
ØTurnbull F S

GREATER MANCHESTER
Colonels
Connolly C E

Lieutenant Colonels
Newman M
Sloan R

Majors
Boyce J TD
Brotherton M J
Cornmell T
ØFearon S
Joynes G
Motteram E
O'Callaghan R MBE
Taylor S

Warr P
Williams J
Williams M

Captains
Allen P
Barlow W BEM
Brooks C
Buckland A
Callaghan W A
Frost L M
Gregori A
Harmston T
Leadbetter K H
MacDonald R C
McColm M J
ØMotteram G H
Ridings E
Sheldon A
Tasker D TD
Taylor S T
Wild C
Woolfenden E A
Young M

Lieutenants
Hall D
Hamlett R
McGuinness A
Scollick M A
ØSwift A
Wood J M

2nd Lieutenants

MERSEYSIDE

County Cadet Commandant
_____

Cadet Executive Officer
Maj G J Corbett
_____

Lieutenant Colonels
Thomson I H

Majors
Alexander C J
Doyle A
ØDoyle D F
Feeney A J
Johnston S C
Laidler H P
McKenzie T P
Rouch D V
Saeed A
Sinclair R S
Whitbread P A

Captains
Ball N D C
Brougham A G
Coker T M
Cummins I M
MacIver C J
Rogers V J
ØWade M T
Wareing P J

Lieutenants

Brady M J
ØBrighouse F A
Corns P B
Dooley D
Edwards J T
Hay R M
Hellon P E
Higham J
Lane D J
McCutcheon G
Moreland J P
Ryan J E
Singleton S J
ØStevens V
Winrow B W

2nd Lieutenants
Bowdler N R
Bowen J P
ØDawson L C
Hastings G
Morgan M A
Ravenscroft K M
Tumilty I J
Williams D

NORFOLK
County Cadet Commandant
_____

Cadet Executive Officer
_____

Colonels
Mizen M R

Lieutenant Colonels
Green M M

Majors
Boston J B
Doughty J F
Keywood J R
ØLawrence J C
O'Neill H B
Pratt S E
Sprules S W
Whitehead D
Wilkinson C G

Captains
Bartrum A D
Cooper D T
Davison D M
Dyke R W
Marshall D
Pratt W G E
Rushton P W

Lieutenants
Anderson S D J
Bagge G J
Crowther G A
Craig W E
Dumbleton D C
ØForeman S A
French K P
Hawkins J L
Holland S H
ØJensen-Meyer L
Lincoln P T
Pickering K A

Raybould J L
Thacker T A H
Uppiah L R

2nd Lieutenants

Curtis P A
Davison S J

1ST (NI) BN

County Cadet Commandant

Cadet Executive Officer

Maj G B Matthews

Colonels

Lieutenant Colonels

Baskin C A
McCleery D G

Majors

Anderson J
Carruthers S H
Killen D E
Matthews G B
McConnell L W
MaGill A T
Taylor R M

Captains

Bowman E I M
Boyd L H
Callaghan R
Caskey T J
Cotter W J
Dickson W
Elliott E G
Mayberry J B
McMillan J S H
ØMorrison G A
Scott W R
Shields D N

Lieutenants

Carton J P
Elliott F M S P
Forster T S
Green R I N
Hughes P R
McCord S S
Morrow M T
Perry M
Ridley M
Robinson T C
ØStyles V M
Terrett W H
Tolland J
Watson S J

2nd Lieutenants

Donnell S
ØMcFarland L R
Wray P

2ND (NI) BN

Cadet Executive Officer

Colonels

Lieutenant Colonels

Gregg W M

Majors

Faulkner R
Hagan T J
Hollinger T
McConnell J N
Moffett K
Pollock T
ØTurkington E R
Warnock M V

Captains

ØBennington A
Blair R T
Boyd W M
Crozier J D
Forsythe S E
ØGreen E V
Keys A B
ØMacKintosh H R
McCloskey G
McFall T R
ØMcVeigh D
ØSleator K
Steele T
Stronge A J
ØTyler J C

Lieutenants

Bashford T R
Beetson B
ØBerry A E
Bashford T R
Butterworth C M
Cooper A H
Cooper C I
Davidson T W J
Duncan I K
Fergus W G L
Ferguson G
Glass M R
Lawther D G
ØLoughrey K
ØMcMillen P
Paterson G S *TD*
Paton K
Patton E J
ØPatton J
ØRoss J M
Topping P F W
Watters R J

2nd Lieutenants

Anderson S A
Chatterley P J
Martin R H

NORTHUMBRIA

County Cadet Commandant

Col J P P Anderson

Cadet Executive Officer

Maj J J Condon

Lieutenant Colonels

Gerrish M H *MBE*
Smith D A

Majors

Fenwick M F
Grey M
Herron E R C
Huggan R O
James R
Laker A K
Stout K D P
Thompson T A
Watson G A
White B M

Captains

Allen D
Bowles V C D
Burnett A J
Fairbairn D W
Gentle D A
Hardyman M K J
Hogg D
Hutchinson C
Jerdan A
Lafferty J
Shewan J W
Spencer J J
Sunley D
Warren J R
Woods A W

Lieutenants

Bowles C J
Daniels J L
de Planta de Wildenberg R M G
Ewart M
Fram P
ØGracen Y
Haggerty K M
Knowles S
Laker N
Ludden A M
McDonald J L
ØNoble K
Pegg R D
Price D G
Rogan P J
Setterfield J W
Sillence C R
Stenton K
Thompson S N
White M J

2nd Lieutenants

Brown L G
Carr P J
ØGribbin G
Jobson K W
Newman S R
Richfield J O
ØStark A C
Thompson J Q W

NOTTINGHAMSHIRE

County Cadet Commandant

Col T S Richmond *MBE*

Deputy Commandant

Lt Col D A Newsham

Lieutenant Colonels

Majors

Atherton N D
Burt A W
Cook A B
Holloway G E
Lowe M G R
Newbury G

Captains

Baker J M
Chadburn D M
ØCharlesworth J D
Croydon N P D
ØCurling A E
Eaton F A
Hay D P
Munroe J M
Prout N M
Saint S
Wilds T

Lieutenants

Ara M A
Bentham D
Corrigan J
Creamer A D
Gaughan M S
Hayter A J
ØHenson B C
ØHolland L D
Warren N D
Saint S
Stoor H B
Theakstone A
Watson M A
Zdan M A G

2nd Lieutenants

Calton T
Dhamu A S
Eaton T P
ØGilbert A R
Offless C

ORKNEY INDEPENDENT CADET BTY

County Cadet Commandant

Maj M E Walters

Lieutenants

Durrand A B

2nd Lieutenants

OXFORDSHIRE RGJ BN

County Cadet Commandant

Cadet Executive Officer

Colonels

Hordle R I

Lieutenant Colonels

Vince M

Majors

Allen C T
Bell D J
Butler B R
Clements E G
Lynch-Blosse R H
Maxwell B J
Miles M
Thompson D J

Captains

Allington P
Bone A J
Caldwell-Nichols C J
Charles S R
Cossins D J
Dixon P S
Elliott R
Grafton C
Gratwohl E M
Hames A W N
Hanson S
Harland M
Lathey M
Nilsson O E
Osborne C S
Paine J A
Vince M A F
Wilson S L

Lieutenants

ØHall J Y
Hall S A
ØHamblin M B
Murray R W
Phillips W I
Small M D
Smith V G
Spinner P
Stephens C A
White R B

2nd Lieutenants

Allington RP
Duffus W G
ØHall A E
Mackenzie R O
Munro N M
Pratt P G

POWYS

Colonels

Blythe G E J

Lieutenant Colonels

Van-Rees T J *MBE*

Majors

Ahmed K
Evans W B
Head G A
Hurley D T P

Price M C G
Ridge I F
Saunders D J
Williams B J

Captains

Burge N D
Coleman D H
Evans J R
Gray R
Hughes R G J
Hunt P A
Kavanagh W
Pugh P D
Stone P L
Watson P M

Lieutenants

Cook D F L
Duggan J R
Gulley C T
ØGulley B
Harrison M G
Herbert K J
Jones S R
Lord V L
Morrison M J
Newman M P
Roberts D A
ØRoberts J S
ØSmith B
Williams G C

2nd Lieutenants

ØDavies C A
Hopkins D M
ØRoberts R A
Tranter P H

SHETLAND INDEPENDENT CDT BTY

Lieutenants

2nd Lieutenants

ØJenson-Rutland A-M L

SHROPSHIRE

County Cadet Commandant

Lt Col M J Watkins

Cadet Executive Officer

Majors

Budryk K M
Keogh M
Smith G K

Captains

Bassett M A
ØBilton F T
Briggs M J
Collins L J
Cowan D B
Ellis P T
Kingston P F
Maher J C
Mark R T

Salt F A

Lieutenants
Bellis G
Carney A *TD*
Fill D
Saywell A
Steed W
ØTipton Y A

2nd Lieutenants
ØFoulkes-Williams M T
ØFrancis A J
Mounteney M P
Samuel J R

SOMERSET CDT BN LI

County Cadet Commandant

Col D K W Farrant

Cadet Executive Officer

Lieutenant Colonels
Robson J P P

Majors
Crease T N
Deakin D M
Horsey A P M
Hughes A H
Motram W J
Norman R P
Palmer J R
ØPreston C M M
Richardson P M

Captains
Broom P D
Bunce P M
Elliott R J U
Evans R E
Hamilton K
Howlett A D
Lozuet D F
Slipper J J L
Smith A S G
Trunks A J

Lieutenants
ØClancy A M
Dunford R E
Fudge I A
Lech P
ØMadill J C F
ØOrr G
Pearce A J
Robson D P
Rodgers B J
Scriven S F
Smith F L
ØTaylor M L
Tuhey K M F
Vile P A D
ØWilson L M *TD*
White T D

2nd Lieutenants
Bennett S D
Clements J S
Kitching J G
ØProthero G

STAFFORDSHIRE AND WEST MIDLAND NORTH SECTOR

County Cadet Commandant

Cadet Executive Officer
Maj N H Hay

Colonels
Hill D J

Lieutenant Colonels
Buckle A T G

Majors
Emery B W
Harris R D
Lucas M
Oldfield T G
Sandham E

Captains
Blundell P L
ØClarke D C
Fuller W L M
Hadley S G
Hughes D C
Keates D J
Knutton K J
Mychajluk S
Nijjar R S
Pickin C J
Reader B
Sedgwick C T
Stephens D R
Upton K G
Van Falier A J

Lieutenants
ØBartlam S C
Bettany S P
Blake H E
Collins M S
Finney C M
Harrison S
Hill S R
Howells M J
Hutchins D M
McMullen S V
Park G J
Penny R M
Pirie N
Price K
ØRobinson M J
Robinson R L
Westwood D N

2nd Lieutenants
Adcock N
Davies R J
McNair J W
Scrivener A W
Wurr G R

SUFFOLK

County Cadet Commandant
Maj C P Burrell-Saward

Cadet Executive Officer

Lieutenant Colonels
Smye M L

Majors
Denny P W
Goldson A P
Ives M A
Symonds J A
Thorpe M W
Woods M S

Captains
Askew E
Burchell A D
Catt J H
Jackson G L
Jarvis R C
McDaid R A
Nelson B
Pratt W G
Turner G L

Lieutenants
Adams M J
ØBradshaw C L
ØCadman T C
Cole M E
Davey K P
Day G J
Fenwick G G V W
Forster B L
Ibinson G
Lawn B A
Nicholson P D
Pearl J S
Pemberton C A
Pretty C J
Rigewell E B
Rosher L M
Scales T L
Sinclair R D
Smart D
ØTaylor S
ØTyrrell J M
Tyrrell J M
West R J

2nd Lieutenants
Jones D L
Kirby A M J

SURREY

County Cadet Commandant

Col D K G Cox*ACIB*

Cadet Executive Officer

Maj J K Stewardson

Majors

Adkin M Q
Fordham C H
Nicholson N P
Taylor J B R
Wright P J

Captains

ØBurrell-Taylor V J
Horwood G J
Mulder E A
ØMcCauliffe R E
ØMorris K
Newbury J W
Newman D J
Tandy I C
Williams D T H
ØWright J E

Lieutenants

ØBarber F
Blackwell L G
Crome G P
Blowers A M
Devey J
Dodge T M
Flint J K
ØHarte J A
Hayter T J
Risby G A
Ross J H D
Shepherd R
Shipton D J
Stewart I H
Stott J M
Cooney B J
White C J

2nd Lieutenants

Davies T A
ØDodge A F
Jones C R
ØMcCauliffe H K
Marsh J J
Phelan R M
Potashnick M L
Wilson R A

SUSSEX

County Cadet Commandant
Cadet Executive Officer

Lieutenant Colonels

Newton R D *MBE*

Majors

Gillam G E
Harrison G

Holland A P
Moneypenny P J G
Morris A J
Rusbridger D J

Captains

Blackwell D J
Britton G D
Brown R I
Bustard K R
Fotheringham J S
Greenwood F H N *MBE*
Harmes J W
Kilgarriff G A
Pettitt E B
Pollitt F S
Smith R T
ØTrimm-Allen P C

Lieutenants

Blundell B C
Burberry D
ØBurton A C
Dexter M A
Evans L R
Gaffney A G
Hooley M J
Penfold C R
Philpott A

2nd Lieutenants

Clinker P T
ØForte E A
ØHaddrell V
Jennings A J
Harman M A
ØHarrison S
ØMurray K G
ØNeuhaus B A
Welsh W T
Wild J

WARWICKSHIRE AND WEST MIDLAND SOUTH SECTOR

County Cadet Commandant

Col R J Carruthers

Cadet Executive Officer

Lieutenant Colonels

Smith N J

Majors

Baker J H E
Brant P R A
Mytton E J
Redding B M W
Shaw T A
Winckles D

Captains

Ball S A
Barber D R
Burnell M
Hayden P
ØHope P M

Jemmett T M
Nolan M A
Pritchard D
Robertson I D
Snape A J
Sharkey A J *TD O St J*
Saunders P L

Lieutenants

Buncle A J
Curran P
Grubb I J
Hadley J D
Leech A V
Marsh K I
ØNotice A M
Peel R G
Reavley C J
Robinson K P
Ruston A A
Tyndall C L
Young B R

2nd Lieutenants

Bailey N
Gordon M J
Holt E J
Marley N P

WEST LOWLAND BN

County Cadet Commandant
Cadet Executive Officer

Colonels

Steele D K P *MBE*

Lieutenant Colonels

Charteris J A *MBE*
Gallacher J

Majors

Beveridge S E P
Docherty J
Donnell R H
Fulton A
Gillies J
Holt F G
Johnstone D C
Mathews W
McLay H D
Milroy C J A
Reid P

Captains

Caufield T A
ØClarke A M
Dempsey G C
Donald N BEM
Lee F
McAllister T E
Nesbit I
Taplin D J
West J R
ØWhyte M A

Lieutenants

ØDempsey E
Hamilton T C
McGerty J

McIntyre H E
Moffat B
Munro R
ØPickering F M
Stevenson G J P
Tait M
Taplin D J
Woodness C M

2nd Lieutenants

ØCumming R E C
Currie R H
Dunbar I S
Hay A W
ØIreland G
McWilliams A J
Riddell G E D
Wilson T

WILTSHIRE

County Cadet Commandant

Cadet Executive Officer

_____

Colonels

Dobson P H

Lieutenant Colonels

Douglas P L P *OBE*

Majors

Bazter P M
Delaney K J
Venus S J *MBE*
Wilcox S H

Captains

Bartoszewski R K
Bennett P A
ØEdwards S E
Field M R *TD*
Fielding D M R
Griffin M P
Hyslop R A
Lister M J
Roberts A

Lieutenants

Beggs J B M
Bradshaw J P

Carlile R W
ØEdlridge P A
Fell J A
Frizzell B J
Gray R
Hogg D J
Holt J
Johnston A
ØMatthias D K
Rogers A P
Taylor K V
Upton S D

2nd Lieutenants

Matthias M
ØTurner M A T
Wheeler R G
White P J
Williams S A

YORKSHIRE (N&W)

County Cadet Commandant

Col S Ashby *MBE*

_____

Cadet Executive Officer

_____

Lieutenant Colonels

Alexander G
Martin P

Majors

Cole P R
Fewster F *MBE TD*
Hall R
Hooks A
Johnson B
Pope T F
Render M D
Taylor S B
Temple I P

Captains

Anderson J A
Baxendale M C
Bestington D
Evans T B A
Evans T B A
Firth K G
Fortune B S

Gell H
Halliwell A D
Hardy P D *MBE*
Hebden J W
Hewson M E
Hills R E
Marren S A
Morris D W
Mummery W K J
Rashid M H
Semper B L
Sparks D L
Sykes B
Turner N J
ØUnderhill S
Wheller R K
Williams P W
Wootton M J

Lieutenants

Ainsworth P S
Ashby A J
Bell M
Benson J
Bradley A
Bridgeford M L
Bryan D
Chalk J D
Coleman S M
ØFisher K
Greenlee J
Lawson R W
Lister P J
Lomas I C
Lund H W
Major S
ØMillett A E
ØMorris A S
Neal G
ØOddy S E
Parker A
Pashby A J
Penfold C
Semper M I
Steel C
ØSumner M
Turner D A S
Waites P A J
Wise A K

2nd Lieutenants

Bagshaw E
Lynch J L
Whittaker S T

RESERVE FORCES & CADETS ASSOCIATIONS

(Arranged alphabetically)

Note - In some cases in these lists the rank shown against an officer's name is honorary.

COUNCIL OF RESERVE FORCES & CADETS ASSOCIATIONS
(Duke of York's HQ, Kings Road, Chelsea, London SW3 4SG)
(Tel: 0207-730-6122 DFTS: 94631-5587)
(Fax: 0207-414-5589 DFTS: 94631-5589)

President . . . . .The *Rt Hon The Lord* Freeman
Chairman . . . . .Col M J E Taylor *CBE TD DL*
Vice-Chairmen . . . . .Brig M E Browne *CBE TD DL*
Air Vice Marshal A F C Hunter *CBE AFC DL*
Commodore I R Pemberton *RD** DL*
Col P J C Robinson *TD DL*
Col Sir David Trippier *RD JP DL*
Secretary . . . . .Air Vice Marshal A J Stables *CBE FRAeS* RAF (Retd)
Deputy Secretary . . . . .Air Cdre D C Andrews *MBE FRIN* RAF (Retd)

Note: Each Reserve Forces & Cadets Association is represented on this Council by its President, Vice Presidents, Chairman, Vice Chairmen and Secretary.

EAST ANGLIA

President

S C Whitbread Esq JP *(HM Lord-Lieutenant of the County of Bedfordshire)*

Vice-Presidents

J G P Crowden K Esq JP *(HM Lord-Lieutenant of the County of Cambridgeshire)*
The *Lord* Braybrooke JP *(HM Lord-Lieutenant of the County of Essex)*
S A Bowes Lyon Esq JP *(HM Lord-Lieutenant of the County of Hertfordshire)*
Sir Timothy Colman KG JP DCL *(HM Lord-Lieutenant of the County of Norfolk)*
The *Right Honourable The Lord* Belstead PC JP *(HM Lord-Lieutenant of the County of Suffolk)*

Chairman

Col N H Kelsey *OBE TD*

Vice-Chairmen

Cdr T C Haile *RNR** RD* (Retd)
Col A D Chissel *TD*
Air Commodore J A F Ford RAF

County Chairmen

Col M J Simmonds *TD* (Beds)
Lt Col P G R Horrell *TD DL* (Cambs)
Lt Col W I M Allan *TD* (Essex)
Lt Col J D Sainsbury *OBE TD* (Herts)
Lt Col R E S Drew (Norfolk)
Col J G Aldous *OBE* (Suffolk)

Secretary

Col J S Houchin *OBE*

Deputy Secretary

Lt Col J A Allan *TD*

"Springfield Tyrells", 250 Springfield Road
Chelmsford, Essex CM2 6BU
Tel: 01245 354262 Mil: 94651 xxxx
DDI: 01245 244800
Fax: 01245 492398 Mil: 94651 4723
E-mail: offman@rfcanglia.demon.co.uk
Internet: www.reserve-forces-anglia.org

EAST MIDLAND

President

Sir Andrew Buchanan *Bt (HM Lord-Lieutenant Nottinghamshire)*

Vice Presidents

T G M Brooks Esq JP *(HM Lord-Lieutenant Leicestershire)*
Mrs B K Cracroft-Eley *(HM Lord-Lieutenant Lincolnshire)*
Lady Juliet Townsend LVO *(HM Lord-Lieutenant Northamptonshire)*
J K Bather Esq *(HM Lord-Lieutenant Derbyshire)*
Air Chief Marshal *Sir* Thomas Kennedy *GCB AFC (HM Lord-Lieutenant Rutland)*

Chairman

Brig M E Browne *CBE TD DL*

Vice Chairmen

Col G B Roper *TD*
Maj G G Simpson *TD DL*
Col A A F Terry *TD DL*
Air Cdre A J Griffin AFC
Col I R Keers *OBE DL*
Col R Merryweather *TD DL*
Cdr P R Moore *RD** RNR

Chief Exective

Brig W J Hurrell *CBE*

6 Clinton Terrace, Derby Road
Nottingham NG7 1LZ
Tel: 0115 947 6508 Fax: 0115 947 3406

GREATER LONDON

President

The *Lord* Imbert *QPM JP*

Vice Presidents

Field Marshal *Sir* John Chapple *GCB CBE DL*
Col *Sir* Greville Spratt *GBE TD JP DL*

Chairman

Brig A P Verey *QVRM TD*

Vice Chairmen

Cmdr J McK Ludgate *RD* DL RNR*
Col M E Hatt-Cook *OBE RD**
Col G E Godbold *OBE TD DL*
Col I W B McRobbie *OBE TD DL*
Col J C Power *TD*

Secretary

Col P C Cook

Duke of York's Headquarters
Chelsea, London SW3 4RY
Tel: (Civ) 020-7730-8131 Fax: 020-7414 5560
Tel: (Mil) 94631 5503 Fax: 94631 5560

381

HIGHLANDS

President

Air Vice Marshal G A Chesworth *CB OBE DFC (HM Lord-Lieutenant Moray)*

Vice Presidents

John D B Smart *(HM Lord-Lieutenant Kincardine)*
The Lord Provost of the City of Aberdeen
Lt Col J Stirling *CBE TD (HM Lord-Lieutenant Stirling and Falkirk)*
The Earl of Airlie *KT GCVO PC (HM Lord-Lieutenant Angus)*
Cllr J A S McPherson *CBE JP (HM Lord-Lieutenant Banffshire)*
Maj G T Dunnett *TD DL (HM Lord-Lieutenant Caithness)*
The Lord Provost of the City of Dundee
George Marwick *(HM Lord-Lieutenant Orkney)*
John H Scott *(HM Lord-Lieutenant Shetland)*
E A Brodie of Lethen *(HM Lord-Lieutenant Nairn)*
Angus D M Farquarson *OBE (HM Lord-Lieutenant Aberdeenshire)*
Capt R W K Stirling *TD JP (HM Lord-Lieutenant Ross and Cromarty)*
Brig D D G Hardie *TD JP (HM Lord-Lieutenant Dunbartonshire)*
Mrs Margaret Dean *(HM Lord-Lieutenant Fife)*
Sir David Montgomery *Bt JP (HM Lord-Lieutenant Perth and Kinross)*
Maj Gen D Houston *CBE (HM Lord-Lieutenant Sutherland)*
Col R C Stewart *CBE TD (HM Lord-Lieutenant Clackmannan)*
Lord Gray of Contin *MP (HM Lord-Lieutenant Inverness)*
The Duke of Argyll *(HM Lord-Lieutenant Argyll and Bute)*

Chairman

Lt Col G S Johnston *OBE TD DL*

Vice Chairmen

Lt Col V P Mason
Col R L Steele
Maj A C Oag *TD*
Brig A G Dorward *TD*
Capt T R Woolley *RD* RNR
Gp Capt J P Dacre RAF (Retd)

Secretary

Col J R Hensman *OBE*

"Seathwood" 365 Perth Road
Dundee DD2 1LX
Tel: 01382 668283 Fax: 01382 566442
E-mail: info@hrfca.co.uk

LOWLANDS

President

Lt Gen *Sir* Norman Arthur *KCB (Brig Queen's Body Guard for Scotland)*

Vice Presidents

The Lord Provost of the City of Edinburgh
The Lord Provost of the City of Glasgow
Maj A R Trotter
Capt G W Burnet *LVO (Brig Queen's Body Guard for Scotland)*
Maj *Sir* Hew Hamilton-Dalrymple *Bt KCVO (Capt Queen's Body Guard for Scotland)*
The Rt Hon The Earl of Morton
Cameron Parker Esq *OBE*
Dr J Paterson-Brown *CBE*
Capt R C Cunningham-Jardine *(Member Queen's Body Guard for Scotland)*
Maj E S Orr Ewing
Capt J D B Younger *(Secretary Queen's Body Guard for Scotland)*
Maj R Y Henderson *TD (Brig Queen's Body Guard for Scotland)*
G K Cox Esq *MBE JP*

Chairman

Col D A Scott *OBE TD*

Vice Chairmen

Capt C J P Hall *RD* RNR
Col D J Cameron *TD*
Col N J F Dalrymple Hamilton *OBE TD DL*
Col J W Mackay *TD*
Col A G Smith
Lt Col I Ballantyne
Lt Col R C Hambleton *TD*
Maj W S Turner *MC*
Gp Capt D A Needham

Secretary

Col R S B Watson *OBE* ret pay

Lowland House
60 Avenuepark Street
Glasgow G20 8LW
Tel: 0141-945 4951 Fax: 0141-945 4869
E-mail: info@lowland.rcfa.org.uk

NORTH WEST OF ENGLAND AND THE ISLE OF MAN

President

Col W A Bromley-Davenport *JP (HM Lord-Lieutenant of Cheshire)*

Vice Presidents

Col J B Timmins *OBE TD JP (HM Lord-Lieutenant of Greater Manchester)*
His Excellency Air Marshal I D Macfadyen *CB OBE (HM Lieutenant-Governor Isle of Man)*
Col A W Waterworth *JP (HM Lord-Lieutenant of Merseyside)*
Col J A Cropper *(HM Lord-Lieutenant of Cumbria)*
Col *The Rt Hon The Lord* Shuttleworth *JP (HM Lord-Lieutenant of Lancashire)*

Chairman

Col *Sir* David Trippier *RD JP DL*

Vice Chairmen

Cdre R H Walker *RD** DL* RNR
Lt Col C T Hillock *RD* RMR
Col J A Harkon *MBE TD*
Maj D Gee *TD DL*
Col S H Spackman *TD DL*
Gp Capt M Bruce *RAF*

Chief Executive

Col G J O Wells-Cole *OBE* ret pay

Alexandra Court
28 Alexandra Drive
Aigburth, Liverpool L17 8YE
Tel: 0151-727-4552 Fax: 0151-727-8133
E-mail: nwrfca@compuserve.com

NORTHERN IRELAND

President

Maj W J Hall *JP (HM Lord-Lieutenant Down)*

Vice Presidents

Col *The Rt Hon The Earl of* Erne *JP (HM Lord-Lieutenant Fermanagh)*
Col *The Lord* O'Neill *TD JP (HM Lord-Lieutenant Antrim)*
Mr D Desmond *CBE (HM Lord-Lieutenant Londonderry)*
His Grace The Duke of Abercorn *(HM Lord-Lieutenant Tyrone)*
Col *The Right Hon The Earl of* Caledon *JP (HM Lord-Lieutenant*
Col J T Eaton *CBE TD JP (HM Lord-Lieutenant City of Londonderry)*
Lady Carswell *OBE (HM Lord-Lieutenant City of Belfast)*

Chairman

Col S M Elder *TD DL*

Vice Chairmen

Lt Col R W C T Barbour *MBE TD*
Maj K Maginnis
The Viscountess Brookeborough
Maj S Irwin *TD*
Col J M Steele *CB OBE TD DL*
Lt Col C T Hogg *MBE UD JP DL*
Col A H Reid *OBE TD JP DL*
Cdr N J E Reynolds *RD*
Gp Capt B G Freeman *OBE*
Maj W B S Buchanan *MBE TD*

Secretary

Brig I N Osborne *OBE*

25 Windsor Park
Belfast BT9 6FR
Tel: 028 9066 5024 Fax: 028 9066 2809
E-mail: secretary@rfcani.co.uk

383

NORTH OF ENGLAND

President

Sir Paul Nicholson *(HM Lord-Lieutenant Durham)*

Vice Presidents

Sir John Riddell *Bt CVO KG GCVO TD (HM Lord-Lieutenant Northumberland)*
Lord Crathorne *(HM Lord-Lieutenant North Yorkshire)*
Nigel Sherlock Esq *(HM Lord-Lieutenant Tyne & Wear)*

Chairman

Col A A E Glenton *CBE TD DL*

Vice Chairmen

Capt A I B Moffat *RD DL* RNR
Col J G W Feggetter *TD QHS*
Col W P Catesby *DL*
Col D W Herring *TD QHS*
Col A W Illingworth *TD*
Avm A F C Hunter *CBE AFC DL*

Secretary

Brig N G R Hepworth *OBE* ret pay

53 Old Elvet
Durham DH1 3JJ
Tel: 0191-384 7202 Fax: 0191-384 0918
E-mail: ne.reserveforces@virgin.net

SOUTH EAST

President

P L Wroughton Esq *JP (HM Lord-Lieutenant Berkshire)*

Vice Presidents

The Right Hon Lord Kingsdown *KG (HM Lord-Lieutenant Kent)*
Mrs F M Fagan *JP (HM Lord-Lieutenant Hampshire)*
C D J Bland Esq *JP (HM Lord-Lieutenant Isle of Wight)*
H Brunner Esq *JP (HM Lord-Lieutenant Oxfordshire)*
Mrs S J F Goad *JP (HM Lord-Lieutenant Surrey)*
Sir Nigel Mobbs *JP (HM Lord-Lieutenant Buckinghamshire)*
H R Wyatt Esq *(HM Lord-Lieutenant West Sussex)*
Mrs P K Stewart-Roberts *OBE (HM Lord-Lieutenant East Sussex)*

Chairman

Col J R G Putnam *CBE TD DL*

Vice Chairmen

Lt Col C H Ainsley *TD*
C J Prideaux Esq *DL*
Col W H F Stevens *OBE*
Lt Col R C B Dixon *TD DL*
Brig J N B Mogg *DL*
Col P A D Storie-Pugh *MBE TD ADC*
Col D E Stevens *OBE TD DL*
Cdr D J Belfield *RD**
Gp Capt R Dixon *OBE*
Capt M C Griffiths *TD DL*
Lt Col G H Wright *TD DL*

Secretary

Brig J S W Powell *OBE*

Seely House, Shoe Lane
Aldershot, Hants GU11 2HJ
Tel: 01252 357605 Fax: 01252 357620
E-mail: h@serfca.co.uk

WALES

President

Capt N Lloyd-Edwards *GCStJ RD* LLB JP* RNR *(HM Lord-Lieutenant for South Glamorgan)*

Vice Presidents

Sir David Mansel Lewis *KCVO KStJ BA JP (HM Lord-Lieutenant for Dyfed)*
Professor E Sunderland *OBE (HM Lord-Lieutenant for Gwynedd)*
M A McLaggan Esq *MA KStJ JP (HM Lord-Lieutenant for Mid Glamorgan)*
The Hon Mrs S Legge Bourke *LVO (HM Lord-Lieutenant for Powys)*
Commodore R C Hastie *CBE RD* JP* RNR *(HM Lord-Lieutenant for West Glamorgan)*
Clwyd - vacant
Gwent - vacant

Chairman

Col P Eyton-Jones *TD DL*

Vice Chairman (Naval)

Cdr J M D Curteis *SBStJ RD* FCA DL* RNR

Vice Chairmen (Military)

Col G E J Blythe *BSc*
Lt Col D G Clarke *TD JP*
Col D W Forrest *TD***

Vice Chairman (Air)

Air Cmdr A J Park *CBE*

Secretary

Brig W A Mackereth *DL*

Deputy Secretary (North Wales)

Major P J Mullings *MBE*

Centre Block, Maindy Barracks
Cardiff DF4 3YE
Tel: 029 20 220251 (Cardiff Mil Ext 8205)
Fax: 029 20 224828 (Cardiff Mil: Ext 8313)
E-mail: info@rfca-wales.org.uk

WESSEX

President

Lady Gass *MA JP (HM Lord-Lieutenant for Somerset)*

Vice Presidents

J N Tidmarsh Esq *MBE JP (HM Lord-Lieutenant for the City and County of Bristol)*
Lady Mary Holborrow *JP (HM Lord-Lieutenant for Cornwall)*
E Dancer Esq *CBE KStJ (HM Lord-Lieutenant for Devon)*
Captain M Fulford-Dobson *JP CVO* RN *(HM Lord-Lieutenant for Dorset)*
H W G Elwes Esq *JP (HM Lord Lieutenant for Gloucestershire)*
Lt Gen *Sir* Maurice Johnston *KCB OBE (HM Lord-Lieutenant for Wiltshire)*

Chairman

Cdre I R Pemberton *RD** DL* RNR

Vice Chairman

Col M E Kelsey *TD* (Bristol)
Wg Cdr M J Metherell *BA* (Cornwall)
Col J E B Hills *TD* (Devon)
Col D G Thomas (Dorset)
Col J F Penley *OBE TD* (Gloucestershire)
Brig J Hemsley (Somerset)
Lt Col J R Arkell *TD DL* (Wiltshire)
Cmdr J F Holmes *RD** RNR (Naval)
Col R A Hooper *MA FRSA DL* RM (Marine)
Wg Cdr A S Donaldson *AE BA RAuxAF* (Air)

Chief Executive/Secretary

Brig B C Jackman *OBE MC*

2 Beaufort Road
Clifton, Bristol BS8 2JS
Tel: 0117 973 4045
Fax: 0117 974 3154
E-mail: hq@reserve-forces-wessex.org.uk

Deputy Chief Executive

Col C J Constable

Assistant Secretary

Maj C E Marsh *TD*

385

WEST MIDLAND

President

Mr James Hawley *TD JP MA (HM Lord-Lieutenant for Staffordshire)*

Vice Presidents

Mr M Dunne *JP (HM Lord-Lieutenant for Warwickshire)*
Mr A E H Heber-Percy *(HM Lord-Lieutenant for Shropshire)*
R R Taylor *OBE KStJ JP (HM Lord-Lieutenant for West Midlands)*
Col *Sir* Thomas Dunne *KCVO KStJ JP (HM Lord-Lieutenant for Hereford & Worcester)*

Chairman

Col P J C Robinson *TD DL*

Vice Chairman

Cdr R J Symonds *RD* RNR
Maj S P Etheridge *MBE TD JP*
Col R L Cariss *MBE TD*
Col T M Evans *TD DL*
Col T D C Lloyd *TD*
Air Vice Marshal M D Smart

Secretary/Chief Executive

Brig J M Patrick *MBE* ret pay

Tennal Grange, Tennal Road
Harborne, Birmingham B32 2HX
Tel: 0121 427 5221 Fax: 0121 427 8380

YORKSHIRE AND THE HUMBER

President

The Earl of Scarbrough *(HM Lord-Lieutenant South Yorkshire)*

Vice Presidents

The Lord Crathorne *(HM Lord-Lieutenant North Yorkshire)*
R Marriott *TD (HM Lord-Lieutenant East Riding of Yorkshire)*
J Lyles *CBE JP (HM Lord-Lieutenant West Yorkshire)*

Chairman

Col E C York *TD DL*

Vice Chairmen

Commodore P R Sutermeister RN
Brig G B Smalley *OBE TD*
Col C J Tattersall *TD DL*
Air Cdre W G Gambold *FIMgt* RAF (R)

Secretary

Brig N F Wood ret pay

20 St George's Place
York YO24 1DS
Tel: 01904 623081 Fax: 01904 622245

COMBINED CADET FORCE ASSOCIATION
E Block, Duke of York's Headquarters, London SW3 4RR
(Tel: 020 7730 9733 Fax: 020 7730 8264)

Captain General . . . . .THE QUEEN
President . . . . .Air Marshal *Sir* Timothy Garden *KCB*
Vice Presidents
  Royal Navy . . . . .Maj Gen (Retd) A M Keeling *CB CBE* (Late RM)
  Army . . . . .Maj Gen (Retd) P C Shapland *CB MBE*
  RAF . . . . .Air Vice Marshal (Retd) J D L Feesey *AFC*
Chairman .Maj Gen (Retd) M T Tennant *CB*
Vice Chairman . . . . .Wg Cdr A V M Murray *MA* RAFVR(T)
Hon Treasurer . . . . .Cdr A G Brown RNR
Secretary . . . . .Brig J E Neeve

ARMY CADET FORCE ASSOCIATION
E Block, Duke of York's Headquarters, London SW3 4RR
(Tel: 020 7730 9733 Fax: 020 7730 8264)

Patron . . . . .THE QUEEN
Colonel-in-Chief . . . . .Field Marshal *HRH The Prince* Philip *Duke of* Edinburgh
                                              KG KT OM GBE AC QSO
President . . . . .Gen *Sir* Michael Wilkes *KCB CBE*
Vice President . . . . .Lt Gen *Sir* David Scott-Barrett *KBE MC*
                                              Chief Constable P Clare *QPM DL BA(Hons)*
Chairman . . . . .Lt Gen *Sir* Anthony Denison-Smith *KBE*
Vice Chairmen . . . .*The Rt Hon Lord* Trefgarne
                                              Maj Gen (Retd) J D Stokoe *CB CBE*
                                              Brig (Retd) R B MacGregor-Oakford *CBE MC*
                                              Mr A C Chambers
Hon Treasurer . . . . .Col K Bruce-Smith *TD*
General Secretary . . . . .Brig J E Neeve
DeputyGeneral Secretary . . . . .Lt Col A G C Horridge

THE ROYAL GIBRALTAR REGIMENT

(formerly The Gibraltar Defence Force 1939-1958)

Regimental Crest

A shield bearing the Castle and Key of Gibraltar superimposed on a decorative backing depicting the blue sky of the Mediterranean together with its sea and a three part scroll below with the inscription "NULLI EXPUGNABILIS HOSTI". The whole surmounted by the Queen's crown.

Commissions

Granted by the Governor of Gibraltar on behalf of Her Majesty the Queen

Agents . . . . Nat West Bank Ltd, 57 Line Wall Road, Gibraltar

Regimental Headquarters. . . . . Devil's Tower Camp, BFPO 52

Regimental March . . . . .The British Grenadiers
RA Slow March

Alliances

The Royal Anglian Regiment
The Royal Regiment of Artillery
Corps of Royal Engineers
The Royal Irish Regiment

Commander in Chief . . . . The Governor of Gibraltar

Honorary Colonel . . . . Lt Col (Retd) J J Porral *OBE ED JP*

Authorised Abbreviation . . . . .RG

Affiliations

HMS Calpe
19 (Gibraltar 1779-83) Battery Royal Artillery
21 (Gibraltar 1779-83) Battery Royal Artillery

Regulars	Jurado W	010699	Canessa P X *BSc ED*	110997
	O'Shea A D J	280499	Dellipiani M D *ED*	010400
Lieutenant Colonels	Risso C	011098	Sanguinetti M G *ED*	010400
			Wawn C J N *BA ED*	110997
	Lieutenants			
Brancato F P *psc*	011198			
	Lopez I S	120498	*Captains*	
Majors	McComb D	100400		
			Collado D *ED*	010296
Alman M G	300999	*2nd Lieutenants*	Navas J C	011098
Borg A M	010797			
Perez J C	300998	Williamson J R	090898	*Lieutenants*	
Randall M J	010995			
			Khubchand K	011298
Captains		**Volunteers**		
			2nd Lieutenants	
Bonfante A W	010497	*Majors*	Chichon M C	310799
Freyone D D	060896	Canessa P H *ED*	011194	Payas J A	130698

SECTION V

391

INDEX

SUBJECT INDEX

A

394

501898 Austin C G, 123
539677 Austin F, 320
536042 Austin G R, 250
551201 Austin J S, 110
546484 Austin J S, 175
533932 Austin M R, 242
471191 Austin R P M, 271
522319 Austin W J, 318
Austin R, 345
527489 Austin R C, 362
552215 Auty J B, 295
504309 Averty J T, 335
506353 Aveyard B, 319
505922 Avison B P, 140
540169 Avison B, 362
548732 Axcell J P, 306
532956 Axtell S D, 336
550297 Axten A, 362
527943 Axup R R, 266
551967 Aylett D J, 339
511352 Ayling K S, 305
548844 Aylward A C, 141
548783 Aylward G L, 251
500804 Aylwin-Foster N R F, 119
547853 Ayo L P, 184
549203 Ayre P W, 301
Ayres R J, 345
544506 Azzopardi M, 298

B

554405 Babb P L, 340
540448 Babbage S F, 249
554117 Babbington J M, 343
486592 Baber J H, 265
546710 Babicki A A, 251
541312 Babicki J W, 251
514855 Babington D J, 217
530244 Babington D, 362
Bach Lord, 13, 14, 15
548526 Back J D, 120
548845 Back S C, 136
520982 Backhouse R, 342
Backhouse W H, 35
492915 Backler J A A, 265
552817 Bacon A C, 338
539213 Bacon C, 125
504644 Bacon G A, 315
529410 Bacon H C, 255
503747 Bacon K T, 19, 265
551077 Bacon M D, 280
547091 Bacon M J, 278
506635 Bacon R J, 237
541067 Bacon R J W, 242
498906 Bacon S J, 177
503747 Bacon K, 38
551238 Badcock C, 118
552576 Badcock D L, 343
511368 Badcock W C, 362
523937 Baddeley M W, 262
550890 Badder P W, 245
542650 Badger J, 263
488662 Badgery J, 211
495129 Badham-Thornhill M L, 123
520432 Badman S J G, 123
506699 Badruddin P, 362
537639 Baff J, 362
538894 Bage S J, 297
Bage I, 345
Bagga H S, 72
524995 Baggaley D, 280
551000 Bagge G J, 362
Baggs A C, 345
540279 Bagley N S, 134
498907 Bagnall A R K, 145
Bagnall Sir Anthony, 13
360763 Bagnall Sir Nigel, 93
510446 Bagnall-Oakeley M A, 239
551239 Bagnold R A, 172
552301 Bagshaw C E I, 120
534873 Bagshaw J D, 147
553072 Bagshaw E, 362
545633 Baguley J B, 362
536043 Baidwan J S, 249
546303 Baigent I F, 278
526532 Bailes M D, 143
527710 Bailey B J, 294
531412 Bailey C, 107
503748 Bailey C W, 131
551461 Bailey D J S, 208
520262 Bailey D J W, 248
553133 Bailey D W, 137
553553 Bailey I P, 219
552702 Bailey J, 282
494267 Bailey J B A, 121
518605 Bailey J C, 191
549305 Bailey J D, 302
550405 Bailey K G H, 252
499584 Bailey K V, 230
545328 Bailey M C, 244

516307 Bailey M S, 268
516553 Bailey N J W, 111
504789 Bailey P, 335
530997 Bailey P D, 177
497882 Bailey P R S, 191
539345 Bailey R, 337
544272 Bailey S D, 258
554471 Bailey S T, 324
535966 Bailey T S, 270
543123 Bailey V E, 342
495130 Bailey W A, 130
494267 Bailey J B A, 17, 27
Bailey L, 345
552035 Bailey N, 362
Bailey S M, 345
Bailey W N, 345
541542 Bailie K B, 217
513991 Baillie P F, 265
505195 Baillon R J F, 218
495131 Bain A G, 174
550923 Bain N J, 143
543895 Bain R, 288
Bain J, 345
538833 Bainbridge J, 362
515823 Baines C, 249
527721 Baines J J, 261
513838 Baines M, 140
522778 Baines M L, 297
536595 Bainger A J, 256
Bainimarama Ratu Voreque, 82
530271 Baird D R, 307
553054 Baird J, 325
507245 Baird J N, 218
554214 Baird M E, 324
535427 Baird P C, 324
544871 Baker A, 125
540005 Baker A G, 301
539090 Baker A K, 250
521155 Baker B C, 322
544273 Baker B G, 172
511488 Baker D, 248
547017 Baker D M, 297
519505 Baker E D, 331
554131 Baker G B, 302
534125 Baker G V, 133
545723 Baker H, 252
537344 Baker H J, 311
535456 Baker H K, 311
553134 Baker J A, 127
490082 Baker J C, 335
482682 Baker J G, 90, 129
540914 Baker J P, 301
538675 Baker K H, 241
543725 Baker L E M, 251
520160 Baker M A, 300
551734 Baker M A S, 137
552245 Baker M S, 259
554081 Baker N, 338
520288 Baker N A, 277
544870 Baker N D, 143
533380 Baker N G, 319
527914 Baker N L, 291
549454 Baker N P, 186
544190 Baker P, 324
503749 Baker P B, 249
526566 Baker P C, 140
525269 Baker P H S, 123
501374 Baker P J, 336
512565 Baker P J A, 237
547373 Baker P L, 267
528208 Baker P M, 301

523587 Cheung S N, 335
543490 Chick C G, 230
554190 Chick D, 339
503781 Chick J A, 131
525835 Child C J S, 240
534772 Child K A B, 269
548874 Child S E, 214
523472 Childerley P, 281
551741 Childs S P L, 144
527890 Chilton G, 336
Chiluba F J T, 81
Chimbayo J G, 80
555374 Chinery J P, 325
504014 Chinneck P J E, 315
522351 Chisholm A C, 311
553578 Chisholm A R T, 343
549485 Chisholm G J P, 246
542147 Chisholm R A J, 211
Chisholm Sir John, 62
553908 Chishti S K K, 324
491420 Chisnall R M, 177
493339 Chissel A D, 305, 380
515950 Chiswell J R, 218
544641 Chitrabahadur Gurung, 225
540920 Chitraj Limbu, 227
530661 Chittenden H B, 249
528246 Chittock B, 364
519795 Chitty R O M, 115
534956 Chivers M A, 256
Chiwenga C G, 83
Chiziko M D, 80
545517 Chohan M J, 245
500809 Cholerton I D, 201
533117 Chorley J P, 288
536883 Chorley W E, 337
484746 Chown J D B, 330
525860 Chrisp A H R, 293
534323 Christer D A, 364
549181 Christian M R Rev, 234
494473 Christian P A, 364
552249 Christie D, 259
551198 Christie D G, 271
554944 Christie G A, 339
542670 Christie J M, 161
527789 Christie M P, 218
542982 Christie T S B, 165
544818 Christie G, 364
Christmas M R, 352
554519 Christodoulou T L K, 343
542227 Christopher C D, 244
534631 Christopher C H, 269
535492 Christopher R J, 124
552697 Christophers G J, 364
Christopherson R J, 33
541545 Chrystal D, 142
542228 Chubb G K, 243
536922 Chudha S S, 324, 364
534027 Chudleigh C J H, 202
544889 Church I J, 135
538301 Church K B, 244
538234 Church S A, 242
531427 Churcher G P, 171
549829 Churcher R, 364
538683 Churchill A M, 141
521291 Churchley C J, 125
486614 Chuter J W, 253
515951 Chynoweth M, 204
497722 Ciaglinski R Z A, 268
545423 Ciaralli-Parenzi A, 302
498895 Cima K H, 18, 129
513542 Cinnamon R, 318
516574 Ciotti M, 318

503782 Clacher A D C, 238
550208 Clack J D, 252
497722 Claglinski R Z A, 90
549412 Clancy A M, 364
551220 Clapham M P, 278
512786 Clapham N G, 305
538551 Clapham N W J, 271
527790 Clapp G B, 171
509500 Clapp R N, 139
533187 Clapp D J, 364
Clapp I A, 352
Clapper M S, 352
542278 Clare C J, 282
541952 Clare G A, 251
548875 Clare R J, 212
Clare P, 386
515952 Claridge C R, 174
536128 Claridge M, 269
539548 Claridge M K, 242
533046 Clark A C, 244
550642 Clark A R, 246
534001 Clark A V, 219
504910 Clark C R, 123
479192 Clark H D, 330
532046 Clark H I M, 166
544296 Clark H J L, 167
547304 Clark J, 281
532591 Clark J A, 333
535666 Clark J E, 117
548496 Clark J L, 134
506825 Clark J W, 139
529604 Clark K E, 142
552327 Clark L, 144
545489 Clark M J M, 293
537402 Clark M L, 242
546502 Clark M P, 245
555714 Clark N P, 298
505739 Clark N R, 131
537817 Clark P, 295
549683 Clark P I C, 325
541430 Clark P J, 278
544077 Clark P R, 283
552281 Clark P W J, 288
499597 Clark R C D, 123
525963 Clark R N W, 276
545053 Clark S, 303
553187 Clark S G G, 231
549975 Clark S J, 242
531054 Clark S L, 311
540791 Clark S L A, 263
546748 Clark S M G, 293
548736 Clark T L, 252
554072 Clark V G, 339
516711 Clark C W, 364
Clark D A, 352
540995 Clark D A, 364
502205 Clark M A, 364
544787 Clark P S, 364
Clark R T, 58
506793 Clark W G C, 364
551162 Clarke A G, 120
547107 Clarke A J, 126
543236 Clarke A J, 314
545415 Clarke A S, 297
544891 Clarke A W, 202
552888 Clarke B S, 334
542928 Clarke C J, 337
554501 Clarke C S, 343
518745 Clarke D, 257
554480 Clarke D M, 295
539972 Clarke D S, 124
551257 Clarke G J, 141

553501 Clarke G J, 148
521084 Clarke G R, 288
544297 Clarke I, 258
537331 Clarke J R, 244
529476 Clarke J R, 256
527188 Clarke K J, 256
552153 Clarke K L, 243
550643 Clarke K M, 242
530302 Clarke M F, 277
512498 Clarke N L, 309
522325 Clarke P, 296
517095 Clarke P S, 307
494404 Clarke P W, 130
552591 Clarke R A, 136
548877 Clarke R A H, 245
545934 Clarke R J, 200
538173 Clarke R M, 297
551743 Clarke R S, 246
543446 Clarke S A, 142
548335 Clarke S J G, 231
492692 Clarke S K E, 85, 130
506766 Clarke S R, 342
514372 Clarke T, 336
552328 Clarke T N, 127
493694 Clarke T P, 122
537522 Clarke T P, 287
505887 Clarke A M, 364
543639 Clarke D C, 364
Clarke D G, 384
549826 Clarke J P E, 364
550312 Clarke J W, 364
554748 Clarke N, 364
Clarke R, 347
Clarke R J, 347
Clarke S, 347
553569 Clarkson G J, 339
Clarkson Her Excellency
The Right
HonourableAdrienne, 67
528539 Clarkson M A, 255
Clarkson A H, 7
530413 Clash M A, 326
518394 Clasper J C, 248
Clasper P, 45
520909 Clauson J G, 324
516576 Claydon C J, 230
543479 Claydon L E, 251
511006 Claydon M N, 205
Claydon K, 347
553166 Clayton A A, 257
545454 Clayton A L, 334
551744 Clayton B G, 165
531519 Clayton C G, 134
520433 Clayton J W, 304
542307 Clayton P J, 200
529788 Clayton P S, 134
535471 Clayton R L, 105
549776 Clayton S M, 338
Clayton R L, 347
Clayton V A, 347
540802 Cleary A C, 337
532187 Cleave R C, 195
541878 Cleaver P, 219
533547 Clee A C, 133
551003 Clee E F, 143
518400 Clee CBB, 97
526783 Cleeton D C, 243
533028 Cleeve S F, 262
541734 Clegg C J, 219
525345 Clegg C J P, 219
552030 Clegg G E, 283
533538 Clegg P J, 300

550197 Davies P J, 271	547686 Davis M W, 143	519416 Deacon GHJ, 103
532524 Davies P L, 326	488416 Davis P A, 171	518234 Deahl M P, 321
505040 Davies P M, 130	536623 Davis P V, 190	536298 Deakin G A, 115
552972 Davies P M, 271	507430 Davis R, 201	520624 Deakin G C, 183
525721 Davies R, 243	504208 Davis R B, 139	536868 Deakin H K, 110
551575 Davies R A, 184	498078 Davis R E C, 300	512941 Deakin S F, 171
533051 Davies R G, 211	514841 Davis R R, 131	553657 Deakin V E, 343
539411 Davies R G, 241	551750 Davis S G, 143	548716 Deakin D J, 365
532818 Davies R J, 319	551595 Davis E W, 365	544491 Deakin D M, 365
535883 Davies R S, 231	489440 Davis M K, 365	549220 Deakin P, 365
506829 Davies S, 189	Davis P F, 348	542835 Deal L A, 337
555703 Davies S D, 308	548159 Davison G, 219	deAlwis E A D A S, 75
554128 Davies S D L, 324	504757 Davison G M, 318	532819 Deamer S C, 334
518882 Davies S H L, 123	546507 Davison L E, 263	525046 Dean A J, 318
497399 Davies S J, 131	520082 Davison M, 257	533820 Dean A M, 262
549322 Davies S J J, 250	546438 Davison M A, 324	552714 Dean A W M, 282
541590 Davies S L, 141	503719 Davison M F L, 300	529301 Dean B J, 342
549500 Davies S M, 196	485709 Davison M J, 237	548891 Dean E R E, 114
526087 Davies S P, 116	548591 Davison P, 325	554954 Dean F K M, 325
542312 Davies S P, 245	537183 Davison P J, 133	543786 Dean M P, 258
549720 Davies S W, 135	523279 Davison S, 330	550649 Dean P J, 231
548158 Davies T E A, 206	545374 Davison D M, 365	521613 Dean P R, 240
532763 Davies T J, 275	539917 Davison E R, 365	540490 Dean T A, 142
543421 Davies T J, 282	554245 Davison S J, 365	535733 Dean B A, 365
547897 Davies T M D, 127	513391 Davy K R, 281	Dean C E, 348
523627 Davies V, 335	537782 Daw T M, 172	506463 Dean C E, 365
554635 Davies V R, 338	540770 Dawber D W, 305	Dean M E, 381
541259 Davies W H L, 105	546329 Dawe C A, 337	Dean P G, 348
Davies A, 348	539412 Dawes A P L, 124	534917 Dean S J, 365
543184 Davies A J, 365	529874 Dawes C M, 302	522900 Deane J C B, 257
553550 Davies C A, 365	536392 Dawes E J M, 124	549861 Deane M B, 288
483179 Davies D A, 365	553251 Dawes J M, 144	Deane His Excellency The
518320 Davies E M, 365	535962 Dawes S P, 134	Honourable Sir William,
Davies G A, 348	539743 Dawes A L, 365	68
522245 Davies G J, 365	543928 Dawson A G, 219	533446 Deans A J, 269
487476 Davies G L, 222	525354 Dawson A S, 240	520626 Deans G, 141
545725 Davies I A, 365	551751 Dawson B G, 127	541257 Deans J A B, 275
Davies I M, 348	531354 Dawson E J, 261	538950 Deans P, 142
518440 Davies J A, 365	493700 Dawson G W, 130	536625 Deans R, 277
496129 Davies J B, 365	541372 Dawson J F, 125	529484 Dear A M, 256
540744 Davies J P, 223	509507 Dawson L I M, 239	Dearing A P, 348
Davies J R, 348	545897 Dawson M, 126	525573 Dearman B T, 142
545134 Davies MD, 103	542676 Dawson N S, 230	520987 Deas A J, 240
552848 Davies R J, 365	525839 Dawson T J, 269	547004 Deas G D, 342
542405 Davies R M, 365	Dawson C H, 348	517118 Deasy S, 262
523772 Davies R P, 365	Dawson G, 348	548594 Debenham A J, 305
508535 Davies S, 365	Dawson K, 348	548890 De Borchgrave Daltena S
544182 Davies S A, 365	554848 Dawson L C, 365	G, 148
Davies S R, 348	521151 Dawson P, 365	529351 DeBretton Gordon H S,
538510 Davies T A, 365	542571 Day A C, 262	119
551678 Davies T A, 365	540942 Day A R, 278	549755 Decarteret G A, 365
Davies T E, 348	549985 Day A S, 136	554971 Deck M D, 319
485318 Davies-Jenkins S C A, 365	546888 Day B J W, 134	491446 Deed A P, 177
553249 Davies-Jones R L, 206	540026 Day C B, 127	548071 Deegan D A, 142
544306 Davis A K, 126	535116 Day C G, 124	544735 Deegan A C, 365
523351 Davis A T, 240	487477 Day C J R, 107	549986 Deeley A W, 204
516788 Davis C, 268	493533 Day D C, 214	523352 Deer A L, 315
529482 Davis C J, 241	548253 Day J N, 263	529606 Deere R E J, 165
547546 Davis C N, 342	553779 Day K E, 338	509730 Deery E L, 335
517821 Davis E A, 139	535501 Day M J, 124	540467 DeFerry-Foster R J, 110
525188 Davis J, 230	552841 Day M S, 263	533925 DeGale J S, 241
512973 Davis J A, 330	551680 Day P J, 143	537332 Dehnel S H, 146
513136 Davis J E, 335	547117 Day T W, 141	491441 DeHochepied Larpent A L
545853 Davis J E, 338	487477 Day C J R, 85	D, 305
527216 Davis J W, 296	535416 Day G J, 365	534231 Deighan M E P, 336
539833 Davis L J, 327		Day J K, 348	529382 Deighton P, 317
515963 Davis M, 140		Day R E, 348	536230 DeLabilliere J A D, 211
530172 Davis M, 142		Day R T, 348	533939 DeLabilliere S D D, 230
505952 Davis M J, 238	524622 Day S K, 365	498920 DeLaHaye B G, 156
529483 Davis M J, 240		Day Sir John, 40	550412 Delaney N, 343
551271 Davis M T, 202	441683 Day C J R, 18	540081 Delaney K J, 365
540161 Davis M W, 108		Daynes E, 348	539468 Delap S B, 242

531998 Dillon D N, 240
547768 Dillon F G, 366
544639 Dilparsad Limbu, 225
533896 Dilworth R J, 133
549377 Dilworth T M, 276
540673 Dimmock A, 126
521253 Dimmock R G, 257
553001 Din S U, 325
554634 Dinan M J, 302
541366 Dineen J J, 204
458539 Dineley G, 322
550655 Dines S J, 245
545529 Dingle M A, 177
543734 Dingsdale H M, 231
550410 Dinley S J, 274
553928 Dinmore A J, 342
544691 Dinnig A W, 323
548895 Dinnis O R, 143
506692 d'Inverno J G, 303
515569 Disley L C, 366
519467 Disley M, 366
548162 Disney R L, 243
548113 Disney M J, 366
536406 Disney-Spiers P S, 282
491812 Diss M, 366
502537 Ditchfield R, 309
       Diven L D M, 56
550656 Dix S E, 270
555032 Dixon A J, 340
547600 Dixon A R, 204
553471 Dixon B, 219
517968 Dixon C A, 238
538884 Dixon C A, 319
510962 Dixon C G, 322
551753 Dixon C M, 144
525443 Dixon F M, 318
552291 Dixon J, 297
524071 Dixon J, 326
548896 Dixon L, 259
495503 Dixon M F, 254
535502 Dixon M J D, 124
504594 Dixon M S, 122
521615 Dixon M W, 240
551542 Dixon P A, 202
483889 Dixon P R C, 177
519537 Dixon R, 276
507250 Dixon R G, 119
516855 Dixon S G, 318
535131 Dixon S M, 335
542888 Dixon W S, 301
532580 Dixon W T, 323
545075 Dixon P S, 366
       Dixon Q, 58
       Dixon R, 383
       Dixon R C B, 383
499417 Dixon T E, 349, 366
       Dixon-Carter C, 65
506636 Dixon-Warren R A, 238
       Dlamini S, 82
504211 Dobbie D M, 328
539180 Dobbie V A, 276
552157 Dobbie W A C, 165
       Dobbie W I C, 65
552353 Dobbin A S, 178
520772 Dobbs G L A, 261
522229 Dobbs M J, 128
550657 Dobeson C G, 106
541904 Dobrowski J S, 366
530070 Dobson C H F, 205
538829 Dobson D, 156
548130 Dobson I R, 143
550658 Dobson M J, 150

545661 Dobson O J, 266
521616 Dobson R M, 330
       Dobson P E, 349
473665 Dobson P H, 366
542602 Dobson R B, 366
518097 Docherty A J, 183
542176 Docherty A W, 337
546870 Docherty D A, 324
541592 Docherty D W, 242
549791 Docherty E A, 320
544311 Docherty J A, 126
507981 Docherty J S, 294
553254 Docherty J W A, 144
501766 Docherty J, 366
516683 Dockray L, 326
553894 Dodd J D, 308
536915 Dodd J M, 301
546987 Dodd O M, 251
504445 Dodds G C W, 130
541534 Dodds R L, 282
       Dodds M, 87
549717 Dodge A F, 366
546082 Dodge T M, 366
537970 Dodgson K P, 242
531775 Dods D M, 301
508171 Dodson M P, 165
       Dodson M F, 70
554044 Dodson P C, 366
532898 Doherty A J, 133
524998 Doherty C M, 336
491443 Doherty D B, 237
548499 Doherty D J, 111
504204 Doherty D J, 303
500585 Doherty J A, 326
539556 Doherty J W, 126
541836 Doherty M, 276
552158 Doherty O B, 111
532716 Doherty P J, 142
518338 Doherty P J, 318
547898 Doherty S P, 112
       Doherty J R C, 349
543282 Doig A J, 262
540190 Doig J R, 263
532795 Doig M J, 134
507431 Dolamore M I, 238
544587 Dolan J C, 280
549956 Doliczny R M, 250
548897 Dollar MPF, 98
541919 Dolling D P, 142
494046 Dolphin A, 336
548123 Dominguez L L, 330
544312 Dommett M N, 172
488420 Donaghy C P, 27, 139
551951 Donald M, 282
518222 Donald N, 301, 366
540577 Donaldson C I, 337
544780 Donaldson D F T, 337
485716 Donaldson G N, 29, 138
532790 Donaldson K S, 307
505026 Donaldson S G, 122
546967 Donaldson S J, 342
       Donaldson A S, 384
530032 Donaldson D S, 366
545092 Donaldson G, 366
543650 Donegan P T, 302
552873 Donegan S L, 339
551702 Donkersley E F, 339
535503 Donnachie J P, 242
486874 Donnell R H, 366
553944 Donnell S, 366
541233 Donnellan R J, 219
519546 Donnelly A G, 323

554958 Donnelly C T, 297
514054 Donnelly J P S, 197
553800 Donnelly S R, 329
538909 Donnelly W C J, 336
543032 Donnini J M, 175
542125 Donnithorne N C, 302
527430 Donnithorne L, 366
540027 Donoghue C, 242
554215 Donoghue G F, 329
531651 Donoghue J M, 331
539368 Donoghue S J, 262
553255 Donohoe G R, 127
528466 Donohoe J K, 134
548164 Donohoe T A, 137
527112 Donovan J M, 156
541593 Donovan J M, 231
519655 Donovan P J, 240
537319 Donovan S A, 141
548489 Donovan S J, 324
540960 Donovan D, 366
534003 Dooley M S, 140
549215 Dooley D, 366
518784 Doran M J, 214
534155 Doran S E E, 337
483891 Dore M I V, 90, 122
555339 Dorey S J, 366
527494 DoreyLJ L J, 366
547736 Dorins H L, 319
554800 Dorling I J, 329
501585 Dorman C G, 130
544453 Dorman K F, 329
524217 Dornan H G, 336
547899 Dornan M A A, 127
553293 Dorrington C J, 287
512767 Dorrington P J, 335
516587 Dorset S, 265
       Dorward A G, 381
553256 Dougall G C, 259
546508 Dougall I, 157
528078 Dougan W J, 262
522089 Dougherty A D, 366
540140 Doughty E, 142
518339 Doughty H A, 322
503287 Doughty J F, 366
       Doughty S J, 349
501586 Doughty WSG, 95
554492 Douglas A R, 339
548898 Douglas A S, 135
545530 Douglas A S J, 160
518427 Douglas A V Rev, 316
551532 Douglas B M J, 325
513150 Douglas C, 19, 39, 268
531099 Douglas D G, 301
540651 Douglas G, 142
495506 Douglas G A, 166
513872 Douglas J C, 217
513873 Douglas J M, 240
501587 Douglas J S, 216
532372 Douglas K P, 156
547352 Douglas M R, 290
543202 Douglas R, 249
541234 Douglas R A, 133
512124 Douglas R W, 268
527428 Douglas A, 366
547444 Douglas A J W, 366
544717 Douglas K, 366
509407 Douglas P L P, 366
540530 Douglas R A L, 223
530474 Douglass P K, 230
541235 Doust A J, 297
536528 Douthwaite S P, 258
553679 Dove G K, 339

433

525375 Guinness D E M, 290
483921 Gullan P H, 218
Gulland J R, 350
550294 Gulley B, 369
545097 Gulley C T, 369
496498 Gulley W G, 369
546772 Gullidge P M N Rev, 316
546772 Gullidge P, 369
549753 Gulwell R R, 369
535532 Gumm I R, 309
Gunaratne W M S, 76
Gunasinghe C S D, 76
Gunawardena L C R, 75
554854 Gundabolu S S R, 325
526880 Gunning C P, 123
531471 Gunning J S, 141
Gunning A M, 350
504819 Gunns J M, 130
482746 Gunson J N, 238
544087 Gunson S J W, 144
Gunson J B, 33
514185 Gunter P V, 281
536573 Gupta S, 250
Gupta R K, 73
545807 Guptaman Gurung, 223
545112 Gurney I, 251
Gurney C J H, 5
535296 Gurung K, 143
540128 Gurung S, 223
Gust T B, 351
512474 Guthrie A P, 305
548189 Guthrie F D, 143
543840 Guthrie H C, 251
548190 Guthrie W D, 190
461440 Guthrie Sir Charles, 93
511980 Gutkowski J A, 326
Gutteridge S C D, 351
553287 Guy D J, 232
547001 Guy J M, 342
532173 Guy P S, 323
533556 Guy W P R, 217
513057 Guzkowska M A J, 334
541011 Gwilliam D J, 330
547318 Gwilliam G R W, 298
512741 Gwizdala J P A, 294
534218 Gwynn P P J, 342
506195 Gwynn G, 369
549235 Gwynne I, 150
Gwynn-Jones P LI, 18
548502 Gwyther R J, 134
515429 Gwyther G D, 369
553997 Gyanbahadur Limbu, 224
548062 Gyanbahadur Limbu, 227
518111 Gyorffy T A, 255

H

548077 Hacker A G, 324
487498 Hackett J R M, 205
499710 Hackett R L M, 199
527364 Hackford A A, 318
528442 Hacking F J, 336
527527 Hacking J, 369
550688 Hackney A R, 114
542988 Hackney S R D, 199
Hackworth T W, 7
507591 Hacon A N, 123
550003 Hadadine L A, 242
Haddad P F, 69
517145 Hadden W A, 322
549801 Haddock D L, 338
549730 Haddock J W S, 126
526362 Haddow R J, 256
555660 Haddrell V, 369
545185 Haden N D, 306
544332 Haden N J, 178
540479 Haden W J, 326
530085 Hadfield A N, 207
502518 Hadfield G F Rev, 234
495519 Hadfield K J, 18, 138
501406 Hadfield J D, 369
539759 Hadfield P, 369
550689 Hadley W R, 279
Hadley J D, 369
547653 Hadley S G, 369
521768 Hadnett R G, 368
524038 Haendel A E G, 323
544784 Haensel D G, 125
481782 Haes R E, 177
494925 Hagan T J, 368
554613 Hagerty A J, 338
536808 Haggerty B S, 311
515108 Haggerty J H, 294
549431 Haggerty K M, 368
550974 Hagues P H, 266
511847 Haig A J R, 230
547015 Haig S D, 324
546519 Haigh A W, 126
519535 Haigh B, 275
518729 Haigh C, 239
544520 Haigh K, 242
552668 Haigh M A, 340
542074 Haigh P A, 295
Haile T C, 380
543015 Hailstone G C, 142
553288 Hain V M, 137
481496 Haines D H, 322
553289 Haines R E, 127
516604 Haines S R, 123
503107 Hainge C M, 131
537304 Hair F J, 134
540037 Hair J C, 249
543939 Hair P S, 270
542148 Hairsine A C, 257
548575 Hairsine H J, 251
Haj B Y, 80
551774 Hakes C J, 127
548927 Hakes R T, 223
548813 Haldane A G, 251
530381 Haldane G E, 311
531905 Haldane J, 302
526821 Haldenby R, 123
535105 Hale D M, 243
492005 Hale L R O, 333
547920 Hale P J, 143
552719 Hale P J, 252
500269 Haley K J, 334

541864 Halffman E M, 114
536634 Halford-Macleod A A R, 293
546244 Halford-Macleod J P A, 120
472552 Halford-MacLeod A P L, 34, 368
Halfpenny D, 58
545549 Halksworth B D, 257
482748 Hall A D, 254
553889 Hall A H, 304
501305 Hall A J, 298
528235 Hall A W, 322
548191 Hall B R H, 217
526941 Hall C J, 120
501114 Hall C R, 327
553551 Hall D, 297
539570 Hall D E, 256
520327 Hall D L, 323
553031 Hall D P, 148
547921 Hall D R, 243
546873 Hall E C, 325
552611 Hall E J, 343
527911 Hall F J, 319
536147 Hall G R, 292
541403 Hall G S, 282
553723 Hall G T, 127
540330 Hall G W, 229
528973 Hall I E, 269
547605 Hall I L, 172
527952 Hall I P, 231
495343 Hall I R M, 177
517873 Hall I T, 300
546423 Hall J, 211
548192 Hall J A, 186
526557 Hall J A, 336
548193 Hall J C, 245
546163 Hall J E, 319
520367 Hall J W, 211
554099 Hall K, 339
520561 Hall L P, 240
552381 Hall M C, 266
555109 Hall M P, 308
482749 Hall N S C, 229
496308 Hall N St J, 191
534065 Hall P, 258
531158 Hall P A, 258
532766 Hall P A, 274
542895 Hall P C, 219
555024 Hall P J, 338
540941 Hall R E W, 302
502435 Hall R G R, 130
547922 Hall R J, 192
527113 Hall R J Rev, 234
503630 Hall R P, 165
530206 Hall R P, 305
552926 Hall S A, 250
499712 Hall S C, 237
550004 Hall S E, 259
521633 Hall S J, 119
553927 Hall S M, 338
524913 Hall S R, 123
545719 Hall T, 142
538972 Hall T A, 244
540426 Hall T A, 256
489533 Hall T E, 87, 119
511460 Hall V H, 268
551214 Hall A E, 368
Hall C J, 381
527462 Hall D, 368
544514 Hall D B, 368
Hall J M F C, 5, 44

438

547621 Hesketh P G, 136
552194 Heslop L M, 325
536380 Heslop P R, 342
548339 Hesslewood K B, 231
541618 Hetherington A E, 207
　　　　Hettiarachchi G, 75
535559 Heward R M, 262
547367 Hewett I S, 270
540535 Hewett M, 133
544338 Hewins D J, 136
502922 Hewitt B, 139
548941 Hewitt C A, 125
496309 Hewitt C A, 236
524312 Hewitt C T D, 145
521053 Hewitt G M, 181
491470 Hewitt R S, 139
528592 Hewitt R W, 123
536108 Hewitt J E, 368
532147 Hewlett M S J, 290
541756 Hewson A, 134
548667 Hewson G A, 259
545970 Hewson R J, 135
　　　　Hewson D I, 351
491264 Hewson M E, 368
554763 Hext D M, 368
536520 Hey B, 307
535520 Heycock D J, 219
552614 Heyes G M T, 343
547620 Heyes P A, 135
546239 Heyes S M, 319
519775 Heyes T P O, 297
542709 Heywood A C R, 120
527870 Heywood J W, 250
536286 Heywood S G, 241
504463 Hibbert J C, 239
553307 Hibbert J M, 266
548204 Hibbert K D, 172
519682 Hibbert N S, 123
524313 Hibbert R J, 230
527454 Hibbs-Owen D, 326
526302 Hick R B, 240
549863 Hicketts J L, 136
524807 Hickey D P, 368
552394 Hickie M D J, 150
518122 Hickie P L, 123
530764 Hickling A, 142
539596 Hickman A, 337
543376 Hickman K C, 211
546155 Hickman M E, 172
512898 Hickman S J, 296
542865 Hicks C E, 283
491471 Hicks C F, 218
544917 Hicks G E J, 202
538502 Hicks I R, 322
495526 Hicks P E D, 147
　　　　Hicks D M, 351
551990 Hickson G L, 231
514573 Hickson M G, 238
550858 Hickson S, 245
539576 Higgens S G, 132
554170 Higgins A D, 206
550353 Higgins A J N, 230
522586 Higgins J R C, 294
553308 Higginson J C, 144
540550 Higgs A R A, 174
548942 Higgs B Y, 141
545630 Higgs J H, 318
547471 Higgs J M, 219
552395 Higgs J S, 214
531452 Higgs S C, 309
544201 Higgs S J, 266
545025 Higgs S L, 280

510240 Higham C J, 335
539988 Higham J, 368
501608 Hignett J J, 131
553577 Hike C L, 320
545808 Hikmatbahadur Gurung, 223
　　　　Hildick B G, 351
500827 Hile N F W, 122
530177 Hiles R G, 309
518905 Hill A G, 140
551297 Hill A J, 136
548943 Hill A L, 143
525321 Hill A P, 296
550452 Hill B L N, 259
553477 Hill C A, 319
548205 Hill C D F, 215
552396 Hill C J E M, 184
505270 Hill D A, 185
534437 Hill D A, 281
545552 Hill E C, 200
555720 Hill E G, 340
533082 Hill G P, 319
553773 Hill G R, 339
546156 Hill I C W, 196
526778 Hill J, 219
514742 Hill J A, 255
540806 Hill J C, 323
534999 Hill J D, 124
536642 Hill J G, 141
549388 Hill J H, 174
541947 Hill J J, 251
548786 Hill J L, 287
523452 Hill J L, 330
545972 Hill J R, 214
527587 Hill K A K, 319
547257 Hill L S, 287
548206 Hill M C, 220
550435 Hill M J, 135
494428 Hill M K, 277
548574 Hill N E, 251
502440 Hill N L, 292
525234 Hill P F, 248
546920 Hill P J, 339
518123 Hill R J, 313
542710 Hill R J A, 136
526167 Hill R J T, 125
542711 Hill S, 202
553309 Hill S A, 108
552788 Hill S G, 318
551665 Hill S M, 338
548944 Hill S M D, 259
547931 Hill S R G, 231
515480 Hill S T, 311
536643 Hill T, 142
525870 Hill T A S, 160
　　　　Hill A M, 351
536644 Hill A P, 223
484520 Hill D J, 368
554749 Hill G T, 368
545094 Hill J M, 368
527495 Hill K F, 368
554791 Hill L A, 368
　　　　Hill R A D, 351
543632 Hill S R, 368
　　　　Hill T J, 351
533355 Hillary L T J Rev, 234
555775 Hillery A L, 339
550453 Hillman C G, 259
552397 Hillman C P G A, 231
　　　　Hillock C T, 382
536535 Hills G B, 258
525990 Hills P E, 283

487084 Hills P L Rev, 234
535282 Hills P R, 297
　　　　Hills J E B, 384
493095 Hills R E, 368
522297 Hillsdon J, 337
549064 Hillyard E J, 302
504677 Hillyer C G, 237
550420 Hilsdon J, 292
520663 Hilton A C, 132
536259 Hilton B D, 172
540271 Hilton C, 336
523647 Hilton D L, 336
555040 Hilton J, 319
528056 Hilton K A, 295
549538 Hilton M J, 245
505694 Hilton P J, 307
　　　　Hilton K B, 351
529057 Himbury S J E, 230
546525 Hinchliffe J P, 192
522129 Hinchliffe R G, 296
　　　　Hind J R, 351
519683 Hinde M G, 187
487508 Hinde P N, 211
　　　　Hindle D J, 351
513444 Hindley R J W, 230
540684 Hindmarsh N J, 133
522947 Hinds P A, 257
543392 Hinds S S, 126
　　　　Hinds The Hon Samuel A A, 81
490519 Hine R N, 119
552700 Hines S E, 282
　　　　Hiney T B F, 7
536645 Hing M J, 242
500274 Hingston P J, 147
554104 Hinkin J, 339
552698 Hinks M, 368
536049 Hinsley D E, 250
554874 Hinton A, 319
516378 Hinton G P P G, 123
535946 Hinton S G B, 328
553271 Hinton C, 368
547145 Hinxman T L B, 223
549888 Hiorns J S, 143
541956 Hipkins J R D, 266
514929 Hirani A, 322
551043 Hirani S, 324
555498 Hird J A, 340
535000 Hirst S A, 242
543302 Hirst T D, 257
　　　　Hirst K J, 351
551298 Hiscock J J, 279
514011 Hiskett M W, 174
530918 Hislop A R, 133
495349 Hislop G F, 216
507459 Hitchcock I G, 131
508794 Hitchcock D, 368
550698 Hitching R M, 178
554824 Hitchings B J, 303
546996 Hitchings G A, 306
527925 Hitchman S C, 294
539190 Hitman Gurung, 223
539191 Hitman Gurung, 223
552663 Hitman Gurung, 226
517123 Hoad A S, 318
504016 Hoad N A, 248
522709 Hoal W J, 230
527135 Hoare J C G, 240
542168 Hoban D M, 134
549539 Hoban J, 245
553926 Hobbs A P, 340
519520 Hobbs C M, 248

444

	(Retd) Yahya A J J, 81
503119	Jammes R F, 119
495537	Jammes R R, 122
	Jamset C, 352
547148	Janaway A S, 136
548217	Janes A C, 278
547939	Janes C M, 127
517415	Janes J R E, 190
554615	Janes P A, 266
552413	Janvier C E, 270
548765	Janvrin E D C, 223
516612	Jaques P W, 254
544348	Jaques V A, 252
552414	Jardine C L, 144
550012	Jardine D I, 172
546231	Jarman N J, 127
534392	Jarratt D G, 211
521126	Jarrett K J, 320
547262	Jarrett M H, 311
550415	Jarrett M J D, 324
	Jarron J C, 89
550013	Jarvill C M, 136
519957	Jarvill M K, 315
539585	Jarvill R G, 230
547940	Jarvis A R G, 134
546111	Jarvis D M, 324
547149	Jarvis D O W, 219
553574	Jarvis R C M Rev, 235
495188	Jarvis S A M, 253
538725	Jarvis T J, 133
	Jarvis I, 62
489871	Jarvis R C, 370
	Jarvis R T, 58
	Jarvis S A M, 19
494398	Jarvis-Bicknell T C, 181
554402	Jarymowycz J D, 340
501500	Jasper S A, 38, 119
502054	Jay A C, 334
522388	Jay R E, 239
551536	Jayakumar R, 324
550137	Jayaprasad Gurung, 223
	Jayaratne K J C, 75
	Jayasinghe R M, 76
	Jayasundara G B W, 75
	Jayathilake D R A B, 76
	Jayathilake W A A P B, 76
537363	Jayatilaka M N D P, 322
	Jayawardenepsc T W, 76
	Jayaweera S, 75
542837	Jayes J A, 337
501036	Jeanes P A, 370
537441	Jeavons M D, 257
530099	Jee S P, 277
533306	Jeevaratnam E A J, 248
546533	Jeeves K A, 143
526592	Jefferies C L, 281
507051	Jefferies I D, 277
537786	Jefferies N J, 250
524914	Jefferies R, 160
517765	Jefferies R A, 190
547305	Jefferies P, 370
	Jefferis T J, 352
503211	Jefferson I D, 294
513440	Jefferson N T, 122
543205	Jefferson P G, 249
536237	Jefferson P T I, 202
551306	Jeffery B K, 141
545666	Jeffery E, 263
543842	Jeffery N P, 251
534749	Jeffery R G F, 250
525235	Jeffery S L, 248
554753	Jeffery T C, 297

510828	Jeffery W R, 335
	Jeffery M K, 67
551305	Jefford T E, 110
495189	Jeffrey D R, 236
537442	Jeffrey J P, 262
470540	Jeffrey R S, 275
545361	Jeffreys Z S, 302
	Jeffreys A P, 352
498883	Jeffreys K E, 370
525385	Jeffries P A, 239
544349	Jeffries T, 301
	Jeffries T, 352
485761	Jelf A M F, 171
549547	Jelf C E, 116
550709	Jellard H P, 195
540618	Jelley H W, 126
520537	Jemmett T M, 370
539877	Jeng M, 249
518922	Jenkins B W, 124
552779	Jenkins C J, 278
528494	Jenkins D, 269
510241	Jenkins D A, 281
539587	Jenkins D E, 242
553879	Jenkins D J, 282
527485	Jenkins D M, 322
536310	Jenkins G A, 242
520670	Jenkins H A, 140
550014	Jenkins I G, 136
492155	Jenkins J H, 268
516213	Jenkins J H, 322
540537	Jenkins L D, 134
515906	Jenkins L J, 335
534069	Jenkins M A, 258
541627	Jenkins M A, 263
553965	Jenkins M G, 136
547008	Jenkins P C, 258
535824	Jenkins P J L, 334
520999	Jenkins R J, 330
552415	Jenkins R T V, 252
517285	Jenkins S G, 239
529898	Jenkins T P, 311
	Jenkins G E, 352
	Jenkins I L, 61
515906	Jenkins L, 370
	Jenkins M, 352
497585	Jenkinson R J, 130
550015	Jenkinson S F, 244
548960	Jenner G E J, 127
546707	Jenner S A, 302
523881	Jennings A D, 240
544926	Jennings D J, 126
531302	Jennings D J, 303
545722	Jennings E R M, 250
543219	Jennings G, 301
545245	Jennings H M, 243
539369	Jennings J, 263
550710	Jennings J C, 270
542281	Jennings J P Rev, 316
541650	Jennings J R, 143
503847	Jennings P F A, 197
524320	Jennings P J, 240
550711	Jennings S J, 270
554237	Jennings A J, 370
	Jennings C N H, 352
	Jennings M R, 352
	Jennings P, 48
537838	Jensen-Meyer L, 370
553651	Jenson-Rutland A-M L, 370
554161	Jephcote R A, 302
535155	Jepson D H, 142
550867	Jepson D J, 319

537302	Jerdan A, 370
542720	Jermy S P, 242
535524	Jermy T E, 370
551786	Jerome F J E, 206
529711	Jervis P N, 333
550901	Jessermino M J, 245
536673	Jewell C D, 262
531356	Jewell K C, 342
549778	Jeys M C, 338
542838	Jivan N, 337
552417	Joannou E, 135
495871	Joannou B, 370
522827	Joannou J, 370
537443	Job C J T, 184
503848	Jobbings T N, 239
554623	Jobson K W, 370
518132	Joels B D, 255
538983	John C W, 242
535447	John J C, 202
537764	John M P, 270
534011	John P F, 249
502896	John S E, 238
516381	John T, 174
497724	John R B, 370
554140	John R D, 370
515533	John-Lewis M P, 370
515224	Johns K I, 318
550355	Johns P M, 343
506859	Johns S C, 139
520671	Johns S J, 171
	Johns A R, 352
	Johns P F, 352
	Johns Sir Richard, 7
501296	Johns W A, 370
545902	Johns W P, 370
526126	Johnson A, 258
527906	Johnson A, 309
515024	Johnson A, 335
544525	Johnson A G, 182
522797	Johnson A M, 309
551307	Johnson A R, 127
547941	Johnson A S, 144
543713	Johnson A T, 187
519301	Johnson B, 335
552619	Johnson B D, 343
540619	Johnson B G W, 141
491158	Johnson C D, 123
551733	Johnson C J D, 325
548746	Johnson C M, 308
497183	Johnson D A, 254
553319	Johnson E L, 266
550016	Johnson F K, 127
549769	Johnson G, 280
546926	Johnson G A, 244
550922	Johnson G R, 143
541323	Johnson I A, 262
522548	Johnson I A E, 296
515481	Johnson I C, 311
483679	Johnson I H, 130
545667	Johnson I P, 269
543950	Johnson J, 257
540348	Johnson J, 337
520439	Johnson J C, 307
548477	Johnson J D, 337
530937	Johnson K, 135
541961	Johnson K G, 184
540093	Johnson K L, 270
493738	Johnson M, 122
535627	Johnson M, 336
484494	Johnson M K, 321
534840	Johnson N, 174
533901	Johnson N A, 177

449

546822	Knowles E, 329	
538993	Knowles G W, 342	
539807	Knowles J C, 151	
519331	Knowles J D, 301	
489911	Knowles J E, 237	
546539	Knowles M A, 126	
554726	Knowles P E, 302	
537327	Knowles R B, 165	
	Knowles P J N, 353	
545885	Knowles S, 370	
528188	Knowles T, 370	
547156	Knowles-Jackson T J, 211	
552029	Knox A, 283	
547950	Knox B J, 188	
537839	Knox D, 303	
505754	Knox D E, 294	
485766	Knox P J, 199	
549149	Knox P J, 245	
511865	Knox R A, 177	
538193	Knox R J I, 219	
523883	Knox T H, 132	
496209	Knudsen N P, 253	
537999	Knurbin M M, 256	
533237	Knutton K J, 370	
516910	Kocan M K, 322	
	Kochar S B S, 72	
500106	Koder P C, 332	
546321	Koenen C A J, 334	
529532	Kohler G M, 256	
541132	Kolczak R, 257	
	Komba G M S, 79	
	Konstacka L, 353	
515153	Koss R A, 294	
545309	Kottritsch S J, 249	
538513	Kovar I Z, 323	
535296	Krishna Gurung, 226	
	Krishna Vijay, 74	
541652	Krishnabahadur Gurung, 227	
548492	Krishnabahadur Gurung, 226	
550305	Krishnakumar Thapa, 223	
548427	Krishnaparsad Gurung, 223	
	Krishnaratne H M N, 75	
552933	Krishnkumar Rai, 223	
	Krlic M, 353	
540950	Krstic S A, 125	
548967	Krykunivsky N V, 246	
551864	Krysa-Clark J, 324	
552208	Krysinski H L, 338	
	Kufuor J A, 77	
521535	Kuhle C G, 132	
	Kulatunga D V S Y, 75	
	Kulatunga P S B, 75	
	Kumar C R S, 72	
	Kumar Sudhir, 73	
	Kumar V G, 73	
520516	Kumik P C, 328	
512226	Kyle I H, 330	
554138	Kyle J W, 293	
	Kynaston L E, 370	
551312	Kyte P D, 204	
550437	Kyzer K E, 337	

L

507475	Laborda M A, 255	
517289	Labouchere D H, 110	
552422	Labram A F, 144	
520762	Lacey G J, 274	
486682	Lacey J D, 177	
552916	Lacey J F, 325	
508860	Lacey M G, 122	
	Lacey G J, 30	
	Lacey J D, 353	
549889	Lacey J D C, 370	
	Lacey R G, 353	
	Lacey , 15	
535425	Lack S L E L, 319	
547158	Lacken J F, 134	
543170	Ladbrook M B, 297	
541359	Ladd J A P, 305	
546283	Ladds P, 135	
536292	Ladds R W E, 305	
552844	Lade S J, 263	
512507	Laden R ST L, 238	
528631	Laden D M, 370	
512632	Ladley R J, 177	
521216	Lafferty J, 370	
543789	Lagadu S P, 258	
539140	Laher R A I, 249	
523884	Lai T J, 217	
522396	Laidlaw A N, 171	
502899	Laidler R J, 254	
525991	Laidler H P, 370	
	Laidler P, 353	
549552	Laing A C, 219	
539838	Laing D M, 337	
533979	Laing M A, 199	
	Laing Sir Martin, 353	
496885	Laird J, 238	
498041	Laird R J, 317	
549349	Laird D M, 370	
490525	Lake A P B, 204	
539221	Lakeman A, 282	
537300	Laker A K, 370	
551178	Laker N, 370	
551685	Lakey G, 136	
548505	Lakin N P H, 134	
552767	Lalbahadur Gurung, 223	
542277	Lalitbahadur Gurung, 223	
532810	Lalitchandra Dewan, 223	
539202	Lally C W, 370	
501631	Lalor S F N, 288	
543401	Lamb A T, 301	
526266	Lamb A W, 230	
549341	Lamb C R, 278	
543311	Lamb G B, 142	
495192	Lamb G C M, 165	
546665	Lamb J, 174	
542577	Lamb J A, 262	
547676	Lamb J C, 278	
549949	Lamb J M, 325	
488458	Lamb K I F, 254	
488155	Lamb M E, 307	
496314	Lamb P A, 261	
542332	Lamb S C, 125	
492701	Lambe B C, 121	
536677	Lambert A N, 230	
546929	Lambert A P, 244	
518143	Lambert C F, 105	
499989	Lambert C G, 171	
526777	Lambert D N, 219	
544661	Lambert M G, 133	
540053	Lambert M W A, 244	
517400	Lambert P J, 268	

543493	Lambert R, 231	
509449	Lambert S J, 268	
503361	Lambert W A, 326	
529865	Lambert B J, 370	
539393	Lambert-Gorwyn M, 125	
546540	Lambeth J O, 143	
545491	Lambirth S J, 330	
518284	Lambton J A, 300	
554857	Lamki L, 325	
545106	Lammiman S A, 241	
539243	Lammin D, 370	
553017	Lamont I, 343	
553328	Lamont K A, 246	
546134	Lamont T B, 338	
	Lamont His Excellency D A, 58	
539697	Lampard B, 211	
545410	Lancaster A J, 282	
483804	Lancaster J A S, 149	
531664	Lancaster J M, 297	
547524	Lancaster T, 338	
553329	Lance P C, 152	
	Land W M A, 353	
533827	Landon J, 174	
551086	Lane B C, 126	
551846	Lane B J, 339	
535190	Lane B K E, 305	
532205	Lane C A M, 165	
554796	Lane C J, 312	
499737	Lane G S, 130	
519540	Lane I B F, 276	
518800	Lane J F, 132	
544768	Lane J J S, 108	
532182	Lane K F, 125	
531646	Lane M G P, 171	
522397	Lane P J I, 241	
506768	Lane P R L, 122	
496465	Lane R, 318	
553233	Lane R A, 143	
546541	Lane S, 204	
498274	Lane S A, 261	
513445	Lane W G, 301	
551624	Lane D J, 370	
552423	Lane-Fox ES, 98	
489550	Lang J D, 123	
524607	Lang J M, 297	
494033	Lang N G W, 122	
494439	Lang S E L, 114	
528971	Lang S M, 256	
510754	Lang V, 262	
520679	Lang W R S, 132	
544103	Lang J A, 370	
	Lang R M, 16	
488306	Langan J, 370	
500061	Langford C D, 238	
517976	Langford D E, 268	
523060	Langford D P, 248	
519689	Langford P J, 132	
539999	Langford T P, 142	
551313	Langham S J R, 257	
551221	Langhorn D G, 278	
522742	Langley G E, 296	
533189	Langley J A G, 141	
541877	Langley J S, 250	
536678	Langman B M W, 107	
531853	Langridge S R, 241	
543077	Langston C M Rev, 234	
488280	Langton C R, 89, 151	
497453	Lanham J W, 265	
497454	Lanham M R, 237	
	Lankadeva A, 76	
541533	Lankester C M, 301	

458

513805	McAlinden B P, 296
552307	McAlister B A, 339
507491	McAlister I R, 166
547007	McAllister D G, 342
532815	McAllister E J, 326
503174	McAllister H K, 333
535656	McAllister P D, 249
551716	McAllister R J, 108
535167	McAllister T E, 372
	McAlpine Sir William, 354
	McAlpine The Hon David, 41
540554	McAndie A M, 336
521011	McAneny B, 300
544948	McAnulty K H, 141
514594	McArthur A, 240
527588	McArthur A, 318
518405	McArthur D J, 335
548793	McArthur J J, 302
543373	McArthur P J, 257
518387	McArthur R, 165
494339	McAslan A R R, 129
539910	McAulay D, 167
531640	McAulay H M, 159
	Mcaulay H, 354
543022	McAuley J, 323
551326	McAuley L, 263
537341	McAuslan I A, 314
554097	McAvan J O, 343
546662	McAvock S G, 271
534072	McAvoy D A, 254
533474	McAvoy N J, 256
532672	McBain A F, 318
510717	McBirnie D, 268
521812	McBride C, 318
542341	McBride D, 329
510859	McBride G W, 308
533904	McBride H G M, 249
529156	McBride J, 292
549150	McBride J C, 245
527828	McBride T D, 231
542179	McBride A, 372
531938	McBroom R J, 248
538296	McBryde J B H, 327
489560	McCabe M C, 130
	McCabe P, 43
551149	McCaferty L F, 343
553094	McCafferty W A Rev, 234
546552	McCaffrey P S, 126
	McCahon W E, 354
526650	McCaig D J, 305
507027	McCall B W, 254
546346	McCall D, 126
515731	McCall P J, 238
508684	McCall R, 262
528447	McCall S, 336
	McCall B W, 50
534735	McCallin E J, 298
542738	McCallion S E J, 134
543963	McCallum G A R, 135
	McCallum C D, 354
	McCallum K I R, 354
553739	McCammon D W, 208
551549	McCann E L, 136
535906	McCann G J, 301
539333	McCann J F, 337
499988	McCann K G, 56, 217
531782	McCappin T R, 300
541311	McCarraher C F, 334
	McCarroll S A, 354
540421	McCartan J M, 295
532690	McCarten P D, 243

519069	McCarthy C A, 326
547016	McCarthy D A, 310
535639	McCarthy D J, 320
549245	McCarthy D L, 282
542739	McCarthy H, 135
548637	McCarthy K J, 319
531989	McCarthy L D L, 256
553235	McCarthy M, 174
546896	McCarthy M D, 134
551085	McCarthy M P, 126
495554	McCarthy P T, 253
549672	McCarthy S, 274
	McCarthy P T, 25
533342	McCartney R C Rev, 234
550289	McCartney R J, 331
517368	McCartney W N, 309, 372
540422	McCauley S P, 124
553290	McCauliffe H K, 372
534860	McCauliffe R E, 372
	McCausland N W, 40
521062	McClean B C W, 255
529006	McClean C T, 256
546856	McClean J A, 217
519476	McClean J C, 300
551927	McClean K D, 333
552434	McCleery D K, 217
552867	McCleery I A, 339
540538	McCleery J W, 125
504286	McCleery D G, 372
	McCleery N, 44
549571	McClellan M S, 110
544030	McClellan P A, 134
541201	McClellan P R, 242
544346	McClellan S A, 242
543597	McClelland A E, 274
533686	McClelland J, 271
554129	McClelland S, 339
	McClelland S E, 43
542449	McCloskey A G, 337
494705	McCloskey G, 372
543791	McClung J, 258
540478	McClung M T, 301
520912	McClure C, 335
546912	McClure J, 337
534600	McClure S, 230
524837	McClurg H W, 342
535026	McCluskey A J, 250
547358	McCluskey D, 263
537836	McCluskey J R, 243
511643	McCluskey D, 372
546615	McCluskey M, 372
512797	McCoig M J, 317
535027	McCole A S, 141
543898	McColl E M, 275
540585	McColl J K, 141
495202	McColl J C, 52, 94
540820	McColm M J, 372
509546	McComb A W T, 139
512885	McComb S A F, 275
550737	McComb S J G, 136
528688	McCombe R C, 329
552886	McComiskey M H, 325
553582	McConaghy A D, 339
507493	McConaghy A J W, 131
544761	McConnachie R J, 135
543439	McConnell A G, 309
496242	McConnell D C, 300
551156	McConnell J F, 343
553347	McConnell J J, 137
529540	McConnell S J, 140
521013	McConnell J N, 372
517228	McConnell L W, 372

	McConnell-Wood T I, 354
543130	McConway K, 330
511051	McCord A C J, 217
494976	McCord I M, 261
547709	McCord S S, 372
523547	McCorkell J, 318
525053	McCormack D M, 300
545069	McCormack L, 125
523284	McCormack P J Rev, 234
547472	McCormack R H, 148
542740	McCormack T S, 242
543509	McCormick C, 337
548240	McCormick E J, 245
532796	McCormick I G, 134
544813	McCormick L R, 191
515136	McCormick R J, 275
543422	McCourt A L, 282
535640	McCourt G R, 243
518154	McCourt L D, 301
493753	McCourt R L, 311
543316	McCoy R, 245
534327	McCoy P, 372
547228	McCracken A, 259
555768	McCracken I H, 334
501653	McCracken W A, 294
543826	McCrann J S D, 245
544766	McCreadie K E, 172
550905	McCreanor A P, 245
533244	McCreath D W, 278
549833	McCreath V H E, 334
549911	McCreedy N, 143
531165	McCreesh D, 258
543067	McCrindle G M, 142
536218	McCrorie W, 266
537966	McCrum D, 177
520951	McCShaw R H, 372
547412	McCuaig D D, 280
551418	McCullagh M, 343
541308	McCulloch A J R Rev, 234
511584	McCulloch D B, 261
500970	McCulloch J A, 238
532631	McCulloch J R, 281
542638	McCulloch W S, 219
536261	McCulloch JW, 103
514596	McCullough GMD, 97
513599	McCurdie I M, 248
498931	McCurdy J A M, 160
532018	McCurrach J L, 256
548988	McCurry R R, 219
534629	McCutcheon K A, 277
543714	McCutcheon L C, 174
517955	McCutcheon P, 160
542641	McCutcheon G, 372
541202	McDade G A, 204
534355	McDaid R A, 372
535827	McDermott R P, 174
551224	McDill P J A, 278
529996	McDonald A M, 275
537636	McDonald G, 337
541339	McDonald G M, 266
543592	McDonald H B W, 126
550401	McDonald I, 337
546001	McDonald J S, 219
554757	McDonald K M, 280
551489	McDonald M R, 172
550102	McDonald P C, 304
553349	McDonald S S, 217
544365	McDonald V, 242
546084	McDonald J L, 372
519927	McDonald M P, 372
546648	McDonnell C, 282
519696	McDonnell I M, 318

460

522723 McLean A J, 296
554502 McLean A M, 343
553196 McLean A P, 276
487136 McLean I S, 330
533184 McLean P C, 331
550738 McLean R C, 148
549708 McLean L M, 372
554786 McLean N, 372
McLean V F P, 355
McLean-Inglis A R, 355
547413 McLeavy J A, 126
538452 McLees S D, 319
547965 McLeish R N, 157
549209 McLellan E L, 144
521983 McLellan J H, 326
483971 McLelland P D, 171
545336 McLelland R J, 244
McLelland P D, 30
552440 McLeman J F S, 106
552677 McLenaghan C J, 343
553699 McLenaghan J R, 325
540850 McLennan J V, 251
535547 McLennan Fordyce D, 290
522856 McLeod A B, 240
518389 McLeod A R, 156
519827 McLeod G, 303
552121 McLeod G S, 324
544722 McLeod P W, 204
McLeod K C, 67
526374 McLeod-Jones M I, 219
McLoughlin E M, 18
527556 McLuckie A J, 293
527627 McMachan T L, 281
509112 McMahon H E, 238
550031 McMahon J D, 190
510353 McMahon M J, 238
531166 McMahon P, 258
532010 McMahon S C, 241
483973 McMahon W A, 229
547250 McMahon T W, 372
549058 McManus K J C, 219
544547 McMaster B C, 165
534036 McMaster J M, 324
526776 McMaster W C, 372
McMeechan E D, 295
538019 McMeekin N S, 276
545574 McMenamin J J, 263
McMenemey J D S, 355
534074 McMenemy J B, 258
537020 McMenemy P, 248
525149 McMillan B A, 314
513222 McMillan C S, 337
522542 McMillan D W, 328
505070 McMillan J M, 281
547229 McMillan P, 259
532489 McMillan J S H, 372
498550 McMillen P, 372
545575 McMonagle L M, 135
543907 McMullan E A, 324
516180 McMullen T M, 63, 278
548720 McMullen S V, 372
544242 McMurdo R J, 125
519697 McMurtrie T D, 211
528007 McMurtry I A, 249
543511 McNab G, 339
516310 McNair R W L, 240
555025 McNair J W, 372
553968 McNairn M S, 319
517033 McNally B F, 306
539777 McNally M K, 266
489563 McNally N J, 238
543792 McNally O P, 258

529688 McNamara D A, 278
496321 McNamara G M, 130
539070 McNamee A M, 372
536317 McNaney T L, 372
McNarn M R, 68
551658 McNaughton P A, 219
553890 McNaughton C P, 372
553350 McNay G J, 161
545626 McNee M, 297
554203 McNee P A J, 251
522184 McNeil D R, 342
523132 McNeil I N, 256
537621 McNeil K A, 242
543562 McNeil L, 271
552441 McNeil R J, 178
541204 McNeil R J, 241
484912 McNeil A, 222
507826 McNeil J, 372
McNeile M T H, 355
506001 McNeill G J, 140
521391 McNeill M L, 336
543848 McNeill V E, 266
548244 McNelis M J, 219
553475 McNelly I, 143
537168 McNicholas J J K, 250
531502 McNicholas P, 185
McNicoll , 15
502903 McNinch H H, 253
509551 McNulty P J, 230
532984 McParlin P I, 318
529544 McPhee M N J, 133
550113 McPhee W A, 231
McPhee I A, 31
496322 McPherson A M, 253
515007 McPherson I, 125
525095 McPherson I A, 238
541373 McPherson R A, 125
McPherson J A S, 381
545436 McQuade K L, 270
483807 McQueen P D P, 229
528918 McQueenie S S, 190
513158 McQuilton K C, 258
538392 McRae A D, 241
539823 McRae S C V, 242
547292 McRae W, 297
497779 McRae J R, 372
525444 McRobb N P, 124
497664 McRobbie I W B, 317, 380
523393 McRory P, 124
535577 McSkimming G J, 355
544726 McSorley P N, 372
538785 McSpadden R M, 319
520076 McSporran D R, 174
548990 McSweeney D J, 326
528128 McTurk P S, 143
550193 McVeigh S Rev, 316
530973 McVeigh D, 372
527303 McVey A G J, 241
518026 McVey G S, 264
505871 McVicar I H, 333
McWhinnie L P, 335
555042 McWhirter R, 355
552831 McWilliam C, 339
McWilliams A J, 372
Mdadlala-Routledge
Nozizwe, 71
521584 Meaby D A, 372
543175 Meacock T W, 184
539836 Mead A J C, 326
537468 Mead J R, 125
547076 Mead N K, 251
518638 Mead W, 238

531261 Mead AJ, 95
Mead E F, 355
553573 Meaden C D, 372
542900 Meades A, 174
540699 Meadowcroft S N, 141
542453 Meads J R P, 372
527012 Mear J E, 335
550120 Meares P S, 372
506480 Mears A J, 122
526833 Mears C J, 124
523660 Mears C N, 305
553486 Mears G O, 338
550032 Mears L C, 245
536162 Mears P R C, 172
Meating R G, 67
500381 Medcalf M F, 238
554110 Meddeman M J, 302
545576 Medhurst-Cocksworth C R, 120
539614 Medley J C, 262
490537 Medley R G, 237
522897 Medway N B, 336
520380 Mee J B, 239
530479 Meech L K, 230
Meedin T F, 76
536315 Meehan RDC, 103
490927 Meek A D, 54, 191
498181 Meeke B A, 217
552635 Meeks C, 339
533389 Meeson G V, 328
553952 Megahey P W L, 333
545187 Megaw G P, 295
532528 Megaw R M E, 336
551451 Meggison T, 211
500726 Mehers S I, 123
535914 Mehigan C P, 243
534342 Mehrlich P R, 196
536400 Mehta N V, 326
Mehta S S, 72
Mehta Y K, 72
Meier A L, 42
Meight R A, 355
Meikle R S, 355
528455 Meinertzhagen R D, 140
552041 Mekhbahadur Gurung, 227
553619 Melbourne F P, 186
517297 Meldon P, 261
542868 Meldrum C R, 283
547966 Meldrum T S, 126
550739 Melia M C, 178
542344 Mellar T B, 177
551980 Melley C R, 325
519053 Mellin D J, 372
531126 Melling K, 336
542741 Melling R I, 172
Melling R J, 355
551507 Mellor A D, 136
541350 Mellor I, 323
534809 Mellor I J, 280
493836 Mellor S G, 247
539011 Mellor S L, 242
Mellor W J A, 68
501513 Mellows W A N, 229
Mellows Professor A R, 64
545812 Melnyk L D, 135
525399 Melnyk E J F V, 151
523394 Melrose S R C, 240
549574 Melson N J M, 118
547432 Melville J, 126
516625 Melville J L, 105
549295 Melville P C F, 290
499747 Melvin R A M S, 59, 129

467

468

548671	Oliver C B, 259	503632	Ormerod I S, 238	547981	Otter S T G, 178
550949	Oliver D M, 114	514610	Ormerod J C, 110	543003	Ottewell H V, 211
509899	Oliver D M, 317	548257	Ormerod P M P, 151	493763	Ottowell C M S, 311
508881	Oliver G G, 174	540060	Ormiston C J, 278	507996	Oughton R A B, 265
543326	Oliver G J, 143	537746	Ormiston C J, 337	553629	Outram D R, 373
543778	Oliver J, 244	534960	Ormiston T, 243		Ovens A J, 356
552806	Oliver J C, 325	545772	Ormston B, 373		Overend A E M, 356
544962	Oliver J N, 110	547632	Orourke J S, 324	553576	Overland M A, 373
550607	Oliver J P, 302	552752	Orourke K, 245	539254	Overton M A J M, 305
538712	Oliver M G, 297	514026	O'Rourke C H, 313	551541	Overton V J, 146
491509	Oliver M R, 238	539017	O'Rourke L, 141	514090	Overy T B, 373
518557	Oliver M W, 258	537279	Orpen M A, 337	532265	Ovey R J D, 214
517309	Oliver P J, 240	507505	Orpen-Smellie G R, 218	540315	Owen A J, 337
551019	Oliver P J R, 324	525405	Orpin B P, 328	501351	Owen A M, 262
526220	Oliver G R, 373	547980	Orpin D J, 174	551343	Owen A R, 279
	Oliver S J, 356	545100	Orpin P J, 373	502477	Owen C L, 318
525613	Olley G W J, 269	551341	Orr D R, 144	509561	Owen C R, 140
499553	Olley J B, 130	549307	Orr D S A, 324	505462	Owen C W, 183
549841	Olliff R Rev, 234	546932	Orr G, 245	547634	Owen G, 324
497067	Olney M, 330	551096	Orr H A, 337	521680	Owen G L, 230
536243	Olney R A, 230	504490	Orr I A, 160	536717	Owen G S, 297
	Olof H M, 356	530978	Orr J C M, 230	541165	Owen J D, 244
549588	Olsen T A L, 152	522416	Orr J N N, 114	488474	Owen J M, 119
524640	Olson M, 373	530674	Orr L E, 250	517961	Owen J P, 248
497220	Olver J J, 321	540879	Orr P A B, 135	538751	Owen K A, 142
543970	O'Malley C G S, 223	514740	Orr R, 318	539018	Owen M D, 297
542093	Omand D W, 259	531026	Orr R J, 133	539328	Owen P D, 295
552543	Omara J M, 263	531760	Orr R K, 277	545217	Owen P F R R, 310
	Ombu V K, 79	528415	Orr S A, 166	546564	Owen P G, 257
554073	Omeara T J, 332	544823	Orr G, 373	552085	Owen R, 334
554174	Oneill C N, 136		Orr J A, 356	493490	Owen R D J R, 313
553812	Oneill M B, 338	515417	Orr-Cooper S J, 301	490797	Owen R G, 19, 253
546277	Oneill M J, 117	538646	Orrell J B J, 151	539925	Owen R J, 283
535628	O'Neill B J E, 336	537295	Orrell-Jones V F H, 133	551906	Owen R M, 314
540487	O'Neill G, 337	525406	OrrEwing D R, 163	506756	Owen S F, 237
526569	O'Neill H S, 116		OrrEwing E S, 381	513544	Owen S P, 115
550778	O'Neill S S M, 136	550039	Orvis R J, 127		Owen A, 356
531509	O'Neill V K, 133	550779	Orwin D R, 217	538334	Owen D, 373
	O'Neill J M, 356	546635	Orwin D W, 217		Owen D L, 356
543132	O'NeilRoe G C B, 195	544963	Osborn A, 198		Owen J P, 356
539439	O'NeilRoe R H D, 195	540948	Osborn J P, 373		Owen M A, 356
507260	Ong E J, 301	508069	Osborne B M, 335	548419	Owens A M, 282
539958	Ong S T, 301	530628	Osborne C, 243	534240	Owens C M, 336
550038	Ongaro R J, 106	531027	Osborne D G S, 230	528928	Owens J P C, 133
521744	Onslow M P D, 156	552642	Osborne G E, 178	543716	Owens P S, 257
	Onslow P S, 356	521276	Osborne J, 314	547801	Owens S K, 337
554953	Ooi S W, 325	552876	Osborne J M, 143	554010	Owers R A, 338
537366	Oommen J, 248	544385	Osborne M C, 266	522002	Owers R C, 249
554534	Oosterveen G M, 343	530979	Osborne M J, 297	529998	Owsley R M, 318
545117	Opie N J, 251	519237	Osborne M R, 336	541167	Owsnett N, 257
529791	Oram M, 373	496326	Osborne P G, 238	523040	Oxborough R J, 238
555758	Orange S J, 325	549590	Osborne R C A, 190	495565	Oxlade S J, 204
533789	Orchard R M, 134		Osborne C J, 356	514612	Oxley J A G, 290
	Orchard-Lisle P, 66	539746	Osborne C S, 373	544386	Oxley P J, 125
534279	Orcheston-Findlay G G, 120		Osborne I N, 382	536080	Ozanne A M, 120
		551233	Osborne-Smith L, 338		
554973	Ord C, 320	516925	Osborn-Smith B R, 288		
538645	Ord N E, 163	529439	Osbourn C P, 243		
522993	O'Regan J, 328	527337	O'Shea R J Rev, 316		
526254	O'Regan S W, 336	550040	Osman T R, 128		
543971	O'Reilly C, 151	509345	Osment P A, 139		
546780	O'Reilly J E, 282	527384	Osmond G I P, 124		
503887	O'Reilly M S M, 109	526097	Osullivan P A, 311		
554898	O'Reilly J, 67, 373	515808	O'Sullivan E M, 322		
	O'Reilly T, 70	504958	O'Sullivan G A, 238		
549355	Orejda H A, 330	491717	O'Sullivan J P J, 130		
534103	Orfanelli R T A, 263	521679	O'Sullivan J S S, 218		
477691	Orford K J, 334	498597	Oswald C J R, 255		
544384	Organ P A, 244	546656	Oswin N, 117		
550562	Oriordan P D, 293	512440	Othen A, 131		
546197	O'Riordan K D, 250	554968	Otoole J A, 338		
549240	Orman C A, 282		Ottaway R R, 70		

469

P

532128 Pace J W, 326
551344 Pack D T, 223
547982 Packer P M, 266
555806 Padambahadur Gurung, 224
545367 Padambahadur Limbu, 223
       Paddison N, 356
542503 Paden E L, 177
547389 Paden E O, 337
509562 Padgett S, 185
       Padha K C, 74
       Padmanabhan S, 72
526610 Paffard G F, 373
480108 Pagan C W, 296
524118 Page A G, 133
540389 Page A J, 133
549899 Page A M B, 297
526661 Page B, 307
513353 Page C S T, 149
497593 Page C T, 197
552693 Page E A, 334
512953 Page J D, 218
518166 Page N A, 132
528061 Page R C, 317
544964 Page R M, 135
       Page F V, 356
       Page K R M, 356
531975 Pagent B, 373
509795 Paget D W, 294
546450 Paget D W, 320
547230 Pain P J, 258
496516 Paine A P, 253
520389 Paine M C, 294
545396 Paine R B, 259
515838 Paine S L, 322
538260 Paine J A, 373
526132 Painter D E, 257
498789 Painter N J, 131
550780 Paintin E J, 146
554095 Pajger S D, 343
       Pal Krishan, 72
536366 Palframan A M, 281
549592 Palfrey R J, 192
545493 Palfreyman S, 142
532348 Palfreyman R, 373
549880 Palin B J, 276
518335 Paling N J, 305
547603 Pallant S N, 177
544172 Pallent S, 373
551091 Pallett B C, 329
551907 Palmer A D, 343
533644 Palmer A H, 230
523066 Palmer A R, 135
551345 Palmer B, 244
545581 Palmer C, 116
541168 Palmer C, 124
537754 Palmer C C D, 125
543717 Palmer C H, 257
487558 Palmer D F, 139
517058 Palmer D M, 317
554464 Palmer D P, 343
500992 Palmer I P, 248
551801 Palmer J A E, 152
506013 Palmer J C, 222
549593 Palmer J G K, 127
534341 Palmer J M, 250
551490 Palmer J N, 308
509564 Palmer J R M, 113
533311 Palmer J V, 249
536138 Palmer K L, 269

529552 Palmer M, 199
548258 Palmer M C A, 192
527060 Palmer N S, 292
494449 Palmer P, 238
530741 Palmer R A, 134
497959 Palmer R J, 321
545032 Palmer R T J, 297
493764 Palmer R W, 265
527282 Palmer S P, 300
487557 Palmer A M D, 18, 94
       Palmer C C, 356
535087 Palmer J R, 373
552676 Palmer T C, 373
516709 Palucci T A, 373
530675 Pambakian S, 248
       Panabokke S V, 75
543042 Panchabir Rai, 223
       Panday Hon Basdeo, 80
525811 Pandya V V K, 324
514947 Pani C K, 247
513554 Pankhurst J A, 373
551587 Pankhurst S T, 373
534428 Pannell J D, 373
550781 Pannett J G A, 232
550431 Panton C J, 306
504959 Panton J F, 187
521743 Panton S I, 319
531829 Pape S R, 323
530125 Papenfus J R, 124
513151 Paphiti A S, 31, 57, 271
539092 Papworth J E J, 250
511059 Paramore A, 239
553687 Pardew G, 143
537473 Pardy D C, 132
542350 Parfitt A J, 141
538422 Parfitt K D, 297
493558 Parfitt P, 138
529325 Paris A B Rev, 234
552450 Paris D, 259
527744 Paris H V I, 256
502755 Parish J B, 229
494663 Parish M C, 183
525883 Park A J, 277
538483 Park B W, 190
554808 Park C K, 252
551046 Park C L, 252
494556 Park D A M, 296
523404 Park D E, 241
550467 Park R, 259
511553 Park R J J, 122
495216 Park T A, 197
       Park A J, 384
526228 Park G J, 373
536085 Park J E, 373
551154 Parke F S, 266
550782 Parke M P, 144
523955 Parker A G, 132
513925 Parker A G, 239
532483 Parker A J, 125
540061 Parker A J, 242
532707 Parker C J, 171
520533 Parker C J R, 248
552110 Parker D A, 252
549042 Parker E A, 136
554797 Parker E M, 295
511892 Parker H J, 132
549153 Parker I, 245
499482 Parker J C, 305
553366 Parker M, 246
553457 Parker M D Rev, 234
517311 Parker N B, 319
546251 Parker N J, 126

491510 Parker N P, 229
496852 Parker N R, 60, 214
505326 Parker N R M, 185
551683 Parker P G, 293
517583 Parker P J, 248
547418 Parker P V Rev, 316
534645 Parker R J, 125
549354 Parker S M, 325
514692 Parker T, 280
548483 Parker A, 373
506139 Parker A G, 373
       Parker C, 381
       Parker D C, 66
       Parker G J, 34
532678 Parker K, 373
       Parker P V, 356
       Parker R J, 356
549850 Parkes S, 373
541248 Parkes S, 373
549678 Parkes J R, 288
502220 Parkes N G, 300
543313 Parkes N M, 266
546769 Parkes S K, 262
536827 Parkes Z E C, 126
528008 Parkhouse D A F H, 249
545337 Parkin D, 244
516085 Parkin E J, 335
528387 Parkin S A, 336
486388 Parkinson A D, 333
553367 Parkinson A J, 144
548672 Parkinson A J, 259
538095 Parkinson C E A, 126
496647 Parkinson D C, 218
552451 Parkinson D J, 137
533778 Parkinson D R, 141
524349 Parkinson R E, 240
539846 Parkinson R I B, 133
541718 Parkinson R J, 142
       Parkinson J M, 356
541169 Parks A F W, 126
553093 Parks P T, 127
494450 Parle M E, 238
492781 Parnell C J, 321
534152 Parnell C M, 337
551059 Parnell D D, 343
552452 Parnell J L, 230
532150 Parnell M H, 297
552549 Parnham H L, 295
546933 Parr C, 245
547480 Parr D B, 302
536828 Parr R L, 244
       Parrish M, 356
501516 Parrott A J, 238
495372 Parrott D E P, 238
527271 Parrott D W, 318
536245 Parrott J D, 124
543112 Parrott J M, 125
497018 Parrott L A, 275
515781 Parrott W J, 319
550400 Parry A, 339
528930 Parry A J, 241
539813 Parry I L, 142
549378 Parry J S, 276
543329 Parry M J, 219
548999 Parry N J, 246
551460 Parry R E, 219
537868 Parry R H, 292
502374 Parry S A, 318
505327 Parry S J, 318
516633 Parry RJ, 103
528598 Parry-Jones D B, 265
524891 Parselle S P Rev, 234

529112	Rogers E H B, 374	
523973	Rogers M, 374	
484015	Rogers PB, 97	
546846	Rogers R J, 374	
539991	Rogers V J, 374	
516699	Rogers W, 374	
547999	Rogerson P C, 244	
	Rogerson C D, 359	
541327	Rolfe C F, 262	
549018	Rolfe G L, 244	
533779	Rolfe P C, 328	
486734	Rolfe-Smith B P S, 218	
526599	Rolland I A, 328	
	Rolle D, 83	
504583	Rollins A, 334	
497498	Rollins JW, 217	
550423	Rollins S E A, 252	
551064	Rollison F M, 338	
547791	Rollo J A S, 251	
496550	Rollo N H, 129	
498777	Rollo S J, 237	
	Rollo N H, 52	
	Rollo W R, 17	
504027	Rollo WR, 97	
495378	Rollo-Walker R M J, 90, 211	
548275	Romanovitch A P G, 251	
505905	Romberg C R, 87, 122	
543008	Romilly S W, 177	
532285	Ronaghan T W A, 307	
542209	Ronald C N A, 305	
515738	Ronaldson D A A, 261	
489593	Rook R, 236	
550802	Rook T W, 259	
	Rook-Blackstone S, 359	
486735	Rooke J L K, 122	
551228	Rooker A D, 278	
522505	Rooms M A, 248	
531618	Rooney C A, 337	
527897	Rooney J J P, 336	
530046	Rooney J J, 374	
541150	Roose J J, 133	
542082	Rooth F G, 258	
526637	Ropel M A, 132	
529318	Roper C B, 124	
548000	Roper O N, 212	
537370	Roper T J, 312	
	Roper G B, 380	
	Roper R W, 16	
532943	Rorie P A, 303	
537484	Rorison A, 256	
538423	Rosborough P, 297	
550803	Roscoe W J F, 152	
527161	Rose A J, 262	
531402	Rose C A H, 337	
510257	Rose C J, 131	
532460	Rose C J S, 241	
507531	Rose D J, 187	
554094	Rose D J, 343	
538187	Rose I R B, 332	
524765	Rose R J J, 181	
541328	Rose S, 263	
552535	Rose W K C, 310	
537649	Rose A J, 374	
	Rose L, 65	
	Rose Tan Sri Ahmad Saruji bin Che, 78	
549081	Rosedale L, 374	
551468	RoseLarner J F, 332	
528009	Rosell P A E, 250	
548001	Rosen H W, 148	
492552	Rosenberg B C, 321	
544230	Rosenfeld S W, 217	
	Roser P W, 60	
552872	Rosewall L J A, 338	
541687	Rosher L M, 375	
550470	Rosie L R, 259	
539443	Rosier S D, 124	
499764	Roskelly C M D W, 107	
542620	Roskelly J H E Rev, 234	
552757	Roskelly J K, 245	
	Roskilly N, 359	
517316	Ross A C G, 114	
516032	Ross A G, 44, 140	
543247	Ross B M, 165	
538299	Ross B N H, 336	
497927	Ross C A M, 123	
546466	Ross C R, 223	
517587	Ross D A, 248	
548572	Ross D H, 251	
520704	Ross E T, 114	
535604	Ross F J, 133	
539032	Ross G D, 159	
492977	Ross H A, 139	
493781	Ross I A M, 130	
537874	Ross I L J, 294	
497499	Ross I W, 254	
524237	Ross J E, 243	
482820	Ross J H D, 305	
548534	Ross K S, 314	
539131	Ross M, 207	
508945	Ross M, 330	
510746	Ross M C, 123	
551016	Ross M J, 343	
537211	Ross M L, 124	
484016	Ross N D, 253	
547701	Ross P, 187	
493780	Ross R J V, 199	
540065	Ross S J, 204	
539649	Ross W J, 125	
517007	Ross C A, 375	
537130	Ross C M, 375	
525541	Ross D, 375	
485005	Ross D G, 375	
554234	Ross I K, 375	
	Ross J A, 359	
	Ross J H D, 375	
548718	Ross J M, 375	
550171	Ross K R, 375	
509142	Ross R A, 375	
513643	Rossi D R, 326	
522506	Rossiter N D, 248	
491189	Rossiter P R, 236	
551479	RossMcNairn J E, 306	
537532	RossRussell D, 133	
536463	Ross-Wilson A W M, 290	
549019	Rostron J A, 219	
495225	Rotchell L R, 254	
	Rothnie N, 359	
525184	Rothwell A, 269	
523181	Rothwell M J R, 291	
547408	Rothwell S M J, 282	
	Rothwell D A, 359	
	Rothwell P N, 359	
500180	Rouch D V, 375	
527199	Roud S C, 375	
541025	Roud W C, 375	
504499	Rough M A, 139	
530416	Roughley J P, 278	
543340	Roughton N H, 126	
526520	Roughton S A, 248	
539839	Roulston P, 251	
551904	Round J A, 252	
538649	Rous J A E, 148	
543720	Rous R W J, 151	
534281	Rouse B R, 116	
505343	Rouse J F, 254	
493063	Rouse P A R, 138	
550058	Rouse R A, 245	
495577	Rouse R L, 261	
537246	Rouse C T, 375	
	Rouse M J, 359	
541484	Rout A J, 171	
524372	Routh C A, 294	
553731	Routh S A, 308	
546938	Routledge C J, 245	
538760	Routledge S J, 183	
495226	Row N A, 261	
521830	Rowan D, 326	
516685	Rowan J F, 248	
553514	Rowan J R, 108	
553392	Rowbotham V S, 137	
506890	Rowe A G, 238	
540197	Rowe C A, 333	
550059	Rowe C C, 128	
534019	Rowe E C, 309	
528939	Rowe M H, 239	
548629	Rowe M P, 320	
506024	Rowe N D J, 222	
550441	Rowe P D, 297	
485820	Rowe R G, 18, 32, 216	
	Rowe D R, 359	
	Rowe G A, 359	
537865	Rowe J W K, 375	
	Rowe K W, 359	
547535	Rowe T L, 375	
545035	Rowell J F, 231	
544405	Rowell P J, 135	
524971	Rowland P C Rev, 234	
550978	Rowland T J, 266	
543341	Rowland T L, 249	
	Rowland D, 359	
495539	Rowland-Jones S D, 229	
553394	Rowlands A, 200	
553393	Rowlands A N, 198	
530131	Rowlands D L, 133	
527467	Rowlands L J, 296	
544267	Rowlands M A, 270	
549711	Rowlands M H Rev, 234	
547780	Rowlands M T, 338	
553454	Rowlands P, 136	
541992	Rowlands T K, 251	
534552	Rowles G R, 320	
547672	Rowles N W, 278	
554404	Rowley A J, 338	
541335	Rowley D N, 266	
507532	Rowley J, 140	
527938	Rowley J, 318	
509570	Rowley R K, 237	
	Rowley C H, 359	
501687	Rowlinson D E, 138	
520940	Rowney M R, 305	
553560	Roworth S A, 127	
551124	Rowsell A M, 282	
551362	Rowson A C J, 136	
547296	Rowson S A, 301	
513363	Roxburgh AM, 103	
548313	Roy H, 159	
538177	Royce A A D, 190	
491526	Roycroft M J, 236	
506025	Royds J C, 293	
542210	Roylance E K, 265	
549796	Royle A P, 338	
552112	Royston C L, 252	
540437	Ruane J A, 375	
541812	Rudd A R, 297	

484

487

494

Z

RFEA Limited
(Regular Forces Employment Association)

Established 1885, Incorporated 1996 and formerly known as the National Association for Employment of Regular Sailors Soldiers and Airmen

HEAD OFFICE: 49 Pall Mall, London SW1Y 5JG
Telephone: 020 7321 2011 Facsimile: 020 7839 0970
E-mail: rfea@primex.co.uk www.rfea.org.uk

Patrons: HER MAJESTY THE QUEEN
HER MAJESTY QUEEN ELIZABETH THE QUEEN MOTHER

President: Vice Admiral Sir Geoffrey Dalton KCB
Chairman: Lieutenant General Sir Roderick Cordy-Simpson KBE CB
Chief Executive: Major General M F L Shellard CBE
Head of Field Operations: Derek Lawrence-Brown
Controller of Finance: Omar Binbasilar

Branches	Employment Consultant	Postal Address	Tel & Fax No
ABERDEEN	Phillip Wilcock	46a Union Street, Aberdeen AB10 1BD	01224 644493
BEDFORD	Dave Tompson	TA Centre, 28 Bedford Rd, Kempston, Beds MK42 8AJ	01234 351573
BELFAST	Les Kelly	Northern Ireland War Memorial Building, Waring Street, Belfast BT1 2EU	028 9043 5037*
BIRMINGHAM	David House MBE	2nd Floor, City Gate, 25 Moat Lane, Birmingham B5 6BH	Tel: 0121 622 3052 Fax: 0121 622 3383
BRISTOL	Paul Lucas	3rd Floor, 4 Colston Avenue, Bristol BS1 4TT	0117 922 0277
BURY ST EDMUNDS	Ken Ruston	Room 4, 90 Guildhall Street, Bury St Edmunds IP33 1PR	Tel: 01284 700 530 Fax: 01284 760 577
CARDIFF	Peter Holmes	Maindy Barracks, Cardiff CF4 3YE	Tel: 029 2022 8842 Fax:0870 705 1524
CARLISLE	David Clark	The Castle, Carlisle, Cumbria CA3 8UR	01228 523 736
CHATHAM	Peter Jackson Dip Gd	9 New Road, Rochester, Kent ME1 1BG	01634 408 696
CHELMSFORD	David Taylor	The Gate House, AMT Centre, Upper Chase, Writtle Road, Chelmsford CM2 0BN	01245 261171
CHELTENHAM	Bob Preston	Potter House, St Annes Road, Cheltenham, GL52 2SS	01242 251612
CHESTER	Bob Bacon	156 Percival Road, Chester, Cheshire CH2 4AN	01244 390759
DARLINGTON	Jim Snaddon	4th Floor, Northgate House, St Augustine's Way Darlington DL1 1XA	Tel: 01325 286480 Fax: 01325 384084
DERBY	Ted Morgan	The College Business Centre, Uttoxeter New Road Derby DE22 3WZ	01332 371 217
EDINBURGH	Frank McGuinness BEM	New Haig House, Logie Green Road, Edinburgh EH7 4HQ	Tel: 0131 557 1747 Fax: 0131 557 5819
EXETER	Graham Hume	Wyvern Barracks, Exeter, Devon EX2 6AF	01392 257 005
GLASGOW	Bill Clark	Haig House, 1 Fitzroy Place, Glasgow G3 7RJ	0141 229 0739
LEEDS	Bernard Foster	Harewood Barracks, Regent Street, Leeds LS7 1AT	Tel: 0113 246 9065 Fax: 0113 243 2958
LINCOLN	Robert Oxbury	Cobb Hall Centre, St Paul's Lane, Ballgate Lincoln LN1 3AX	01522 519 194
LIVERPOOL	John Mullans	Suite 43 Oriel Chambers, 14 Water Street Liverpool L2 8TD	0151 236 4989
LONDON - INNER	Jenny Hughes	49 Pall Mall, London SW1Y 5JG	Tel: 020 7321 2688 Fax: 020 7930 8035
LONDON - OUTER (replaced Acton & Brighton)	Colin Acreman	49 Pall Mall, London SW1Y 5JG	Tel: 020 7321 2177 Fax: 020 7930 8035
MANCHESTER	John Nicholson	TA Centre, Belle Vue, Manchester M12 5PW	0161 223 1945
NEWCASTLE-UPON-TYNE	Brian Jones	4th Floor, Mea House, Ellison Place, Newcastle-upon-Tyne NE1 8XS	Tel: 0191 222 0654 Fax: 0191 261 7321
NORTHAMPTON	Elenore Lowry	TA Centre,Clare Street, Northampton NN1 3JQ	01604 632326
NORWICH	Paul Fidler	TA Centre, Britannia House, 325 Aylsham Road Norwich NR3 2AB	01603 405222
NOTTINGHAM	Gary Nathan	19 Malvern Road, Nottingham NG3 5HA	0115 960 2134
PERTH (replaced DUNDEE)	Terry Ellison	Room 5, Lower Ground Floor, 4 Atholl Place Perth PH1 5ND	01738 580412
PLYMOUTH	Joanne (Jo) Jones	Raglan Cottage, MOD Mt Wise Business Park Devonport, Plymouth PL1 4JH	Tel: 01752 501743 Fax: 01752 501709
PORTSMOUTH	Ken Wilkinson	2(b) Tipner Road, Stamshaw, Portsmouth PO2 8QP	023 9267 7846
PRESTON	Roger Buttery	Fulwood Barracks, Fulwood, Preston, Lancs PR2 8AA	01772 709707
READING	Barry Slater FISM	Watlington House, Watlington Stret, Reading RG1 4RJ	0118 957 3178
SALISBURY	Allan Sanders	27 Castle Street, Salisbury, Wilts SP1 1TT	Tel: 01722 335134 Fax: 01722 323779
SHEFFIELD	Steve Bates FECI	2nd Floor, 9 Paradise Square, Sheffield S1 2DE	0114 272 6847
SHREWSBURY (reopened)	Peter Westwell	Building 4, Copthorne Barracks, Copthorne Road Shrewsbury SY3 7LT	01743 289001
STOKE-ON-TRENT	John Marland	Martin Leake House, TA Centre, Waterloo Road Cobridge, Stoke-on-Trent ST6 3HJ	01782 208 680
SWANSEA	Terry Cokeley BEM	TA Centre, The Grange, West Cross, Swansea SA3 5LB	01792 405608

THE OFFICERS' ASSOCIATION

PATRON
HM THE QUEEN

PRESIDENTS
Admiral of the Fleet Sir Julian Oswald GCB
General Sir John Waters GCB CBE JP
Air Chief Marshal Sir Michael Graydon GCB CBE FRAeS

The Officers' Association provides services which are available to ex-officers of the Royal Navy (including Royal Marines), the Army and the Royal Air Force, and their widows and dependants, including those who held Commissions in the Womens' Services.

Services include:

Employment: Combining outplacement, job finding and recruitment, the Employment Department provides a unique, cost-effective service for any officer leaving the Armed Forces or those who, in later life, up to age 65, may be seeking a new job. For service leavers the department works closely with The Coutts Transition Partnership, who have been contracted to provide resettlement services for MOD, DMOS.

Benevolence: Financial assistance is given to those in financial distress; cash grants on a one-off basis towards specific items; continuing allowances to those on very small incomes; help towards home fees for those who through age or infirmity can no longer remain in their home, and can find no suitable Home within their means; and in special circumstances, help with education and training fees.

Homes Advice: Providing advice on Homes for the elderly as well as offering information on the entitlement to benefits.

A Country Home: Running "Huntly", a delightful country home at Bishopsteignton, South Devon, which affords comfort and security for ex-officers at or over the age of 65, both male and female, who do not need special nursing care. Selection is made with due regard to need and financial assistance can be given towards the very modest fees if necessary.

Bungalows: Running a 12-bungalow estate at Leavesden, Hertfordshire, for disabled ex-officers and their families.

All enquiries should be made to:

The General Secretary
The Officers' Association
48 Pall Mall, London SW1Y 5JY
Tel: 020 7389 5204 Fax: 020 7930 9053

THE
ROYAL PATRIOTIC FUND
CORPORATION

FOUNDED 1854

REORGANISED UNDER THE PATRIOTIC FUND
REORGANISATION ACT, 1903, AND THE ROYAL PATRIOTIC FUND
CORPORATION ACT, 1950
Registered Charity Number 207476

President: HRH Prince Michael of Kent KCVO
Vice-President: General Sir Robert Pascoe KCB MBE

The Corporation administers a number of funds for the benefit of widows, children and dependants of *deceased officers and other ranks* of the Naval, Military and Air Forces of the Crown.

Over £430,000 is distributed annually in allowances, grants, school bursaries and in the provision of television sets/licences to the widows of servicemen.

Regular allowances are paid to widows of officers and other ranks where need exists.

Grants are made to meet particular requirements.

Bursaries and educational grants are available to assist with the payment of school fees where special need exists.

Applications for assistance should be made through local branches of SSAFA Forces Help or through the War Pension's Agency.

Further information may be obtained from the Secretary
Royal Patriotic Fund Corporation
40 Queen Anne's Gate, London SW1H 9AP.
Telephone: 020 7233 1894. Facsimile: 020 7233 1799

Royal United Services Institute for Defence Studies
Whitehall, London, SW1A 2ET
Tel: 020-7930-5854 Fax: 020 7321-0943 Web Site: www.rusi.org

The Aim of the RUSI

- keep you informed and up-to-the minute on both current and developing defence issues;
- provide depth and breadth to your interests, knowledge and expertise;
- act as neutral ground for and encourage the exchange of opinions and ideas, both in person and in print.

The RUSI is independent of government and other political affiliations. We are dedicated to the study and vigorous debate of all issues of defence and international security, focusing particularly on Britain's interests, but set in a wide international context. We aim to develop fresh thinking and to develop options with an analysis of their implications. Our work ranges from defence procurement, technology and management, through the military sciences and strategic studies, to the causes, prevention and resolution of conflicts. We aim to make a difference.

Individual Membership is open to those serving in the armed forces and to members of the public who have a responsibility or simply an interest in defence and security matters.

The fees to be a 'Member' for a year are £ 53.00 and include receipt of the bi-monthly RUSI Journal, the bi-annual World Defence Systems, use of the Library, Reading Room and access to Lectures.

The fees to be a 'Full Member' for a year are £ 102.00 and include the above publications, plus receipt of the monthly RUSI Newsbrief and occasional Whitehall Papers.

A **40% discount** is given for the first year of Individual Membership and thereafter for those aged 30 or under.

Mess Membership offers the flexibility needed by a UK-based mess or unit, who wish its personnel to use the Institute. Mess members receive 1 full set of RUSI publications and access to the building as well as lectures for up to 5 members of the mess or unit per visit. The fees begin at £ 285.00 per year.

For further details, please contact the Membership Secretary by Post, Fax, E-mail: membership@rusi.org or log on to our Web-site: www.rusi.org
Founded in 1831 Patron: Her Majesty Queen Elizabeth Charity No 21063

. It has an
excellent academic record and a strong reputation in sport, music and drama.
Opportunities abound for pupils to excel in a wide range of activities.

Academic work for 11-16-year-olds follows the National Curriculum. In the Sixth
Form a wide range of AS, A and ANVQ courses is offered. The vast majority
of Sixth Form leavers enter university. There is a comprehensive programme of
educational visits, international exchanges and trips and expeditions abroad. Pupils
are given every opportunity to discover and to develop their various interests and
talents.

Entry is by tests in English and Mathematics with a good Headteacher's report.

Further information can be obtained from: The Headmaster's Personal Assistant.

QUEEN VICTORIA SCHOOL DUNBLANE

Patron: HRH The Duke of Edinburgh KG KT OM GBE
HER MAJESTY'S COMMISSIONERS
President: The Secretary of State for Scotland
Chairman: Lieutenant General Sir John MacMillan KCB CBE
and 15 others

The School provides stable and uninterrupted boarding education for the sons and
daughters of Scottish Service personnel or any service personnel who are serving, or
have served, in Scotland. Queen Victoria School is set in 45 acres of beautiful
Perthshire countryside, easily accessible by road, rail or air.

Pupils are normally admitted into Primary 7 at the age of 10/11 but may be registered
for entry from the age of seven onwards. However, consideration will be given, in
particular circumstances, to applications made after these dates.

Applications must reach the school by 31st December to be considered for admission
for the following August. Admissions are academically non-selective and decisions rest
with the Admissions Board, held in February each year

The School offers a wide and balanced curriculum following the Scottish educational
system leading to Standard Grade, Intermediate 2, Higher and Advanced Higher.

Queen Victoria School aims to provide a happy, stable and homely environment in
which pupils can achieve their full academic potential, raise their esteem and partici-
pate in a full and energetic boarding life. Pastoral care, which is given a high priority,
is aimed at promoting the welfare and happiness of each individual child and includes
careers advice, healthcare, emotional support, character development as well as
spiritual and moral guidance.

Increasingly pupils move on to Further and Higher Educations but the careers links
with the three Services remain strong.

For further information please write to:

Headmaster, Queen Victoria School, Dunblane, Perthshire FK15 0JY
Tel: 0131-310-2901 (Headmaster's Secretary) 0131-310-2902 (Bursar's Secretary).

THE ARMY DEPENDANTS' TRUST
President: The Adjutant General

The Army Dependants' Trust (ADT) was formed on 1 January 2000 from a merger of the Army Officers' Dependants Fund and The Soldiers' Dependants Fund. The Trust is a charity and its aim is to make a discretionary grant for the immediate needs of a widow, widower and/or dependants of a member who dies in Service, whilst members of the Trust, irrespective of cause or place of death.

Membership of the Trust is open to all Regular Officers, R Irish (full-time), Gurkha and NRPS Officers. FTRS, TA and Reserve Officers when called-out/volunteering for full-time Service, but only for the duration of that Service. Retired Officers may also re-join the Trust when re-employed under the RO scheme or as ACOs.

The subscription is £5 per annum for married, widowed, separated and divorced members and £3 for single members. Retired Officers and ACOs will initially pay £10 per annum. Current discretionary grants are up to £6,000 for single members and up to £10,000 for other categories.

Full details and the Rules of the Trust are contained in AGAIs, Vol 3, Ch 88 and the Trust's address is:

Secretary
The Army Dependants' Trust
Building 43
Trenchard Lines
Upavon
Wiltshire SN9 6BE
Telephone: Upavon Mil Ext 5734/5736
01980-615734/615736

ROYAL CAMBRIDGE HOME FOR SOLDIERS' WIDOWS
82/84 HURST ROAD
EAST MOLESEY, SURREY

Patron:
HER MAJESTY THE QUEEN
Lady President: HRH PRINCESS ALICE, DUCHESS OF GLOUCESTER
Chairman of the Council: GEN SIR JEREMY MACKENZIE *GCB OBE*
Superintendent: MRS I O YARNELL
Chairman of theTrustees: BRIG SIR HENY LEE *CBE*

The Home was founded in 1851, in memory of Field Marshall H R H Adolphus Frederick, Duke of Cambridge KG, to provide a home for widows of NCOs and Privates of the Regular Army. Now it is open also to women, single or widowed, who have served in the Regular, Territorial or Reserve Army, QARANC, FANY'S and wives of soldiers who have been admitted to the Royal Hospital Chelsea and who are in need of residential care.

The Home offers an enhanced quality of life for up to 30 ladies in private bed-sitting rooms which residents are encouraged to furnish themselves.

The Committee urgently appeal for applications.

THE OFFICERS' PENSIONS SOCIETY

An attractive secure pension is an essential ingredient of any modern employment package. It goes with salary, with allowances for travel and accommodation, with provision for healthcare and so on. Pensions take many forms - occupational, personal etc - and they are usually 'portable' on change of job. One thing they have in common is that their importance increases with age and into retirement.

The Officers' Pensions Society was formed immediately after the Second World War with commendable foresight to look after the pensions interests of members of the Armed Forces. It exists today for exactly the same purpose. It is a membership organisation with over 50,000 members and operates as a business, with annual subscriptions providing the income to support its activities.

The Society has brought about many improvements in the pensions and benefits now available to all ranks, not just officers, and their dependants. Its activities are, therefore, of critical interest to everyone, both serving and retired. It is especially important for everyone to take an early interest in his or her pension arrangements - and joining the Society is one practical way of doing this. For example, members of the Society are kept informed of matters relating to Service Retired Pay, pensions and related financial matters through its popular journal 'Pennant' that is published twice a year.

Membership is currently restricted to officers but the fact is that any changes the Society achieves apply universally to all ranks of all three Services. Membership policy is under review and is likely to be extended to embrace all ranks from mid 2001.

The annual subscription is £20.00 (or £1.75 per month) for officers and £9.00 for widows/widowers and dependants of deceased officers.

Further information and application forms can be obtained from:

The Membership Secretary
The Officers' Pensions Society
68 South Lambeth Road
Vauxhall, London SW8 1RL
Telephone 020 7820 9988
Fax 020 7820 9948

ALEXANDRA HOUSE
(Royal United Services Short Stay Residence for Service Children)
20 Crownhill Fort Road, Crownhill, Plymouth PL6 5BX
Telephone: Plymouth (01752) 781888
Patron: HRH Princess Alexandra, The Hon Lady Ogilvy GCVO
President: The Naval Base Commander, HM Naval Base, Devonport

---

The Foundation (formerly based at Newquay) has, since 1839, looked after the children of all ranks of the Armed Services. The Short Stay Residence is established in a modern house to meet the *immediate* need that may arise for whatever reason, that renders the parents temporarily unable to look after their children themselves. In essence, the Foundation acts as an "Immediate Aunt". The problem is met AT ONCE, at any hour of day or night, and the children are cared for, placed in schools and, by arrangement, given whatever special instruction, treatment or maintenance they need for up to three months whilst the family problem is resolved.

The House is run as a family house - NOT as an Institution - and the House-Mother and her team of dedicated and caring staff, are qualified and experienced in child care. Voluntary financial grants and donations enable the House to keep charges to parents to a very low level.

Urgent and emergency enquiries should be made by telephone, as above. Routine correspondence should be addressed to the Comptroller.

Grants, covenants, donations and legacies are especially valuable as the Foundation is a Registered Charity (No 202922). An outline of the tax advantages to the donor, or his estate, may be obtained from the Comptroller, to whom all routine correspondence should be addressed.

Urgent and emergency enquiries should be made to the House-Mother by telephone, as above.